ANALYTICAL
SOLID GEOMETRY

ANALYTICAL SOLID GEOMETRY

[For B.Sc./B.A. Classes as per UGC model curriculum & also useful for different competitive examinations]

SHANTI NARAYAN

Formerly, Dean of Colleges
University of Delhi, Delhi
(Formerly, Principal, Hans Raj College, Delhi)

Revised By

P.K. MITTAL

M.Sc., Ph.D.
Head of Mathematics Department
Govt. Post Graduate College
RISHIKESH *(Uttaranchal)*

S. CHAND
PUBLISHING

S Chand And Company Limited

(ISO 9001 Certified Company)

S Chand And Company Limited

(ISO 9001 Certified Company)

Head Office: Block B-1, House No. D-1, Ground Floor, Mohan Co-operative Industrial Esta
New Delhi – 110 044 | Phone: 011-66672000

Registered Office: A-27, 2ⁿᵈ Floor, Mohan Co-operative Industrial Estate, New Delhi – 110 04
www.**schandpublishing**.com; e-mail: **info@schandpublishing.com**

Branches

Ahmedabad	:	Ph: 27542369, 27541965; ahmedabad@schandpublishing.com
Bengaluru	:	Ph: 22354008, 22268048; bangalore@schandpublishing.com
Bhopal	:	Ph: 4274723, 4209587; bhopal@schandpublishing.com
Bhubaneshwar	:	Ph: 2951580; bhubaneshwar@schandpublishing.com
Chennai	:	chennai@schandpublishing.com
Guwahati	:	Ph: 2738811, 2735640; guwahati@schandpublishing.com
Hyderabad	:	hyderabad@schandpublishing.com
Jaipur	:	Ph: 2291317, 2291318; jaipur@schandpublishing.com
Jalandhar	:	Ph: 4645630; jalandhar@schandpublishing.com
Kochi	:	Ph: 2576207, 2576208; cochin@schandpublishing.com
Kolkata	:	Ph: 23357458, 23353914; kolkata@schandpublishing.com
Lucknow	:	Ph: 4065646; lucknow@schandpublishing.com
Mumbai	:	Ph: 25000297; mumbai@schandpublishing.com
Nagpur	:	nagpur@schandpublishing.com
Patna	:	Ph: 2260011; patna@schandpublishing.com
Ranchi	:	Ph: 2361178; ranchi@schandpublishing.com
Sahibabad	:	Ph: 2771238; info@schandpublishing.com

First Edition 1939
Subsequent Editions and Reprints 1942, 44, 46, 49, 50, 52, 54, 55, 57, 59, 61, 65, 69, 71, 72, 75, 78, 80, 82, 83, 85, 87, 88, 90, 92, 94, 95, 97, 98, 99, 2001, 2002, 2005, 2006, 2007 (Twice), 2008, 2009, 2010 (Twice), 2011, 2012, 2013, 2014 (Twice), 2016, 2017 (Twice), 2018
Reprint 2019 (Twice)

ISBN: 978-81-219-2661-4   **Product Code:** H6GTY68MATH10ENAQ0XR

PRINTED IN INDIA

By Vikas Publishing House Private Limited, Plot 20/4, Site-IV, Industrial Area Sahibabad, Ghaziabad – 201 010 and Published by S Chand And Company Limited, Block B-1, House No. D-1, Ground Floor, Mohan Co-operative Industrial Estate, New Delhi – 110 044

PREFACE TO THE SEVENTEENTH EDITION

In the present edition, I have tried my level best to accommodate Questions upto the year 2005 of most of the Indian Universities, which have been asked in B.Sc. examinations. All the mistakes have been removed. Now the book is in bigger size with new get-up. Constructive suggestions for improvement of this book will be highly appreciated.

P.K. Mittal
(Reviser)

PREFACE TO THE SIXTEENTH EDITION

This book, originally written about 49 years ago. During the intervening period. It has been revised and re-printed several times. Since its last revision in 1977, tremendous changes in the trend of studies have taken place which necessitated thorough revision of the book. But, it was really a very difficult task to revise this perfect well-written book of late Shri Shanti Narayan. Since a long time undoubtedly, it was a book loved by teachers and students alike.

I took up the task to revise the book with great devotion to meet the rapidly changing demands of students interested in self-study and appearing in different competitive examinations. Keeping this view, a large variety of illustrative solved examples have been included in every chapter. As per new syllabus of B.Sc. 3-year Courses, a new chapter on Confocal Conicoids has been added.

This book, in the present form, is an humble effort to make it more useful to students and teachers.

I Owe my special gratitude to Shri Ravindra Kumar Gupta, Managing Director, S. Chand & Company Ltd., for giving me the opportunity to revise the book of late Shri Shanti Narayan, an eminent Indian Mathematician.

I also acknowledge my sincere thanks to Shri Navin Joshi, General Manager (S&M) for providing necessary assistance in this revision work.

As the need for improvement is never ending, I will look forward to receive valuable and useful suggestions from our readers for further improvement in the book.

P.K. Mittal
(Reviser)

PREFACE TO THE FIRST EDITION

This book is intended as an introduction to Analytical Solid Geometry and covers as much of the subject as generally expected of students going up for the B.A.., B.Sc., Pass and Honours examinations of our Universities.

I have endeavoured to develop the subject in a systematic and logical manner. To help the beginner. As for as possible the elementary parts of the subject have been presented in simple and lucid mànner and fairly large number of solved examples to illustrate various type of methods have been introduced. The books already existing in the market cover a rather extensive ground and consequently comparative lesser attention is paid to the introductory portion than is necessary for a beginner.

The book contains nummerous exercises of varied types in a graded form. Some of these have been selected from various examination papers and standard works to the publishers and authors, I offer my best thanks.

I am extremely indebted to Professor Sita Ram Gupta, M.A., P.E.S., of the Government College, Lahore, who very kindly went through the manuscript with great care and keen interest and suggested a large number of extremely valuable improvements.

I shall be very grateful for any suggestions for improvements or corrections of text or examples.

Shanti Narayan

Lahore :
June, 1939.

CONTENTS

1

Co-ordinates

INTRODUCTION

In a plane the position of a point is determined by an ordered pair (x, y) of real numbers, obtained with reference to two straight lines in the plane generally at right angles. The position of a point in *space* is, however, determined by an ordered triad (x, y, z) of real numbers. We now proceed to explain as to how this is done.

1.1. CO-ORDINATES OF A POINT IN SPACE

Let $X'OX$, $Z'OZ$ be two perpendicular straight lines determining the XOZ-plane. Through O, their point of intersection, called the *origin*, draw the line $Y'OY$ perpendicular to the XOZ-plane so that we have three mutually perpendicular straight lines

$$X'OX, Y'OY, Z'OZ$$

known as *Rectangular Co-ordinate Axes**. The positive directions of the axes are indicated by arrow heads. These three axes, taken in pairs, determine the three planes,

$$XOY, YOZ \text{ and } ZOX$$

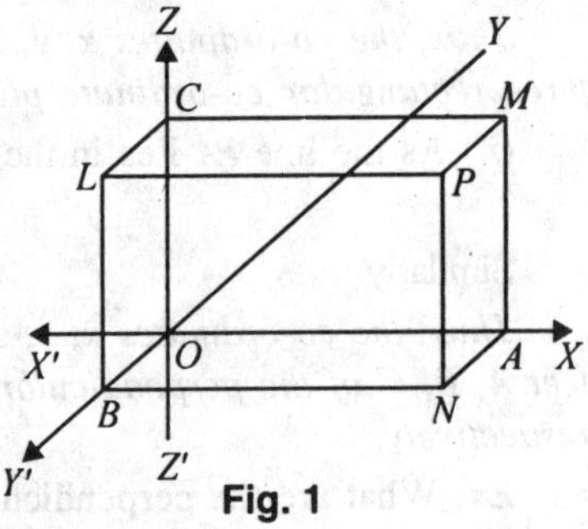

Fig. 1

or briefly the XY, YZ, ZX planes mutually at right angles, known as *Rectangular Co-ordinate Planes*.

Through *any* point, P, in space, draw three planes parallel to the three co-ordinate planes (being also perpendicular to the corresponding axes) to meet the axes in A, B, C.

Let $OA = x$, $OB = y$ and $OC = z$.

These three numbers x, y, z taken in this order determined by the point P, are called the co-ordinates of the point P.

We refer to the ordered triad (x, y, z) formed of the co-ordinates of the point P as the point P itself.

Any one of these x, y, z will be positive or negative according as it is measured from O, along the corresponding axis, in the positive or the negative direction.

Conversely, given an ordered triad (x, y, z) of numbers, we can find the point whose co-ordinates are x, y, z. To do this, we proceed as follows :

(i) Measure OA, OB, OC along OX, OY, OZ equal to x, y, z respectively.

(ii) Through the points A, B, C draw planes parallel to the co-ordinate planes YZ, ZX, XY respectively.

The point of intersection of these three planes is the required point P.

---

* The plane XOZ containing the lines $X'OX$ and $Z'OZ$ may be imagined as the plane of the paper; the line OY as pointing towards the reader and OY' behind the paper.

Note. The three co-ordinate planes divide the whole space in eight compartments which are known as *eight octants* and since each of the co-ordinates of a point may be positive or negative, there are 2^3 (= 8) points whose co-ordinates have the same numerical values and which lie in the eight octants, one in each.

1.1.1. Further Explanation about Co-ordinates

In § 1.1 above, we have learnt that in order to obtain the co-ordinates of a point P, we have to draw three planes through P respectively parallel to the three co-ordinate planes. The three planes through P and the three co-ordinate planes determine a parallelopiped whose consideration leads to three other useful constructions for determining the co-ordinates of P.

The parallelopiped, in question, has six rectangular faces consisting of three pairs of parallel planes, *viz.*,

$$PMAN, LCOB; PNBL, MAOC; PLCM, NBOA \qquad (See\ Fig.\ 1)$$

(*i*) We have

$x = OA = CM = LP$ = perpendicular from P on the YZ-plane;

$y = OB = AN = MP$ = perpendicular from P on the ZX-plane;

$z = OC = AM = NP$ = perpendicular from P on the XY-plane.

Thus, the co-ordinates x, y, z of a point P, are the perpendicular distances of P from the three rectangular co-ordinate planes YZ, ZX and XY respectively.

(*ii*) As the line PA lies in the plane $PMAN$ which is perpendicular to the line OA^*, we have

$$PA \perp OA.$$

Similarly $PB \perp OB$ and $PC \perp OC$

Thus, the co-ordinates x, y, z of a point P are also the distances from the origin O of the feet A, B, C of the perpendiculars from the point P to the co-ordinate axes $X'X$, $Y'Y$ and $Z'Z$ respectively.

Ex. What are the perpendicular distances of a point (x, y, z) from the co-ordinate axes ?

$$[\textbf{Ans.}\ \sqrt{y^2 + z^2},\ \sqrt{z^2 + x^2},\ \sqrt{x^2 + y^2}]$$

(*iii*) We have (Fig. 1)

$NP = AM = OC = z$;

$AN = OB = y$;

$OA = x$.

Thus, (Fig. 2) if we draw the line PN perpendicular to the XY-plane meeting it at N and the line NA parallel to the line, OY meeting OX at A, we have

$$OA = x, AN = y, NP = z.$$

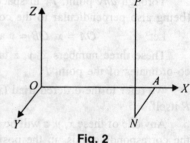

Fig. 2

EXAMPLE

In which octant the following points lie

(*i*) $(-1, -2, -3)$, (*ii*) $(a, b, -c)$, (*iii*) (a, b, c), (*iv*) $(-a, -b, c)$?

Sol. (*i*) Since all the three co-ordinates are negative hence, $(-1, -2, -3)$ lies in octant $OX'Y'Z'$ (Fig. 1).

(*ii*) Similarly $(a, b, -c)$ is a point in the octant $OXYZ'$.

(*iii*) It is a point in the octant $OXYZ$.

(*iv*) It is a point in the octant $OX'Y'Z$.

---

*A line perpendicular to a plane is perpendicular to every line in the plane.

EXERCISES

1. In Fig. 1, write down the co-ordinates of the point $A, B, C; L, M, N$ when the co-ordinates of P are (x, y, z).

2. Show that for every point (x, y, z) on the ZX-plane, $y = 0$.

3. Show that for every point (x, y, z) on the Y-axis, $x = 0, z = 0$.

4. What is the locus of a point (x, y, z) for which

    (i) $x = 0$,   (ii) $y = 0$,   (iii) $z = 0$,

    (iv) $x = a$,   (v) $y = b$,   (vi) $z = c$.

5. What is the locus of a point (x, y, z) for which

    (i) $y = 0, z = 0$,   (ii) $z = 0, x = 0$,   (iii) $x = 0, y = 0$,

    (iv) $y = b, z = c$,   (v) $z = c, x = a$,   (vi) $x = a, y = b$.

6. P is any point (x, y, z), and α, β, γ are the angles which OP makes with X-axis, Y-axis and Z-axis respectively, show that

$$\cos \alpha = x/r, \cos \beta = y/r, \cos \gamma = z/r,$$

where $r = OP$.

7. Find the lengths of the edges of the rectangular parallelopiped formed by planes drawn through the points $(1, 2, 3)$ and $(4, 7, 6)$ parallel to the co-ordinate planes.

                                                       [**Ans.** 3, 5, 3]

1.2. DISTANCE BETWEEN TWO POINTS

To find the distance between two given points $P(x_1, y_1, z_1)$ and $Q(x_2, y_2, z_2)$.

Through the points P, Q draw planes parallel to the co-ordinate planes to form a rectangular parallelopiped whose one diagonal is PQ.

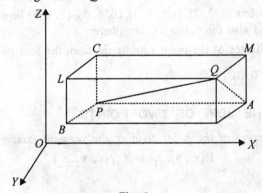

Fig. 3

Then

$$APCM, NBLQ; LCPB, QMAN; BPAN, LCMQ$$

are the three pairs of parallel faces of this parallelopiped.

Now, PA is the distance between the planes drawn through the points P and Q parallel to the YZ-plane and is, therefore, equal to the difference between their x-co-ordinates.

$\therefore$ $PA = x_2 - x_1.$

Similarly $AN = y_2 - y_1,$ ...(i)

and $NQ = z_2 - z_1.$

The line AQ lies in the plane $QMAN \perp PA$

$\Rightarrow \qquad\qquad AQ \perp PA$

$\Rightarrow \qquad\qquad PQ^2 = PA^2 + AQ^2 \qquad\qquad\qquad\qquad\qquad\qquad\qquad$ ...(ii)

$\angle ANQ$ is a rt. angle

$\Rightarrow \qquad\qquad AQ^2 = AN^2 + NQ^2 \qquad\qquad\qquad\qquad\qquad\qquad\qquad$ ...(iii)

From (i), (ii) and (iii), we obtain

$$PQ^2 = PA^2 + AQ^2 = PA^2 + AN^2 + NQ^2$$

$$= (x_2 - x_1)^2 + (y_2 - y_1)^2 + (z_2 - z_1)^2.$$

Thus, the distance between the points (x_1, y_1, z_1) and (x_2, y_2, z_2) is

$$\sqrt{(x_2 - x_1)^2 + (y_2 - y_1)^2 + (z_2 - z_1)^2}$$

Cor. Distance from the origin. When P coincides with the origin O, we have $x_1 = y_1 = z_1$ = 0 so that we obtain,

$$OQ^2 = x_2{}^2 + y_2{}^2 + z_2{}^2$$

Note. The reader should notice the similarity of the formula obtained above for the distance between two points with the corresponding formula in plane co-ordinate geometry. Also refer § 1.3.

EXERCISES

1. Find the distance between the points $(4, 3, -6)$ and $(-2, 1, -3)$. **[Ans. 7]**
2. Show that the points $(0, 7, 10)$, $(-1, 6, 6)$, $(-4, 9, 6)$ form an isosceles right-angled triangle.
3. Show that the three points $(-2, 3, 5)$, $(1, 2, 3)$, $(7, 0, -1)$ are collinear.
4. Show that the points $(3, 2, 2)$, $(-1, 1, 3)$, $(0, 5, 6)$, $(2, 1, 6)$ lie on a sphere whose centre is $(1, 3, 4)$. Find also the radius of the sphere. **[Ans. 3]**
5. Find the co-ordinates of the point equidistant from the four points $(a, 0, 0)$, $(0, b, 0)$,

   $(0, 0, c)$ and $(0, 0, 0)$. $\left[\textbf{Ans. } \dfrac{1}{2}a, \dfrac{1}{2}b, \dfrac{1}{2}c\right]$

1.3. DIVISION OF THE JOIN OF TWO POINTS

To find the co-ordinates of the point dividing the segment joining the points

$$P(x_1, y_1, z_1) \text{ and } Q(x_2, y_2, z_2)$$

in the ratio $m : n$.

Let $R(x, y, z)$ be the point dividing the segment PQ in the ratio $m : n$.

Draw PL, QM, RN perpendiculars to the XY-plane.

The line PL, QM, RN clearly lie in one plane so that the points L, M, N lie in the straight line which is the intersection of this plane with the XY-plane.

The line through R parallel to the line LM shall lie in the same plane. Let it intersect PL and QM at H and K respectively.

The triangles HPR and QRK are similar.

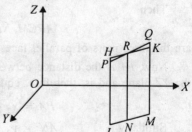

Fig. 4

$$\Rightarrow \quad \frac{m}{n} = \frac{PR}{RQ} = \frac{PH}{KQ} = \frac{NR - LP}{MQ - NR} = \frac{z - z_1}{z_2 - z}$$

$$\Rightarrow \quad z = \frac{mz_2 + nz_1}{m + n}.$$

Similarly, by drawing perpendiculars to the *XY* and *YZ*-planes, we obtain

$$y = \frac{my_2 + ny_1}{m + n} \text{ and } x = \frac{mx_2 + nx_1}{m + n}$$

The point *R* divides *PQ* internally or externally according as the ratio *m* : *n* is positive or negative.

Thus, the co-ordinates of the point which divides the join of the points (x_1, y_1, z_1) *and* (x_2, y_2, z_2) *in the ratio m : n are*

$$\left(\frac{mx_2 + nx_1}{m + n}, \frac{my_2 + ny_1}{m + n}, \frac{mz_2 + nz_1}{m + n} \right)$$

Cor. 1. Co-ordinates of the middle point. In case *R* is the middle point of *PQ*, we have

$$m : n :: 1 : 1$$

$$\Rightarrow \quad x = \frac{1}{2}(x_1 + x_2), \ y = \frac{1}{2}(y_1 + y_2), \ z = \frac{1}{2}(z_1 + z_2).$$

Cor. 2. Co-ordinates of a point on the join of two points. Putting *k* for *m/n*, we see that the co-ordinates of the point *R* which divides *PQ* in the ratio *k* : 1 are

$$\left(\frac{kx_2 + x_1}{1 + k}, \frac{ky_2 + y_1}{1 + k}, \frac{kz_2 + z_1}{1 + k} \right)$$

To every value of $k \neq -1$, there corresponds a point *R* on the line *PQ* and to every point *R* on the line *PQ* corresponds some value of *k*, viz., *PR/RQ*.

Thus, we see that the point

$$\left(\frac{kx_2 + x_1}{1 + k}, \frac{ky_2 + y_1}{1 + k}, \frac{kz_2 + z_1}{1 + k} \right) \qquad \dots(i)$$

lies on the line *PQ* whatever value $k \neq -1$ may have and *conversely any* given point on the line *PQ* is obtained by giving *some* suitable value to *k* other than -1. This idea is sometimes expressed by saying that (*i*) is the *general co-ordinates* of a point on the line joining $P(x_1, y_1, z_1)$ and $Q(x_2, y_2, z_2)$.

The set of points of the line joining the points (x_1, y_1, z_1) and (x_2, y_2, z_2) is

$$\left[\left(\frac{kx_2 + x_1}{1 + k}, \frac{ky_2 + y_1}{1 + k}, \frac{kz_2 + z_1}{1 + k} \right); k \neq -1 \right]$$

In other words, the line joining the points (x_1, y_1, z_1) and (x_2, y_2, z_2) is the set

$$\left[\left(\frac{kx_2 + x_1}{1 + k}, \frac{ky_2 + y_1}{1 + k}, \frac{kz_2 + z_1}{1 + k} \right); k \neq -1 \right].$$

EXAMPLES

1. *Find the ratio in which the line joining the points* (2, 4, 5), (3, 5, – 4) *is divided by the xy-plane.*

Sol. Co-ordinates of a point that divides the line joining the given point in the ratio $k : 1$ is

$$\left(\frac{3k + 2}{k + 1}, \frac{5k + 4}{k + 1}, \frac{-4k + 5}{k + 1} \right)$$

For a point on xy-plane, $z = 0$, i.e.,

$$\frac{-4k + 5}{k + 1} = 0, \text{ or } k = \frac{5}{4}.$$

Hence, the xy-plane divides the line in the ratio $5 : 4$.

Putting $k = \dfrac{5}{4}$, the co-ordinates of the point are $\left(\dfrac{23}{9}, \dfrac{41}{9}, 0 \right)$.

2. *Given that* $P(3, 2, -4)$, $Q(5, 4, -6)$, $R(9, 8, -10)$ *are collinear, find the ratio in which* Q *divides* PR.   *(Rohilkhand, 1993)*

Sol. Let Q divides PR in the ratio $k : 1$. Now x-co-ordinate of Q should be

$$\frac{9k + 3}{k + 1} = 5, \text{ or } k = \frac{1}{2}.$$

Hence, the required ratio is $1 : 2$.

3. *Show that the centroid of the tetrahedron whose vertices are* (x_r, y_r, z_r), $r = 1, 2, 3, 4$ *is*

$$\left\{ \frac{1}{4}(x_1 + x_2 + x_3 + x_4), \frac{1}{4}(y_1 + y_2 + y_3 + y_4), \frac{1}{4}(z_1 + z_2 + z_3 + z_4) \right\}.$$

Sol. Let G_1 be the centre of gravity of the triangular face ABC. G_1 divides the median BE in the ratio $1 : 2$. Co-ordinates of E are

$$\left(\frac{x_1 + x_3}{2}, \frac{y_1 + y_3}{2}, \frac{z_1 + z_3}{2} \right).$$

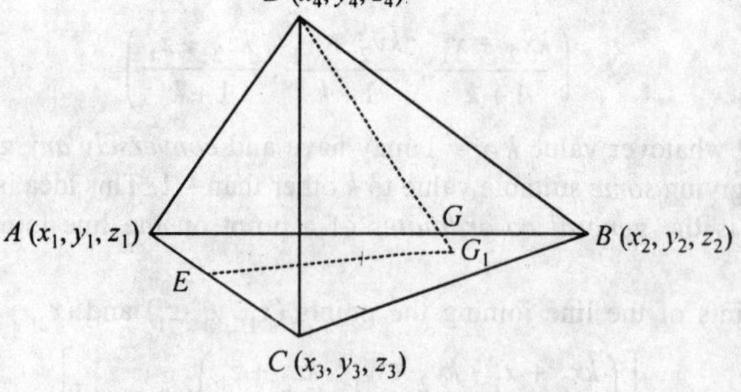

Fig. 5

Hence, G_1 will be

$$\left[\frac{2 \cdot \dfrac{1}{2}(x_1 + x_3) + x_2}{2 + 1}, \frac{2 \cdot \dfrac{1}{2}(y_1 + y_3) + y_2}{2 + 1}, \frac{2 \cdot \dfrac{1}{2}(z_1 + z_3) + z_2}{2 + 1} \right]$$

i.e., $\left(\dfrac{x_1 + x_2 + x_3}{3}, \dfrac{y_1 + y_2 + y_3}{3}, \dfrac{z_1 + z_2 + z_3}{3} \right).$

Centre of gravity $G(x, y, z)$ of the tetrahedron lies on DG_1 and divides it in the ratio $3 : 1$.

$$\therefore \qquad x = \frac{3 \cdot \frac{1}{3}(x_1 + x_2 + x_3) + x_4}{3 + 1} = \frac{x_1 + x_2 + x_3 + x_4}{4}$$

Similarly, $\quad y = \dfrac{y_1 + y_2 + y_3 + y_4}{4}$ and $z = \dfrac{z_1 + z_2 + z_3 + z_4}{4}$.

4. *Find the ratio in which the sphere $x^2 + y^2 + z^2 = 350$ divides the line joining the points $(3, -1, 2)$ and $(9, -3, 6)$.*

Sol. Let the line joining the two points intersect the sphere at the point (x_1, y_1, z_1) and this divides the join of two points in the ratio $k : 1$. Then

$$x_1^2 + y_1^2 + z_1^2 = 350 \qquad \qquad \text{...(i)}$$

and $\qquad x_1 = \dfrac{9k + 3}{k + 1}, \; y_1 = \dfrac{-3k - 1}{k + 1}, \; z_1 = \dfrac{6k + 2}{k + 1}$

$$\Rightarrow \quad \left(\frac{9k + 3}{k + 1}\right)^2 + \left(\frac{-3k - 1}{k + 1}\right)^2 + \left(\frac{6k + 2}{k + 1}\right)^2 = 350$$

$$\Rightarrow \quad (3k + 1)^2 = 25(1 + k)^2$$

$$\Rightarrow \quad (3k + 1) = \pm 5(1 + k) \Rightarrow k = -2, \text{ or } k = -3/4.$$

Hence, the required ratios are $-2 : 1$ and $-3 : 4$.

5. *From any point $(1, -2, 3)$, lines are drawn to meet the sphere $x^2 + y^2 + z^2 = 4$ and they are divided in the ratio $2 : 3$. Prove that the points of section lie on a sphere.*

Sol. Let the line through $(1, -2, 3)$ meets the sphere in point (x_1, y_1, z_1). Hence,

$$x_1^2 + y_1^2 + z_1^2 = 4 \qquad \qquad \text{...(1)}$$

Let the point (α, β, γ) divide the line joining the points $(1, -2, 3)$ and (x_1, y_1, z_1) in the ratio $2 : 3$.

Then

$$\alpha = \frac{2 \cdot x_1 + 3 \cdot 1}{2 + 3} \quad \Rightarrow \quad x_1 = \frac{5\alpha - 3}{2}$$

$$\beta = \frac{2 \cdot y_1 + 3(-2)}{2 + 3} \quad \Rightarrow \quad y_1 = \frac{5\beta + 6}{2}$$

$$\gamma = \frac{2 \cdot z_1 + 3 \cdot 3}{2 + 3} \quad \Rightarrow \quad z_1 = \frac{5\gamma - 9}{2}$$

From (1), we have

$$\frac{(5\alpha - 3)^2}{4} + \frac{(5\beta + 6)^2}{4} + \frac{(5\gamma - 9)^2}{4} = 4$$

$$\Rightarrow \quad 25\alpha^2 + 25\beta^2 + 25\gamma^2 - 30\alpha + 60\beta - 90\gamma + 210 = 0$$

$$\Rightarrow \quad 5\alpha^2 + 5\beta^2 + 5\gamma^2 - 6\alpha + 12\beta - 18\gamma + 22 = 0.$$

Hence, locus of (α, β, γ) will be

$$x^2 + y^2 + z^2 - \frac{6}{5}x + \frac{12}{5}y - \frac{18}{5}z + \frac{22}{5} = 0,$$

which is a sphere.

EXERCISES

1. Find the co-ordinates of the points which divide the line joining the points $(2, -4, 3)$ $(-4, 5, -6)$ in the ratios

    (i) $(1 : -4)$ and (ii) $(2 : 1)$.   **[Ans.** (i) $(4, -7, 6)$; (ii) $(-2, 2, -3)$**]**

2. $A(3, 2, 0)$, $B(5, 3, 2)$, $C(-9, 6, -3)$ are three points forming a triangle, AD, the bisector of the angle BAC, meets BC at D. Find the co-ordinates of the point D.

$$\left[\textbf{Ans. } \frac{38}{16}, \frac{57}{16}, \frac{97}{16}\right]$$

3. Find the ratio in which the line joining the point
$$(2, 4, 5), (3, 5, -4)$$
    is divided by the YZ-plane.   **[Ans.** $-2 : 3$**]**

4. Find the ratio in which the XY-plane divides the join of
$$(-3, 4, -8) \text{ and } (5, -6, 4).$$
    Also obtain the point of intersection of the line with the plane. **[Ans.** 2; $(7/3, -8/3, 0)$**]**

5. The three points $A(0, 0, 0)$, $B(2, -3, 3)$, $C(-2, 3, -3)$, are collinear. Find the ratio in which each point divides the segment joining the other two.

                  [Ans. $AB/BC = -1/2$, $BC/CA = -2$, $CA/AB = 1$**]**

6. Show that the following triads of points are collinear :

    (i) $\{(2, 5, -4), (1, 4, -3), (4, 7, -6)\}$ (ii) $\{(5, 4, 2), (6, 2, -1), (8, -2, -7)\}$.

7. Find the ratios in which the join of the points $(3, 2, 1)$, $(1, 3, 2)$ is divided by the locus of the equation $3x^2 - 72y^2 + 128z^2 = 3$.   **[Ans.** $-2 : 1$; $1 : -2$**]**

8. $A(4, 8, 12)$, $B(2, 4, 6)$, $C(3, 5, 4)$, and $D(5, 8, 5)$ are four points; show that the lines AB and CD intersect.

9. Show that the point $(1, -1, 2)$, is common to the lines which join $(6, -7, 0)$ to $(16, -19, -4)$ and $(0, 3, -6)$ to $(2, -5, 10)$.

10. Show that the set of points on the plane determined by the three points (x_1, y_1, z_1), (x_2, y_2, z_2) and (x_3, y_3, z_3) is

$$\left[\left(\frac{lx_1 + mx_2 + nx_3}{l + m + n}, \frac{ly_1 + my_2 + ny_3}{l + m + n}, \frac{lz_1 + mz_2 + nz_3}{l + m + n}\right); l + m + n \neq 0\right].$$

11. Show that the centroid of the triangle with vertices (x_r, y_r, z_r), $r = 1, 2, 3$ is

$$\left(\frac{x_1 + x_2 + x_3}{3}, \frac{y_1 + y_2 + y_3}{3}, \frac{z_1 + z_2 + z_3}{3}\right).$$ *(Bundelkhand, 1997)*

1.4. TETRAHEDRON

Tetrahedron is a figure bounded by four planes, not all of which pass through the same point. It has four vertices, each vertex arising as a point of intersection of three of the four planes. It has six edges; each edge arising as the line of intersection of two of the four planes ($^4C_2 = 6$).

To construct a tetrahedron, we start with three points A, B, C, and any point D, not lying on the plane determined by the points A, B, C. Of the tetrahedron, thus formed, the four points A, B, C, D are the four vertices, the four triangles ABC, BCD, CAD, ABD are the four faces, and the lines AB, CD; BC, AD; CA, BD are the six edges.

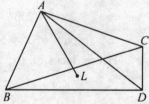

Fig. 6

The two edges *AB*, *CD* joining separately the points *A*, *B* and *C*, *D* are called a pair of *opposite edges*. Similarly *BC*, *AD* and *CA*, *DB* are the two other pairs of opposite edges*.

EXERCISES

1. The four lines drawn from the vertices of a tetrahedron to the centroids of the opposite faces meet in a point which is at three-fourths of the distance from each vertex to the opposite face.

2. Show that the three lines joining the mid-points of opposite edges of a tetrahedron meet in a point.

1.5. ANGLE BETWEEN TWO LINES

The meaning of the angle between two intersecting, *i.e.*, coplanar lines, is already known to the student. We now give the definition of the angle between two non-coplanar lines, also sometimes called *skew* lines.

Def. *The angle between two* **non-coplanar,** *i.e.*, *non-intersecting lines is the angle between two intersecting lines drawn from any point parallel to each of the given lines.*

Note 1. To justify the definition of angle between two non-coplanar lines, as given above, it is necessary to show that this angle is independent of the position of the point through which the parallel lines are drawn, but here we simply assume this result.

Note 2. The angle between a given line and the co-ordinate axes are the angles which the line drawn through the origin parallel to the given lines makes with the axes.

(*Kumaon, 1995, 2001; Kanpur, 1999*)

1.6. DIRECTION COSINES OF A LINE

Let α, β, γ be the angles which any line makes with the positive directions of the co-ordinate axes. Then cos α, cos β, cos γ re called the *direction cosines* of the given line and are generally denoted by *l*, *m*, *n* respectively.

Ex. What are the direction cosines of the axes of co-ordinates ?

[**Ans.** 1, 0, 0; 0, 1, 0; 0, 0, 1]

1.6.1. A Useful Relation

If O be the origin of co-ordinates and (*x*, *y*, *z*) *the co-ordinates of a point P, then*

$$x = lr, \, y = mr, \, z = nr,$$

l, *m*, *n* *being the direction cosines of the line OP and r, the length of the segment OP.*

Through the point *P* draw the line *PL* perpendicular to the *X*-axis so that *OL* = *x*.

From the right-angled triangle *OPL*, we have

$$\frac{OL}{OP} = \cos \angle LOP \; \Rightarrow \; \frac{x}{r} = l \; \Rightarrow \; x = lr.$$

---

* The three points, A, B, C may be imagined as lying on the plane of the paper and the point D as lying above this plane.

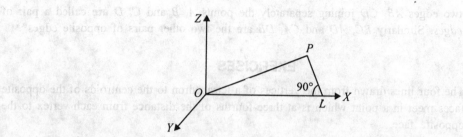

Fig. 7

Similarly, we have

$$y = mr, \ z = nr.$$

1.7. RELATION BETWEEN DIRECTION COSINES

If l, m, n are the direction cosines of a line, then

$$l^2 + m^2 + n^2 = 1,$$

i.e., the sum of the squares of the direction cosines of every line is one.

         (Kumaon, 1996, 98, 2001; Kanpur, 1998, 2001, 2005; Gorakhpur, 2002)

Let OP be drawn through the origin parallel to the given lines so that l, m, n are the cosines of the angles which the line OP makes with the co-ordinate axes OX, OY, OZ respectively (*Refer Fig. 7*).

Let (x, y, z) be the co-ordinates of any point P on this line.

Let $OP = r.$

We have $x = lr, \ y = mr, \ z = nr.$

Squaring and adding, we obtain

$$x^2 + y^2 + z^2 = (l^2 + m^2 + n^2)\,r^2$$

$$\Rightarrow \qquad r^2 = OP^2 = x^2 + y^2 + z^2 = (l^2 + m^2 + n^2)\,r^2$$

$$\Rightarrow \qquad l^2 + m^2 + n^2 = 1.$$

Cor. If a, b, c be three numbers *proportional* to the direction cosines l, m, n of a line, we have

$$\frac{l}{a} = \frac{m}{b} = \frac{n}{c} = \pm \frac{\sqrt{l^2 + m^2 + n^2}}{\sqrt{a^2 + b^2 + c^2}} = \pm \frac{1}{\sqrt{a^2 + b^2 + c^2}}$$

$$\Rightarrow \qquad l = \pm \frac{a}{\sqrt{a^2 + b^2 + c^2}}, \ m = \pm \frac{b}{\sqrt{a^2 + b^2 + c^2}}, \ n = \pm \frac{c}{\sqrt{a^2 + b^2 + c^2}},$$

where the same sign, positive or negative, is to be chosen throughout.

Direction Ratios. From above, we see that a set of three numbers which are proportional to the direction cosines of a line are sufficient to specify the direction of a line. Such numbers are called the **direction ratios** or **direction numbers** of the line. Thus, if a, b, c be the direction ratios of a line, its direction cosines are

$$\pm \frac{a}{\sqrt{\Sigma a^2}}, \ \pm \frac{b}{\sqrt{\Sigma a^2}}, \ \pm \frac{c}{\sqrt{\Sigma a^2}}.$$

Note. It is easy to see that if a line OP through the origin O makes angles α, β, γ with OX, OY, OZ, then the line OP' obtained by producing OP backwards through O will make angles $\pi - \alpha$,

$\pi - \beta$, $\pi - \gamma$ with the axes OX, OY, OZ. Thus, if

$$\cos \alpha = l, \cos \beta = m, \cos \gamma = n$$

are the direction cosines of OP, then

$$\cos (\pi - \alpha) = -l, \cos (\pi - \beta) = -m, \cos (\pi - \gamma) = -n$$

are the direction cosines of OP' i.e., of the line OP produced backwards.

Thus, if we ignore the two senses of a line, we can think of the direction cosines l, m, n or $-l$, $-m$, $-n$, determining the direction of one and the same line. This explains the ambiguity in the sign obtained above.

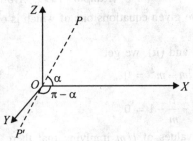

Fig. 8

Note. The student should always make a distinction between direction cosines and direction ratios. It is only when l, m, n are direction cosines, that we have the relation

$$l^2 + m^2 + n^2 = 1.$$

EXAMPLES

1. *If α, β, γ be the angles which a line makes with the positive direction of the axes, prove that*

$$sin^2 \alpha + sin^2 \beta + sin^2 \gamma = 2.$$

(Gorakhpur, 1999, 2001; Bundelkhand, 1998; Rohilkhand, 1998)

Sol. We have

$$l = \cos \alpha, \ m = \cos \beta, \ n = \cos \gamma$$

$\therefore \qquad \cos^2 \alpha + \cos^2 \beta + \cos^2 \gamma = 1$

$\Rightarrow \qquad 1 - \sin^2 \alpha + 1 - \sin^2 \beta + 1 - \sin^2 \gamma = 1$

$\Rightarrow \qquad \sin^2 \alpha + \sin^2 \beta + \sin^2 \gamma = 2.$

2. *The vertices of a triangle ABC are the points $(-1, 2, -3)$, $(5, 0, -6)$ and $(0, 4, -1)$ respectively. Determine the direction ratios of the bisector of the angle BAC.*

Sol. We have

$$AB = \sqrt{(5+1)^2 + (0-2)^2 + (-6+3)^2} = 7$$

and $\qquad AC = 3$

By geometry, the bisector of angle BAC will divide the side BC in the ratio $7 : 3$.

Hence, co-ordinates of D are

$$\left[\frac{7 \cdot 0 + 3 \cdot 5}{7 + 3}, \frac{7 \cdot 4 + 3 \cdot 0}{7 + 3}, \frac{7 \cdot (-1) + 3 \cdot (-6)}{7 + 3} \right]$$

$$\Rightarrow \left(\frac{3}{2}, \frac{14}{5}, -\frac{5}{2} \right).$$

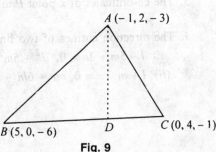

Fig. 9

Hence, the direction ratios of bisector AD are

$$\left\{\frac{3}{2}-(-1)\right\}, \left\{\frac{14}{5}-2\right\}, \left\{\frac{-5}{2}-(-3)\right\}$$

$\Rightarrow$ 25, 8, 5.

3. *The direction cosines* $l, m, n,$ *of two lines are connected by the relations*

$$l + m + n = 0 \qquad \qquad ...(i)$$

$$2lm + 2ln - mn = 0 \qquad \qquad ...(ii)$$

ind them.   *(Kanpur. 1999; Avadh, 2006; Poorvanchal, 1998)*

Sol. We shall solve the two given equations one of which is of the first degree and the other of second degree in l, m, n.

Eliminating n between (i) and (ii), we get

$$2l^2 - lm - m^2 = 0$$

$\Rightarrow$ $$2\left(\frac{l}{m}\right)^2 - \frac{l}{m} - 1 = 0 \qquad \qquad ...(iii)$$

This equation gives two values of l/m implying that there are two lines. Let l_1, m_1, n_1; l_2, m_2, n_2 be the direction cosines of these lines.

The two roots of the quadratic equation (iii) in l/m are 1 and $- 1/2$.

Also $\qquad l_1 + m_1 + n_1 = 0 \Rightarrow \dfrac{l_1}{m_1} + 1 + \dfrac{n_1}{m_1} = 0 \Rightarrow \dfrac{n_1}{m_1} = -2$

$$l_2 + m_2 + n_2 = 0 \Rightarrow \frac{l_2}{m_2} + 1 + \frac{n_2}{m_2} = 0 \Rightarrow \frac{n_2}{m_2} = -\frac{1}{2}$$

Thus, we have

$$\frac{l_1}{1} = \frac{m_1}{1} = \frac{n_1}{-2} = \frac{1}{\sqrt{6}} \Rightarrow l_1 = \frac{1}{\sqrt{6}}, m_1 = \frac{1}{\sqrt{6}}, n_1 = -\frac{2}{\sqrt{6}}$$

$$\frac{l_2}{1} = \frac{m_2}{-2} = \frac{n_2}{1} = \frac{1}{\sqrt{6}} \Rightarrow l_2 = \frac{1}{\sqrt{6}}, m_2 = -\frac{2}{\sqrt{6}}, n_2 = -\frac{1}{\sqrt{6}}.$$

EXERCISES

1. 6, 2, 3 are direction ratios of a line. What are the direction cosines ?

[**Ans.** 6/7, 2/7, 3/7]

2. What are the direction cosines of lines equally inclined to the axes ? How many such lines are there ?   *(Kanpur, 1996, Banglore, 2001)* [**Ans.** $(1/\sqrt{3}, 1/\sqrt{3}, 1/\sqrt{3})$; 4]

3. The co-ordinates of a point P are (3, 12, 4). Find the direction cosines of the line OP.

[**Ans.** 3/13, 12/13, 4/13]

4. The direction cosines of two lines are determined by the relations

) $l - 5m + 3n = 0$, $7l^2 + 5m^2 - 3n^2 = 0$;   *(Kumaon 2006, Kanpur, 199*

(ii) $l + m - n = 0$, $mn + 6ln - 12lm = 0$.

$$\left[\begin{array}{l} \textbf{Ans.} \ (i) \ \dfrac{1}{\sqrt{14}}, \dfrac{2}{\sqrt{14}}, \dfrac{3}{\sqrt{14}}; -\dfrac{1}{\sqrt{6}}, \dfrac{1}{\sqrt{6}}, \dfrac{2}{\sqrt{6}}; \\ \\ \quad (ii) \ \dfrac{1}{\sqrt{26}}, \dfrac{3}{\sqrt{26}}, \dfrac{4}{\sqrt{26}}; \dfrac{1}{\sqrt{14}}, \dfrac{2}{\sqrt{14}}, \dfrac{3}{\sqrt{14}} \end{array}\right]$$

1.8. PROJECTION ON A STRAIGHT LINE

1.8.1. Projection of a Point on a Line

The foot of the perpendicular from a given point on a given straight line is called the orthogonal projection (or simply projection) *of the point on the line.*
This projection is the same point where the plane through the given point and perpendicular to the given line meets the line.

Thus, in Fig. 1, page 1, the point A is the projection of the point P on X-axis; also the points B and C are the projections of the point P on Y-axis and Z-axis respectively.

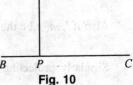

Fig. 10

1.8.2. Projection of a Segment on Another Line

The projection of a segment AB on a line CD is the segment $A'B'$ where A', B' are the projections of points A, B respectively on the line CD.

Clearly the projection $A'B'$ of the segment AB is the intercept made on CD by planes perpendicular to the line CD through the points A and B.

Ex. The co-ordinates of a point P are (x, y, z). What are the projections of the segment OP on the co-ordinate axes ?

Theorem. *The projection of a segment AB on a line CD is AB cos* θ*, where* θ *is the angle between the lines AB and CD.*

Let the planes through the points A and B perpendicular to the line CD meet the line CD in A', B' respectively so that $A'B'$ is the projection of AB. Through the point A draw a line $AP \parallel CD$ to meet the plane through the point B at P.

Now $\qquad\qquad\qquad AP \parallel CD$

$\Rightarrow \qquad\qquad\qquad \angle PAB = \theta.$

Also BP lies in the plane which is perpendicular to AP

$\Rightarrow \qquad\qquad\qquad \angle APB = 90°.$

Hence, $\qquad\qquad\qquad AP = AB \cos \theta$

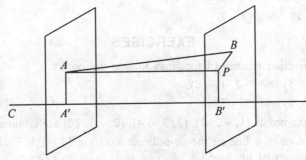

Fig. 11

Clearly $A'B'PA$ is a rectangle implying that

$$AP = A'B'.$$

Hence, $\qquad\qquad A'B' = AB \cos \theta.$

Cor. Direction cosines of the join of two points.

To find the direction cosines of the line joining the two points

$$P(x_1, y_1, z_1) \text{ and } Q(x_2, y_2, z_2).$$

Let the points L, M be the feet of the perpendicular drawn from the points P, Q to the X-axis respectively so that we have

$$OL = x_1, \ OM = x_2.$$

Projection of the segment PQ on X-axis $= LM$

$$= OM - OL = x_2 - x_1.$$

Also if l, m, n be the direction cosines of the line PQ, the projection of PQ on X-axis $= l \cdot PQ$.

$$l \cdot PQ = x_2 - x_1.$$

Similarly projecting PQ on Y-axis and Z-axis, we get

$$m \cdot PQ = y_2 - y_1,$$
$$n \cdot PQ = z_2 - z_1.$$

From these we obtain the relations*,

$$\frac{x_2 - x_1}{l} = \frac{y_2 - y_1}{m} = \frac{z_2 - z_1}{n} = PQ.$$

Thus, the direction cosines of the line joining the two points

$$(x_1, y_1, z_1) \ and \ (x_2, y_2, z_2)$$

are proportional to

$$x_2 - x_1, y_2 - y_1, z_2 - z_1.$$

EXAMPLE

The projection of a line on the axes are 2, 3, 6. What is the length of the line ?

Sol. Let PQ be the length of the line and $[l, m, n]$ be the direction cosines. Then,

projection on x-axis, $PQ \cdot l = 2,$

projection on y-axis, $PQ \cdot m = 3,$

projection on z-axis, $PQ \cdot n = 6.$

Squaring and adding, we get

$$PQ^2 \ (l^2 + m^2 + n^2) = 2^2 + 3^2 + 6^2$$

$\Rightarrow \qquad PQ^2 = 49 \ \Rightarrow \ PQ = 7.$

EXERCISES

1. Find the direction cosines of the lines joining the points
   (*i*) $(4, 3, -5)$ and $(-2, 1, -8)$.   [**Ans.** 6/7, 2/7, 3/7]
   (*ii*) $(7, -5, 9)$ and $(5, -3, 8)$.   [**Ans.** 2/3, -2/3, 1/3]
2. Show that the points $(1, -2, 3)$, $(2, 3, -4)$, $(0, -7, 10)$ are collinear.
3. The projections of a line on the co-ordinate axes are 12, 4, 3. Find the length and the direction cosines of the line.   [**Ans.** 13; (12/13, 4/13, 3/13)]

1.8.3. Projection of a Broken Line

If P_1, P_2, P_3, ..., P_n be a number of points in space, then the sum of the projections of the segments

$$P_1P_2, \ P_2P_3, \ ....., \ P_{n-1}P_n$$

on any line is equal to the projection of the segment P_1P_n on the same line.

---

*The relations can be given in this form only if none of l, m, n is zero.

Let $$Q_1, Q_2, Q_3, ..., Q_n$$
be the projections of the points
$$P_1, P_2, P_3, ..., P_n$$
on the given line. Then,
$$Q_1Q_2 = \text{projection of } P_1P_2$$
$$Q_2Q_3 = \text{projection of } P_2P_3$$
and so on.

Also $$Q_1Q_n = \text{projection of } P_1P_n.$$

As $Q_1, Q_2, Q_3, ..., Q_n$ lie on the same line, we have for all relative positions of these points on the line, the relation
$$Q_1Q_2 + Q_2Q_3 + ... + Q_{n-1}Q_n = Q_1Q_n.$$

Hence, the result.

1.8.4. Projection of the Join of Two Points on a Line

To show that the projection of the segment joining the points
$$P(x_1, y_1, z_1) \text{ and } Q(x_2, y_2, z_2)$$
on a line with direction cosines, l, m, n is
$$(x_2 - x_1)\, l + (y_2 - y_1)\, m + (z_2 - z_1)\, n.$$

Through P, Q draw planes parallel to the co-ordinate planes to form a rectangular parallelopiped whose one diagonal is PQ (See Fig. 3, page 3).

Now
$$PA = x_2 - x_1, \ AN = y_2 - y_1, \ NQ = z_2 - z_1.$$

The lines PA, AN, NQ are respectively parallel to X-axis, Y-axis, Z-axis. Therefore, their respective projections on the line with direction cosines l, m, n are
$$(x_2 - x_1)\, l, \ (y_2 - y_1)\, m, \ (z_2 - z_1)\, n.$$

As the projection of the segment PQ on any line is equal to the sum of the projections of the segments PA, AN, NQ on that line, the required projection is
$$(x_2 - x_1)\, l + (y_2 - y_1)\, m + (z_2 - z_1)\, n.$$

EXERCISES

1. $A\,(6, 3, 2)$, $B\,(5, 1, 4)$, $C\,(3, -4, 7)$, $D\,(0, 2, 5)$ are four points. Find the projections of the segment AB on the line CD and the segment CD on the line AB.

[**Ans.** $- 13/7; - 13/3$]

2. Show by projection that if P, Q, R, S are the points $(6, -6, 0)$, $(-1, -7, 6)$, $(3, -4, 4)$, $(2, -9, 2)$ respectively, then $PQ \perp RS$.

1.9. ANGLE BETWEEN TWO LINES

To find the angle between lines whose direction cosines are (l_1, m_1, n_1) and (l_2, m_2, n_2).

(*Garhwal, 1999; Kumaon, 2002, 2004; Kanpur, 1997; Patna, 2003*)

Let OP_1, OP_2 be lines through the origin parallel to the given line so that the cosines of the angles which OP_1 and OP_2 make with the axes are l_1, m_1, n_1 and l_2, m_2, n_2 respectively and the angle between the given lines is the angle between OP_1 and OP_2. Let this angle be θ.

Let the co-ordinates of P_2 be (x_2, y_2, z_2).

The projection of the segment OP_2 joining
$$O\ (0, 0, 0) \text{ and } P_2\ (x_2, y_2, z_2)$$
on the line OP_1 with direction cosines
$$l_1, m_1, n_1$$
is $\qquad (x_2 - 0)\ l_1 + (y_2 - 0)\ m_1 + (z_2 - 0)\ n_1 = l_1 x_2 + m_1 y_2 + n_1 z_2.$

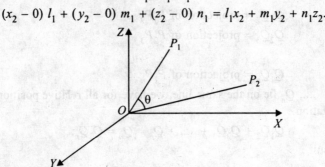

Fig. 12

Also this projection is $OP_2 \cos \theta.$

$\therefore \qquad OP_2 \cos \theta = l_1 x_2 + m_1 y_2 + n_1 z_2.$

But $\qquad x_2 = l_2 \cdot OP_2, y_2 = m_2 \cdot OP_2, z_2 = n_2 \cdot OP_2 \qquad$ (§ 1.6.1)

$\therefore \qquad OP_2 \cos \theta = (l_1 l_2 + m_1 m_2 + n_1 n_2)\ OP_2$

$\Rightarrow \qquad \cos \theta = l_1 l_2 + m_1 m_2 + n_1 n_2.$

Second Method. Suppose $OP_1 = r_1, OP_2 = r_2.$

Let the co-ordinates of the points P_1, P_2 be (x_1, y_1, z_1) and (x_2, y_2, z_2) respectively, so that
$$x_1 = r_1 l_1, \quad y_1 = r_1 m_1, \quad z_1 = r_1 n_1 \qquad (\S\ 1.6.1)$$
$$x_2 = r_2 l_2, \quad y_2 = r_2 m_2, \quad z_2 = r_2 n_2.$$

We have
$$P_1 P_2^{\ 2} = (x_2 - x_1)^2 + (y_2 - y_1)^2 + (z_2 - z_1)^2$$
$$= (x_2^{\ 2} + y_2^{\ 2} + z_2^{\ 2}) + (x_1^{\ 2} + y_1^{\ 2} + z_1^{\ 2}) - 2\ (x_1 x_2 + y_1 y_2 + z_1 z_2)$$
$$= r_2^{\ 2} + r_1^{\ 2} - 2 r_2 r_1\ (l_1 l_2 + m_1 m_2 + n_1 n_2). \qquad \qquad …(i)$$

Also from the cosine rule in Trigonometry, we have
$$P_1 P_2^{\ 2} = r_1^{\ 2} + r_2^{\ 2} - 2 r_1 r_2 \cos \theta. \qquad \qquad …(ii)$$

Therefore, from (i) and (ii), we obtain
$$r_1^{\ 2} + r_2^{\ 2} - 2 r_1 r_2 \cos \theta = P_1 P_2^{\ 2} = r_1^{\ 2} + r_2^{\ 2} - 2 r_1 r_2\ (l_1 l_2 + m_1 m_2 + n_1 n_2)$$
$$\Rightarrow \qquad \cos \theta = l_1 l_2 + m_1 m_2 + n_1 n_2.$$

Cor. 1. sin θ and tan θ. The expressions for $\sin \theta$ and $\tan \theta$ in a convenient form are obtained as follows :
$$\sin^2 \theta = 1 - \cos^2 \theta = 1 - (l_1 l_2 + m_1 m_2 + n_1 n_2)^2$$
$$= (l_1^{\ 2} + m_1^{\ 2} + n_1^{\ 2})\ (l_2^{\ 2} + m_2^{\ 2} + n_2^{\ 2}) - (l_1 l_2 + m_1 m_2 + n_1 n_2)^2$$
$$= (l_1 m_2 - l_2 m_1)^2 + (m_1 n_2 - m_2 n_1)^2 + (n_1 l_2 - n_2 l_1)^2.$$

$$\Rightarrow \qquad \sin\theta = \pm \sqrt{\Sigma(l_1 m_2 - l_2 m_1)^2}.$$

Also $\qquad \tan\theta = \dfrac{\sin\theta}{\cos\theta} = \pm \dfrac{\sqrt{\Sigma(l_1 m_2 - l_2 m_1)^2}}{\Sigma l_1 l_2}.$

Cor. 2. If the direction cosines of two lines be proportional to a_1, b_1, c_1 and a_2, b_2, c_2, so that their actual values are

$$\pm \frac{a_1}{\sqrt{a_1^2 + b_1^2 + c_1^2}}, \pm \frac{b_1}{\sqrt{a_1^2 + b_1^2 + c_1^2}}, \pm \frac{c_1}{\sqrt{a_1^2 + b_1^2 + c_1^2}};$$

$$\pm \frac{a_2}{\sqrt{a_2^2 + b_2^2 + c_2^2}}, \pm \frac{b_2}{\sqrt{a_2^2 + b_2^2 + c_2^2}}, \pm \frac{c_2}{\sqrt{a_2^2 + b_2^2 + c_2^2}},$$

and if θ be the angle between the given lines, we have

$$\cos\theta = \pm \frac{a_1 a_2 + b_1 b_2 + c_1 c_2}{\sqrt{a_1^2 + b_1^2 + c_1^2}\ \sqrt{a_2^2 + b_2^2 + c_2^2}},$$

$$\sin\theta = \pm \frac{\sqrt{(a_1 b_2 - a_2 b_1)^2 + (b_1 c_2 - b_2 c_1)^2 + (c_1 a_2 - c_2 a_1)^2}}{\sqrt{a_1^2 + b_1^2 + c_1^2}\ \sqrt{a_2^2 + b_2^2 + c_2^2}};$$

$$\tan\theta = \pm \frac{\sqrt{\Sigma(a_1 b_2 - a_2 b_1)^2}}{\Sigma a_1 a_2}.$$

The expression for $\tan\theta$ is the same whether we use direction cosines or direction ratios.

Cor. 3. Conditions for perpendicularity and parallelism.

(*i*) The given lines are perpendicular

$$\Rightarrow \qquad\qquad\qquad \theta = 90°$$

$$\Rightarrow \qquad\qquad\qquad \cos\theta = 0$$

$$\Rightarrow \qquad\qquad a_1 a_2 + b_1 b_2 + c_1 c_2 = 0.$$

(*ii*) The given lines are parallel

$\Rightarrow \qquad$ the lines through the origin drawn parallel to the lines coincide.

$\Rightarrow \qquad$ the direction cosines of the lines are the same.

$\Rightarrow \qquad$ the direction ratios of the lines are proportional.

EXAMPLES

1. *Find the direction cosines of the line which is perpendicular to the lines with direction cosines proportional to* $(1, -2, -2)$, $(0, 2, 1)$.

Sol. If l, m, n be the direction cosines of the line perpendicular to the given lines, we have

$$l(1) + m(-2) + n(-2) = 0 \Rightarrow l - 2m - 2n = 0,$$

$$l(0) + m(2) + n(1) = 0 \Rightarrow 0l + 2m + n = 0.$$

These give $\dfrac{l}{2} = \dfrac{m}{-1} = \dfrac{n}{2}.$

$$\therefore \qquad l = \frac{2}{\sqrt{2^2 + (-1)^2 + 2^2}} = \frac{2}{3}, \ m = -\frac{1}{3}, \ n = \frac{2}{3}.$$

2. l_1, m_1, n_1; l_2, m_2, n_2 *are the direction cosines of two mutually perpendicular lines. Show that the direction cosines of the line perpendicular to them both are*

$$m_1n_2 - m_2n_1, \ n_1l_2 - n_2l_1, \ l_1m_2 - l_2m_1.$$

(Garhwal, 1996; Poorvanchal, 1997)

Sol. If l, m, n be the direction cosines of the required line, we have

$$ll_1 + mm_1 + nn_1 = 0$$

$$ll_2 + mm_2 + nn_2 = 0$$

$$\Rightarrow \qquad \frac{l}{m_1n_2 - m_2n_1} = \frac{m}{n_1l_2 - n_2l_1} = \frac{n}{l_1m_2 - l_2m_1} = \frac{\sqrt{\Sigma l^2}}{\sqrt{\Sigma (m_1n_2 - m_2n_1)^2}} = \frac{1}{\sin\theta},$$

where θ is the angle between the given lines. As $\theta = 90°$, we have $\sin\theta = 1$. Hence, the result.

3. *A line makes angles* α, β, γ, δ *with the four diagonals of a cube, prove that*

$$\cos^2\alpha + \cos^2\beta + \cos^2\gamma + \cos^2\delta = \frac{4}{3}.$$

(Avadh, 1996, 97; Garhwal, 1997, 99; Kanpur, 1998)

Sol. Let a be the length of each side of the cube. Taking three coterminous edges OA, OB, OC as axes, the co-ordinates of various vertices will be A $(a, 0, 0)$, L $(a, a, 0)$, B $(0, a, 0)$, N $(0, a, a)$, C $(0, 0, a)$, M $(a, 0, a)$, P (a, a, a) and O $(0, 0, 0)$.

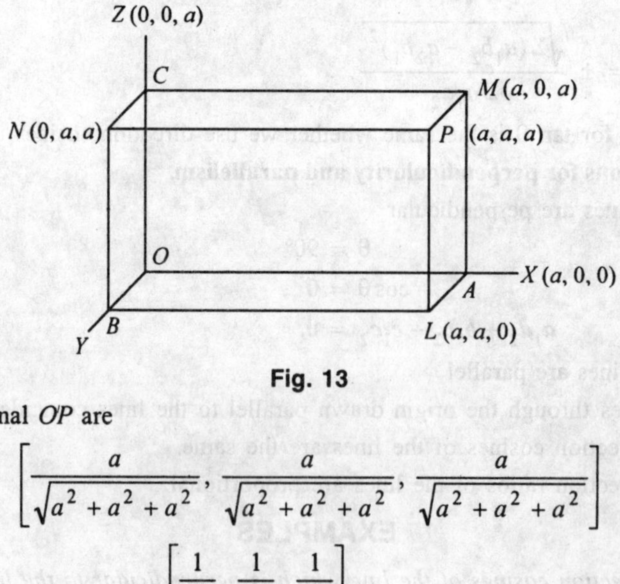

Fig. 13

d.c.'s of diagonal OP are

$$\left[\frac{a}{\sqrt{a^2 + a^2 + a^2}}, \ \frac{a}{\sqrt{a^2 + a^2 + a^2}}, \ \frac{a}{\sqrt{a^2 + a^2 + a^2}} \right]$$

$$\Rightarrow \qquad \left[\frac{1}{\sqrt{3}}, \ \frac{1}{\sqrt{3}}, \ \frac{1}{\sqrt{3}} \right]$$

Similarly, d.c.'s of AN are $\left[-\frac{1}{\sqrt{3}}, \ \frac{1}{\sqrt{3}}, \ \frac{1}{\sqrt{3}} \right]$

of BM are $\left[\frac{1}{\sqrt{3}}, \ \frac{1}{\sqrt{3}}, \ -\frac{1}{\sqrt{3}} \right]$

and of CL are $\left[\frac{1}{\sqrt{3}}, \ \frac{1}{\sqrt{3}}, \ -\frac{1}{\sqrt{3}} \right].$

If [l, m, n] be the d.c.'s of a line which makes angles α, β, γ, δ with these four diagonals of the cube, then

$$\cos \alpha = \frac{l + m + n}{\sqrt{3}}, \quad \cos \beta = \frac{-l + m + n}{\sqrt{3}}, \quad \cos \gamma = \frac{l - m + n}{\sqrt{3}} \text{ and } \cos \delta = \frac{l + m - n}{\sqrt{3}}$$

Hence,

$$\cos^2 \alpha + \cos^2 \beta + \cos^2 \gamma + \cos^2 \delta$$

$$= \frac{1}{3} [(l + m + n)^2 + (-l + m + n)^2 + (l - m + n)^2 + (l + m - n)^2]$$

$$= \frac{4}{3}.$$

4. *Show that the straight lines whose direction cosines are given by the equations*

$$al + bm + cn = 0, \quad ul^2 + vm^2 + wn^2 = 0$$

are perpendicular or parallel according as

$$a^2 (v + w) + b^2 (w + u) + c^2 (u + v) = 0 \text{ or } a^2/u + b^2/v + c^2/w = 0.$$

(Meerut, 2001; Bundelkhand, 1996; Gorakhpur, 2000;
Avadh, 1998; Kumaon, 2003; Garhwal, 1996, 98)

Sol. Eliminating l, between the given relations, we have

$$\frac{u (bm + cn)^2}{a^2} + vm^2 + wn^2 = 0$$

$$\Rightarrow \quad (b^2 u + a^2 v) m^2 + 2ubcmn + (c^2 u + a^2 w) n^2 = 0. \qquad \ldots(i)$$

If the lines be parallel, their direction cosines are equal so that the two values of m/n must be equal. The condition for this is

$$u^2 b^2 c^2 = (b^2 u + a^2 v)(c^2 u + a^2 w)$$

$$\Rightarrow \quad \frac{a^2}{u} + \frac{b^2}{v} + \frac{c^2}{w} = 0.$$

Again, if l_1, m_1, n_1 and l_2, m_2, n_2 be the direction cosines of the two lines then equation (i) gives

$$\frac{m_1}{n_1} \cdot \frac{m_2}{n_2} = \frac{m_1 m_2}{n_1 n_2} = \frac{c^2 u + a^2 w}{b^2 u + a^2 v}$$

$$\Rightarrow \quad \frac{m_1 m_2}{c^2 u + a^2 w} = \frac{n_1 n_2}{b^2 u + a^2 v}$$

Similarly the elimination of n, gives, (or by symmetry)

$$\frac{l_1 l_2}{b^2 w + c^2 v} = \frac{m_1 m_2}{a^2 w + c^2 u}$$

Thus, we have

$$\frac{l_1 l_2}{b^2 w + c^2 v} = \frac{m_1 m_2}{a^2 w + c^2 u} = \frac{n_1 n_2}{b^2 u + a^2 v} = k, \text{ say.}$$

$$\Rightarrow \quad l_1 l_2 + m_1 m_2 + n_1 n_2 = k (b^2 w + c^2 v + a^2 w + c^2 u + b^2 u + a^2 v)$$

For perpendicular lines

$$l_1 l_2 + m_1 m_2 + n_1 n_2 = 0.$$

Thus, the condition for perpendicularity is

$$a^2 (v + w) + b^2 (w + u) + c^2 (u + v) = 0.$$

5. $l_1, m_1, n_1; l_2, m_2, n_2$ *are the direction cosines of two concurrent lines. Show that the direction cosines of the lines bisecting the angle between them are proportional to*

$$l_1 \pm l_2, \, m_1 \pm m_2, \, n_1 \pm n_2. \qquad \text{(Garhwal 2006)}$$

Sol. Let the lines concur at the origin O and let OA, OB be the two lines. Take points A, B on the two lines such that $OA = OB = r$, say. Also take a point A' on AO produced such that $AO = OA'$. Let C, C' be the mid-points of AB and $A'B$. Then OC, OC' are the required bisectors. The result, now, follows from the fact that the co-ordinates of A, B, A' respectively are

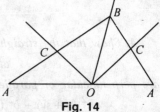

$$(l_1 r, \, m_1 r, \, n_1 r); \, (l_2 r, \, m_2 r, \, n_2 r); \, (- l_1 r, \, - m_1 r, \, - n_1 r).$$

Fig. 14

6. *Show that the angles between the four diagonals of a rectangular parallelopiped are*

$$\cos^{-1} [(\pm a^2 \pm b^2 \pm c^2)/(a^2 + b^2 + c^2)];$$

a, b, c being the edges of the parallelopiped. *(Kanpur, 1997; Meerut, 1996)*

Sol. Take one of the vertices O of the parallelopiped as origin and the three rectangular faces through it as the three rectangular co-ordinate planes. *(See* Fig. 1, page 1*)*. Let

$$OA = a, \, OB = b, \, OC = c.$$

The lines OP, AL, BM, CN are the four diagonals of the parallelopiped.

The co-ordinates of

$$A, B, C \text{ are } (a, 0, 0); \, (0, b, 0); \, (0, 0, c).$$
" $$L, M, N \text{ are } (0, b, c); \, (a, 0, c); \, (a, b, 0).$$
" $$O, P \text{ are } (0, 0, 0); \, (a, b, c).$$

Direction cosines of the line OP are $\dfrac{a}{\sqrt{\Sigma a^2}}, \, \dfrac{b}{\sqrt{\Sigma a^2}}, \, \dfrac{c}{\sqrt{\Sigma a^2}};$

Direction cosines of the line AL are $\dfrac{-a}{\sqrt{\Sigma a^2}}, \, \dfrac{b}{\sqrt{\Sigma a^2}}, \, \dfrac{c}{\sqrt{\Sigma a^2}};$

Direction cosines of the line BM are $\dfrac{a}{\sqrt{\Sigma a^2}}, \, \dfrac{-b}{\sqrt{\Sigma a^2}}, \, \dfrac{c}{\sqrt{\Sigma a^2}};$

Direction cosines of the line CN are $\dfrac{-a}{\sqrt{\Sigma a^2}}, \, \dfrac{b}{\sqrt{\Sigma a^2}}, \, \dfrac{-c}{\sqrt{\Sigma a^2}};$

The angle between OP and CN, therefore, is

$$\cos^{-1} \frac{a^2 + b^2 - c^2}{a^2 + b^2 + c^2}.$$

Similarly the angle between any one of the six pairs of diagonals can be found.

7. *If $l_1, m_1, n_1; l_2, m_2, n_2; l_3, m_3, n_3$ are the direction cosines of three mutually perpendicular lines, show that the line whose direction cosines are proportional to $l_1 + l_2 + l_3, \, m_1 + m_2 + m_3, \, n_1 + n_2 + n_3$ makes equal angles with them.* *(Kanpur, 2002)*

Sol. Since the given lines are mutually perpendicular, hence

$$l_1 l_2 + m_1 m_2 + n_1 n_2 = 0 \qquad \ldots(1)$$
$$l_2 l_3 + m_2 m_3 + n_2 n_3 = 0 \qquad \ldots(2)$$
$$l_1 l_3 + m_1 m_3 + n_1 n_3 = 0 \qquad \ldots(3)$$

Let θ be the angle between the line whose d.c.'s are $[l_1, m_1, n_1]$ and the line whose d.c.'s are proportional to $l_1 + l_2 + l_3, m_1 + m_2 + m_3, n_1 + n_2 + n_3$; then

$$\cos\theta = \frac{l_1 (l_1 + l_2 + l_3) + m_1 (m_1 + m_2 + m_3) + n_1 (n_1 + n_2 + n_3)}{\sqrt{(l_1 + l_2 + l_3)^2 + (m_1 + m_2 + m_3)^2 + (n_1 + n_2 + n_3)^2}}$$

$$= \frac{1}{\sqrt{3}}, \text{ from (1), (2) and (3)}$$

which is independent of $l_1, m_1, n_1; l_2, m_2, n_2; l_3, m_3, n_3$.

Hence, the given line makes equal angles with the three lines.

8. *If a variable line in two adjacent positions had direction cosines $l, m, n; l + \delta l, m + \delta m, n + \delta n$, show that the small angle $\delta\theta$ between two positions is given by*

$$\delta\theta^2 = \delta l^2 + \delta m^2 + \delta n^2. \qquad \textit{(Kanpur, 1997; Avadh, 2003)}$$

Sol. Since $[l, m, n]$ and $[l + \delta l, m + \delta m, n + \delta n]$ are d.c.'s, hence

$$l^2 + m^2 + n^2 = 1 \qquad \ldots(1)$$

and $\qquad (l + \delta l)^2 + (m + \delta m)^2 + (n + \delta n)^2 = 1$

$$\Rightarrow \qquad \delta l^2 + \delta m^2 + \delta n^2 = -2 (l\delta l + m\delta m + n\delta n) \qquad \ldots(2)$$

Now, $\qquad \cos\delta\theta = l(l + \delta l) + m(m + \delta m) + n(n + \delta n)$

$$= l^2 + m^2 + n^2 + l\delta l + m\delta m + n\delta n$$

$$= 1 - \frac{1}{2}\{\delta l^2 + \delta m^2 + \delta n^2\}, \text{ from (1) and (2)}$$

$$\Rightarrow \qquad \delta l^2 + \delta m^2 + \delta n^2 = 2(1 - \cos\delta\theta) = 2 \cdot 2 \sin^2 \frac{\delta\theta}{2}$$

$$= 4\left(\frac{1}{2}\delta\theta\right)^2 = \delta\theta^2.$$

9. *O, A, B, C are four points not necessarily lying in the same plane and such that $OA \perp BC$ and $OB \perp CA$. Prove that $OC \perp AB$.*

What well-known theorem does this become if four points are coplanar?

The result of this example may also be stated thus:

"If two pairs of opposite edges of a tetrahedron be at right angles, then so is the third."

(Kanpur, 1997)

Sol. Take the point O as origin and any three mutually perpendicular lines through O as co-ordinate axes.

Let $(x_1, y_1, z_1), (x_2, y_2, z_2), (x_3, y_3, z_3)$ be the co-ordinates of the points A, B, C respectively.

$$OA \perp BC \Rightarrow x_1(x_2 - x_3) + y_1(y_2 - y_3) + z_1(z_2 - z_3) = 0 \qquad \ldots(i)$$
$$OB \perp CA \Rightarrow x_2(x_3 - x_1) + y_2(y_3 - y_1) + z_2(z_3 - z_1) = 0. \qquad \ldots(ii)$$

Adding (i) and (ii), we obtain

$$x_3(x_2 - x_1) + y_3(y_2 - y_1) + z_3(z_2 - z_1) = 0 \Rightarrow OC \perp AB.$$

EXERCISES

1. Find the angles between the lines whose direction ratios are

 (*i*)　$5, -12, 13; -3, 4, 5$.　　　　　　　　　　　　　　　**[Ans.** $\cos^{-1}(1/65)$**]**

 (*ii*)　$1, 1, 2; \sqrt{3} - 1, -\sqrt{3} - 1, 4$.　　　　　　　　**[Ans.** $\pi/3$**]**

2. If A, B, C, D are the points $(3, 4, 5), (4, 6, 3), (-1, 2, 4)$ and $(1, 0, 5)$, find the angle between CD and AB.　　　　　　　　　　　　　　　　　　　　**[Ans.** $\cos^{-1}(4/9)$**]**

3. Find the angle between any two diagonals of a cube.　　　　**[Ans.** $\cos^{-1}(1/3)$**]**

4. Show that a line can be found perpendicular to the three lines with direction cosines proportional to $(2, 1, 5), (4, -2, 2), (-6, 4, -1)$. Hence, show that if these three lines be concurrent, they are also coplanar.

5. Find the direction cosines of a line which is perpendicular to the lines whose direction ratios are $1, 2, 3; -1, 3, 5$.　　　　**[Ans.** $1/\sqrt{90}, -8/\sqrt{90}, 5/\sqrt{90}$**]**

6. l_1, m_1, n_1 and l_2, m_2, n_2 are the direction ratios of two intersecting lines. Show that lines through the intersection of these two with direction ratios

$$l_1 + kl_2, \; m_1 + km_2, \; n_1 + kn_2$$

are coplanar with them; k being a number whatsoever.

 (Show that they all have a common perpendicular direction.)

7. Show that three concurrent lines with direction cosines

$$(l_1, m_1, n_1), (l_2, m_2, n_2), (l_3, m_3, n_3)$$

are coplanar if and only if

$$\begin{vmatrix} l_1 & m_1 & n_1 \\ l_2 & m_2 & n_2 \\ l_3 & m_3 & n_3 \end{vmatrix} = 0$$
　　　　　　　　　　　　　　　　　　　　　　　　　　　　(Kumaon, 2003)

8. Show that the join of points $(1, 2, 3), (4, 5, 7)$ is parallel to the join of the points $(-4, 3, -6), (2, 9, 2)$.

9. Show that the points $(4, 7, 8), (2, 3, 4), (-1, -2, 1), (1, 2, 5)$ are the vertices of a parallelogram.

10. Show that the points $(5, -1, 1), (7, -4, 7), (1, -6, 10), (-1, -3, 4)$ are the vertices of a rhombus.

11. Show that the points $(0, 4, 1), (2, 3, -1), (4, 5, 0) (2, 6, 2)$ are the vertices of a square.

12. $A(1, 8, 4), B(0, -1 \cdot 1, 4), C(2, -3, 1)$ are three points and D is the foot of the perpendicular from A on BC. Find the co-ordinates of D.　　　　**[Ans.** $4, 5, -2$**]**

13. Find the point in which the join of $(-9, 4, 5)$ and $(11, 0, -1)$ is met by the perpendicular from the origin.　　　　　　　　　　　　　　　　　　　　　**[Ans.** $1, 2, 2$**]**

14. $A(-1, 2, -3), B(5, 0, -6), C(0, 4, -1)$ are three points. Show that the direction cosines of the bisectors of the angle BAC are proportional to $(25, 8, 5)$ and $(-11, 20, 23)$.

 [Hint. Find the co-ordinates of the points which divide BC in the ratio $AB : AC$.]

15. Find the angle between the lines whose direction cosines are given by the equations $3l + m + 5n = 0$ and $6mn - 2nl + 5lm = 0$.　　　　**[Ans.** $\cos^{-1} 1/6$**]**

16. Show that the pair of lines whose direction cosines are given by $3lm - 4ln + mn = 0$, $l + 2m + 3n = 0$ are perpendicular.

17. Find the angle between the lines whose direction cosines satisfy the equations $l + m + n = 0$ and $2nl + 2lm - mn = 0$.　　　　*(Rohilkhand, 1993; Avadh, 1999; Patna, 2003)*

18. Show that the straight lines whose d.c.'s are given by $l + m + n = 0$, $2mn + 3nl - 5lm = 0$
    are perpendicular to each other.   (*Meerut, 2000, 2005*)

19. Find the angle between the lines $l + m + n = 0$, $\dfrac{mn}{q-r} + \dfrac{nl}{r-p} + \dfrac{lm}{p-q} = 0$.

    [Ans. $\pi/3$]

20. Show that the straight lines whose d.c.'s are given by $a^2 l + b^2 m + c^2 n = 0$, $mn + nl + lm$
    $= 0$ will be parallel if $a + b + c = 0$.

21. Show that the straight lines whose direction cosines are given by
    $$al + bm + cn = 0, \ fmn + gnl + hlm = 0,$$
    are perpendicular if
    $$f/a + g/b + h/c = 0,$$
    are parallel if
    $$\sqrt{af} \pm \sqrt{bg} \pm \sqrt{ch} = 0.$$
    (*Rohilkhand, 2003; Avadh, 2001, 2005; Meerut, 1999; Kumaon, 2001; Kanpur, 1996*)

22. If, in a tetrahedron $OABC$,
    $$OA^2 + BC^2 = OB^2 + CA^2 = OC^2 + AB^2$$
    then its pairs of opposite edges are at right angles.

23. l_1, m_1, n_1 and l_2, m_2, n_2 are two directions inclined at an angle φ, to each other. Show that
    $$\frac{l_1 + l_2}{2\cos\dfrac{1}{2}\varphi}, \ \frac{m_1 + m_2}{2\cos\dfrac{1}{2}\varphi}, \ \frac{n_1 + n_2}{2\cos\dfrac{1}{2}\varphi}$$
    are the direction cosines of the line which bisects the angle between these two directions.

24. Show that the direction equally inclined to the three mutually perpendicular directions
    $$l_1, m_1, n_1; \ l_2, m_2, n_2; \ l_3, m_3, n_3$$
    is given by the direction cosines
    $$\frac{l_1 + l_2 + l_3}{\sqrt{3}}, \ \frac{m_1 + m_2 + m_3}{\sqrt{3}}, \ \frac{n_1 + n_2 + n_3}{\sqrt{3}}.$$ (*Kanpur, 1996*)

25. Show that the area of the triangle whose vertices are the origin and the points (x_1, y_1, z_1),
    and (x_2, y_2, z_2) is
    $$\frac{1}{2}\sqrt{(y_1 z_2 - y_2 z_1)^2 + (z_1 x_2 - z_2 x_1)^2 + (x_1 y_2 - x_2 y_1)^2}$$

26. $l_1, m_1, n_1; \ l_2, m_2, n_2; \ l_3, m_3, n_3$ are the direction cosines of three mutually perpendicular
    lines; show that
    $$l_1, l_2, l_3; \ m_1, m_2, m_3; \ n_1, n_2, n_3$$
    are also the direction cosines of three mutually perpendicular lines. Hence, show that

$$\begin{cases} l_1^2 + m_1^2 + n_1^2 = 1, \\ l_2^2 + m_2^2 + n_2^2 = 1, \\ l_3^2 + m_3^2 + n_3^2 = 1, \\ l_1 l_2 + m_1 m_2 + n_1 n_2 = 0, \\ l_2 l_3 + m_2 m_3 + n_2 n_3 = 0, \\ l_3 l_1 + m_3 m_1 + n_3 n_1 = 0, \end{cases} \qquad \begin{cases} l_1^2 + l_2^2 + l_3^2 = 1, \\ m_1^2 + m_2^2 + m_3^2 = 1, \\ n_1^2 + n_2^2 + n_3^2 = 1, \\ l_1 m_1 + l_2 m_2 + l_3 m_3 = 0, \\ m_1 n_1 + m_2 n_3 + m_3 n_3 = 0, \\ n_1 l_1 + n_2 l_2 + n_3 l_3 = 0 \end{cases}$$

OBJECTIVE QUESTIONS

I. Multiple Choice Questions

Note : *For each of the following questions, four alternatives are given for the answer. Only one of them is correct. Choose the correct alternative.*

1. Point $(-1, -2, -3)$ lies in the octant :

   (a) *OXYZ'*   (b) *OX'YZ*   (c) *OXY'Z*   (d) *OX'Y'Z'*.

2. The co-ordinates of the point equidistant from the four points $(a, 0, 0)$, $(0, b, 0)$, $(0, 0, c)$ and $(0, 0, 0)$ are :

   (a) $(2a, 2b, 2c)$ (b) (a, b, c) (c) $(a/2, b/2, c/2)$ (d) $(a/3, b/3, c/3)$.

   (Avadh, 2004)

3. The ratio in which the line joining $(2, 4, 5)$, $(3, 5, -4)$ is divided by the *YZ*-plane is :

   (a) $2 : 3$ (b) $3 : 2$ (c) $-2 : 3$ (d) $4 : -3$.

   (Avadh, 2004)

4. If $A(0, 0, 0)$, $B(2, -3, 3)$, $C(-2, 3, -3)$ are three collinear points, then C divides BA in the ratio :

   (a) $-1 : 2$ (b) $-2 : 1$ (c) $1 : 1$ (d) $1 : 2$.

   (Avadh, 2003)

5. The three mutually perpendicular planes divide the space into :

   (a) 6 parts   (b) 8 parts   (c) 4 parts   (d) 3 parts.

   (Kanpur, 2002)

6. Equation of *yz*-plane is :

   (a) $x = 0$ (b) $y = 0$ (c) $z = 0$ (d) $y = 0, z = 0$.

7. The equation of *XOY*-plane is :

   (a) $x = 0$ (b) $y = 0$ (c) $z = 0$ (d) $z = c, c \neq 0$.

   (Kanpur, 2001)

8. The equation of *z*-axis is :

   (a) $z = 0$ (b) $y = 0, z = 0$ (c) $x = 0, y = 0$ (d) $z = 0, x = 0$.

   (Kanpur, 2001)

9. If AB is any segment, XX' is a line and θ is the angle between them, then the projection of AB on XX' is :

   (a) $AB \sin \theta$ (b) $AB \cos \theta$ (c) $AB \tan \theta$ (d) None of these.

10. If l, m, n are the d.c.'s of a line, then $l^2 + m^2 + n^2$ is equal to :

    (a) 0 (b) 1 (c) ∞ (d) None of these.

    (Avadh, 2001, 2005)

11. The direction cosines of a line which is equally inclined to the positive direction of the axes are :

    (a) $1, 1, 1$ (b) $0, 0, 0$ (c) $\dfrac{1}{\sqrt{2}}, \dfrac{1}{\sqrt{2}}, \dfrac{1}{\sqrt{2}}$ (d) $\dfrac{1}{\sqrt{3}}, \dfrac{1}{\sqrt{3}}, \dfrac{1}{\sqrt{3}}$.

    (U.P.P.C.S. 2000, Rohilkhand, 2003; Kanpur, 2002)

12. If l, m, n and l', m', n' be the c.c.'s of two lines, then the angle between them is :

    (a) $\cos^{-1}(ll' + mm' + nn')$ (b) $\sin^{-1}(ll' + mm' + nn')$

    (c) $\tan^{-1}(ll' + mm' + nn')$ (d) None of these.

13. If α, β, γ, δ be the angles made by a line with four diagonals of cube, then $\cos^2 \alpha + \cos^2 \beta + \cos^2 \gamma + \cos^2 \delta$ is equal to :

(a) 0   (b) 1/3   (c) 2/3   (d) 4/3.

(Avadh, 2003)

14. The direction cosines of a line equally inclined to three mutually perpendicular lines having d.c.'s $l_1, m_1, n_1; l_2, m_2, n_2; l_3, m_3, n_3$ are :

(a) $l_1 + l_2 + l_3, m_1 + m_2 + m_3, n_1 + n_2 + n_3$

(b) $\dfrac{l_1 + l_2 + l_3}{\sqrt{3}}, \dfrac{m_1 + m_2 + m_3}{\sqrt{3}}, \dfrac{n_1 + n_2 + n_3}{\sqrt{3}}$

(c) $\dfrac{l_1 + l_2 + l_3}{3}, \dfrac{m_1 + m_2 + m_3}{3}, \dfrac{n_1 + n_2 + n_3}{3}$.

(d) None of these.

15. If P is any point (x, y, z) and β be the angle which OP makes with y-axis, then :

(a) $r = y \sin \beta$ (b) $y = r \sin \beta$ (c) $r = y \cos \beta$ (d) $y = r \cos \beta$.

16. The direction cosines of x-axis are :

(a) [1, 0, 0]   (b) [0, 1, 0]   (c) [0, 0, 1]   (d) [1, 1, 1].

(Kanpur, 2001, 2003)

17. If l, m, n are the d.c.'s of a line, then :

(a) $l^2 + m^2 + n^2 = 0$ (b) $l^2 + m^2 + n^2 = 1$ (c) $l + m + n = 0$ (d) $l = m = n = 1$.

18. Which of the following triplets gives the direction cosines of a line ?

(a) 1, 1, 1   (b) 1, – 1, 1   (c) 1, 1, – 1   (d) $\dfrac{1}{\sqrt{3}}, \dfrac{1}{\sqrt{3}}, \dfrac{1}{\sqrt{3}}$.

19. If the direction cosines of a line are $\left(\dfrac{1}{c}, \dfrac{1}{c}, \dfrac{1}{c} \right)$, then :

(a) $c > 0$ (b) $0 < c < 1$ (c) $c = \pm \sqrt{3}$ (d) $c > 2$.

(Avadh, 2003)

20. If α, β, γ are the angles which a half ray makes with the positive directions of the axes, then $\sin^2 \alpha + \sin^2 \beta + \sin^2 \gamma$ is equal to :

(a) 1   (b) 2   (c) 0   (d) – 1.   *(Garhwal, 2006*

21. The direction cosines of a line equally inclined with co-ordinate axes are :

(a) 1, 1, 1   (b) 1, 0, 0   (c) 0, 1, 0   (d) $\dfrac{1}{\sqrt{3}}, \dfrac{1}{\sqrt{3}}, \dfrac{1}{\sqrt{3}}$.

(Avadh, 2001)

22. If $[a, b, c]$ and $[a', b', c']$ are the direction ratios of two perpendicular lines, then :

(a) $a/a' = b/b' = c/c'$ (b) $aa' + bb' + cc' = 0$

(c) $aa' + bb' + cc' = 1$ (d) $a + b + c = a' + b' + c'$.

23. The projection of the line joining (3, 4, 5) and (4, 5, 3) on the line joining (– 1, 2, 4) and (1, 0 , 5) is :

(a) 4/3   (b) 2/3   (c) 8/3   (d) 1/3.

24. The angle between the lines whose direction ratios are 1, 1, 2; $\sqrt{3} - 1, -\sqrt{3} - 1, 4$ is :

(a) $\cos^{-1} (1/65)$ (b) $\pi/6$ (c) $\pi/3$ (d) $\pi/4$.

25. The direction cosines of the line joining the points $(4, 3, -5)$ and $(-2, 1, -8)$ are :

 (a) $[2, 4, -13]$ (b) $[6, 2, 3]$ (c) $[6/7, 2/7, 3/7]$ (d) None of these.

26. If the vertices of a triangle are $A(1, 4, 2)$, $B(-2, 1, 2)$, $C(2, -3, 4)$, then the angle B is equal to :

 (a) $\cos^{-1}(1/\sqrt{3})$ (b) $\pi/2$ (c) $\cos^{-1}(\sqrt{6}/3)$ (d) $\cos^{-1}(\sqrt{3})$.

27. The angle between the lines whose direction cosines are given by the equations $l^2 + m^2 - n^2 = 0$, $l + m + n = 0$ is :

 (a) $\cos^{-1}(2/\sqrt{3})$ (b) $\cos^{-1}(\sqrt{3})$ (c) $\pi/3$ (d) $\pi/2$.

28. The straight lines whose direction cosines are given by $al + bm + cn = 0$, $fmn + gnl + hlm = 0$ are perpendicular if :

 (a) $f/a + g/b + h/c = 0$ (b) $\sqrt{a/f} + \sqrt{b/g} + \sqrt{c/h} = 0$

 (c) $\sqrt{af} = \sqrt{bg} = \sqrt{ch}$ (d) $\sqrt{a/f} = \sqrt{b/g} = \sqrt{c/h}$.

29. Direction cosines of the line which is perpendicular to the lines whose direction ratios are $1, -1, 2$ and $2, 1, -1$ are given by :

 (a) $\left[\dfrac{-1}{\sqrt{35}}, \dfrac{5}{\sqrt{35}}, \dfrac{3}{\sqrt{35}}\right]$ (b) $\left[\dfrac{-1}{\sqrt{35}}, \dfrac{-5}{\sqrt{35}}, \dfrac{3}{\sqrt{35}}\right]$

 (c) $\left[\dfrac{1}{\sqrt{35}}, \dfrac{5}{\sqrt{35}}, \dfrac{-3}{\sqrt{35}}\right]$ (d) None of these.

30. If O be the origin and $P(2, 3, 4)$ and $Q(1, b, 1)$ be two points such that $OP \perp OQ$ then $b = ?$

 (a) 2   (b) -2

 (c) No such real b exists   (d) None of these.   (Avadh, 2003)

ANSWERS

1. (d)	2. (c)	3. (c)	4. (b)	5. (b)	6. (a)	7. (c)	8. (c)
9. (b)	10. (b)	11. (d)	12. (a)	13. (d)	14. (b)	15. (d)	16. (a)
17. (b)	18. (d)	19. (c)	20. (b)	21. (d)	22. (b)	23. (a)	24. (c)
25. (c)	26. (b)	27. (c)	28. (a)	29. (a)	30. (b)		

II. Fill in the Blanks

Note : *Fill in the blanks "......." so that the following statements are complete and correct.*

1. Three mutually perpendicular co-ordinate planes divide the space into .... parts.

2. Point $(-a, -b, c)$ lies in the octant ....

3. Distance between the points $(4, 3, -6)$ and $(-2, 1, -3)$ is ....

4. Direction cosines of x-axis are ....

5. If α, β, γ be the angles which a line makes with the positive directions of the axes, then $\sin^2\alpha + \sin^2\beta + \sin^2\gamma = $ ....

6. The distance of the point (a, b, c) from x-axis is ....   (Kanpur, 2001)

7. The ratio in which the yz-plane divides the join of the points $(-2, 4, 7)$ and $(3, -5, 8)$ is ....

8. Angle between the lines whose direction ratios are $1, 1, 2$; $\sqrt{3} - 1, -\sqrt{3} - 1, 4$ is ....

9. The direction cosines of a line which is equally inclined to the positive direction of the axes are ....

10. If a, b, c are direction ratios, then $a^2 + b^2 + c^2$ is .... to unity.

ANSWERS

1. eight; 2. $OX'Y'Z$; 3. 7; 4. 1, 0, 0; 5. 2;

6. $\sqrt{b^2 + c^2}$; 7. 2 : 3; 8. $\pi/3$; 9. $\dfrac{1}{\sqrt{3}}, \dfrac{1}{\sqrt{3}}, \dfrac{1}{\sqrt{3}}$; 10. Not equal.

III. True/False Statements

Note : *Write 'T' for true and 'F' for false statements.*

1. The three co-ordinate planes divide the whole space into eight parts called octants.

2. Middle point of line joining (x_1, y_1, z_1) and (x_2, y_2, z_2) is $\left(\dfrac{x_1 + x_2}{2}, \dfrac{y_1 + y_2}{2}, \dfrac{z_1 + z_2}{2} \right)$.

3. If l, m, n be the direction cosines of a line, then $l^2 + m^2 + n^2 = 0$.

4. Two lines whose d.c.'s are l_1, m_1, n_1 and l_2, m_2, n_2 are parallel if $l_1 l_2 + m_1 m_2 + n_1 n_2 = 0$.

5. Angle between any two diagonals of a cube is $\cos^{-1}(1/3)$.

6. If the direction cosines of a line are $\left(\dfrac{1}{c}, \dfrac{1}{c}, \dfrac{1}{c} \right)$, then $c > 0$.

ANSWERS

1. T 2. T 3. F 4. F 5. T 6. F

2

The Plane

GENERAL EQUATION OF FIRST DEGREE

An equation of the first degree in x, y, z is of the form

$$ax + by + cz + d = 0$$

where a, b, c are given real numbers and a, b, c are not all zero. The condition that a, b, c are not all zero is equivalent to the single condition $a^2 + b^2 + c^2 \neq 0$.

We are now interested in the locus of the points whose co-ordinates satisfy an equation of first degree viz.,

$$ax + by + cz + d = 0, \quad a^2 + b^2 + c^2 \neq 0.$$

It will be shown that this locus is a plane. To show this, we make use of the characteristic property of a plane which we give below :

A geometrical locus is a plane if it is such that if P and Q are any two points on the locus then every point of the line PQ is also a point on the locus.

2.1. THEOREM

Every equation of the first degree in x, y, z represents a plane.

(Avadh, 1998; Garhwal, 2000, 2004)

Consider the equation

$$ax + by + cz + d = 0, \quad a^2 + b^2 + c^2 \neq 0.$$

The locus of this equation will be a plane if *every* point of the line joining *any* two points on the locus also lies on the locus.

Let

$$P(x_1, y_1, z_1) \text{ and } Q(x_2, y_2, z_2)$$

be two points on the locus, so that we have

$$ax_1 + by_1 + cz_1 + d = 0 \qquad \text{...}(i)$$
$$ax_2 + by_2 + cz_2 + d = 0 \qquad \text{...}(ii)$$

Multiplying (*ii*) by k and adding to (*i*), we get

$$a(x_1 + kx_2) + b(y_1 + ky_2) + c(z_1 + kz_2) + d(1 + k) = 0$$

$$\Rightarrow \quad a\frac{x_1 + kx_2}{1 + k} + b\frac{y_1 + ky_2}{1 + k} + c\frac{z_1 + kz_2}{1 + k} + d = 0$$

Assuming that $k \neq -1$, the relation (*ii*) shows that the point

$$\left(\frac{x_1 + kx_2}{1 + k}, \frac{y_1 + ky_2}{1 + k}, \frac{z_1 + kz_2}{1 + k} \right)$$

is also a point on the locus for every value of $k \neq -1$.

Thus, every point on the straight line joining any two *arbitrary points* on the locus also lies on the locus. The given equation, therefore, represents a plane. Hence, every equation of the first degree in x, y, z represents a plane.

Ex. Find the co-ordinates of the points where the plane

$$ax + by + cz + d = 0, \ a^2 + b^2 + c^2 \neq 0$$

meets the three co-ordinate axes.

2.2. CONVERSE OF THE PRECEDING THEOREM

We shall now show that *the equation of every plane is of the first degree i.e.*, is of the form

$$ax + by + cz + d = 0,$$

where

$$a^2 + b^2 + c^2 \neq 0.$$

Consider any plane. Let p be the length of the perpendicular from the origin to the plane and let l, m, n be the direction cosines of this perpendicular.

We shall show that for any point (x, y, z) on the plane, we have the relation

$$lx + my + nz = p$$

implying that the equation of the plane is of the first degree.

Let K be the foot of the perpendicular from the origin O to the plane. Let $OK = p$ and let l, m, n be its direction cosines. Take any point $P(x, y, z)$ on the plane.

Now PK lies in the plane

$$\Rightarrow \qquad\qquad PK \perp OK$$

$\Rightarrow$ the projection of OP on $OK = OK = p.$

Also the projection of the segment OP joining the points

$$O(0, 0, 0) \text{ and } P(x, y, z)$$

on the line OK with direction cosines

$$l, \ m, \ n$$

is $\qquad l(x - 0) + m(y - 0) + n(z - 0) = lx + my + nz.$

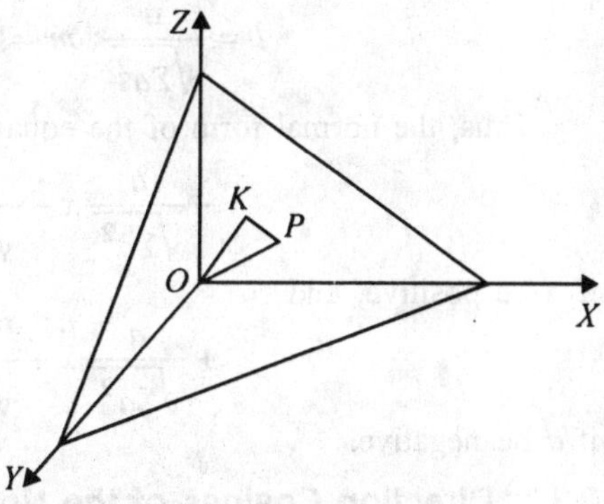

Fig. 15

It follows that

$$lx + my + nz = p.$$

This equation, being satisfied by the co-ordinates of any point $P(x, y, z)$ on the given plane, is the equation of the plane.

Note 1. The equation

$$lx + my + nz = p,$$

is called the **normal** form of the equation of a plane.

(Garhwal, 1999; Kumaon, 2004; Patna, 2003)

Note 2. The plane whose equation is

$$ax + by + cz + d = 0$$

is referred to as

$$ax + by + cz + d = 0$$

itself *i.e.*, we often refer to an equation of the plane itself as the plane.

Ex. Find the equation of the plane containing the lines through the origin with direction cosines proportional to $(1, -2, 2)$ and $(2, 3, -1)$.   **[Ans.** $4x - 5y - 7z = 0]$

2.3. TRANSFORMATION TO THE NORMAL FORM

To transform the equation

$$ax + by + cz + d = 0, \quad a^2 + b^2 + c^2 \neq 0$$

to the normal form

$$lx + my + nz = p.$$

As these two equations represent the same plane, we have

$$-\frac{d}{p} = \frac{a}{l} = \frac{b}{m} = \frac{c}{n} = \pm \frac{\sqrt{a^2 + b^2 + c^2}}{\sqrt{l^2 + m^2 + n^2}} = \pm \sqrt{a^2 + b^2 + c^2}.$$

Thus, $d/p = \pm \sqrt{a^2 + b^2 + c^2}$. As p, according to our convention, is always positive, we shall take positive or negative sign with the radical according as, d, is negative or positive.

Thus, if d be positive, we have

$$l = -\frac{a}{\sqrt{\Sigma a^2}}; \; m = -\frac{b}{\sqrt{\Sigma a^2}}; \; n = -\frac{c}{\sqrt{\Sigma a^2}}; \; p = +\frac{d}{\sqrt{\Sigma a^2}};$$

and if d be negative, we have

$$l = \frac{a}{\sqrt{\Sigma a^2}}; \; m = \frac{b}{\sqrt{\Sigma a^2}}; \; n = \frac{c}{\sqrt{\Sigma a^2}}; \; p = -\frac{d}{\sqrt{\Sigma a^2}}.$$

Thus, the normal form of the equation $ax + by + cz + d = 0$ is

$$-\frac{a}{\sqrt{\Sigma a^2}} x - \frac{b}{\sqrt{\Sigma a^2}} y - \frac{c}{\sqrt{\Sigma a^2}} z = -\frac{d}{\sqrt{\Sigma a^2}},$$

if d be positive, and

$$+\frac{a}{\sqrt{\Sigma a^2}} x + \frac{b}{\sqrt{\Sigma a^2}} y + \frac{c}{\sqrt{\Sigma a^2}} z = -\frac{d}{\sqrt{\Sigma a^2}}$$

if d be negative.

2.3.1. Direction Cosines of the Normal to a Plane

From above we deduce that *the direction cosines of the normal to a plane are proportional to the coefficients of x, y, z in its equation or* that the coefficients of x, y, z are direction ratios of the normal *to the plane*.

Thus,

$$a, b, c$$

are direction ratios of the normal to the plane

$$ax + by + cz + d = 0.$$

Ex. 1. Find the direction cosines of the normals to the planes

(i) $2x - 3y + 6z = 7$,   (ii) $x + 2y + 2z - 1 = 0$.

[**Ans.** (i) 2/7, – 3/7, 6/7; (ii) 1/3, 2/3, 2/3]

Ex. 2. Show that the normals to the planes

$$x - y + z = 1, \; 3x + 2y - z + 2 = 0$$

are perpendicular to each other.

2.3.2. Angle Between Two Planes

Angle between two planes is equal to the angle between the normals to them from any point.

It follows that the angle between the two planes

$$ax + by + cz + d = 0, \; a_1 x + b_1 y + c_1 z + d_1 = 0$$

being equal to the angle between the lines with direction ratios

$$a, b, c; a_1, b_1, c_1$$

is
$$\cos^{-1}\left\{\frac{aa_1 + bb_1 + cc_1}{\sqrt{\Sigma a^2}\,\sqrt{\Sigma a_1^2}}\right\}.$$

Cor. Parallelism and perpendicularity of two planes. Two planes are parallel or perpendicular according as the normals to them are parallel or perpendicular.

Thus, the two planes

$$ax + by + cz + d = 0,\ a_1 x + b_1 y + c_1 z + d_1 = 0$$

will be parallel, if

$$a, b, c\ and\ a_1, b_1, c_1$$

are direction ratios of the same line and will be perpendicular, if

$$aa_1 + bb_1 + cc_1 = 0.$$

EXERCISES

1. Find the angles between the following pairs of planes

   (*i*) $2x - y + 2z = 3$; $3x + 6y + 2z = 4$ **[Ans.** $\cos^{-1}(4/21)$**]**

   (*ii*) $2x - y + z = 6$; $x + y + 2z = 7$ **[Ans.** $\pi/3$**]**

   (*iii*) $3x - 4y + 5z = 0$; $2x - y - 2z = 5$ **[Ans.** $\pi/2$**]**

2. Show that the equations

$$ax + by + r = 0,\ by + cz + p = 0,\ cz + ax + q = 0$$

represent planes respectively perpendicular to the *XY*, *YZ*, *ZX* planes.

3. Show that $ax + by + cz + d = 0$ represents planes, perpendicular respectively to *YZ*, *ZX*, *XY* planes, if a, b, c separately vanish (Similar to Ex. 2).

4. Show that the plane

$$x + 2y - 3z + 4 = 0$$

is perpendicular to each of the planes

$$2x + 5y + 4z + 1 = 0,\ 4x + 7y + 6z + 2 = 0.$$

2.4. DETERMINATION OF A PLANE UNDER GIVEN CONDITIONS

The *general* equation $ax + by + cz + d = 0$ of a plane contains *three* arbitrary constants (ratios of the coefficients a, b, c, d) and, therefore, a plane can be found to satisfy three conditions each giving rise to only one relation between the constants. The three constants can then be determined from the three resulting relations.

We give below a few sets of conditions which determine a plane :

   (*i*) passing through *three* non-collinear points;

   (*ii*) passing through *two* given points and perpendicular to a given plane;

   (*iii*) passing through a given point and perpendicular to *two* given planes.

2.4.1. Cor. Intercept Form of the Equation of a Plane

To find the equation of a plane in terms of the intercepts a, b, c which it makes on the axes.

(Kumaon, 1995)

The intercept of a plane on any co-ordinate axis is the distance of the point where the plane meets the axis from the origin taken with the appropriate sign.

We, of course, suppose here that the plane does not pass through the origin so that none of a, b, c is zero.

Let the origin of the plane be

$$Ax + By + Cz + D = 0. \qquad \qquad ...(i)$$

The plane not passing through the origin, we have

$$D \neq 0.$$

The points $(a, 0, 0)$, $(0, b, 0)$, $(0, 0, c)$ lying on the plane (i), we have

$$aA + D = 0 \implies -\frac{A}{D} = \frac{1}{a}$$

$$bB + D = 0 \implies -\frac{B}{D} = \frac{1}{b}$$

$$cC + D = 0 \implies -\frac{C}{D} = \frac{1}{c}.$$

The equation (1) can be rewritten as

$$-\frac{A}{D}x - \frac{B}{D}y - \frac{C}{D}z = 1$$

so that after substitution, we obtain

$$\frac{x}{a} + \frac{y}{b} + \frac{z}{c} = 1,$$

as the required equation of the plane.

2.4.2. Plane Through Three Points

To find the equation of the plane through the three non-collinear points

$$x_1, y_1, z_1), (x_2, y_2, z_2), (x_3, y_3, z_3). \qquad (Kumaon, 1998, 2000, 03, 04, Banglore, 2001$$

Let the required equation of the plane be

$$ax + by + cz + d = 0. \qquad \qquad ...(i)$$

As the given points lie on the plane (i), we have

$$ax_1 + by_1 + cz_1 + d = 0, \qquad \qquad ...(ii)$$

$$ax_2 + by_2 + cz_2 + d = 0, \qquad \qquad ...(iii)$$

$$ax_3 + by_3 + cz_3 + d = 0. \qquad \qquad ...(iv)$$

Eliminating a, b, c, d from $(i) - (iv)$, we have

$$\begin{vmatrix} x & y & z & 1 \\ x_1 & y_1 & z_1 & 1 \\ x_2 & y_2 & z_2 & 1 \\ x_3 & y_3 & z_3 & 1 \end{vmatrix} = 0$$

which is the required equation of the plane.

Cor. The equation of the plane which makes intercepts a, b, c respectively on the three co-ordinate axes is

$$\frac{x}{a} + \frac{y}{b} + \frac{z}{c} = 1$$

in that this is the plane through the 3 points $(a, 0, 0)$, $(0, b, 0)$, $(0, 0, c)$.

Note. In actual numerical exercises, the student would find it more convenient to follow the method of the first example below.

EXAMPLES

1. *Find the equation of the plane through the points*
$$P(2, 2, -1), Q(3, 4, 2), R(7, 0, 6).$$

Sol. The general equation of a plane through $P(2, 2, -1)$ is
$$a(x-2) + b(y-2) + c(z+1) = 0 \quad \text{(Refer 4, § 2.5, p. 35)} \quad ...(i)$$
It will pass through Q and R, if
$$a + 2b + 3c = 0$$
$$5a - 2b + 7c = 0.$$

These give
$$\frac{a}{20} = \frac{b}{8} = \frac{c}{-12} \quad \text{or} \quad \frac{a}{5} = \frac{b}{2} = \frac{c}{-3}.$$

Substituting these values in (i), we have
$$5(x-2) + 2(y-2) - 3(z+1) = 0$$
$$\Rightarrow \qquad 5x + 2y - 3z - 17 = 0$$
as the required equation.

2. *Find the equation of the plane through the points*
$$(2, 2, 1) \text{ and } (9, 3, 6),$$
and perpendicular to the plane
$$2x + 6y + 6z = 9.$$

(Kanpur, 1997, 1999; Avadh, 1995; Rohilkhand, 1996; Bundelkhand, 1995, 1998; Poorvanchal, 1995, 1997)

Sol. Any plane through $(2, 2, 1)$ is
$$a(x-2) + b(y-2) + c(z-1) = 0. \qquad ...(i)$$
It passes through $(9, 3, 6)$
$$\Rightarrow \qquad a(9-2) + b(3-2) + c(6-1) = 0$$
$$\Rightarrow \qquad 7a + b + 5c = 0 \qquad ...(ii)$$

The plane (i) is perpendicular to the given plane
$$\Rightarrow \qquad 2a + 6b + 6c = 0 \qquad ...(iii)$$

From (ii) and (iii), we have
$$\frac{a}{-24} = \frac{b}{-32} = \frac{c}{40} \Rightarrow \frac{a}{3} = \frac{b}{4} = \frac{c}{-5}.$$

Substituting in (i), we see that the equation of the required plane is
$$3(x-2) + 4(y-2) - 5(z-1) = 0 \Leftrightarrow 3x + 4y - 5z = 9.$$

EXERCISES

1. Find the equation of the plane through the three points $(1, 1, 1)$, $(1, -1, 1)$, $(-7, -3, -5)$ and show that it is perpendicular to the XZ plane. **[Ans.** $3x - 4z + 1 = 0$**]**

2. Obtain the equation of the plane passing through the point $(-2, -2, 2)$ and containing

3. If, from the point P (a, b, c), perpendiculars PL, PM be drawn to YZ and ZX planes, find the equation of the plane OLM.   [**Ans.** $bcx + cay - abz = 0$]

4. Show that the four points $(-6, 3, 2)$, $(3, -2, 4)$, $(5, 7, 3)$ and $(-13, 17, -1)$ are coplanar.

5. Show that the points $(6, -4, 4)$, $(0, 0, -4)$ intersects the join of $(-1, -2, -3)$, $(1, 2, -5)$.

6. Show that $(-1, 4, -3)$ is the circumcentre of the triangle formed by the points $(3, 2, -5)$, $(-3, 8, -5)$, $(-3, 2, 1)$.

7. Show that the equations of the three planes passing through the points, $(1, -2, 4)$, $(3, -4, 5)$ and perpendicular to the XY, YZ, ZX planes are $x + y + 1 = 0$; $x - 2z + 7 = 0$; $y + 2z = 6$ respectively.

8. Obtain the equation of the plane which passes through the point $(-1, 3, 2)$ and is perpendicular to each of the two planes $x + 2y + 2z = 5$; $3x + 2y + 2z = 8$.
     [**Ans.** $2x - 4y + 3z + 8 = 0$]

9. Find the equation of the plane which passes through $A (-1, 1, 1)$ and $B (1, -1, 1)$ and is perpendicular to the plane $x + 2y + 2z = 5$.   (*Gorakhpur, 2000*)
     [**Ans.** $2x + 2y - 3z + 3 = 0$]

10. Find the intercepts of the plane $2x - 3y + z = 12$ on the co-ordinate axes.
     [**Ans.** $6, -4, 12$]

11. A plane meets the co-ordinate axes A, B, C such that the centroid of the triangle ABC is the point (a, b, c), show that the equation of the plane is $x/a + y/b + z/c = 3$.
     (*Rohilkhand, 2000; Meerut, 2000; Kumaon, 2003, Meerut, 2005, Calcutta, 2005*)

12. Find the equations of the two planes which pass through the points $(0, 4, -3)$, $(6, -4, 3)$, other than the plane through the origin, which cut off from the axes intercepts whose sum is zero.   [**Ans.** $2x - 3y - 6z = 6$; $6x + 3y - 2z = 18$]

13. A variable plane is at a constant distance p from the origin and meets the co-ordinate axes in A, B, C. Show that the locus of the centroid of the tetrahedron $OABC$ is $x^{-2} + y^{-2} + z^{-2} = 16p^{-2}$.   (*Kanpur, 1997; Kumaon, 1999; Agra, 1998*)

2.5. SYSTEMS OF PLANES

The equation of a plane satisfying two conditions will involve one arbitrary constant which can be chosen in an infinite number of ways, thus giving rise to an infinite number of planes, called a *System of planes*.

The arbitrary constant which is different for different members of the system is called a *Parameter.*

Similarly the equation of a plane satisfying one condition will involve two parameters.

The following are the equations of a few systems of planes involving one or two parameters :

1. The equation
$$ax + by + cz + k = 0$$
represents the system of planes parallel to a given plane
$$ax + by + cz + d = 0,$$
k being the parameter.

Thus, the set of planes parallel to a given plane
$$ax + by + cz + d = 0$$
is $\{ax + by + cz + k = 0; k$ is any number$\}$.

2. The equation
$$ax + by + cz + d = 0$$
represents the system of planes perpendicular to given line with direction ratios a, b, c; d being the parameter.   (§ 2.3.1)

3. The equation
$$(ax + by + cz + d) + k (a_1x + b_1y + c_1z + d_1) = 0 \qquad ...(1)$$
represents the system of planes through the line of intersection of the planes
$$ax + by + cz + d = 0, \qquad ...(2)$$
$$a_1x + b_1y + c_1z + d_1 = 0; \qquad ...(3)$$
k being the parameter, for the equation (1), being of the first degree in x, y, z, represents a plane; and it is evidently satisfied by the co-ordinates of the points which satisfy (2) and (3), whatever value k may have.

4. The equation
$$A (x - x_1) + B (y - y_1) + C (z - z_1) = 0,$$
represents the system of planes passing through the point (x_1, y_1, z_1) where the required *two* parameters are the two ratios of the coefficients A, B, C; for, the equation is of the first degree and is clearly satisfied by the point (x_1, y_1, z_1) whatever be the ratios of the coefficients.

EXAMPLES

1. *Find the equation of the plane passing through the intersection of the planes*
$$x + y + z = 6 \text{ and } 2x + 3y + 4z + 5 = 0$$
and the point $(1, 1, 1)$.

Sol. The plane
$$x + y + z - 6 + k (2x + 3y + 4z + 5) = 0 \qquad ...(i)$$
passes through the intersection of the given planes for all values of k.

It will pass through $(1, 1, 1)$ if
$$- 3 + 14k = 0 \implies k = 3/14$$
Putting $k = 3/14$ in (i), we obtain
$$20x + 23y + 26z - 69 = 0,$$
which is the required equation of the plane.

2. *Find the equation of the plane passing through the lines of intersection of the planes*
$$2x - y = 0 \text{ and } 3z + y = 0$$
are perpendicular to the plane
$$4x + 5y - 3z = 8. \qquad \text{(Gorakhpur, 1999 Garhwal, 2006)}$$

Sol. The plane
$$2x - y + k (3z - y) = 0 \iff 2x - (1 + k) y + 3kz = 0$$
passes through the line of intersection of the given planes whatever value k may have. This plane is perpendicular to
$$4x + 5y - 3z = 8$$
$$\implies \qquad 2·4 - (1 + k)·5 + 3k (- 3) = 0 \implies 14k = 3 \implies k = 3/14.$$
Thus, the required equation is
$$2x - y + \left(\frac{3}{14}\right)(3z - y) = 0 \iff 28x - 17y + 9z = 0.$$

3. *Obtain the equation of the plane through the point* (x_1, y_1, z_1) *and parallel to the plane* $ax + by + cz + d = 0$.

Sol. The plane
$$ax + by + cz + k = 0$$
is parallel to the given plane for all values of k.

It will pass through (x_1, y_1, z_1), if

$$ax_1 + by_1 + cz_1 + k = 0.$$

Subtracting, we get

$$a(x - x_1) + b(y - y_1) + c(z - z_1) = 0$$

as the required equation.

4. *Find the equation to a plane through* $P(a, b, c)$ *and perpendicular to OP, where O is the origin.*

Sol. Obviously, OP will be the normal from the origin to the plane. Direction cosines of OP are

$$\left(\frac{a}{\sqrt{a^2 + b^2 + c^2}}, \frac{b}{\sqrt{a^2 + b^2 + c^2}}, \frac{c}{\sqrt{a^2 + b^2 + c^2}} \right)$$

and length of OP is $\sqrt{a^2 + b^2 + c^2}$. Hence, the equation of the required plane will be

$$\left(\frac{a}{\sqrt{a^2 + b^2 + c^2}} \right) x + \left(\frac{b}{\sqrt{a^2 + b^2 + c^2}} \right) y + \left(\frac{c}{\sqrt{a^2 + b^2 + c^2}} \right) z = \sqrt{a^2 + b^2 + c^2}$$

or

$$ax + by + cz = a^2 + b^2 + c^2.$$

5. *A point P moves on a fixed plane* $x/a + y/b + z/c = 1$. *The plane through P perpendicular to OP meets the axes in A, B, C The planes through A, B, C parallel to co-ordinate planes intersect in Q. Show that the locus of Q is*

$$\frac{1}{x^2} + \frac{1}{y^2} + \frac{1}{z^2} = \frac{1}{ax} + \frac{1}{by} + \frac{1}{cz}.$$

(Kanpur, 1996, 98; Agra, 1996)

Sol. Let the point be $P = (\alpha, \beta, \gamma)$. Hence

$$\frac{\alpha}{a} + \frac{\beta}{b} + \frac{\gamma}{c} = 1 \qquad \qquad \dots(1)$$

Equation of the plane perpendicular to OP is

$$\alpha x + \beta y + \gamma z = d.$$

But it passes through $P(\alpha, \beta, \gamma)$, we have

$$d = \alpha^2 + \beta^2 + \gamma^2.$$

Hence, equation of plane through P and perpendicular to OP is

$$\alpha x + \beta y + \gamma z = \alpha^2 + \beta^2 + \gamma^2 \qquad \qquad \dots(2)$$

$$\Rightarrow \quad OA = \frac{\alpha^2 + \beta^2 + \gamma^2}{\alpha}, \quad OB = \frac{\alpha^2 + \beta^2 + \gamma^2}{\beta}, \quad OC = \frac{\alpha^2 + \beta^2 + \gamma^2}{\gamma}.$$

So the planes through A, B, C parallel to the planes YOZ, ZOX, XOY intersect in the point Q whose co-ordinates are

$$x = \frac{\alpha^2 + \beta^2 + \gamma^2}{\alpha}, \quad y = \frac{\alpha^2 + \beta^2 + \gamma^2}{\beta}, \quad z = \frac{\alpha^2 + \beta^2 + \gamma^2}{\gamma}.$$

With the help of (1),

$$\frac{1}{x^2} + \frac{1}{y^2} + \frac{1}{z^2} = \frac{1}{\alpha^2 + \beta^2 + \gamma^2}$$

and
$$\frac{1}{ax} + \frac{1}{by} + \frac{1}{cz} = \frac{\frac{\alpha}{a} + \frac{\beta}{b} + \frac{\gamma}{c}}{\alpha^2 + \beta^2 + \gamma^2} = \frac{1}{\alpha^2 + \beta^2 + \gamma^2}, \text{ from (1)}.$$

Hence, required locus is
$$\frac{1}{x^2} + \frac{1}{y^2} + \frac{1}{z^2} = \frac{1}{ax} + \frac{1}{by} + \frac{1}{cz}.$$

6. *The plane lx + my = 0 is rotated about its line of intersection with the plane z = 0 through an angle α. Prove that the equation of the plane in its new position is*

$$lx + my \pm z \sqrt{l^2 + m^2} \tan \alpha = 0. \qquad (Meerut, 1998; Gorakhpur, 2003)$$

Sol. The equation of a plane through the line of intersection of the planes $lx + my = 0$ and $z = 0$, is
$$lx + my + \lambda z = 0.$$

This plane makes an angle α with the plane $lx + my = 0$.

$$\therefore \qquad \cos \alpha = \frac{l^2 + m^2}{\sqrt{(l^2 + m^2)(l^2 + m^2 + \lambda^2)}}$$

$$\therefore \qquad \cos^2 \alpha = \frac{l^2 + m^2}{(l^2 + m^2 + \lambda^2)}$$

$$\Rightarrow \qquad \lambda = \pm \sqrt{(l^2 + m^2)} \tan \alpha.$$

Hence, required plane is

$$lx + my \pm z \sqrt{l^2 + m^2} \tan \alpha = 0.$$

7. *A triangle, the lengths of whose sides are a, b and c is placed so that the middle points of the sides are on the axes. Show that the equation to the plane is*

$$x/\alpha + y/\beta + z/\gamma = 1,$$

where $\alpha^2 = \dfrac{(b^2 + c^2 - a^2)}{8}$, $\beta^2 = \dfrac{(c^2 + a^2 - b^2)}{8}$, $\gamma^2 = \dfrac{(a^2 + b^2 - c^2)}{8}$. *(Kanpur, 1995)*

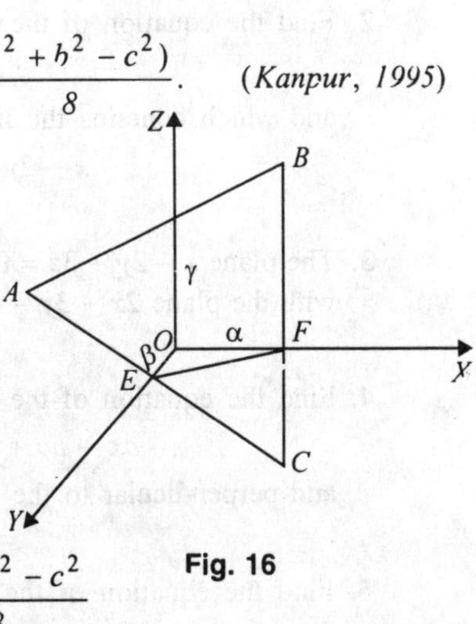

Sol. Let α, β, γ be the intercepts that the plane makes with the axes. E and F are the mid-points of AC and BC. Therefore, EF is parallel to and half of AB.

Fig. 16

$$\therefore \qquad EF^2 = OE^2 + OF^2 = \alpha^2 + \beta^2.$$

But
$$EF = \frac{AB}{2} = \frac{c}{2} \Rightarrow \alpha^2 + \beta^2 = \frac{c^2}{4}$$

Similarly, $\beta^2 + \gamma^2 = a^2/4$ and $\gamma^2 + \alpha^2 = b^2/4$.

Adding, $\alpha^2 + \beta^2 + \gamma^2 = \dfrac{a^2 + b^2 + c^2}{8}$

$$\Rightarrow \qquad \gamma^2 = \frac{a^2 + b^2 + c^2}{8} - \frac{c^2}{4} = \frac{a^2 + b^2 - c^2}{8}$$

Similarly, $\alpha^2 = \dfrac{b^2 + c^2 - a^2}{8}$, $\beta^2 = \dfrac{c^2 + a^2 - b^2}{8}$.

Hence, the equation of plane is
$$x/\alpha + y/\beta + z/\gamma = 1, \text{ where } \alpha^2, \beta^2, \gamma^2 \text{ as given above}.$$

8. *A plane meets a set of three mutually perpendicular planes in the sides of a triangle whose angles are A, B and C. Show that the first plane makes with the other planes angles the squares of whose cosines are*

$$\cos B \cot C, \; \cot C \cot A, \; \cot A \cot B.$$

Sol. Let the plane be

$$x/a + y/b + z/c = 1.$$

Co-ordinates of A, B, C are $(a, 0, 0)$, $(0, b, 0)$ and $(0, 0, c)$.

d.r.'s of AB and AC are $a, -b, 0$ and $a, 0, -c$ respectively.

Since A is angle between AB and AC, we have

$$\tan A = \frac{\sqrt{\Sigma (m_1 n_2 - m_2 n_1)^2}}{l_1 l_2 + m_1 m_2 + n_1 n_2} = \frac{\sqrt{a^2 b^2 + b^2 c^2 + c^2 a^2}}{a^2}$$

$$\tan B = \frac{\sqrt{a^2 b^2 + b^2 c^2 + c^2 a^2}}{b^2}, \quad \tan C = \frac{\sqrt{a^2 b^2 + b^2 c^2 + c^2 a^2}}{c^2}$$

If α be the angle between $x = 0$ and the plane, then

$$\cos \alpha = \frac{1/a}{\sqrt{1/a^2 + 1/b^2 + 1/c^2}} = \frac{bc}{\sqrt{a^2 b^2 + b^2 c^2 + c^2 a^2}}$$

$$\Rightarrow \quad \cos^2 \alpha = \frac{b^2 c^2}{(a^2 b^2 + b^2 c^2 + c^2 a^2)} = \cot B \cot C, \text{ etc.}$$

EXERCISES

1. Obtain the equation of the plane through the intersection of the planes

$$x + 2y + 3z + 4 = 0 \text{ and } 4x + 3y + 2z + 1 = 0$$

and the origin.   **[Ans.** $3x + 2y + z = 0$**]**

2. Find the equation of the plane which is perpendicular to the plane

$$5x + 3y + 6z + 8 = 0$$

and which contains the line of intersection of the planes

$$x + 2y + 3z - 4 = 0, \; 2x + y - z + 5 = 0.$$

[Ans. $51x + 15y - 50z + 173 = 0$**]**

3. The plane $x - 2y + 3z = 0$ is rotated through a right angle about the line of intersection with the plane $2x + 3y - 4z - 5 = 0$, find the equation of the plane in its new position.

(Avadh, 2004) **[Ans.** $22x + 5y - 4z - 35 = 0$**]**

4. Find the equation of the plane through the line of intersection of the planes

$$ax + by + cz + d = 0, \; a_1 x + b_1 y + c_1 z + d_1 = 0$$

and perpendicular to the XY plane.   *(Gorakhpur, 2001)*

[Ans. $x (ac_1 - a_1 c) + y (bc_1 - b_1 c) + z (dc_1 - d_1 c) = 0$**]**

5. Find the equation of the plane through the point $(2, 3, 4)$ and parallel to the plane $5x - 6y + 7z = 3$. *(Kumaon 2005)* **[Ans.** $5x - 6y + 7z = 20$**]**

6. Find the equation of the plane through $(2, 3, -4)$ and $(1, -1, 3)$ parallel to the x-axis.

(Avadh, 1999, 2001; Gorakhpur, 2002)

[Ans. $7y + 4z - 5 = 0$**]**

7. A variable plane is at a constant distance $3p$ from the origin and meets the axes in A, B and C. Show that the locus of the centroid of the triangle ABC is $x^{-2} + y^{-2} + z^{-2} = p^{-2}$. *(Kumaon, 1997, 2001)*

8. Find the equation of the plane that passes through the point $(3, -3, 1)$ and is normal to the line joining the points $(3, 4, -1)$ and $(2, -1, 5)$. *(Rohilkhand, 2004)*

[**Ans.** $x + 5y - 6z + 18 = 0$]

9. Obtain the equation of the plane that bisects the segment joining the points $(1, 2, 3)$, $(3, 4, 5)$, at right angles. [**Ans.** $x + y + z = 9$]

10. A variable plane passes through a fixed point (a, b, c) and meets the co-ordinate axes in A, B, C. Show that the locus of the point common to the planes through A, B, C parallel to the co-ordinate planes is

$$a/x + b/y + c/z = 1. \qquad \text{(Agra, 1996; Poorvanchal, 1997)}$$

2.6. TWO SIDES OF A PLANE

Consider any plane. Two points P and Q which do not lie on the plane lie on the different or the same side of plane according as the segment PQ has or does not have a point in common with the plane.

We proceed to determine a criterion for two given points to lie on the same or different sides of a given plane and show that:

Two points $A(x_1, y_1, z_1)$, $B(x_2, y_2, z_2)$ lie on the same or different sides of the plane

$$ax + by + cz + d = 0,$$

according as the expressions

$$ax_1 + by_1 + cz_1 + d, \; ax_2 + by_2 + cz_2 + d$$

are of the same or different signs.

Let the line AB meet the given plane in the point P and let P divide AB in the ratio $r : 1$ so that r is positive or negative according as P divides AB internally or externally, *i.e.*, according as A and B lie on the opposite or the same side of the plane.

Since the point P whose co-ordinates are

$$\left(\frac{rx_2 + x_1}{r+1}, \; \frac{ry_2 + y_1}{r+1}, \; \frac{rz_2 + z_1}{r+1} \right)$$

lies on the same plane, we have

$$a\frac{rx_2 + x_1}{r+1} + b\frac{ry_2 + y_1}{r+1} + c\frac{rz_2 + z_1}{r+1} + d = 0$$

$$\Rightarrow \qquad r(ax_2 + by_2 + cz_2 + d) + (ax_1 + by_1 + cz_1 + d) = 0,$$

$$\Rightarrow \qquad r = -\frac{ax_1 + by_1 + cz_1 + d}{ax_2 + by_2 + cz_2 + d}$$

This shows that r is negative or positive according as

$$ax_1 + by_1 + cz_1 + d, \; ax_2 + by_2 + cz_2 + d$$

are of the same or different signs.

Thus, the theorem is proved.

Ex. Show that the origin and the point $(2, -4, 3)$ lie on different sides of the plane $x + 3y - 5z + 7 = 0$.

2.7. LENGTH OF THE PERPENDICULAR FROM A POINT TO A PLANE

To find the perpendicular distance of the point

$$P(x_1, y_1, z_1)$$

from the plane

$$lx + my + nz = p.$$

The equation of the plane which passes through the point

$$P(x_1, y_1, z_1)$$

and is parallel to the given plane is

$$lx + my + nz = p_1$$

where

$$lx_1 + my_1 + nz_1 = p_1.$$

Let OKK' be the perpendicular from the origin O to the two parallel planes meeting them in K and K' so that

$$OK = p \text{ and } OK' = p_1.$$

Draw the line PL perpendicular to the given plane. We have

$$LP = OK' - OK$$

$$= p_1 - p = lx_1 + my_1 + nz_1 - p.$$

Cor. *To find the length of the perpendicular from the point*

$$(x_1, y_1, z_1)$$

to the plane as $ax + by + cz + d = 0$.

The normal form of the given equation being

$$\pm \frac{a}{\sqrt{\Sigma a^2}} x \pm \frac{b}{\sqrt{\Sigma a^2}} y \pm \frac{c}{\sqrt{\Sigma a^2}} z \pm \frac{d}{\sqrt{\Sigma a^2}} = 0.$$

the required length of the perpendicular is

$$\pm \frac{ax_1 + by_1 + cz_1 + d}{\sqrt{(a^2 + b^2 + c^2)}}.$$

EXAMPLES

1. *Find the distance between the parallel planes $x + 2y - 3z + 1 = 0$ and $2x + 4y - 4z + 5 = 0$.*

Sol. The perpendicular distances of the origin from the two planes are

$$\frac{1}{\sqrt{1 + 4 + 4}} = \frac{1}{3} \text{ and } \frac{5}{\sqrt{4 + 16 + 16}} = \frac{5}{6}$$

As the two distances are positive, the two planes lie on the same side of the origin. Hence, the required distance between two planes is $\dfrac{5}{6} - \dfrac{1}{3} = \dfrac{1}{2}$.

2. *Find the locus of a point, the sum of the squares of whose distances from the planes $x + y + z = 0$, $x - z = 0$, $x - 2y + z = 0$ is 9.*

Sol. Let the co-ordinates of the point be (α, β, γ). Its distances from the given planes are

$$\frac{\alpha + \beta + \gamma}{\sqrt{3}}, \frac{\alpha - \gamma}{\sqrt{2}}, \frac{\alpha - 2\beta + \gamma}{\sqrt{6}}$$

We are given that

$$\left(\frac{\alpha + \beta + \gamma}{\sqrt{3}}\right)^2 + \left(\frac{\alpha - \gamma}{\sqrt{2}}\right)^2 + \left(\frac{\alpha - 2\beta + \gamma}{\sqrt{6}}\right)^2 = 9$$

$$\Rightarrow \quad 6\alpha^2 + 6\beta^2 + 6\gamma^2 = 54 \Rightarrow \alpha^2 + \beta^2 + \gamma^2 = 9$$

Hence, the locus of (α, β, γ) is

$$x^2 + y^2 + z^2 = 9.$$

3. *Two systems of rectangular axes have the same origin. If a plane cuts them at distances a, b, c and a', b', c' respectively from the origin, prove that*

$$1/a^2 + 1/b^2 + 1/c^2 = 1/a'^2 + 1/b'^2 + 1/c'^2.$$

(Kanpur, 1997; Garhwal, 1998; Rohilkhand, 1999)

Sol. Equations of the plane w.r.t. two systems are

$$x/a + y/b + z/c = 1$$

and
$$x/a' + y/b' + z/c' = 1.$$

Since origin is common to both, hence the perpendicular distances of these planes from the origin must be equal. Hence,

$$\frac{1}{\sqrt{1/a^2 + 1/b^2 + 1/c^2}} = \frac{1}{\sqrt{1/a'^2 + 1/b'^2 + 1/c'^2}}$$

or
$$1/a^2 + 1/b^2 + 1/c^2 = 1/a'^2 + 1/b'^2 + 1/c'^2.$$

EXERCISES

1. Find the distances of the points (2, 3, 4) and (1, 1, 4) from the plane

$$3x - 6y + 2z + 11 = 0 \qquad\qquad \text{[Ans. 1; 16/7]}$$

2. Show that distances between the parallel planes

$$2x - 2y + z + 3 = 0 \text{ and } 4x - 4y + 2z + 5 = 0$$

is 1/6. *(Avadh, 1995)*

(The distance between two parallel planes is the distance of any point on one from the other.)

3. Find the locus of the point whose distance from the origin is three times its distance from the plane $2x + 2z = 3$.

[Ans. $3x^2 + 3z^2 - 4xy + 8xz - 4yz - 12x + 6y - 12z + 9 = 0$]

4. Show that (1/8, 1/8, 1/8) is the incentre of the tetrahedron formed by the four planes $x = 0, y = 0, z = 0, x + 2y + 2z = 1$.

5. Sum of the distances of any number of fixed points from a variable plane is zero; show that the plane passes through a fixed point.

2.7.1. Bisectors of Angles Between Two Planes

Just as we have two bisectors between two given lines, we also have two bisectors between two given planes. Of course, the bisectors are now planes. We have proceed *to find the equations of the bisectors of the angle between the planes*

$$ax + by + cz + d = 0,$$
$$a_1x + b_1y + c_1z + d_1 = 0. \qquad \text{(Rohilkhand, 1998; Garhwal, 2001)}$$

If (x, y, z) be a point on any one of the planes bisecting the angles between the planes, then the perpendiculars from this point to the two planes must be equal (in magnitude) so that

$$\frac{ax + by + cz + d}{\sqrt{(a^2 + b^2 + c^2)}} = \pm \frac{a_1 x + b_1 y + c_1 z + d_1}{\sqrt{(a_1^2 + b_1^2 + c_1^2)}}$$

are the equations of the two bisecting planes.

Of these two bisecting planes, one bisects the acute and the other the obtuse angle between the given planes.

The bisector of the acute angle makes with either of the planes an angle which is less than 45° and the bisector of the obtuse angle makes with either of them an angle which is greater than 45°. This gives a test for determining which angle, acute or obtuse, each bisecting plane bisects.

EXAMPLES

1. *Find the equations of the planes bisecting the angles between the planes*

$$x + 2y + 2z - 3 = 0 \qquad \qquad ...(i)$$
$$3x + 4y + 12z + 1 = 0 \qquad \qquad ...(ii)$$

and specify the one which bisects the acute angle.

Sol. The equations of the two bisecting planes are

$$\frac{x + 2y + 2z - 3}{3} = \pm \frac{3x + 4y + 12z + 1}{13}$$

$$\begin{cases} 2x + 7y - 5z - 21 = 0, & ...(iii) \\ 11x + 19y + 31z - 18 = 0 & ...(iv) \end{cases}$$

If θ be the angle between the planes (i) and (iii), we have

$$\cos \theta = \frac{2}{\sqrt{78}}$$

$$\Rightarrow \qquad \qquad \tan \theta = \frac{\sqrt{74}}{2} > 1$$

$\Rightarrow$ θ is greater than 45°

$\Rightarrow$ the plane (iii) bisects the obtuse angle

$\Rightarrow$ (iv) bisects the acute angle.

2. *Show that the origin lies in the acute angle between the planes $x + 2y + 2z = 9$ and $4x - 3y + 12z + 13 = 0$. Find the planes bisecting the angles between them and point out which bisects the acute angle.*   (*Rohilkhand, 2000; Kanpur, 1995*)

Sol. Equations of the given planes can be written as

$$-x - 2y - 2z + 9 = 0 \qquad \qquad ...(1)$$

and
$$4x - 3y + 12z + 13 = 0 \qquad \qquad ...(2)$$

The bisecting planes are

$$\frac{-x - 2y - 2z + 9}{\sqrt{(1 + 4 + 4)}} = \pm \frac{4x - 3y + 12z + 13}{\sqrt{(16 + 9 + 144)}}$$

or $-13x - 26y - 26z + 117 = \pm (12x - 9y + 36z + 39)$

or $25x + 17y + 62z - 78 = 0$ ...(3)

is the plane bisecting the angle containing the origin, and

$$x + 35y - 10z - 156 = 0 \qquad \qquad ...(4)$$

is the other bisecting plane.

Now, if θ be the angle between (1) and (3), we have

$$\cos \theta = \frac{25 \cdot 1 + 17 \cdot 2 + 62 \cdot 2}{\sqrt{1+4+4}\,\sqrt{25^2 + 17^2 + 62^2}} = \frac{61}{68}$$

$$\therefore \qquad \tan \theta = \sqrt{903}/68$$

which is less than 1, thus θ is less than 45°. Hence, the plane

$$25x + 17y + 62z - 78 = 0$$

bisects the acute angle and, therefore, the origin lies in the acute angle.

Note. Sometimes we distinguish between the two bisecting planes by finding that plane which bisects the angle between the given planes containing the origin. To do this, we express the equations of the given planes so that d and d_1 are positive. Consider the equation

$$\frac{ax + by + cz + d}{\sqrt{(a^2 + b^2 + c^2)}} = \frac{a_1x + b_1y + c_1z + d_1}{\sqrt{(a_1{}^2 + b_1{}^2 + c_1{}^2)}} \qquad \qquad ...(5)$$

Since by virtue of the equality (5), the expressions

$$ax + by + cz + d \text{ and } a_1x + b_1y + c_1z + d_1$$

must have the same sign (denominators being both positive), the points (x, y, z) on the locus lie on the origin or the non-origin side of both the planes, *i.e.*, the points on the locus lie in the angle between the planes containing the origin. Thus, the equation (5) represents the plane bisecting that angle between the planes which contains the origin.

Similarly,

$$\frac{ax + by + cz + d}{\sqrt{(a^2 + b^2 + c^2)}} = -\frac{a_1x + b_1y + c_1z + d_1}{\sqrt{(a_1{}^2 + b_1{}^2 + c_1{}^2)}}$$

represents the plane bisecting the other angle between the given planes.

EXERCISES

1. Find the bisector of the acute angle between the planes

$$2x - y - 2z + 3 = 0, \ 3x - 2y + 6z + 8 = 0.$$

[**Ans.** $23x - 13y + 32z + 45 = 0$]

2. Show that the plane

$$14x - 8y + 13 = 0$$

bisects the obtuse angle between the planes

$$3x + 4y - 5z + 1 = 0, \ 5x + 12y - 13z = 0.$$

3. Find the bisector of that angle between the planes

$$3x - 6y + 2z + 5 = 0, \ 4x - 12y + 3z - 3 = 0$$

which contains the origin. [**Ans.** $67x - 162y + 47z + 44 = 0$]

2.8. JOINT EQUATION OF TWO PLANES

Consider any two planes. We are interested in finding an equation which represents the two planes simultaneously. Thus, we propose to find an equation which will be satisfied if and only if a point lies on *either* of the two planes *i.e.*, either on one plane or the other or both.

Let

$$ax + by + cz + d = 0 \qquad \qquad ...(i)$$

and $$a_1x + b_1y + c_1z + d_1 = 0 \qquad \qquad ...(ii)$$

be the equations of two planes.

Consider the equation

$$(ax + by + cz + d)(a_1x + b_1y + c_1z + d_1) = 0 \qquad \qquad ...(iii)$$

A point (x_1, y_1, z_1) lies on (i)

$\Rightarrow \qquad \qquad ax_1 + by_1 + cz_1 + d = 0$

$\Rightarrow \qquad \qquad (ax_1 + by_1 + cz_1 + d)(a_1x_1 + b_1y_1 + c_1z_1 + d_1) = 0.$

A point (x_1, y_1, z_1) lies on (ii)

$\Rightarrow \qquad \qquad a_1x_1 + b_1y_1 + c_1z_1 + d_1 = 0$

$\Rightarrow \qquad \qquad (ax_1 + by_1 + cz_1 + d)(a_1x_1 + b_1y_1 + c_1z_1 + d_1) = 0.$

A point (x_1, y_1, z_1) lies on (iii)

$\Rightarrow \qquad \qquad (ax_1 + by_1 + cz_1 + d)(a_1x_1 + b_1y_1 + c_1z_1 + d_1) = 0$

$\Rightarrow \qquad \qquad ax_1 + by_1 + cz_1 + d = 0 \text{ or } a_1x_1 + b_1y_1 + c_1z_1 + d_1 = 0.$

$\Rightarrow \qquad (x_1, y_1, z_1)$ lies on the plane (i) or on the plane (ii).

Thus, we have the following :

A point (x, y, z) either lies on the plane (i) or on the plane (ii)

$\Leftrightarrow \qquad (ax + by + cz + d)(a_1x + b_1y + c_1z + d_1) = 0.$

We thus say that

$$(ax + by + cz + d)(a_1x + b_1y + c_1z + d_1) = 0$$

is the equation of the two planes.

2.8.1. *Condition for the homogeneous second degree equation*

$$ax^2 + by^2 + cz^2 + 2fyz + 2gzx + 2hxy = 0 \qquad \qquad ...(i)$$

to represent two planes.   (Kanpur, 1996; Avadh, 2002, 2005)

We suppose that the given equation represents two planes.

Let the equation of the two planes separately be

$$lx + my + nz = 0,$$

and $\qquad \qquad l'x + m'y + n'z = 0.$

There cannot appear constant terms in the separate equations of the planes, for, otherwise, their joint equation will not be homogeneous.

We have

$$ax^2 + by^2 + cz^2 + 2fyz + 2gzx + 2hxy = (lx + my + nz)(l'x + m'y + n'z)$$

$$\Rightarrow \quad \begin{cases} a = ll', \ b = mm', \ c = nn' \\ 2f = m'n + mn', \ 2g = ln' + l'n, \ 2h = lm' + l'm. \end{cases}$$

The required condition which is essentially the condition for the consistency of these equations is obtained on eliminating $l, m, n; l', m', n'$ from the above six relations and this can be easily effected as follows. We have

$$0 = \begin{vmatrix} l & l' & 0 \\ m & m' & 0 \\ n & n' & 0 \end{vmatrix} \times \begin{vmatrix} l' & l & 0 \\ m' & m & 0 \\ n' & n & 0 \end{vmatrix} = \begin{vmatrix} ll' + l'l & l'm + lm' & l'n + ln' \\ lm' + l'm & mm' + m'm & m'n + mn' \\ n'l + nl' & n'm + nm' & n'n + nn' \end{vmatrix}$$

$$= 8 \begin{vmatrix} a & h & g \\ h & b & f \\ g & f & c \end{vmatrix} = 8(abc + 2fgh - af^2 - bg^2 - ch^2).$$

Thus, if the equation
$$ax^2 + by^2 + cz^2 + 2fyz + 2gzx + 2hxy = 0,$$
represents two planes, we have the condition,
$$abc + 2fgh - af^2 - bg^2 - ch^2 = 0.$$

Cor. Angle between planes. If θ be the angle between the planes represented by the equation (i), we have if $ll' + mm' + nn' \neq 0$

$$\tan \theta = \frac{\sqrt{(mn' - m'n)^2 + (nl' - n'l)^2 + (lm' - l'm)^2}}{ll' + mm' + nn'}$$

$$= \frac{2\sqrt{f^2 + g^2 + h^2 - ab - bc - ca}}{a + b + c}.$$

The planes will be at right angles if
$$ll' + mm' + nn' = 0 \iff a + b + c = 0.$$

Ex. Prove that the equation $2x^2 - 6y^2 - 12z^2 + 18yz + 2zx + xy = 0$ represents a pair of planes. Also find the angle between them.   (*Rohilkhand, 1998, 2005; Garhwal, 2000; Kanpur, 2002*)

Sol. $a = 2, b = -6, c = -12, f = 9, g = 1, h = 1/2$. These values satisfy the condition
$$abc + 2fgh - af^2 - bg^2 - ch^2 = 0.$$

$$\tan \theta = \frac{2\sqrt{f^2 + g^2 + h^2 - ab - bc - ca}}{a + b + c} = \frac{2\sqrt{185}}{2(-16)} = -\frac{\sqrt{185}}{16}$$

EXERCISES

Show that the following equations represent pairs of planes and also find the angles between each pair.

(i) $12x^2 - 2y^2 - 6z^2 - 2xy + 7yz + 6zx = 0$.   [**Ans.** $\cos^{-1}(4/21)$]

(ii) $2x^2 - 2y^2 + 4z^2 + 6xz + 2yz + 3xy = 0$.   [**Ans.** $\cos^{-1}(4/9)$]

(iii) Show that the equation

$$\frac{a}{y - z} + \frac{b}{z - x} + \frac{c}{x - y} = 0$$

represents a pair of planes.   (*Garhwal, 1999*)

2.9. ORTHOGONAL PROJECTION ON A PLANE

Corresponding to the notion of projection on a line, we also have that of projection on a plane which we now proceed to consider.

Def. Orthogonal projection on a plane. *The foot of the perpendicular from a point to a given plane is called the orthogonal projection of the point on the plane.*

This plane on which we project is called the plane of the projection.

Thus, (Fig. 1, page 1) L, M, N are respectively the orthogonal projections of the point P on the YZ, ZX and XY planes.

The projection of a curve on a plane is the locus of the projections on the plane of any point on the curve.

The projection on a given plane of the area enclosed by a plane curve is the area enclosed by the projection of the curve on the plane.

In particular, the projection of a straight line on a given plane is the locus of the feet of the perpendiculars drawn from points on the line on the plane.

2.9.1. The following simple results in *Pure Solid Geometry* are assumed without proof :

(1) The projection of a straight line is a straight line.

(2) If a line *AB* in a plane be perpendicular to the line of intersection of this plane with the plane of projection, then the length of its projection is $AB \cos \theta$; θ being the angle between the two planes.

In case a segment *AB* is parallel to the plane of projection, then the length of the projection is the same as that of *AB*.

(3) The projection of the area, *A*, enclosed by a curve in a plane is $A \cos \theta$; θ being the angle between the plane of the curve containing the given area and the plane of projection.

Theorem. *If A_x, A_y, A_z be the areas of the projections of an area, A, on the three co-ordinate planes, then*

$$A^2 = A_x^2 + A_y^2 + A_z^2.$$

Let *l*, *m*, *n* be the direction cosines of the normal to the plane of the area *A*.

Since *l* is the cosine of the angle between the *YZ* plane and the plane of the area *A*, therefore,

$$A_x = lA.$$

Similarly, $$A_y = mA,$$

and $$A_z = nA.$$

Hence $$A_x^2 + A_y^2 + A_z^2 = A^2 (l^2 + m^2 + n^2) = A^2.$$

EXAMPLES

1. *Find the area of the triangle whose vertices are the points*

$$(1, 2, 3), (-2, 1, -4), (3, 4, -2).$$

Sol. To find the area *A* of this triangle, we find the areas A_x, A_y, A_z of the projection of the same on the co-ordinate planes.

The vertices of the projection of the triangle on the *XY* plane are

$$(1, 2, 0), (-2, 1, 0), (3, 4, 0),$$

$$\Rightarrow \qquad A_x = \frac{1}{2} \begin{vmatrix} 1 & 2 & 1 \\ -2 & 1 & 1 \\ 3 & 4 & 1 \end{vmatrix} = -2.$$

Similarly, $$A_y = \frac{1}{2} \begin{vmatrix} 1 & 3 & 1 \\ -2 & -4 & 1 \\ 3 & -2 & 1 \end{vmatrix} = \frac{29}{2}$$

and $$A_z = \frac{1}{2} \begin{vmatrix} 2 & 3 & 1 \\ 1 & -4 & 1 \\ 4 & -2 & 1 \end{vmatrix} = \frac{29}{2}.$$

Therefore, the area of the given triangle

$$= \sqrt{A_x^2 + A_y^2 + A_z^2} = \sqrt{4 + \frac{(29)^2}{4} + \frac{(19)^2}{4}} = \frac{\sqrt{1218}}{2}.$$

2. *A plane makes intercepts OA = a, OB = b and OC = c respectively on the co-ordinate axes. Find the area of △ ABC.*

Sol. Co-ordinates of the points A, B, C are $(a, 0, 0)$, $(0, b, 0)$ and $(0, 0, c)$. Now, if A_x, A_y, A_z be the projections of the area of $\triangle ABC$ on the planes $x = 0$, $y = 0$, $z = 0$ respectively, then

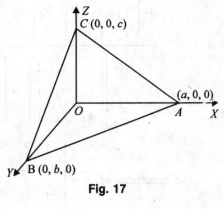

$$A_x = \text{area of } \triangle OBC$$

$$= \frac{1}{2} OB \cdot OC = \frac{1}{2} bc$$

Similarly, $A_y = \frac{1}{2} ac$ and $A_z = \frac{1}{2} ab$.

$\therefore$ Area of $\triangle ABC = \sqrt{A_x^2 + A_y^2 + A_z^2}$

Fig. 17

$$= \frac{1}{2} \sqrt{a^2 b^2 + b^2 c^2 + c^2 a^2}.$$

EXERCISES

1. Find the areas of the triangles whose vertices are the points :

    (i) $(a, 0, 0)$, $(0, b, 0)$, $(0, 0, c)$.   *(ii)* (x_1, y_1, z_1), (x_2, y_2, z_2), (x_3, y_3, z_3).

2. From a point $P(x', y', z')$ a plane is drawn at right angles to OP to meet the co-ordinate axes at A, B, C; prove that the area of the triangle ABC is $r^5/2x'y'z'$, where r is the measure of OP.

2.10. VOLUME OF A TETRAHEDRON

To find the volume of a tetrahedron in terms of the co-ordinates

$$(x_1, y_1, z_1), (x_2, y_2, z_2), (x_3, y_3, z_3), (x_4, y_4, z_4)$$

of its vertices A, B, C, D.   *(Kanpur, 1998, 99; Rohilkhand, 2001)*

Let V be the volume of the tetrahedron $ABCD$.

Then

$$V = \frac{1}{3} \Delta\, p, \qquad \qquad ...(i)$$

where p is the length of the perpendicular AL from a vertex A to the opposite face BCD; and Δ is the area of the triangle BCD.

The equation of the plane BCD is

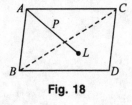

$$\begin{vmatrix} x & y & z & 1 \\ x_2 & y_2 & z_2 & 1 \\ x_3 & y_3 & z_3 & 1 \\ x_4 & y_4 & z_4 & 1 \end{vmatrix} = 0$$

Fig. 18

$$\Leftrightarrow\ x \begin{vmatrix} y_2 & z_2 & 1 \\ y_3 & z_3 & 1 \\ y_4 & z_4 & 1 \end{vmatrix} - y \begin{vmatrix} x_2 & z_2 & 1 \\ x_3 & z_3 & 1 \\ x_4 & z_4 & 1 \end{vmatrix} + z \begin{vmatrix} x_2 & y_2 & 1 \\ x_3 & y_3 & 1 \\ x_4 & y_4 & 1 \end{vmatrix} - \begin{vmatrix} x_2 & y_2 & z_2 \\ x_3 & y_3 & z_3 \\ x_4 & y_4 & z_4 \end{vmatrix} = 0 \qquad ...(i)$$

$\therefore$ The length of the perpendicular, p is equal to

$$\frac{x_1 \begin{vmatrix} y_2 & z_2 & 1 \\ y_3 & z_3 & 1 \\ y_4 & z_4 & 1 \end{vmatrix} - y_1 \begin{vmatrix} x_2 & z_2 & 1 \\ x_3 & z_3 & 1 \\ x_4 & z_4 & 1 \end{vmatrix} + z_1 \begin{vmatrix} x_2 & y_2 & 1 \\ x_3 & y_3 & 1 \\ x_4 & y_4 & 1 \end{vmatrix} - \begin{vmatrix} x_2 & y_2 & z_2 \\ x_3 & y_3 & z_3 \\ x_4 & y_4 & z_4 \end{vmatrix}}{\left\{ \begin{vmatrix} y_2 & z_2 & 1 \\ y_3 & z_3 & 1 \\ y_4 & z_4 & 1 \end{vmatrix}^2 + \begin{vmatrix} x_2 & z_2 & 1 \\ x_3 & z_3 & 1 \\ x_4 & z_4 & 1 \end{vmatrix}^2 + \begin{vmatrix} x_2 & y_2 & 1 \\ x_3 & y_3 & 1 \\ x_4 & y_4 & 1 \end{vmatrix}^2 \right\}^{1/2}} \qquad ...(iii)$$

The numerator of $p = \begin{vmatrix} x_1 & y_1 & z_1 & 1 \\ x_2 & y_2 & z_2 & 1 \\ x_3 & y_3 & z_3 & 1 \\ x_4 & y_4 & z_4 & 1 \end{vmatrix}$.

If Δ_x, Δ_y, Δ_z be the areas of the projections of the triangle on the YZ, ZX, XY planes respectively, we obtain

$$2\Delta_x = \begin{vmatrix} y_2 & z_2 & 1 \\ y_3 & z_3 & 1 \\ y_4 & z_4 & 1 \end{vmatrix}, \quad 2\Delta_y = \begin{vmatrix} x_2 & z_2 & 1 \\ x_3 & z_3 & 1 \\ x_4 & z_4 & 1 \end{vmatrix}, \quad 2\Delta_z = \begin{vmatrix} x_2 & y_2 & 1 \\ x_3 & y_3 & 1 \\ x_4 & y_4 & 1 \end{vmatrix}$$

Therefore the denominator of $p = [4 (\Delta_x^2 + \Delta_y^2 + \Delta_z^2)]^{1/2} = 2\Delta$.

From (i) and (ii), we deduce that the required volume is

$$\frac{1}{3} \Delta p = \frac{1}{6} \begin{vmatrix} x_1 & y_1 & z_1 & 1 \\ x_2 & y_2 & z_2 & 1 \\ x_3 & y_3 & z_3 & 1 \\ x_4 & y_4 & z_4 & 1 \end{vmatrix}.$$

EXAMPLES

1. A, B, C are $(3, 2, 1)$, $(-2, 0, -3)$, $(0, 0, -2)$. Find the locus of P if the volume $PABC = 5$.

Sol. Let (x, y, z) be the co-ordinates of P.

Then

$$\frac{1}{6} \begin{vmatrix} x & y & z & 1 \\ 3 & 2 & 1 & 1 \\ -2 & 0 & -3 & 1 \\ 0 & 0 & -2 & 1 \end{vmatrix} = 5$$

$$\Rightarrow \qquad \begin{vmatrix} x & y & z+2 & 1 \\ 3 & 2 & 3 & 1 \\ -2 & 0 & -1 & 1 \\ 0 & 0 & 0 & 1 \end{vmatrix} = 30 \qquad\qquad [c_3 + 2c_4]$$

$$\Rightarrow \qquad \begin{vmatrix} x & y & z+2 \\ 3 & 2 & 3 \\ -2 & 0 & -1 \end{vmatrix} = 30$$

$$\Rightarrow \qquad 2x - 4z - 8 + 3y = 30$$

$$\Rightarrow \qquad 2x + 3y - 4z = 38.$$

2. *Prove that the four planes* $my + nz = 0$, $nz + lx = 0$, $lx + my = 0$, $lx + my + nz = p$ *form a tetrahedron whose volume is* $\dfrac{2p^3}{3lmn}$.   *(Kumaon 2006, Kanpur, 1995)*

Sol. Solving the given equations taking three planes at a time, we get the vertices of the tetrahedron as

$$(0, 0, 0), \left(\frac{-p}{l}, \frac{p}{m}, \frac{p}{n}\right), \left(\frac{p}{l}, \frac{-p}{m}, \frac{p}{n}\right) \text{ and } \left(\frac{p}{l}, \frac{p}{m}, \frac{-p}{n}\right).$$

With these points as vertices, the volume V of the tetrahedron is given by

$$V = \frac{1}{6} \begin{vmatrix} 0 & 0 & 0 & 1 \\ -p/l & p/m & p/n & 1 \\ p/l & -p/m & p/n & 1 \\ p/l & p/m & -p/n & 1 \end{vmatrix} = \frac{-p^3}{6lmn} \begin{vmatrix} -1 & 1 & 1 \\ 1 & -1 & 1 \\ 1 & 1 & -1 \end{vmatrix}$$

$$= \frac{p^3}{6lmn}(4) = \frac{2}{3}\frac{p^3}{lmn}.$$

3. *Find the volume of a tetrahedron in terms of the lengths of the three edges which meet in a point and of the angles which these edges make with each other in pairs.*

(Agra, 1996; Kanpur, 1996; Avadh, 2003)

Sol. Let $OABC$ be a tetrahedron.

Let $OA = a$, $OB = b$, $OC = c$.

Let $\angle BOC = \lambda$, $\angle COA = \mu$, $\angle AOB = v$.

We take O as origin and any system of three mutually perpendicular lines through O as co-ordinate axes.

Let the direction cosines of the lines OA, OB, OC be

$$l_1, m_1, n_1; l_2, m_2, n_2; l_3, m_3, n_3.$$

Thus, the co-ordinates of A, B, C are

$(l_1 a, m_1 a, n_1 a)$; $(l_2 b, m_2 b, n_2 b)$; $(l_3 c, m_3 c, n_3 c)$ (§ 1.6.1)

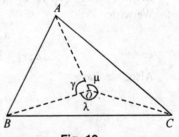

Fig. 19

Therefore, the volume of the tetrahedron $OABC$

$$= \frac{1}{6} \begin{vmatrix} 0 & 0 & 0 & 1 \\ l_1 a & m_1 a & n_1 a & 1 \\ l_2 b & m_2 b & n_2 b & 1 \\ l_3 c & m_3 c & n_3 c & 1 \end{vmatrix} = \frac{1}{6} \begin{vmatrix} l_1 a & m_1 a & n_1 a \\ l_2 b & m_2 b & n_2 b \\ l_3 c & m_3 c & n_3 c \end{vmatrix} = \frac{abc}{6} \begin{vmatrix} l_1 & m_1 & n_1 \\ l_2 & m_2 & n_2 \\ l_3 & m_3 & n_3 \end{vmatrix}$$

Now

$$\begin{vmatrix} l_1 & m_1 & n_1 \\ l_2 & m_2 & n_2 \\ l_3 & m_3 & n_3 \end{vmatrix}^2 = \begin{vmatrix} l_1 & m_1 & n_1 \\ l_2 & m_2 & n_2 \\ l_3 & m_3 & n_3 \end{vmatrix} \times \begin{vmatrix} l_1 & m_1 & n_1 \\ l_2 & m_2 & n_2 \\ l_3 & m_3 & n_3 \end{vmatrix}$$

$$= \begin{vmatrix} \Sigma l_1^2 & \Sigma l_1 l_2 & \Sigma l_1 l_3 \\ \Sigma l_1 l_2 & \Sigma l_2^2 & \Sigma l_2 l_3 \\ \Sigma l_3 l_1 & \Sigma l_3 l_2 & \Sigma l_3^2 \end{vmatrix} = \begin{vmatrix} 1 & \cos \nu & \cos \mu \\ \cos \nu & 1 & \cos \lambda \\ \cos \mu & \cos \lambda & 1 \end{vmatrix}$$

Thus, the volume of the tetrahedron $OABC$

$$= \frac{abc}{6} \begin{vmatrix} 1 & \cos \nu & \cos \mu \\ \cos \nu & 1 & \cos \lambda \\ \cos \mu & \cos \lambda & 1 \end{vmatrix}^{1/2}$$

4. *Show that the volume of the tetrahedron, the equations of whose faces are*

$$a_r x + b_r y + c_r z + d_r = 0, \quad r = (1, 2, 3, 4)$$

is

$$\frac{\Delta^3}{6 D_1 D_2 D_3 D_4}$$

where Δ is the determinant

$$\begin{vmatrix} a_1 & b_1 & c_1 & d_1 \\ a_2 & b_2 & c_2 & d_2 \\ a_3 & b_3 & c_3 & d_3 \\ a_4 & b_4 & c_4 & d_4 \end{vmatrix}$$

and D_1, D_2, D_3, D_4 are the co-factors of d_1, d_2, d_3, d_4 respectively in the determinant Δ.

Sol. Let (x_1, y_1, z_1) be the point of intersection of the three planes

$$a_r x + b_r y + c_r z + d_r = 0, \quad r = (2, 3, 4),$$

so that (x_1, y_1, z_1) is one of the vertices of the tetrahedron.

Let $(x_2, y_2, z_2), (x_3, y_3, z_3), (x_4, y_4, z_4)$ be the other vertices similarly obtained.
We write

$$a_1 x_1 + b_1 y_1 + c_1 z_1 + d_1 = k_1$$

$$\Leftrightarrow \qquad a_1 x_1 + b_1 y_1 + c_1 z_1 + (d_1 - k_1) = 0. \qquad \dots(1)$$

Also, we have

$$a_2 x_1 + b_2 y_1 + c_2 z_1 + d_2 = 0 \qquad \dots(2)$$

$$a_3 x_1 + b_3 y_1 + c_3 z_1 + d_3 = 0 \qquad \dots(3)$$

$$a_4 x_1 + b_4 y_1 + c_4 z_1 + d_4 = 0 \qquad \dots(4)$$

Eliminating x_1, y_1, z_1 from (1), (2), (3), (4), we have

$$\begin{vmatrix} a_1 & b_1 & c_1 & d_1 - k_1 \\ a_2 & b_2 & c_2 & d_2 \\ a_3 & b_3 & c_3 & d_3 \\ a_4 & b_4 & c_4 & d_4 \end{vmatrix} = 0,$$

$$\Rightarrow \qquad \Delta + k_1 \begin{vmatrix} a_2 & b_2 & c_2 \\ a_3 & b_3 & c_3 \\ a_4 & b_4 & c_4 \end{vmatrix} = 0$$

$$\Rightarrow \qquad \Delta - k_1 D_1 = 0 \quad \Rightarrow \quad k_1 = \Delta / D_1$$

Similarly, we have

$$a_2 x_2 + b_2 y_2 + c_2 z_2 + d_2 = k_2 = \Delta / D_2$$
$$a_3 x_3 + b_3 y_3 + c_3 z_3 + d_3 = k_3 = \Delta / D_3$$
$$a_4 x_4 + b_4 y_4 + c_4 z_4 + d_4 = k_4 = \Delta / D_4$$

We, now, have

$$\begin{vmatrix} a_1 & b_1 & c_1 & d_1 \\ a_2 & b_2 & c_2 & d_2 \\ a_3 & b_3 & c_3 & d_3 \\ a_4 & b_4 & c_4 & d_4 \end{vmatrix} \times \begin{vmatrix} x_1 & y_1 & z_1 & 1 \\ x_2 & y_2 & z_2 & 1 \\ x_3 & y_3 & z_3 & 1 \\ x_4 & y_4 & z_4 & 1 \end{vmatrix} = \begin{vmatrix} k_1 & 0 & 0 & 0 \\ 0 & k_2 & 0 & 0 \\ 0 & 0 & k_3 & 0 \\ 0 & 0 & 0 & k_4 \end{vmatrix}$$

$$= k_1 k_2 k_3 k_4 = \frac{\Delta^4}{D_1 D_2 D_3 D_4}.$$

Therefore, the required volume $= \dfrac{\Delta^3}{6 D_1 D_2 D_3 D_4}.$

EXERCISES

1. The vertices of a tetrahedron are $(0, 1, 2)$, $(3, 0, 1)$, $(4, 3, 6)$, $(2, 3, 2)$; show that its volume is 6.

2. A, B, C are three fixed points and a variable point P moves so that the volume of the tetrahedron $PABC$ is constant; show that the locus of the point P is a plane parallel to the plane ABC.

3. A variable plane makes with the co-ordinate planes a tetrahedron of constant volume $64k^3$. Find

   (i) the locus of the centroid of the tetrahedron.   [**Ans.** $xyz = 6k^3$]

   (ii) the locus of the foot of the perpendicular from the origin to the plane.

   [**Ans.** $(x^2 + y^2 + z^2)^3 = 384k^3 xyz$]

4. If the volume of the tetrahedron whose vertices are $(a, 1, 2)$, $(3, 0, 1)$, $(4, 3, 6)$, $(2, 3, 2)$ is 6. Find the value of a.   [**Ans.** 0]

5. Find the volume of the tetrahedron formed by planes whose equations are

$$y + z = 0, \ z + x = 0, \ x + y = 0, \text{ and } x + y + z = 1.$$ [**Ans.** 2/3]

OBJECTIVE QUESTIONS

I. Multiple Choice Questions

Note : *For each of the following questions, four alternatives are given for the answer. Only one of them is correct. Choose the correct alternative.*

1. The equation to a plane in normal form is :

   (a) $\dfrac{x}{a} + \dfrac{y}{b} + \dfrac{z}{c} = 1$ (b) $\dfrac{x}{l} + \dfrac{y}{m} + \dfrac{z}{n} = 1$

   (c) $ax + by + cz = p$ (d) $lx + my + nz = p.$ (*Garhwal, 2004*)

2. The angle between the planes $ax + by + cz + d = 0$ and $a'x + b'y + c'z + d' = 0$ is :

   (a) $\cos^{-1}(aa' + bb' + cc')$ (b) $\sin^{-1}(aa' + bb' + cc')$

   (c) $\cos^{-1}\left[\dfrac{aa' + bb' + cc'}{\sqrt{(\Sigma a^2)(\Sigma a'^2)}}\right]$ (d) $\sin^{-1}\left[\dfrac{aa' + bb' + cc'}{\sqrt{(\Sigma a^2)(\Sigma a'^2)}}\right].$

3. The distance of the point (α, β, γ) from the plane $lx + my + nz = p$ is :

   (a) $| l\alpha + m\beta + n\gamma - p |$ (b) $l\alpha + m\beta + n\gamma$

   (c) $| l\alpha + m\beta + n\gamma + p |$ (d) None of these.

4. The equation $ax^2 + by^2 + cz^2 + 2fyz + 2gzx + 2hxy = 0$ represents a pair of planes passing through the origin if :

   (a) $abc + 2fgh + af^2 + bg^2 + ch^2 = 0$ (b) $abc + 2fgh - af^2 - bg^2 - ch^2 = 0$

   (c) $abc - 2fgh + af^2 + bg^2 + ch^2 = 0$ (d) $abc - 2fgh + af^2 - bg^2 - ch^2 = 0$.

5. The number of arbitrary constants in the equation $Ax + By + Cz + D = 0$ is :

   (a) 4   (b) 3   (c) 2   (d) 1.

6. The equation of the plane through the intersection of two planes $P = 0$ and $Q = 0$ will be :

   (a) $PQ = 0$ (b) $P + \lambda Q = 0$ (c) $P / \lambda Q = 0$ (d) $P = Q = 0$.

   (Avadh, 2005)

7. Two planes $a_1x + b_1y + c_1z + d_1 = 0$ and $a_2x + b_2y + c_2z + d_2 = 0$ are parallel if :

   (a) $a_1a_2 + b_1b_2 + c_1c_2 = 0$ (b) $\dfrac{a_1}{a_2} + \dfrac{b_1}{b_2} + \dfrac{c_1}{c_2} = 0$

   (c) $\dfrac{a_1}{a_2} = \dfrac{b_1}{b_2} = \dfrac{c_1}{c_2}$ (d) None of these.   *(Kanpur, 2001)*

8. Equation to a plane through $P (a, b, c)$ and perpendicular to OP is :

   (a) $x + y + z = abc$ (b) $ax + by + cz = 0$

   (c) $ax + by + cz = a + b + c$ (d) $ax + by + cz = a^2 + b^2 + c^2$.

9. The intercepts made on the axes by the plane $x + 2y - 2z = 9$ are :

   (a) $1, 2, -2$ (b) $\dfrac{1}{9}, \dfrac{2}{9}, -\dfrac{2}{9}$ (c) $9, \dfrac{9}{2}, -\dfrac{9}{2}$ (d) None of these.

   (Avadh, 2003)

10. The intercept on the x-axis of the plane $x + y + z = 1$ is :

    (a) 4   (b) 3   (c) 2   (d) 1.

    (Kanpur, 2002)

11. The intercept on z-axis of the plane $x + y + 2z = 2$ is :

    (a) 1   (b) 2   (c) 3   (d) 4.

    (Kanpur, 2003)

12. Angle between the planes $x + y + z = 1$ and $x - y = 2$ is :

    (a) 0   (b) $\pi/2$ (c) $\pi/3$ (d) $\pi/4$.

    (Kanpur, 2003)

13. The distance between the parallel planes $2x - 2y + z + 1 = 0$ and $4x - 4y + 2z + 3 = 0$ is :

    (a) $\dfrac{1}{6}$ (b) $\dfrac{1}{2}$ (c) $\dfrac{1}{3}$ (d) 0.

    (Avadh, 2003)

14. A plane meets the co-ordinate axes at A, B, C such that the centre of the triangle is $(3, 3, 3)$. The equation of the plane is :

    (a) $x + y + z = 3$ (b) $x + y + z = 9$

    (c) $3x + 3y + 3z = 1$ (d) $9x + 9y + 9z = 1$.

15. The angle between the planes $2x - y + z = 6$, $x + y + 2z = 7$ is :

(a) $\cos^{-1}(4/\sqrt{21})$ (b) $\pi/3$ (c) $\pi/4$ (d) $\pi/2$.

(*Avadh, 2001; Garhwal, 2002*)

16. The equation of the plane passing through the point $(-2, -2, 2)$ and containing the line joining the points $(1, 1, 1)$ and $(1, -1, 2)$ is :

(a) $x + 2y - 3z + 4 = 0$ (b) $3x - 4y + 1 = 0$

(c) $5x + 2y - 3z - 17 = 0$ ·   (d) $x - 3y - 6z + 8 = 0$.

17. If the plane $x - 2y + 3z = 0$ is rotated through a right angle about its line of intersection with the plane $2x + 3y - 4z - 5 = 0$, position is :

(a) $28x - 17y + 9z = 0$ (b) $22x + 5y - 4z - 35 = 0$

(c) $25x + 17y + 52z - 25 = 0$ (d) $x + 35y - 10z - 70 = 0$.

18. The plane $ax + by + cz = 1$ meets the co-ordinates axes in A, B, C. The centroid of the triangle is :

(a) $(3a, 3b, 3c)$ (b) $(a/3, b/3, c/3)$ (c) $(3/a, 3/b, 3/c)$ (d) $(1/3a, 1/3b, 1/3c)$.

19. The distance between the parallel planes $ax + by + cz + d = 0$ and $ax + by + cz + d' = 0$ is :

(a) $\dfrac{|d - d'|}{\sqrt{a^2 + b^2 + c^2}}$ (b) $\dfrac{|d + d'|}{\sqrt{(a^2 + b^2 + c^2)}}$ (c) $\dfrac{d}{\sqrt{(a^2 + b^2 + c^2)}}$ (d) None of these.

20. The equation of the plane through the origin and parallel to the plane $3x - 4y + 5z - 6 = 0$ is :

(a) $3x - 4y + 5z + 6 = 0$ (b) $3x + 4y - 5z + 6 = 0$

(c) $3x - 4y - 5z - 6 = 0$ (d) $3x - 4y + 5z = 0$.

21. The intercepts of the plane $2x - 3y + 4z = 12$ on the co-ordinate axes are given by :

(a) $2, -3, 4$ (b) $6, -4, -3$ (c) $6, -4, 3$ (d) $3, -2, 1.5$.

22. The angle between the two planes $3x - 4y + 5z = 0$ and $2x - y - 2z = 5$ is :

(a) $\pi/3$ (b) $\pi/2$ (c) $\pi/6$ (d) $\pi/4$.

(*Avadh, 2003*)

23. The plane passing through the point (a, b, c) and parallel to the plane $x + y + z = 0$ is :

(a) $x + y + z = a + b + c$ (b) $x + y + z + (a + b + c) = 0$

(c) $x + y + z + abc = 0$ (d) $ax + by + cz = 0$.

24. The equation of the plane through the intersection of the planes $x - 2y + 3z - 4 = 0$, $2x - 3y + 4z - 5 = 0$ and perpendicular to the plane $x + y + z - 1 = 0$ is :

(a) $x - y + 2 = 0$ (b) $x - z + 2 = 0$ (c) $y - z + 2 = 0$ (d) $z - x + 2 = 0$.

25. The distance of the plane $2x - 3y + 6z + 14 = 0$ from the origin is :

(a) 14 (b) 2 (c) -2 (d) 11.

(*Avadh, 2005*)

26. Equation of a plane parallel to x-axis is :

(a) $ax + by + cz + d = 0$ (b) $by + cz + d = 0$

(c) $ax + by + d = 0$ (d) $ax + cz + d = 0$.

27. If the equation $2x^2 - 2y^2 + 4z^2 + 6xz + 2yz + 3xy = 0$ represents a pair of planes, then the angle between the pair of planes is :

(a) $\cos^{-1}(4/9)$ (b) $\cos^{-1}(4/21)$ (c) $\cos^{-1}(4/17)$ (d) $\cos^{-1}(2/3)$.

28. The length of the perpendicular from a point (x_1, y_1, z_1) to a plane $ax + by + cz + d = 0$ is :

   (a) $ax_1 + by_1 + cz_1 + d = 0$ (b) $ax_1 + by_1 + cz_1 - d$

   (c) $\dfrac{ax_1 + by_1 + cz_1 + d}{\sqrt{a^2 + b^2 + c^2}}$ (d) $\dfrac{ax_1 + by_1 + cz_1 + d}{a^2 + b^2 + c^2}$.

29. The equation of the bisector of the obtuse angle between the planes $3x + 4y - 5z + 1 = 0$, $5x + 12y - 13z = 0$ is :

   (a) $11x + 4y - 3z = 0$ (b) $14x - 8y + 13 = 0$

   (c) $x + y + z = 9$ (d) $13x - 7z + 18 = 0$.

ANSWERS

1. (d)	**2.** (c)	**3.** (a)	**4.** (b)	**5.** (b)	**6.** (b)	**7.** (c)	**8.** (d)
9. (c)	**10.** (d)	**11.** (a)	**12.** (b)	**13.** (a)	**14.** (b)	**15.** (b)	**16.** (d)
17. (b)	**18.** (d)	**19.** (a)	**20.** (d)	**21.** (c)	**22.** (b)	**23.** (a)	**24.** (b)
25. (b)	**26.** (b)	**27.** (a)	**28.** (c)	**29.** (b)			

II. Fill in the Blanks

Note : *Fill in the blanks "......." so that the following statements are complete and correct.*

1. $a(x - l) + b(y - m) + c(z - n) = 0$ represents a plane passing through the point ....

   (*Meerut, 2001*)

2. The equation $ax + by + cz + d = 0$ represents a ....

3. $2x + 3y + 4z = 0$ is the equation of a plane which passes through the ....

   (*Meerut, 2001*)

4. Equation of the plane through a given point (x_1, y_1, z_1) and perpendicular to a line whose direction ratios are a, b, c is ....

5. The equation of the plane which cuts off intercepts a, b, c from the axes is ....

6. The direction cosines of normal to the plane $4x - y - 8z + 7 = 0$ directed from the origin to the plane are ....

7. The planes $a_1x + b_1y + c_1z + d_1 = 0$ and $a_2x + b_2y + c_2z + d_2 = 0$ are perpendicular if and only if ....

8. The intercepts made by the plane $3x + 4y + 8z = 2$ on y-axis is ....

9. The equation of the plane parallel to zx-plane and at a distance b from it is given by ....

10. The equation of the plane $x - 2y + 2z - 9 = 0$ in normal form is ....

11. The length of the perpendicular drawn from the point (x_1, y_1, z_1) to the plane $ax + by + cz + d = 0$ is ....

12. The distance between the parallel planes $x + y - z + 4 = 0$ and $x + y - z + 5 = 0$ is ....

13. The angle between the normals to the planes $2x - y + z = 13$ and $x + y + 2z = 9$ is ....

14. Two points (x_1, y_1, z_1) and (x_2, y_2, z_2) will lie on the same side of the plane $ax + by + cz + d = 0$ if $ax_1 + by_1 + cz_1 + d$ and $ax_2 + by_2 + cz_2 + d$ are of the ...... signs.

15. Two planes represented by $ax^2 + by^2 + cz^2 + 2fyz + 2gzx + 2hxy = 0$ will be perpendicular if ....

16. The bisector of the acute angle between the planes $2x - y + 2z + 3 = 0$ and $3x - 2y + 6z + 8 = 0$ is ....

ANSWERS

1. (l, m, n); 2. plane; 3. origin;

4. $a(x - x_1) + b(y - y_1) + c(z - z_1) = 0$; 5. $\dfrac{x}{a} + \dfrac{y}{b} + \dfrac{z}{c} = 1$;

6. $-\dfrac{4}{9}, \dfrac{1}{9}, \dfrac{8}{9}$; 7. $a_1 a_2 + b_1 b_2 + c_1 c_2 = 0$; 8. $\dfrac{1}{2}$;

9. $y = b$; 10. $\dfrac{1}{3} x - \dfrac{2}{3} y + \dfrac{2}{3} z = 3$; 11. $\dfrac{ax_1 + by_1 + cz_1 + d}{\sqrt{a^2 + b^2 + c^2}}$;

12. $\dfrac{1}{\sqrt{3}}$; 13. $\pi/3$; 14. same;

15. $a + b + c = 0$; 16. $23x - 13y + 32z + 45 = 0$.

III. True/False Statements

Note : *Write 'T' for true and 'F' for false statements.*

1. $lx + my + nz = p$ is the general equation of a plane.
2. Direction cosines of the normal to a plane are perpendicular to a plane are proportional to the coefficients of x, y, z in its equation.
3. Equation to a plane through $P(a, b, c)$ and perpendicular to OP is $ax + by + cz = a^2 + b^2 + c^2$.
4. The planes $x - y + z = 7$ and $3x + 2y - z + 9 = 0$ are perpendicular to each other.
5. The planes $3x - 4y + 8z + 7 = 0$ and $6x + 8y + 16z + 9 = 0$ are parallel to each other.

ANSWERS

1. F 2. T 3. T 4. T 5. F

3
Right Line

3.1. REPRESENTATION OF LINE

In this chapter, it is proposed to discuss the manner in which a straight line can be represented. We introduce the method analytically as follows :

Consider any two of the co-ordinate planes say YOZ and ZOX, whose equations are $x = 0$ and $y = 0$ respectively. These two planes intersect in Z-axis.

A point (x, y, z) lies on the Z-plane

$\Leftrightarrow$ {the point (x, y, z) lies on the YOZ plane **and** the point (x, y, z) lies on the ZOX plane}

$\Leftrightarrow$ $x = 0$ **and** $y = 0$.

Thus, we see that a point (x, y, z) lies on the Z-axis if and only if, we simultaneously have $x = 0$, $y = 0$. We are thus, led to say that $x = 0$, $y = 0$ are the two equations of Z-axis.

Consider now any line whatsoever and any two planes through the line. Let

$$ax + by + cz + d = 0 \text{ and } a_1x + b_1y + c_1z + d_1 = 0$$

be the equations of these two planes. Clearly, we have the following statement :

A point (x, y, z) lies on the given line if and only if we simultaneously have

$$ax + by + cz + d = 0 \text{ and } a_1x + b_1y + c_1z + d_1 = 0$$

Thus, we say that

$$ax + by + cz + d = 0 \text{ and } a_1x + b_1y + c_1z + d_1 = 0$$

are the two equations of the line.

It follows that a straight line is represented by **two** *equations of the first degree in x, y, z.*

Of course any given line can be represented by *different pairs* of first degree equations, for we may take *any* pair of planes through the line and the equations of the same will constitute the equations of the line.

In particular, as the X-axis is the intersection of the XZ and XY planes, $y = 0$, $z = 0$ taken together are its equations. Similarly $x = 0$, $z = 0$ are the equations of the Y-axis and $x = 0$, $y = 0$ are the equations of the Z-axis.

EXERCISES

1. What is the locus of the point (x, y, z) which satisfies the following conditions :

   (i) $2x + 3y - 4z + 1 = 0$ and $3x - y + z + 2 = 0$

   (ii) $2x + 3y - 4z + 1 = 0$ or $3x - y + z + 2 = 0$

   (iii) $2x - 3y + 5z + 4 = 0$ and $2x + y + z - 8 = 0$

   (iv) $2x - 3y + 5z + 4 = 0$ or $2x + y + z - 8 = 0$.

2. Find the intersection of the line

   $$x - 2y + 4z + 4 = 0, \ x + y + z - 8 = 0$$

   with the plane

   $$x - y + 2z + 1 = 0.$$
   [Ans. 2, 5, 1]

3.1.1. Equation of the Line Through a Given Point Drawn in a Given Direction

To find the equations of the line passing through a given point $A(x_1, y_1, z_1)$ and having direction cosines l, m, n.   (*Kumaun, 2001, 06*)

Let $P(x, y, z)$ be a point on the given line and let $AP = r$.

Projecting the segment AP on the co-ordinate axes, we obtain

$$x - x_1 = lr, \; y - y_1 = mr, \; z - z_1 = nr \qquad \ldots(i)$$

so that for all points (x, y, z) on the given line, we have

$$x = x_1 + lr, \; y = y_1 + mr, \; z = z_1 + nr.$$

Thus, the set of points on the given line is

$$\{(x_1 + lr, \; y_1 + mr, \; z_1 + nr)\};$$

r being any number.

In case none of l, m, n is zero, we have

$$\frac{x - x_1}{l} = \frac{y - y_1}{m} = \frac{z - z_1}{n} = r.$$

Thus, if $l \neq 0$, $m \neq 0$, $n \neq 0$, or equivalently $lmn \neq 0$,

$$\frac{x - x_1}{l} = \frac{y - y_1}{m} = \frac{z - z_1}{n} \qquad \ldots(ii)$$

are the *two* required equations of the line.

Clearly the equations (*ii*) of the line are not altered if we replace the direction cosines l, m, n by the three numbers proportional to them, so that it suffices to use direction ratios in place of direction cosines while writing down the equation of a line

Cor. From the relation (*i*), we have

$$x = x_1 + lr, \; y = y_1 + mr, \; z = z_1 + nr$$

so that the set of points on the line through the point (x_1, y_1, z_1) and having direction ratios l, m, n is

$$\{(x_1 + lr, \; y_1 + mr, \; z_1 + nr); \; r \text{ being any number}\}.$$

This statement does not depend upon the vanishing or otherwise of any of l, m, n.

We may remark that r is what is known as the parameter here.

Note. The equation

$$\frac{x - x_1}{l} = \frac{y - y_1}{m}$$

of first degree, being free of z, represents the plane through the line drawn perpendicular to the XOY plane. Similar statements may be made about the equations

$$\frac{y - y_1}{m} = \frac{z - z_1}{n}, \; \frac{z - z_1}{n} = \frac{x - x_1}{l}.$$

The two equations

$$(x - x_1)/l = (y - y_1)/m, \; (y - y_1)/m = (z - z_1)/n$$

represent a pair of planes through the given line.

3.1.2. Equation of a Line Through Two Points

To find the equations of the line through two points
$$(x_1, y_1, z_1) \text{ and } (x_2, y_2, z_2).$$

Since

$$x_2 - x_1, \; y_2 - y_1, \; z_2 - z_1$$

are proportional to the direction cosines of the line, the required equations are

$$\frac{x - x_1}{x_2 - x_1} = \frac{y - y_1}{y_2 - y_1} = \frac{z - z_1}{z_2 - z_1}$$

Here we have assumed that none of

$$x_2 - x_1, \; y_2 - y_1, \; z_2 - z_1$$

is zero.

EXAMPLES

1. *Find the co-ordinates of the point of intersection of the line*

$$\frac{x + 1}{1} = \frac{y + 3}{3} = \frac{z - 2}{-2}$$

with the plane $3x + 4y + 5z = 5.$ (*Kumaon, 2004*)

Sol. Let

$$\frac{x + 1}{1} = \frac{y + 3}{3} = \frac{z - 2}{-2} = r,$$

so that the point

$$(r - 1, \; 3r - 3, \; -2r + 2)$$

is a point on the given line for all values of r.

If it also lies on the given plane, we have

$$3r - 3 + 12r - 12 - 10r + 10 = 5 \implies r = 2.$$

Hence, the required point of intersection is $(1, 3, -2)$.

Its distance from the point $(-1, -3, 2)$ is $\sqrt{56}$ which is different from the value 2 of r. (Why ?)

2. *If the axes are rectangular and if l_1, m_1, n_1; l_2, m_2, n_2 are direction cosines, show that the equations to the planes through the lines which bisect the angle between*

$$x/l_1 = y/m_1 = z/n_1; \; x/l_2 = y/m_2 = z/n_2$$

and at right angles to the plane containing them are

$$(l_1 \pm l_2) \, x + (m_1 \pm m_2) \, y + (n_1 \pm n_2) \, z = 0.$$

Sol. The given lines pass through the origin. Co-ordinates of any two points, each of them at a distance r from the origin are (rl_1, rm_1, rn_1) and (rl_2, rm_2, rn_2). The co-ordinates of the middle point P of the line joining these two points are $\frac{1}{2} r \, (l_1 + l_2), \; \frac{1}{2} r \, (m_1 + m_2), \; \frac{1}{2} r \, (n_1 + n_2)$.

The point P clearly lies on one of the bisectors and since the two bisectors are at right angles to each other, hence, OP is normal to the plane passing through the other bisectors. The d.c.'s of OP are proportional to

$$\frac{1}{2} (l_1 + l_2), \; \frac{1}{2} (m_1 + m_2), \; \frac{1}{2} (n_1 + n_2).$$

Hence, one of the required planes is

$$\frac{1}{2} (l_1 + l_2) \, x + \frac{1}{2} (m_1 + m_2) \, y + \frac{1}{2} (n_1 + n_2) \, z = 0.$$

i.e., $(l_1 + l_2) \, x + (m_1 + m_2) \, y + (n_1 + n_2) \, z = 0.$

Similarly, if P lies on the other bisector, its co-ordinates will then be

$$\frac{1}{2}(l_1 - l_2)r, \frac{1}{2}(m_1 - m_2)r, \frac{1}{2}(n_1 - n_2)r.$$

The corresponding plane, therefore, will be

$$(l_1 - l_2)x + (m_1 - m_2)y + (n_1 - n_2)z = 0.$$

3. *Find the image of the point $P(1, 3, 4)$ in the plane*
$$2x - y + z + 3 = 0. \hspace{2cm} (Avadh, 2001, 2003; Meerut, 2005)$$

Sol. If two points P, Q be such that the line is bisected perpendicularly by a plane, then either of the points is the image of the other in the plane.

The line through P perpendicular to the given plane is

$$\frac{x-1}{2} = \frac{y-3}{-1} = \frac{z-4}{1},$$

so that the co-ordinates of Q are of the form

$$(2r + 1, -r + 3, r + 4).$$

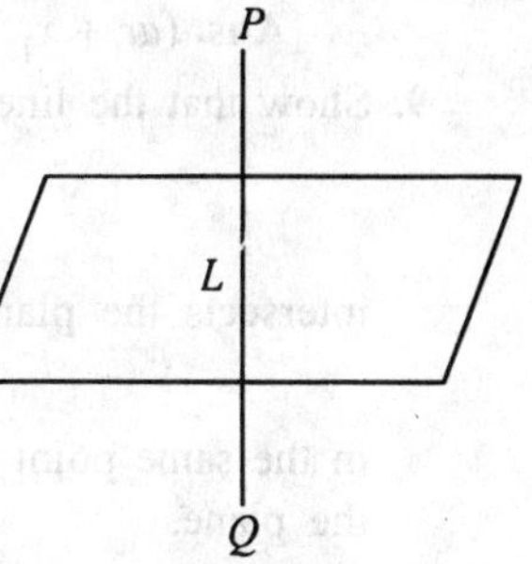

Making use of the fact that the mid-point

$$\left(r + 1, -\frac{1}{2}r + 3, \frac{1}{2}r + 4 \right)$$

Fig. 20

of PQ lies on the given plane, we see that

$$r = -2$$

so that the image of P is $(-3, 5, 2)$.

EXERCISES

1. Find k so that the lines

$$\frac{x-1}{-3} = \frac{y-2}{2k} = \frac{z-3}{2}$$

$$\frac{x-1}{3k} = \frac{y-5}{1} = \frac{z-6}{-5}$$

may be perpendicular to each other.   **[Ans. $-10/7$]**

2. Find two points on the line

$$\frac{x-2}{1} = \frac{y+3}{-2} = \frac{z-5}{2}$$

on either side of $(2, -3, -5)$ and at a distance 3 from it.

[Ans. $(3. -5, -3); (1, -1, -7)$]

3. Find the point where the line joining $(2, -3, 1)$, $(3, -4, -5)$ cuts the plane
$$2x + y + z = 7. \hspace{2cm} \textbf{[Ans. } 1, -2, 7\textbf{]}$$

4. Find the distance of the point $(-1, -5, -10)$ from the point of intersection of the line
$$\frac{1}{2}(x-2) = \frac{1}{4}(y+1) = \frac{1}{12}(z-2) \text{ and the plane } x - y + z = 5. \hspace{0.5cm} \textbf{[Ans. 13]}$$

5. Find the distance of the point $(3, -4, 5)$ from the plane
$$2x + 5y - 6z = 16$$
measured along a line with direction cosines proportional to $(2, 1, -2)$.   **[Ans. 60/7]**

6. Find the equations to the line through $(-1, 3, 2)$ and perpendicular to the plane $x + 2y + 2z = 3$, the length of the perpendicular and the co-ordinates of its foot.

[**Ans.** 2; $(-5/3, 5/3, 2/3)$]

7. Find the co-ordinates of the foot of the perpendicular drawn from the origin to the plane $2x + 3y - 4z + 1 = 0$; also find the co-ordinates of the point which is the image of the origin in the plane. [**Ans.** $(-2/29, -3/29, 4/29)$; $(-4/29, -6/29, 8/29)$]

8. Find the equations to the line through (x_1, y_1, z_1) perpendicular to the plane $ax + by + cz + d = 0$ and the co-ordinates of its foot. Deduce the expression for the perpendicular distance of the given point from the given plane.

[**Ans.** $(ar + x_1, br + y_1, cr + z_1)$, where $r = -(ax_1 + by_1 + cz_1 + d)/(a^2 + b^2 + c^2)$]

9. Show that the line

$$\frac{1}{2}(x - 7) = -(y + 3) = (z - 4)$$

intersects the planes

$$6x + 4y - 5z = 4 \text{ and } x - 5y + 2z = 12$$

in the same point and deduce that the line is coplanar with the line of intersection of the plane.

10. Show that the line

$$(x - 3)/3 = (2 - y)/4 = (z + 1)/1$$

intersects the line

$$x + 2y + 3z = 0, \; 2x + 4y + 3z + 3 = 0.$$

Find also the point of intersection. [**Ans.** $(9, -6, 1)$]

11. Show that the equations to the straight line through (a, b, c) parallel to the X-axis are $y = b, z = c$.

12. Show that $m(x - a) = l(y - b)$, $z = c$ is a straight line perpendicular to the Z-axis.

13. Show that the straight line

$$(x - \alpha)/l = (y - \beta)/m = (z - \gamma)/n$$

meets the locus of the equation

$$ax^2 + by^2 + cz^2 = 1,$$

in two points.

Deduce the conditions for the two points to coincide at (α, β, γ).

[**Ans.** $al\alpha + bm\beta + cn\gamma = 0$; $a\alpha^2 + b\beta^2 + c\gamma^2 = 1$]

14. P is a point on the plane $lx + my + nz = p$ and a point Q is taken on the line OP such that $OP \cdot OQ = p^2$; show that the locus of the point Q is $p(lx + my + nz) = x^2 + y^2 + z^2$.

15. A variable plane makes intercepts on the co-ordinate axes the sum of whose squares is constant and equal to k^2. Find the locus of the foot of the perpendicular from the origin to the plane. [**Ans.** $(x^{-2} + y^{-2} + z^{-2})(x^2 + y^2 + z^2)^2 = k^2$]

16. Show that the equations of the lines bisecting the angles between the lines

$$\frac{x - 3}{2} = \frac{y + 4}{-1} = \frac{z - 5}{-2}, \; \frac{x - 3}{4} = \frac{y + 4}{-12} = \frac{z - 5}{3}$$

are

$$\frac{x - 3}{38} = \frac{y + 4}{-49} = \frac{z - 5}{-17}, \; \frac{x - 3}{14} = \frac{y + 14}{23} = \frac{z - 5}{-35}.$$

3.1.3. Two Forms of the Equation of a Line

It has been seen in §§ 3.1.1, 3.1.2, that the equations of a straight line which we generally employ are of two forms.

One is the form deduced from the consideration that a straight line is completely determined when we know its direction ratios and the co-ordinates of any one point on it, or when any two points on the line are given. This is sometimes referred to as the **Symmetrical form** of the equations of a line.

The second form is deduced from the consideration that a straight line is the locus of points common to any two planes through it. This is sometimes referred to as the **Unsymmetrical form** of the equations of a line.

In fact the symmetrical form takes note only of a special pair of planes through this line, *viz.*, the pair of planes through the line perpendicular to two of the co-ordinate planes.

In the next section, it will be seen how one form of equations can be transferred into the other.

3.1.4. Transformation from the Unsymmetrical to the Symmetrical Form

To transform the equations
$$ax + by + cz + d = 0, \ a_1x + b_1y + c_1z + d_1 = 0,$$
of a line to the symmetrical form.

To transform these equations to the symmetrical form, we require :

  (*i*) *the direction ratios of the line, and*

  (*ii*) *the co-ordinates of any one point on it.*

Let *l*, *m*, *n* be the direction ratios of the line. Since the line lies in both the planes
$$ax + by + cz + d = 0 \ \text{and} \ a_1x + b_1y + c_1z + d_1 = 0,$$
it is perpendicular to the normals to both of them. The direction ratios of the normals to the planes being
$$a, b, c; \ a_1, b_1, c_1,$$
we have
$$\begin{cases} al + bm + cn = 0, \\ a_1l + b_1m + c_1n = 0, \end{cases}$$

$$\Rightarrow \qquad \frac{l}{bc_1 - b_1c} = \frac{m}{ca_1 - c_1a} = \frac{n}{ab_1 - a_1b}.$$

Now, we require the co-ordinates of *any one* point on the line and there is an infinite number of points from which to choose. We, for the sake of convenience, find the point of intersection of the line with the plane $z = 0$. This point which is given by the equations
$$ax + by + d = 0 \ \text{and} \ a_1x + b_1y + d_1 = 0,$$
is

$$\left(\frac{bd_1 - b_1d}{ab_1 - a_1b}, \ \frac{a_1d - ad_1}{ab_1 - a_1b}, \ 0 \right).$$

Thus, in the symmetrical form, the equations of the given line are
$$\frac{x - (bd_1 - b_1d)/(ab_1 - a_1b)}{bc_1 - b_1c} = \frac{y - (a_1d - ad_1)/(ab_1 - a_1b)}{ca_1 - c_1a} = \frac{z - 0}{ab_1 - a_1b}.$$

EXAMPLES

1. *Put in symmetrical form, the equations of the line* $3x - y + z + 1 = 0$, $5x + y + 3z = 0$.
Also find the equation to a plane through $(2, 1, 4)$ *and perpendicular to the given line.*

Sol. Let l, m, n be the direction ratios of the given line. Then, we have

$$3l - m + n = 0$$
$$5l + m + 3n = 0$$

$$\Rightarrow \qquad \frac{l}{1} = \frac{m}{1} = \frac{n}{-2}.$$

Again, suppose the given line intersects the plane $z = 0$ at $(x_1, y_1, 0)$, then

$$3x_1 - y_1 + 1 = 0 \text{ and } 5x_1 + y_1 = 0$$

$$\Rightarrow \qquad x_1 = -1/8, \ y_1 = 5/8$$

Hence, the symmetrical form of the line is

$$\frac{x + 1/8}{1} = \frac{y - 5/8}{1} = \frac{z}{-2}.$$

Equation of any plane perpendicular to the line is

$$x + y - 2z + d = 0$$

But this plane also passes through $(2, 1, 4)$.

Hence, $\qquad\qquad 2 + 1 - 8 + d = 0$ or $d = 5$.

Hence, required plane is

$$x + y - 2z + 5 = 0.$$

2. *Find the equation of the line through the point* $(1, 2, 3)$ *parallel to the line*

$$x - y + 2z = 5, \ 3x + y + z = 6.$$

Sol. Let l, m, n be the direction ratios of the required line. Since it is parallel to the given line, the direction ratios of the given line are also l, m, n. But the given line is the intersection of the two planes $x - y + 2z = 5$ and $3x + y + z = 6$, and hence, lies in both the planes and is perpendicular to the normals of these planes.

$$l \cdot 1 - m \cdot 1 + n \cdot 2 = 0$$

and $\qquad\qquad l \cdot 3 + m \cdot 1 + n \cdot 1 = 0$

$$\Rightarrow \qquad\qquad \frac{l}{-3} = \frac{m}{5} = \frac{n}{4}$$

Thus, the equations of the line in symmetrical form are

$$\frac{x - 1}{-3} = \frac{y - 2}{5} = \frac{z - 3}{4}.$$

3. *Prove that the equations to the line through* (α, β, γ) *at right angles to the lines*

$$\frac{x}{l_1} = \frac{y}{m_1} = \frac{z}{n_1}; \ \frac{x}{l_2} = \frac{y}{m_2} = \frac{z}{n_2}$$

are $\qquad \dfrac{x - \alpha}{m_1 n_2 - m_2 n_1} = \dfrac{y - \beta}{n_1 l_2 - n_2 l_1} = \dfrac{z - \gamma}{l_1 m_2 - l_2 m_1}.$

Sol. Let the dc's of the required line be l, m, n. Since it is perpendicular to the given lines, hence

$$ll_1 + mm_1 + nn_1 = 0 \text{ and } ll_2 + mm_2 + nn_2 = 0.$$

Solving, we get

$$l/(m_1n_2 - m_2n_1) = m/(n_1l_2 - n_2l_1) = n/(l_1m_2 - l_2m_1).$$

Hence, the equations of the required line are

$$\frac{x - \alpha}{(m_1n_2 - m_2n_1)} = \frac{y - \beta}{(n_1l_2 - n_2l_1)} = \frac{z - \gamma}{(l_1m_2 - l_2m_1)}.$$

EXERCISES

1. Find, in a symmetrical form, the equations of the line
$$x + y + z + 1 = 0, 4x + y - 2z + 2 = 0$$
and find its direction cosines.   *(Kanpur, 2001, 2002)*

$$\left[\text{Ans. } \frac{x + 1/3}{1} = \frac{y + 2/3}{-2} = \frac{z}{1}; \frac{1}{\sqrt{6}}, -\frac{2}{\sqrt{6}}, \frac{1}{\sqrt{6}}\right]$$

2. Obtain the symmetrical form of the equations of the line
$$x - 2y + 3z = 4, 2x - 3y + 4z = 5.$$

$$\left[\text{Ans. } (x + 2) = \frac{1}{2}(y + 3) = z\right]$$

3. Find the points of intersection of the line
$$x + y - z + 1 = 0 = 14x + 9y - 7z - 1$$
with the *XY* and *YZ* planes, and hence put down the symmetrical form of its equations.
[**Ans.** $-(x)/2 = (y - 4)/7 = (z - 5)/5$]

4. Find the equation of the plane through the point (1, 1, 1) and perpendicular to the line
$$x - 2y + z = 2, 4x + 3y - z + 1 = 0.$$
[**Ans.** $x - 5y - 11z + 15 = 0$]

5. Find the equations of the line through the point (1, 2, 4) parallel to the line
$$3x + 2y - z = 4, x - 2y - 2z = 5.$$
[**Ans.** $(x - 1)/6 = (2 - y)/5 = (z - 4)/8$]

6. Find the angle between the lines in which the planes
$$3x - 7y - 5z = 1, 5x - 13y + 3z + 2 = 0$$
cut the plane $8x - 11y + z = 0.$ [**Ans.** 90°]

7. Find the angle between the lines
$$3x + 2y + z - 5 = 0 = x + y - 2z - 3,$$
$$2x - y - z = 0 = 7x + 10y - 8z.$$ [**Ans.** 90°]

8. Show that the condition for the lines
$$x = az + b, y = cz + d; x = a_1z + b_1, y = c_1z + d_1,$$
to be perpendicular is
$$aa_1 + cc_1 + 1 = 0.$$ *(Rohilkhand, 2004)*

3.2. ANGLE BETWEEN A LINE AND A PLANE

To find the angle between the line

$$\frac{x - x_1}{l} = \frac{y - y_1}{m} = \frac{z - z_1}{n}$$

and the plane

$$ax + by + cz + d = 0.$$

The angle between a line and a plane is the complement of the angle between the line and the normal to the plane.

Since the direction cosines of the normal to the given plane and of the given line are proportional to a, b, c and l, m, n respectively, we have

$$\sin q = \frac{al + bm + cn}{\sqrt{(a^2 + b^2 + c^2)}\,\sqrt{(l^2 + m^2 + n^2)}},$$

where θ is the required angle.

The straight line is *parallel to the plane*

$$\Rightarrow \qquad\qquad\qquad \theta = 0$$

$$\Rightarrow \qquad\qquad\qquad al + bm + cn = \mathbf{0}.$$

This condition is also evident from the fact that a *line will be parallel to a plane if and only if it is perpendicular to the normal to it.*

EXERCISES

1. Show that the line $\frac{1}{3}(x-2) = \frac{1}{4}(y-3) = \frac{1}{5}(z-4)$ is parallel to the plane

$$2x + y - 2z = 3.$$

2. Find the equations of the line through the point $(-2, 3, 4)$ and parallel to the planes

   $2x + 3y + 4z = 5$ and $3x + 4y + 5z = 6$. $\left[\textbf{Ans. } (x+2) = -\frac{1}{2}(y-3) = (z-4)\right]$

   [**Hint.** The direction ratios, l, m, n of the line are given by the relations $2l + 3m + 4n = 0 = 3l + 4m + 5n$.]

3. Find the equation of the plane through the points

   $$(1, 0, -1), (3, 2, 2)$$

   and parallel to the line

   $$(x-1) = (1-y)/2 = (z-2)/3.$$ [**Ans.** $4x - y - 2z = 6$]

4. Show that the equations of the plane parallel to the join of

   $$(3, 2, -5) \text{ and } (0, -4, -11)$$

   and passing through the points

   $$(-2, 1, -3) \text{ and } (4, 3, 3)$$

   is

   $$4x + 3y - 5z = 10.$$

5. Find the equation of the plane containing the line

   $$2x - 5y + 2z = 6, \ 2x + 3y - z = 5$$

   and parallel to the line $x = -y/6 = z/7$.   [**Ans.** $6x + y - 16 = 0$]

6. Show that the equation of the plane through the line

   $$u_1 \equiv a_1 x + b_1 y + c_1 z + d_1 = 0, \ u_2 \equiv a_2 x + b_2 y + c_2 z + d_2 = 0$$

   and parallel to the line

   $$x/l = y/m = z/n$$

   is

   $$u_1 (a_2 l + b_2 m + c_2 n) = u_2 (a_1 l + b_1 m + c_1 n).$$

7. Find the equation of the plane through the point (f, g, h) and parallel to the lines $x/l_r = y/m_r = z/n_r$; $r = 1, 2$.   [**Ans.** $\Sigma (x - f) (m_1 n_2 - m_2 n_1) = 0$]

8. Find the equations of the two planes through the origin which are parallel to the line
$$(x - 1)/2 = -(y + 3) = -(z + 1)/2$$
and distant 5/3 from it; show that the two planes are perpendicular.

[**Ans.** $2x + 2y + z = 0$, $x - 2y + 2z = 0$]

3.3. CONDITIONS FOR A LINE TO LIE IN A PLANE

To find the conditions for the line
$$\frac{x - x_1}{l} = \frac{y - y_1}{m} = \frac{z - z_1}{n}$$

to lie in the plane
$$ax + by + cz + d = 0.$$

(Kumaon, 2003; Patna, 2003; Rohilkhand, 2005)

The line would lie in the given plane if and only if every point of the line is a point of the plane, *i.e.*, the point
$$(lr + x_1, mr + y_1, nr + z_1)$$
lies on the plane for all values of r implying that the equation
$$r (al + bm + cn) + (ax_1 + by_1 + cz_1 + d) = 0$$
is true for every value of r.

This implies that
$$\begin{cases} al + bm + cn = 0 \\ ax_1 + by_1 + cz_1 + d = 0 \end{cases}$$

which are the required *two* conditions.

These conditions, when geometrically interpreted, state that a line lies in a given plane, if
   (*i*) *the normal to the plane is perpendicular to the line, and*
   (*ii*) *any one point on the line lies in the plane.*

Cor. *The general equation of a plane containing the line*
$$\frac{x - x_1}{l} = \frac{y - y_1}{m} = \frac{z - z_1}{n} \qquad \qquad ...(i)$$

is
$$A (x - x_1) + B (y - y_1) + C (z - z_1) = 0$$

where
$$Al + Bm + Cn = 0. \qquad \qquad ...(ii)$$

Here, A, B, C are parameters subject to the condition (*ii*).

In other words, the set of planes containing the line (*i*) is
$$\{A (x - x_1) + B (y - y_1) + C (z - z_1) = 0, \; Al + Bm + Cn = 0\}$$

EXAMPLES

1. *Find the equation to the plane which passes through the point (x_1, y_1, z_1) and the line*
$$(x - a)/l = (y - b)/m = (z - c)/n. \qquad \qquad (Garhwal, 1998)$$

Sol. The general equation of the plane containing the given line is
$$A (x - a) + B (y - b) + C (z - c) = 0, \qquad \qquad ...(i)$$
where A, B, C are parameters subjected to the condition
$$Al + Bm + Cn = 0 \qquad \qquad ...(ii)$$

The plane (i) will pass through the point (x_1, y_1, z_1), if

$$A(x_1 - a) + B(y_1 - b) + C(z_1 - c) = 0. \qquad ...(iii)$$

Eliminating A, B, C from (i), (ii) and (iii), we have

$$\begin{vmatrix} x - a & y - b & z - c \\ l & m & n \\ x_1 - a & y_1 - b & z_1 - c \end{vmatrix} = 0$$

as the required equation.

2. *Find the equation to the plane containing the line* $\dfrac{x+1}{-3} = \dfrac{y-3}{2} = \dfrac{z+2}{1}$ *and the point*

$(0, 7, -7)$ *and show that the line* $\dfrac{x}{1} = \dfrac{y-7}{-3} = \dfrac{z+7}{2}$ *also lies in the same plane.*

(Garhwal, 2001)

Sol. Let the required equation of plane be

$$Ax + By + Cz + D = 0 \qquad ...(1)$$

The given line will lie in it, if

$$-A + 3B - 2C + D = 0 \qquad ...(2)$$

and
$$-3A + 2B + C = 0. \qquad ...(3)$$

The plane (1) will pass through $(0, 7, -7)$ if

$$0 \cdot A + 7B - 7C + D = 0 \qquad ...(4)$$

Eliminating A, B, C, D from equations (1), (2), (3), (4) the required plane is

$$\begin{vmatrix} x & y & z & 1 \\ -1 & 3 & -2 & 1 \\ -3 & 2 & 1 & 0 \\ 0 & 7 & -7 & 1 \end{vmatrix} = 0$$

$$\Rightarrow \qquad\qquad x + y + z = 0 \qquad ...(5)$$

Now, the line $(x)/1 = (y - 7)/(-3) = (z + 7)/2$ will lie in the plane (5) if the point $(0, 7, -7)$ on the line lies on the plane and the line (dr's $1, -3, 2$) is perpendicular to the normal to the plane(s).

Obviously, both the conditions are satisfied.

3. *Prove that the plane through* (α, β, γ) *and the line* $x = py + q = rz + s$ *is given by*

$$\begin{vmatrix} x & py + q & rz + s \\ \alpha & p\beta + q & r\gamma + s \\ 1 & 1 & 1 \end{vmatrix} = 0. \quad \text{(Garhwal, 1998; Meerut, 2001)}$$

Sol. The given line can be written as

$$x/1 = y + q/p\big/1/p = z + s/r\big/1/r \qquad ...(1)$$

Let equation of any plane be

$$Ax + By + Cz + D = 0 \qquad ...(2)$$

It will pass through line (1), if

$$A \cdot 0 + B(-q/p) + C(-s/r) + D = 0 \qquad ...(3)$$

and
$$A \cdot 1 + B \cdot 1/p + C \cdot 1/r = 0 \qquad ...(4)$$

The plane will pass through (α, β, γ) if

$$A \cdot \alpha + B \cdot \beta + C \cdot \gamma + D = 0 \qquad \text{...(5)}$$

Subtracting (3) from (2) and (5), we get

$$Ax + B(y + q/p) + C(z + s/r) = 0 \qquad \text{...(6)}$$
$$A \cdot \alpha + B(\beta + q/p) + C(\gamma + s/r) = 0 \qquad \text{...(7)}$$

Eliminating A, B, C from (6), (7) and (4)

$$\begin{vmatrix} x & y + q/p & z + s/r \\ \alpha & \beta + q/p & \gamma + s/r \\ 1 & 1/p & 1/r \end{vmatrix} = 0$$

$$\Rightarrow \qquad \begin{vmatrix} x & py + q & rz + s \\ \alpha & p\beta + q & r\gamma + s \\ 1 & 1 & 1 \end{vmatrix} = 0.$$

4. *Find the equations to the line through* (f, g, h) *which is parallel to the plane*

$$lx + my + nz = 0$$

and intersects the line $ax + by + cz + d = 0 = a'x + b'y + c'z + d'.$

Sol. Any plane parallel to $lx + my + nz = 0$ and through (f, g, h) is

$$l(x - f) + m(y - g) + n(z - h) = 0 \qquad \text{...(1)}$$

Any plane through the given line is

$$(ax + by + cz + d) + \lambda(a'x + b'y + c'z + d') = 0$$

If it passes through (f, g, h), then

$$\lambda = -\frac{af + bg + ch + d}{a'f + b'g + c'h + d'}.$$

Hence, the plane becomes

$$\frac{ax + by + cz + d}{af + bg + ch + d} = \frac{a'x + b'y + c'z + d'}{a'f + b'g + c'h + d'} \qquad \text{...(2)}$$

The equations (1) and (2) give the required line.

5. *The axes are rectangular and the plane* $\dfrac{x}{a} + \dfrac{y}{b} + \dfrac{z}{c} = 1$ *meets them in A, B, C. Prove that the equations to BC are* $x/0 = y/b = z - c/- c$; *that the equation to the plane through OX at right angles to BC is* $by = cz$; *that the three planes through OX, OY, OZ at right angles to BC, CA, AB respectively pass through the line* $ax = by = cz$; *and that the co-ordinates of the orthocentre of the triangle ABC are*

$$\left[\frac{a^{-1}}{a^{-2} + b^{-2} + c^{-2}}, \frac{b^{-1}}{a^{-2} + b^{-2} + c^{-2}}, \frac{c^{-1}}{a^{-2} + b^{-2} + c^{-2}} \right].$$

Sol. The given plane meets the axes in points $A(a, 0, 0)$; $B(0, b, 0)$ and $C(0, 0, c)$. Equations of the line through B and C are

$$\frac{x}{0} = \frac{y}{b} = \frac{z - c}{- c} \qquad \text{...(1)}$$

Equation of any plane through OX is

$$y + \lambda z = 0.$$

If BC is perpendicular to above plane,

then, $b/1 = -c/\lambda \Rightarrow \lambda = -c/b$

Hence, the plane is $by = cz$.

Similarly the planes through OY and OZ and at right angles to CA and AB respectively are

$$cz = ax, \quad ax = by.$$

Hence, the three planes pass through the line

$$ax = by = cz. \qquad \qquad \qquad \qquad \qquad ...(2)$$

The orthocentre of the triangle ABC lies where the line (2) meets the given plane.

Any point on (2) is $(r/a, r/b, r/c)$.

If it lies on the given plane, then

$$r = \frac{1}{a^{-2} + b^{-2} + c^{-2}}.$$

Hence, the co-ordinates of the orthocentre are

$$\left[\frac{a^{-1}}{a^{-2} + b^{-2} + c^{-2}}, \frac{b^{-1}}{a^{-2} + b^{-2} + c^{-2}}, \frac{c^{-1}}{a^{-2} + b^{-2} + c^{-2}} \right].$$

EXERCISES

1. Show that the line $x + 10 = (8 - y)/2 = z$ lies in the plane

$$x + 2y + 3z = 6$$

and the line

$$\frac{1}{3}(x - 2) = -(y + 2) = \frac{1}{4}(z - 3) \text{ in the plane}$$

$$2x + 2y - z + 3 = 0.$$

2. Find the equation of the plane containing the line

$$\frac{1}{2}(x + 2) + \frac{1}{3}(y + 3) = -\frac{1}{2}(z - 4)$$

and the point $(0, 6, 0)$.   [**Ans.** $3x + 2y + 6z - 12 = 0$]

3. $\dfrac{x - x_1}{l_1} = \dfrac{y - y_1}{m_1} = \dfrac{z - z_1}{n_1}$ and $\dfrac{x - x_2}{l_2} = \dfrac{y - y_2}{m_2} = \dfrac{z - z_2}{n_2}$ are two straight lines. Find

the equation of the plane containing the first line and parallel to the second.

[**Ans.** $\Sigma (x - x_1)(m_1 n_2 - m_2 n_1) = 0$]

4. Find the equation to the plane containing the line $y/b + z/c = 1$, $x = 0$ and parallel to
the line $x/a + z/c = 1$, $y = 0$.   (*Avadh, 2000; Meerut, 1999*)

[**Ans.** $x/a - y/b - z/c + 1 = 0$]

5. Find the equation to the plane which passes through the z-axis and is perpendicular to
the line

$$\frac{x - 1}{\cos \theta} = \frac{y + 2}{\sin \theta} = \frac{z - 3}{0}.$$ [**Ans.** $x \cos \theta + y \sin \theta = 0$]

6. Show that the equation of the plane which passes through the line

$$\frac{x - 1}{3} = \frac{y + 6}{4} = \frac{z + 1}{2}$$

and is parallel to the line
$$\frac{x-2}{2} = \frac{y-1}{-3} = \frac{z+4}{5},$$

is $26x - 11y - 17z - 109 = 0$ and show that the point $(2, 1, -4)$ lies on it. What is the geometrical relation between the two lines and the plane ?

7. Find the equation of the plane containing the line
$$-\frac{1}{3}(x+1) = \frac{1}{2}(y-3) = (z+2)$$

and the point $(0, 7, -7)$ and show that the line
$$x = \frac{1}{3}(7-y) = \frac{1}{2}(z+7).$$

lies in the same plane.   [**Ans.** $x + y + z = 0$]

8. Find the equation of the plane which contains the line
$$(x-1)/2 = -y - 1 = (z-3)/4$$

and is perpendicular to the plane
$$x + 2y + z = 12.$$ (*Garhwal, 1995*)

Deduce the direction cosines of the projection of the given line on the given plane.

[**Ans.** $9x - 2y - 5z + 4 = 0$; $4k, -7k, 10k$, where $k = \sqrt{165}$]

9. Find the equations, in the symmetrical form, of the projection of the line
$$\frac{1}{2}(x+1) = \frac{1}{3}(y+2) = \frac{1}{4}(z+3)$$

on the plane
$$x - 2y + 3z - 4 = 0.$$

[**Ans.** $(x - 1/4)/10 = (y + 15/8)/29 = (z - 0)/16$]

3.4. COPLANAR LINES. CONDITION FOR THE COPLANARITY OF LINES

To find the condition that two given straight lines

$$\frac{x-x_1}{l_1} = \frac{y-y_1}{m_1} = \frac{z-z_1}{n_1} \qquad \ldots(1)$$

$$\frac{x-x_2}{l_2} = \frac{y-y_2}{m_2} = \frac{z-z_2}{n_2} \qquad \ldots(2)$$

are coplanar.   (*Kanpur, 1995; Kumaon, 2000; Patna, 2003, 2004*)

Sol. First Method. Equation of *any* plane containing the line (1) is
$$A(x-x_1) + B(y-y_1) + C(z-z_1) = 0; \qquad \ldots(i)$$

A, B, C being numbers not all zero satisfying the condition
$$Al_1 + Bm_1 + Cn_1 = 0. \qquad \ldots(ii)$$

The plane (*i*) will contain the line (2) if

(*a*) the point (x_2, y_2, z_2) lies on it

$\Rightarrow \qquad A(x_2 - x_1) + B(y_2 - y_1) + C(z_2 - z_1) = 0 \qquad \ldots(iii)$

(*b*) the line is perpendicular to the normal to the plane

$\Rightarrow \qquad Al_2 + Bm_2 + Cn_2 = 0. \qquad \ldots(iv)$

The two lines will be coplanar if the three linear homogeneous equations (ii), (iii), (iv) in A, B, C are consistent so that

$$\begin{vmatrix} x_2 - x_1 & y_2 - y_1 & z_2 - z_1 \\ l_1 & m_1 & n_1 \\ l_2 & m_2 & n_2 \end{vmatrix} = 0 \qquad \qquad ...(A)$$

which is thus, the required condition for the lines to intersect. Assuming this condition is satisfied, we see that the required equation of the plane is

$$\begin{vmatrix} x - x_1 & y - y_1 & z - z_1 \\ l_1 & m_1 & n_1 \\ l_2 & m_2 & n_2 \end{vmatrix} = 0.$$

This is the equation of the plane containing the two lines.

Second Method. Two lines are coplanar if and only if they intersect or are parallel. We first consider the case of intersection. The condition for intersection may also be obtained as follows :

$$(l_1 r_1 + x_1, \, m_1 r_1 + y_1, \, n_1 r_1 + z_1) \text{ and } (l_2 r_2 + x_2, \, m_2 r_2 + y_2, \, n_2 r_2 + z_2)$$

are the general co-ordinates of the points on the lines (1) and (2) respectively for all values of r_1 and r_2.

In case the lines intersect, these points should coincide for some values of r_1 and r_2. This requires that the following three equations

$$(x_1 - x_2) + l_1 r_1 - l_2 r_2 = 0,$$
$$(y_1 - y_2) + m_1 r_1 - m_2 r_2 = 0,$$
$$(z_1 - z_2) + n_1 r_1 - n_2 r_2 = 0.$$

in r_1, r_2 are consistent, so that we have the condition

$$\begin{vmatrix} x_1 - x_2 & l_1 & l_2 \\ y_1 - y_2 & m_1 & m_2 \\ z_1 - z_2 & n_1 & n_2 \end{vmatrix} = 0 \Leftrightarrow \begin{vmatrix} x_2 - x_1 & y_2 - y_1 & z_2 - z_1 \\ l_1 & m_1 & n_1 \\ l_2 & m_2 & n_2 \end{vmatrix} = 0$$

which is the same condition as (A).

This condition is clearly satisfied if the lines are parallel.

Note 1. In general, the equation

$$\begin{vmatrix} x - x_1 & y - y_1 & z - z_1 \\ l_1 & m_1 & n_1 \\ l_2 & m_2 & n_2 \end{vmatrix} = 0$$

represents the plane which passes through the line (1) and is parallel to the line (2), and the equation

$$\begin{vmatrix} x - x_2 & y - y_2 & z - z_2 \\ l_1 & m_1 & n_1 \\ l_2 & m_2 & n_2 \end{vmatrix} = 0$$

represents the plane which passes through the line (2) and is parallel to the line (1).

In case the lines are coplanar, the condition (A) shows that the point (x_2, y_2, z_2) lies on the first plane and the point (x_1, y_1, z_1) on the second. These two equations are then identical.

Thus, the plane containing two coplanar *lines* is the one which passes through one line and is parallel to the other *or*, through one line and any point on the other.

Note 2. Two lines will intersect if and only if, there exists a point whose co-ordinates satisfy the *four* equations, two of each line so that for intersection, we require that the four linear equations in three unknowns should be *consistent*.

It is sometimes comparatively more convenient to follow this method to obtain the condition of intersection or to prove the fact of intersection of two lines.

Note 3. The condition for the lines whose equations, given in the unsymmetrical form, are

$$a_1 x + b_1 y + c_1 z + d_1 = 0, \quad a_2 x + b_2 y + c_2 z + d_2 = 0;$$
$$a_3 x + b_3 y + c_3 z + d_3 = 0, \quad a_4 x + b_4 y + c_4 z + d_4 = 0;$$

to intersect, is the condition for the consistency of these four equations, *i.e.*,

$$\begin{vmatrix} a_1 & b_1 & c_1 & d_1 \\ a_2 & b_2 & c_2 & d_2 \\ a_3 & b_3 & c_3 & d_3 \\ a_4 & b_4 & c_4 & d_4 \end{vmatrix} = 0.$$

In case, this condition is satisfied, the co-ordinates of the point of intersection are obtained by solving any three of the four equations simultaneously.

EXAMPLES

1. *Show that the lines*

$$\frac{x-4}{1} = \frac{y+3}{-4} = \frac{z+1}{7}, \quad \frac{x-1}{2} = \frac{y+1}{-3} = \frac{z+10}{8}$$

intersect and find the co-ordinates of the point of intersection.

Sol. Now, $(r + 4, -4r - 3, 7r - 1)$ and $(2r' + 1, -3r' - 1, 8r' - 10)$

are the co-ordinates of points on the two lines respectively for all values of r and r'.

The two lines will intersect if the three equations

$$r + 4 = 2r' + 1 \quad \Leftrightarrow \quad r - 2r' + 3 = 0, \qquad \qquad \dots(i)$$
$$-4r - 3 = -3r' - 1 \quad \Leftrightarrow \quad 4r - 3r' + 2 = 0, \qquad \qquad \dots(ii)$$
$$7r - 1 = 8r' - 10 \quad \Leftrightarrow \quad 7r - 8r' + 9 = 0, \qquad \qquad \dots(iii)$$

in two unknowns r, r' are simultaneously true *i.e.*, are consistent.

Now the equations (*i*) and (*ii*) give $r = 1$, $r' = 2$ which also, clearly, satisfy (*iii*). Hence, the lines intersect and the point of intersection obtained by putting $r = 1$ (or $r' = 2$) is $(5, -7, 6)$.

Note. This question can also be solved by first finding the point satisfying the three equations

$$\frac{x-4}{1} = \frac{y+3}{-4}; \quad \frac{y+3}{-4} = \frac{z+1}{7}; \quad \frac{x-1}{2} = \frac{y+1}{-3}$$

and then showing that the same point also satisfies the equation

$$\frac{y+1}{-3} = \frac{z+10}{8}$$

i.e., by showing that the four linear equations in three unknowns x, y, z are consistent.

2. *Show that the lines*

$$\frac{x+3}{2} = \frac{y+5}{3} = \frac{z-7}{-3}, \quad \frac{x+1}{4} = \frac{y+1}{5} = \frac{z+1}{-1}$$

are coplanar and find the equation of the plane containing them.

Sol. The equation of the plane which contains the first line and is parallel to the second is

$$\begin{vmatrix} x+3 & y+5 & z-7 \\ 2 & 3 & -3 \\ 4 & 5 & -1 \end{vmatrix} = 0 \Leftrightarrow 6x - 5y - z = 0.$$

This plane, as may be easily seen, passes through the point $(-1, -1, -1)$ on the second line so that it also contains the second line.

Thus, the two lines are coplanar and the equation of the plane containing them is

$$6x - 5y - z = 0.$$

3. *Show that the lines*

$$\frac{x+5}{3} = \frac{y+4}{1} = \frac{z-7}{-2}$$

$$3x + 2y + z - 2 = 0 = x - 3y + 2z - 3$$

are coplanar and find the equation to the plane in which they lie.

Sol. The *general* equation of the plane through the second line is

$$3x + 2y + z - 2 + k\,(x - 3y + 2z - 13) = 0$$

$$\Leftrightarrow \qquad x\,(3+k) + y\,(2-3k) + z\,(1+2k) - 2 - 13k = 0;$$

k being the parameter.

This will be parallel to the first line

if

$$3\,(3+k) + (2-3k) - 2\,(1+2k) = 0 \Rightarrow k = 9/4.$$

Hence, the equation of the plane which contains the second line and is parallel to the first is

$$21x - 19y + 22z - 125 = 0.$$

This plane clearly passes through the point $(-5, -4, 7)$ and so contains also the first line.

Thus, the two lines are coplanar and lie in the plane

$$21x - 19y + 22z - 125 = 0.$$

4. *If, OA, OB, OC have direction ratios $l_r, m_r, n_r, r = 1, 2, 3$ and OA', OB', OC' bisect the angles BOC, COA, AOB, the planes AOA', BOB', COC' pass through the line*

$$\frac{x}{l_1 + l_2 + l_3} = \frac{y}{m_1 + m_2 + m_3} = \frac{z}{n_1 + n_2 + n_3}.$$

Sol. Let O be the origin, equations of OB and OC are

$$x/l_2 = y/m_2 = z/n_2$$

and $$x/l_3 = y/m_3 = z/n_3$$

Points on these lines at unit distance are (l_2, m_2, n_2) and (l_3, m_3, n_3).

Corresponding point on bisector OA' is

$$\left[\frac{1}{2}(l_2 + l_3), \frac{1}{2}(m_2 + m_3), \frac{1}{2}(n_2 + n_3)\right]$$

$\therefore$ Equations of OA' are

$$\frac{x}{l_2 + l_3} = \frac{y}{m_2 + m_3} = \frac{z}{n_2 + n_3}$$

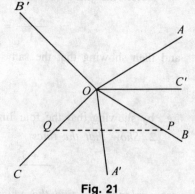

Fig. 21

Now, equation of the plane containing OA and OA', *i.e.*, AOA' is

$$\begin{vmatrix} x & y & z \\ l_1 & m_1 & n_1 \\ l_2 + l_3 & m_2 + m_3 & n_2 + n_3 \end{vmatrix} = 0$$

$$\Rightarrow \begin{vmatrix} x & y & z \\ l_1 & m_1 & n_1 \\ l_1 + l_2 + l_3 & m_1 + m_2 + m_3 & n_1 + n_2 + n_3 \end{vmatrix}$$ (Operating $R_3 + R_2$)

This plane clearly passes through the line

$$\frac{x}{l_1 + l_2 + l_3} = \frac{y}{m_1 + m_2 + m_3} = \frac{z}{n_1 + n_2 + n_3}.$$

Similarly plane BOB' and COC' pass through the same line.

5. *A, A', B, B', C, C' are points on the axes. Show that the lines of intersection of the planes A'BC, AB'C', B'CA, BC'A', C'AB, CA'B' are coplanar.* (*Kanpur, 1996*)

Sol. Let the points A, A', B, B', C, C' be $(a, 0, 0)$, $(a', 0, 0)$, $(0, b, 0)$, $(0, b', 0)$, $(0, 0, c)$, $(0, 0, c')$ respectively.

Equations of the planes $A'BC$ and $AB'C'$ are

$$x/a' + y/b + z/c = 1 \text{ and } x/a + y/b' + z/c' = 1.$$

These equations taken together represent the line of intersection of the planes $A'BC$ and $AB'C'$.

Any plane through this line is

$$(x/a' + y/b + z/c - 1) + \lambda_1 (x/a + y/b' + z/c' - 1) = 0 \qquad ...(1)$$

Similarly, planes through the lines of intersection of $B'CA$, $BC'A'$; $C'AB$, $CA'B'$ are respectively

$$(x/a + y/b' + z/c - 1) + \lambda_2 (x/a' + y/b + z/c' - 1) = 0$$

and $$(x/a + y/b + z/c' - 1) + \lambda_3 (x/a' + y/b' + z/c - 1) = 0$$

In case the three lines are coplanar then for some value of $\lambda_1, \lambda_2, \lambda_3$, the above equations must represent the same plane. This is obviously so, when $\lambda_1 = \lambda_2 = \lambda_3 = 1$; and then the plane becomes

$$x (1/a + 1/a') + y (1/b + 1/b') + z (1/c + 1/c') = 2.$$

EXERCISES

1. Show that the lines

$$\frac{1}{3}(x + 4) = \frac{1}{5}(y + 6) = -\frac{1}{2}(z - 1)$$

$$3x - 2y + z + 5 = 0 = 2x + 3y + 4z - 4$$

are coplanar. Find also the co-ordinates of their point of intersection and the equation of the plane in which they lie. [**Ans.** $(2, 4, -3)$; $45x - 17y + 25z + 53 = 0$]

2. Prove that the lines

$$\frac{x-1}{2} = \frac{y+1}{-3} = \frac{z+10}{8}; \frac{x-4}{1} = \frac{y+3}{-4} = \frac{z+1}{7}$$

intersect. Find also their point of intersection and the plane through them.

[**Ans.** $(5, -7, 6)$; $11x = 6y + 5z + 67$]

3. Prove that the lines

$$\frac{x+1}{3} = \frac{y+3}{5} = \frac{z+5}{7}; \ \frac{x-2}{1} = \frac{y-4}{3} = \frac{z-6}{5}$$

intersect. Find their point of intersection and the plane in which they lie.

[**Ans.** $(1/2, -1/2, -3/2); \ x - 2y + z = 0$]

4. Show that the lines

$$x + 2y - 5z + 9 = 0 = 3x - y + 2z - 5;$$
$$2x + 3y - z - 3 = 0 = 4x - 5y + z + 3$$

are coplanar.

5. Prove that the lines

$$x - 3y + 2z + 4 = 0 = 2x + y + 4z + 1;$$
$$3x + 2y + 5z - 1 = 0 = 2y + z$$

intersect and find the co-ordinates of their point of intersection.   [**Ans.** $(3, 1, -2)$]

6. $x + 2y - z - 3 = 0, \ 3x - y + 2z - 1 = 0,$
$$2x - 2y + 3z - 2 = 0, \ x - y + z + 1 = 0$$

are two given pairs of planes. Show that the line of intersection of the first pair is coplanar with the line of intersection of the latter.

7. Show that the line of intersection of the planes

$$7x - 4y + 7z + 16 = 0, \ 4x + 3y - 2z + 3 = 0$$

is coplanar with the line of intersection of planes

$$x - 3y + 4z + 6 = 0, \ x - y + z + 1 = 0.$$

Obtain the equation of the plane through the two lines. [**Ans.** $3x - 7y + 9z + 13 = 0$]

8. Prove that the lines

$$\frac{x-a}{a'} = \frac{y-b}{b'} = \frac{z-c}{c'} \ \text{and} \ \frac{x-a'}{a} = \frac{y-b'}{b} = \frac{z-c'}{c}$$

intersect and find the co-ordinates of the point of intersection and the equation of the plane in which they lie.   *(Meerut, 2000)*

[**Ans.** $(a + a', b + b', c + c'); \ \Sigma x \, (bc' - b'c) = 0$]

9. Show that the two straight lines

$$x = mz + a, \ y = nz + b, \ \text{and} \ x = m'z + a', \ y = n'z + b'$$

would intersect if and only if

$$(a - a') \, (n - n') = (b - b') \, (m - m').$$

10. Show that the plane containing the two parallel lines

$$x - 4 = -\frac{1}{4}(y - 3) = \frac{1}{5}(z - 2), \ x - 3 = -\frac{1}{4}(y + 2) = \frac{1}{5}z$$

is $11x - y - 3z = 35.$

11. Find the equation of the plane which passes through the line

$$x/l = y/m = z/n,$$

and is perpendicular to the plane containing the lines

$$x/m = y/n = z/l$$

and $x/n = y/l = z/m.$

(U.P.P.C.S., 2004; Garhwal, 1998; Avadh, 1998; Kanpur, 1995)

[**Ans.** $\Sigma \, (m - n) \, x = 0$]

12. Show that the line $x + a = y + b = z + c$ intersect each of the four lines

(*i*) $x = 0$, $y + z = 3a$;   (*ii*) $y = 0$, $z + x = 3b$;   (*iii*) $z = 0$, $x + y = 3c$;

(*iv*) $x + y + z = 3k$, $a (a - k)^{-1} x + b (b - k)^{-1} y + c (c - k)^{-1} z = 0$

at right angles if $a + b + c = 0$.

13. Obtain the condition for the line

$$(x - \alpha)/l = (y - \beta)/m = (z - \gamma)/n$$

to intersect the locus of the equations $ax^2 + by^2 = 1$, $z = 0$.

[**Ans.** $a (\alpha n - l\gamma)^2 + b (\beta n - m\gamma)^2 = n^2$]

3.5. NUMBER OF ARBITRARY CONSTANTS IN THE EQUATIONS OF A STRAIGHT LINE

We have already seen that the general equation of a plane contains **three** arbitrary constants and it will now be shown *that there are four arbitrary constants in the equations of a straight line.*

A given line PQ can be regarded as the intersection of *any* two planes through it. In particular, we may take the two planes perpendicular to two of the co-ordinate planes, say, YZ and ZX planes.

The equations of the planes through a line PQ perpendicular to the YZ and ZX planes are respectively of the forms

$$z = cy + d, \text{ and } z = ax + b$$

which are, therefore, the equations of the line PQ and contain four arbitrary constants a, b, c, d.

Hence, the *equations of a straight line involve four arbitrary constants* as it is always possible to express them in the above form.

The fact that the general equations of a straight line contain four arbitrary constants may also be seen as follows :

We see that the equations

$$\frac{x - x_1}{l} = \frac{y - y_1}{m}; \quad \frac{y - y_1}{m} = \frac{z - z_1}{n}$$

are equivalent to

$$x = \frac{l}{m} y + \frac{(mx_1 - ly_1)}{m}, \quad y = \frac{m}{n} z + \frac{(ny_1 - mz_1)}{n}$$

respectively, so that

$$\frac{l}{m}, \frac{m}{n}, \frac{mx_1 - ly_1}{m}, \frac{ny_1 - mz_1}{n}$$

are the *four* arbitrary constants or parameters.

3.5.1. Determination of Lines Satisfying Given Conditions

We now consider the various *sets of conditions* which determine a line.

We know that the equations of a straight line involve four arbitrary constants and as such any four geometrical conditions, each of which gives rise to one relation between the constants, fix a straight line.

It may be noted that the conditions for a line to intersect a given line or be perpendicular to it separately involve one relation between the constants and hence, three more relations are required to fix the line.

A given condition may sometimes give rise to two relations between the constants as, for instance, the conditions that the required line

(*i*) passes through a given point; (*ii*) has a given direction.

In such cases only two more relations will be required to fix the straight line.

We have already considered equations of a line which

   (*i*) pass through a given point and have a given direction;

   (*ii*) pass through two given points;

   (*iii*) pass through a point and are parallel to two given planes;

   (*iv*) pass through a point and perpendicular to two given lines.

Some further sets of conditions which determine a line are given below :

   (*v*) passing through a given point and intersecting two given lines;

   (*vi*) intersecting two given lines and having a given direction;

   (*vii*) intersecting a given line at right angles and passing through a given point;

   (*viii*) intersecting two given lines at right angles;

   (*ix*) intersecting a given line parallel to a given line and passing through a given point;

   (*x*) passing through a given point and perpendicular to two given lines; and so on.

An Important Note : *If*

$$u_1 = 0 = v_1 \text{ and } u_2 = 0 = v_2$$

be two straight lines, then the general equations of a straight line intersecting them both are

$$u_1 + \lambda_1 v_1 = 0 = u_2 + \lambda_2 v_2,$$

where λ_1, λ_2 are any two numbers.

The line $u_1 + \lambda_1 v_1 = 0 = u_2 + \lambda_2 v_2$ lies in the plane $u_1 + \lambda_1 v_1 = 0$ which again contains the line $u_1 = 0 = v_1$.

The two lines

$$u_1 + \lambda_1 v_1 = 0 = u_2 + \lambda_2 v_2; \ u_1 = 0 = v_1$$

are, therefore, coplanar and hence they intersect.

Similarly, the same line intersects the line $u_2 = 0 = v_2$.

This conclusion will be found very helpful in what follows.

For the sake of illustration, we give below a few examples.

EXAMPLES

1. *Find the equations of the line which passes through the point* $(2, -1, 1)$ *and intersects the lines*

$$2x + y - 4 = 0 = y + 2z; \ x + 3z = 4, \ 2x + 5z = 8.$$

Sol. The line

$$2x + y - 4 + \lambda_1 (y + 2z) = 0, \ x + 3z - 4 + \lambda_2 (2x + 5z - 8) = 0$$

intersects the two given lines for all values of λ_1, λ_2.

The line will pass through the point $(2, -1, 1)$, if

$$-1 + \lambda_1 = 0 \text{ and } 1 + \lambda_2 = 0,$$

$$\Rightarrow \qquad \lambda_1 = 1, \lambda_2 = -1.$$

The required equations, therefore, are

$$x + y + z = 2 \text{ and } x + 2z = 4.$$

2. *Find the equations of the line which intersects each of the two lines*

$$2x + y - 1 = 0 = x - 2y + 3z;$$
$$3x - y + z + 2 = 0 = 4x + 5y - 2z - 3$$

and is parallel to the line

$$\frac{x}{1} = \frac{y}{2} = \frac{z}{3}.$$

Sol. The general equations of the line intersecting the two given lines are

$$2x + y - 1 + \lambda_1 (x - 2y + 3z) = 0 \\ 3x - y + z + 2 + \lambda_2 (4x + 5y - 2z - 3) = 0 \Big\}$$

This will be parallel to the given line if λ_1, λ_2 are so chosen that the two planes representing it are separately parallel to the given line.

This requires

$$(2 + \lambda_1) + 2(1 - 2\lambda_1) + 3(3\lambda_1) = 0 \Rightarrow \lambda_1 = -2/3,$$

and

$$(3 + 4\lambda_2) + 2(-1 + 5\lambda_2) + 3(1 - 2\lambda_2) = 0 \Rightarrow \lambda_2 = -1/2.$$

The required equations of the line, therefore, are

$$4x + 7y - 6z - 3 = 0, \ 2x - 7y + 4z + 7 = 0.$$

3. *A line with direction cosines proportional to 2, 1, 2 meets each of the lines given by the equations*

$$x = y + a = z; \ x + a = 2y = 2z;$$

find the co-ordinates of each of the points of intersection.

Sol. Now $P(r, r - a, r)$ and $P'(2r' - a, r', r')$ are the general co-ordinates of points on the given lines

$$\frac{x}{1} = \frac{y+a}{1} = \frac{z}{1}, \ \frac{x+a}{2} = \frac{y}{1} = \frac{z}{1},$$

so that

$$r - 2r' + a, \ r - r' - a, \ r - r'$$

are direction ratios of the line PP'.

We choose r and r' such that the line PP' has direction cosines proportional to $(2, 1, 2)$. This condition requires that

$$\frac{r - 2r' + a}{2} = \frac{r - r' - a}{1} = \frac{r - r'}{2}$$

$\Rightarrow$

$$r = 3a, \ r' = a.$$

Putting $r = 3a$ and $r' = a$ in the co-ordinates of P and P', we get

$$(3a, 2a, 3a) \text{ and } (a, a, a)$$

as the required points of intersection.

4. *Find the equations of the line which passes through the point $(3 - 1, 11)$ and is perpendicular to the line*

$$\frac{1}{2}x = \frac{1}{3}(y - 2) = \frac{1}{4}(z - 3).$$

Obtain also the foot of the perpendicular.

Sol. The co-ordinates of any point on the given line are

$$2r, \ 3r + 2, \ 4r + 3.$$

This will be the required foot of the perpendicular if the line joining it to the point $(3, -1, 11)$ be perpendicular to the given line. This requires

$$2(2r - 3) + 3(3r + 2 + 1) + 4(4r + 3 - 11) = 0 \Rightarrow r = 1.$$

Therefore, the required foot is (2, 5, 7) and the required equations of the perpendiculars are

$$\frac{x-3}{1} = \frac{y+1}{-6} = \frac{z-11}{4}.$$

EXERCISES

1. Find the equations of the perpendicular from

(i) $(2, 4, -1)$ to $(x+5) = \frac{1}{4}(y+3) = \frac{1}{9}(z-6)$,

(ii) $(-2, 2, -3)$ to $(x-3) = \frac{1}{2}(y+1) = -\frac{1}{4}(z-2)$,

(iii) $(0, 0, 0)$ to $x + 2y + 3z + 4 = 0 = 2x + 3y + 4z + 5$,

(iv) $(-2, 2, -3)$ to $2x + y + z - 7 = 0 = 4x + z - 14$.

Obtain also the feet of the perpendiculars.

[**Ans.** (i) $\frac{1}{6}(x-2) = \frac{1}{3}(y-4) = \frac{1}{2}(z+1)$, $(-4, 1, -3)$

(ii) $\frac{1}{6}(x+2) = -(y-2) = (z+3)$, $(4, 1, -2)$

(iii) $-x/2 = y = z/4$, $(2/3, -1/3, -4/3)$

(iv) $\frac{1}{6}(x+2) = -(y-2) = (z+3)$, $(4, 1, -2)$.]

2. A line with direction cosines proportional to $(7, 4, -1)$ is drawn to intersect the lines

$$\frac{x-1}{3} = \frac{y-3}{-1} = \frac{z+2}{1}, \quad \frac{x+3}{-3} = \frac{y-3}{2} = \frac{z-5}{4}.$$

Find the points of intersection and the length intercepted on it.

[**Ans.** $(7, 5, 0)$, $(0, 1, 1)$, $\sqrt{66}$]

3. Find the line which intersects the lines

$$x + y + z = 1, \ 2x - y - z = 2; \ x - y - z = 3, \ 2x + 4y - z = 4$$

and passes through the point $(1, 1, 1)$. Find also the points of intersection.

$$\left[\textbf{Ans. } x = 1, (y-1)/1 = (z-1)/3; \left(1, \frac{1}{2}, -\frac{1}{2}\right); (1, 0, -2) \right]$$

4. Find the lines drawn from the origin to intersect the lines

$$3x + 2y + 4z - 5 = 0, \ 2x - 3y + 4z + 1 = 0; \ 2x - 4y + z + 6 = 0 = 3x - 4y + z - 3.$$

[**Ans.** $13x - 13y + 4z = 0 = 8x - 12y + 3z$]

5. Obtain the line drawn through the point $(1, 0, -1)$ and intersecting the lines

$$x = 2y = 2z; \ 3x + 4y = 1; \ 4x + 5z = 2.$$

[**Ans.** $-(x-1)/6 = y = (z+1)/9$]

6. Find the equations of the line parallel to $x/2 = y/3 = z/4$ and intersecting the lines

$$9x + y + z + 4 = 0 = 5x + y + 3z; \ x + 2y - 3z - 3 = 0 = 2x - 5y + 3z + 3.$$

[**Ans.** $(x+1)/2 = y/3 = z/4$]

7. Find the equations of the line which passes through the point $(-4, 3, 1)$, is parallel to the plane $x + 2y - z = 5$ and intersects the line

$$-(x+1)/3 = (y-3)/2 = -(x-2)$$

Find also the point of intersection. [**Ans.** $(x+4)/3 = -(y-3) = (z-1); (2, 1, 3)$]

8. Find the distance of the point $(-2, 3, -4)$ from the line
$$(x + 2)/3 = (2y + 3)/4 = (3z + 4)/5$$
measured parallel to the plane
$$4x + 12y - 3z + 1 = 0. \qquad \text{[Ans. 17/2]}$$

9. Find the equations of the straight line through the point $(2, 3, 4)$ perpendicular to the X-axis and intersecting the line $x = y = z$. [Ans. $x = 2, 2y - z = 2$]

10. Find the equations of the straight line through the origin which will intersect the lines
$$(x - 1)/2 = (y + 3)/4 = (z - 5)/3, (x - 4)/2 = (y + 3)/3 = (z - 14) = 4$$
and prove that the secant is divided at the origin in the ratio $1 : 2$.

11. Find the equations of the two lines through the origin which intersect the line
$$(x - 3)/2 = y - 3 = z$$
at angles of $60°$. [Ans. $x = y/2 = -z; x = -y = z/2$]

12. The straight line which passes through the points $(11, 11, 18)$, $(2, -1, 3)$ is intersected by a straight line drawn through $(15, 20, 8)$ at right angles to Z-axis; show that the two lines intersect at the point $(5, 3, 8)$.

13. A straight line is drawn through the origin meeting perpendicularly the straight line through (a, b, c) with direction cosines l, m, n; prove that the direction cosines of the line are proportional to
$$a - lk, b - mk, c - nk \text{ where } k = al + bm + cn.$$

14. From the point $P(a, b, c)$ perpendiculars PA, PB are drawn to the lines $y = 2x, z = 1$, and $y = -2x, z = -1$; find the co-ordinates of A and B.

Prove that, if P moves so that the angle APB is always a right angle, P always lies on the surface $12x^2 - 3y^2 + 25z^2 = 25$.

[**Ans.** $A \{(2b + a)/5, (4b + 2a)/5, 1\}$; $B \{(a - 2b)/5, (4b - 2a)/5, -1\}$]

3.6. THE SHORTEST DISTANCE BETWEEN TWO LINES

To show that the shortest distance between two lines lies along the line meeting them both at right angles.

Let AB, CD be two given lines.

A line is completely determined if it intersects two lines at right angles [*See* § 3.5.1, *Case (viii)*].

Thus, there is one and only one line which intersects the two given lines at right angles, say, at G and H.

GH is, then, the shortest distance between the two lines for, if A, C be *any* two points, one on each of the two given lines,

$\qquad GH$ is the projection of AC on itself

$\Rightarrow \qquad GH = AC \cos \theta$

$\Rightarrow \qquad GH < AC$

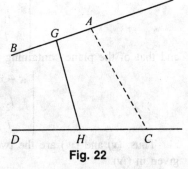

Fig. 22

θ, being the angle between GH and AC. Thus, GH is the shortest distance (S.D.) between the two lines AB and CD.

3.6.1. *To find the magnitude and the equations of the line of shortest distance between two straight lines.* (*Bangalore, 2004*)

Let AB, CD be the two given lines, and GH, the line which meets them both at right angles at G and H. Then GH is the line of shortest distance between the given lines; the length of GH being the magnitude.

Let the equations of the given lines be

$$\frac{x - x_1}{l_1} = \frac{y - y_1}{m_1} = \frac{z - z_1}{n_1},$$ ...(i)

$$\frac{x - x_2}{l_2} = \frac{y - y_2}{m_2} = \frac{z - z_2}{n_2}$$ ...(ii)

and let the shortest distance lie along the line

$$\frac{x - \alpha}{l} = \frac{y - \beta}{m} = \frac{z - \gamma}{n},$$ ...(iii)

Line (iii) is perpendicular to both the lines (i) and (ii)

$$\Rightarrow \qquad \begin{cases} ll_1 + mm_1 + nn_1 = 0, \\ ll_2 + mm_2 + nn_2 = 0, \end{cases}$$

$$\Rightarrow \qquad \frac{l}{m_1 n_2 - m_2 n_1} = \frac{m}{n_1 l_2 - n_2 l_1} = \frac{n}{l_1 m_2 - l_2 m_1};$$

$$= \frac{1}{\sqrt{\Sigma (m_1 n_2 - m_2 n_1)^2}}$$ ...(iv)

The line of shortest distance is perpendicular to both the lines. Therefore, the magnitude of the shortest distance is the projection on the line of shortest distance of the line joining *any* two points, one on each of the given lines (i) and (ii).

Taking the projection of the join of (x_1, y_1, z_1), (x_2, y_2, z_2) on the line with direction cosines l, m, n; we see that the shortest distance

$$= (x_2 - x_1)\, l + (y_2 - y_1)\, m + (z_2 - z_1)\, n,$$

where l, m, n have the values as given in (iv).

To find the equations of the line of shortest distance, we observe that it is coplanar with both the given lines.

The equation of the plane containing the coplanar lines (i) and (iii) is

$$\begin{vmatrix} x - x_1 & y - y_1 & z - z_1 \\ l_1 & m_1 & n_1 \\ l & m & n \end{vmatrix} = 0$$ ...(v)

and that of the plane containing the coplanar lines (ii) and (iii) is

$$\begin{vmatrix} x - x_2 & y - y_2 & z - z_2 \\ l_2 & m_2 & n_2 \\ l & m & n \end{vmatrix} = 0.$$ ...(vi)

Thus, (v) and (vi) are the two equations of the line of shortest distance, where l, m, n are given in (iv).

Note. Other methods of determining the shortest distance are given below where an example has been solved by three different methods.

EXAMPLES

1. *Find the magnitude and the equations of the line of shortest distance between the lines* :

$$\frac{x - 8}{3} = \frac{y + 9}{-16} = \frac{z - 10}{7},$$ ...(i)

$$\frac{x-15}{3} = \frac{y-29}{8} = \frac{z-5}{-5}. \qquad \ldots(ii)$$

Sol. First Method. Let l, m, n be the direction cosines of the line of shortest distance. As it is perpendicular to the two lines, we have

$$\begin{cases} 3l - 16m + 7n = 0, \\ 3l + 8m - 5n = 0. \end{cases}$$

$$\Rightarrow \quad \frac{l}{24} = \frac{m}{36} = \frac{n}{72},$$

$$\Rightarrow \quad \frac{l}{2} = \frac{m}{3} = \frac{n}{6},$$

$$\Rightarrow \quad l = \frac{2}{7}, \ m = \frac{3}{7}, \ n = \frac{6}{7}.$$

The magnitude of the shortest distance is the projection of the join of the points $(8, -9, 10)$, $(15, 29, 5)$, on the line of the shortest distance and is, therefore,

$$= 7 \cdot \frac{2}{7} + 38 \cdot \frac{3}{7} - 5 \cdot \frac{6}{7} = 14.$$

Again, the equation of the plane containing the first of the two given lines and the line of shortest distance is

$$\begin{vmatrix} x-8 & y+9 & z-10 \\ 3 & -16 & 7 \\ 2 & 3 & 6 \end{vmatrix} = 0 \iff 117x + 4y - 41z - 490 = 0.$$

Also the equation of the plane containing the second line and the shortest distance line is

$$\begin{vmatrix} x-15 & y-29 & z-5 \\ 3 & 8 & -5 \\ 2 & 3 & 6 \end{vmatrix} = 0 \iff 9x - 4y - z = 14.$$

Hence, the equations of the shortest distance line are

$$117x + 4y - 41z - 490 = 0 = 9x - 4y - z = 14.$$

Second Method

$$P(3r + 8, -16r - 9, 7r + 10), \ P'(3r' + 15, 8r' + 29, 5r' + 5)$$

are the general co-ordinates of the points on the two lines respectively. The direction cosines of PP' are proportional to

$$3r - 3r' - 7, \ -16r - 8r' - 38, \ 7r + 5r' + 5.$$

Now PP' will be the required line of shortest distance, if it is perpendicular to both the given lines, which requires

$$\begin{cases} 3(3r - 3r' - 7) - 16(-16r - 8r' - 38) + 7(7r + 5r' + 5) = 0, \\ 3(3r - 3r' - 7) + 8(-16r - 8r' - 38) - 5(7r + 5r' + 5) = 0. \end{cases}$$

$$\Rightarrow \qquad 157r + 77r' + 311 = 0 \text{ and } 11r + 7r' + 25 = 0,$$

$$\Rightarrow \qquad r = -1, \ r' = -2.$$

Therefore, the co-ordinates of the point P and P' are

$$(5, 7, 3) \text{ and } (9, 13, 15).$$

Hence, the shortest distance $PP' = 14$ and its equations are

$$\frac{x-5}{2} = \frac{y-7}{3} = \frac{z-3}{6}$$

This method is sometimes very convenient and is specially useful when we require also the points where the line of shortest distance meets the two lines.

Third Method. This method depends upon the following considerations :

Let AB, CD be the given lines and GH, the line of shortest distance between them.

Let 'α' denote the plane which passes through the line AB and is parallel to the line CD and let 'β' denote the plane through the line CD and parallel to the line AB.

The line of shortest distance GH, being perpendicular to both the lines AB, CD is normal to the two planes so that the two planes α, β are parallel.

The length GH of the shortest distance is, therefore, the distance between the parallel planes α and β. This distance between parallel planes being the distance of *any* point on one from the other, we see that it is enough to determine only one plane say 'α' and then the magnitude of the shortest distance is the distance of any point on the second line from the plane 'α'.

Again, we easily see that the plane through the lines AB, GH is perpendicular to the plane 'α' and the plane through CD, GH is perpendicular to the plane 'β' and, therefore, also to 'α'. Thus, GH, *the line of shortest distance, is the line of intersection of the planes separately drawn through AB, CD perpendicular to the plane* 'α'.

We now solve the question.

The equation of the plane containing the line (i) and parallel to the line (ii) is

$$\begin{vmatrix} x-8 & y+9 & z-10 \\ 3 & -16 & 7 \\ 3 & 8 & -5 \end{vmatrix} = 0 \iff 2x + 3y + 6z - 49 = 0 \qquad \ldots(iii)$$

Perpendicular distance of the point $(15, 29, 5)$, lying on the second line, from this plane

$$= \frac{30 + 87 + 30 - 49}{7} = 14$$

which is the required magnitude of the shortest distance.

The equation of the plane through the line (i) perpendicular to the plane (iii) is

$$\begin{vmatrix} x-8 & y+9 & z-10 \\ 3 & -16 & 7 \\ 2 & 3 & 6 \end{vmatrix} = 0 \iff 117x + 4y - 41z - 490 = 0$$

The equation of the plane through (ii) and perpendicular to the plane (iii) is

$$\begin{vmatrix} x-15 & y+29 & z-5 \\ 3 & 8 & -5 \\ 2 & 3 & 6 \end{vmatrix} = 0 \iff 9x - 4y - z = 14 \qquad \ldots(iv)$$

Hence, (iv), (v) are the equations of the line of shortest distance.

2. *Find the shortest distance between the axis of z and the line*

$$ax + by + cz + d = 0, \ a'x + b'y + c'z + d' = 0.$$

(*Kanpur, 1995, 98, 99*; *Garhwal, 1998*; *Gorakhpur, 1999*; *Poorvanchal, 1996*)

Sol. Now the general equation of the plane through the second given line is

$$ax + by + cz + d + k\,(a'x + b'y + c'z + d') = 0$$

$$\Leftrightarrow \qquad (a + ka')\,x + (b + kb')\,y + (c + kc')\,z + (d + kd') = 0 \qquad \qquad ...(i)$$

k being the parameter.

It will be parallel to z-axis whose direction cosines are 0, 0, 1 if the normal to the plane is perpendicular to the z-axis, *i.e.*, if

$$0 \cdot (a + ka') + 0 \cdot (b + kb') + 1 \cdot (c + kc') = 0$$

$$\Rightarrow \qquad\qquad k = -c/c'.$$

Substituting this value of k in (i), we see that the equation of the plane through the second line parallel to the first is

$$(ac' - a'c)\,x + (bc' - b'c)\,y + (dc' - d'c) = 0 \qquad\qquad ...(ii)$$

The required S.D. is the distance of *any* point on the z-axis from the plane (ii) so that

S.D. = perpendicular from $(0, 0, 0)$, (a point on z-axis)

$$= \pm \frac{dc' - d'c}{\sqrt{(ac' - a'c)^2 + (bc' - b'c)^2}}.$$

3. *Prove that the S.D. between the diagonals of rectangular parallelopiped and the edges not meeting it are*

$$\frac{bc}{\sqrt{(b^2 + c^2)}}, \quad \frac{ca}{\sqrt{(c^2 + a^2)}}, \quad \frac{ab}{\sqrt{(a^2 + b^2)}}$$

where a, b, c are the lengths of the edges.

Sol. Let coterminous edges OA, OB, OC be taken as the axes of reference. We will find S.D. between the diagonal OP and edge BL (which does not meet OP). Equations of OP and BL are

$$\frac{x}{a} = \frac{y}{b} = \frac{z}{c} \text{ and } \frac{x}{a} = \frac{y-b}{0} = \frac{z}{0}.$$

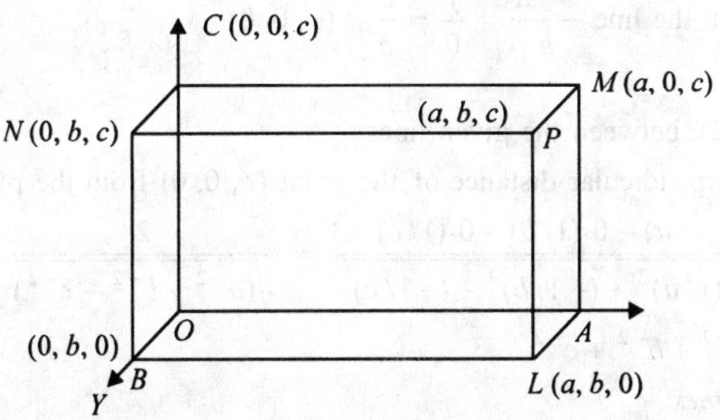

Fig. 23

Let l, m, n be the dc's of S.D., then

$$al + bm + cn = 0$$

and

$$al + 0 \cdot m + 0 \cdot n = 0$$

$$\Rightarrow \qquad l = 0, \; m = \frac{c}{\sqrt{b^2 + c^2}}, \; n = \frac{-b}{\sqrt{b^2 + c^2}}$$

$\therefore$ S.D. = Projection of OB on the line of S.D.

$$= (0 - 0)\,l + (b - 0)\,m + (0 - 0)\,n = bm = \frac{bc}{\sqrt{b^2 + c^2}}.$$

Similarly, S.D.'s between OP and AL and OP and MC are $ca/\sqrt{c^2+a^2}$ and $ab/\sqrt{a^2+b^2}$.

4. *Show that the equation of the plane containing the line*

$$\frac{y}{b}+\frac{z}{c}=1,\ x=0$$

and parallel to the line

$$\frac{x}{a}-\frac{z}{c}=1,\ y=0$$

is

$$\frac{x}{a}-\frac{y}{b}-\frac{z}{c}+1=0$$

and if 2d is the S.D. show that $d^{-2}=a^{-2}+b^{-2}+c^{-2}$.

(Rohilkhand, 2001, 2006; Avadh, 2000; Poorvanchal, 2004)

Sol. The equation of the plane containing the line

$$\frac{y}{b}+\frac{z}{c}-1+\lambda x=0$$

is

$$\left(\frac{y}{b}+\frac{z}{c}-1\right)+\lambda x=0$$

$$\Rightarrow \qquad \lambda x+(1/b)\,y+(1/c)\,z-1=0 \qquad\qquad ...(i)$$

If it is parallel to the line

$$\frac{x}{a}-\frac{z}{c}=1,\ y=0,\ i.e.,\ \frac{x-a}{a}=\frac{y}{0}=\frac{z}{c},$$

then the normal to the plane (i) must be perpendicular to the line and so we have

$$\lambda\cdot a+(1/b)\cdot 0+(1/c)\cdot c=0 \Rightarrow \lambda=-1/a.$$

$\therefore$ From (1) the equation of the required plane is

$$\left(\frac{y}{b}+\frac{z}{c}-1\right)-\frac{1}{a}x=0 \Rightarrow \frac{x}{a}-\frac{y}{b}-\frac{z}{c}+1=0 \qquad\qquad ...(ii)$$

Now, any point on the line $\dfrac{x-a}{a}=\dfrac{y}{0}=\dfrac{z}{c}$ is $(a,0,0)$.

Therefore,

$$2d = \text{S.D. between the given lines}$$

$$= \text{Perpendicular distance of the point }(a,0,0)\text{ from the plane }(i)$$

$$= \frac{a\cdot(1/a)-0\cdot(1/b)-0\cdot(1/c)+1}{\sqrt{(1/a)^2+(-1/b)^2+(-1/c)^2}}=\frac{2}{\sqrt{(a^{-2}+b^{-2}+c^{-2})}}$$

$$\Rightarrow \qquad d^{-2}=a^{-2}+b^{-2}+c^{-2}$$

5. *Two straight lines*

$$\frac{x-\alpha_1}{l_1}=\frac{y-\beta_1}{m_1}=\frac{z-\gamma_1}{n_1},\ \frac{x-\alpha_2}{l_2}=\frac{y-\beta_2}{m_2}=\frac{z-\gamma_2}{n_2}$$

are cut by a third line whose dc's are $\lambda,\ \mu,\ \nu$. *Show that 'd' the length intercepted on the third line is given by*

$$d\begin{vmatrix} l_1 & m_1 & n_1 \\ l_2 & m_2 & n_2 \\ \lambda & \mu & \nu \end{vmatrix}=\begin{vmatrix} \alpha_1-\alpha_2 & \beta_1-\beta_2 & \gamma_1-\gamma_2 \\ l_1 & m_1 & n_1 \\ l_2 & m_2 & n_2 \end{vmatrix}$$

Deduce the length of S.D. between the first two lines.

Sol. Let the third line with dc's λ, μ, ν meet the first line

$$\frac{x-\alpha_1}{l_1} = \frac{y-\beta_1}{m_1} = \frac{z-\gamma_1}{n_1} \qquad \ldots(i)$$

at $\qquad P(\alpha_1 + l_1 r_1, \beta_1 + m_1 r_1, \gamma_1 + n_1 r_1)$.

Then the equation of third line can be written as

$$\frac{x-(\alpha_1+l_1 r_1)}{\lambda} = \frac{y-(\beta_1+m_1 r_1)}{\mu} = \frac{z-(\gamma_1+n_1 r_1)}{\nu} = d \text{ (say)} \qquad \ldots(ii)$$

$\therefore$ The co-ordinates of any point Q at a distance d from the point P on the line (ii) are

$$\alpha_1 + l_1 r_1 + d\lambda, \; \beta_1 + m_1 r_1 + d\mu, \; \gamma_1 + n_1 r_1 + d\nu \qquad \ldots(iii)$$

Now, the point Q is a point on the second line, at a distance d from P. Hence, the point (iii) is the same as $(\alpha_2 + l_2 r_2, \beta_2 + m_2 r_2, \gamma_2 + n_2 r_2)$. Comparing we get

$$d\lambda + \alpha_1 + l_1 r_1 = \alpha_2 + i_2 r_2 \text{ etc.}$$

$$\Rightarrow \qquad d\lambda + (\alpha_1 - \alpha_2) + l_1 r_1 - l_2 r_2 = 0,$$

Similarly, $\qquad d\mu + (\beta_i - \beta_2) + m_1 r_1 - m_2 r_2 = 0,$

$$d\nu + (\gamma_1 - \gamma_2) + n_1 r_1 - n_2 r_2 = 0.$$

Eliminating r_1 and r_2 from these, we get

$$\begin{vmatrix} d\lambda + (\alpha_1-\alpha_2) & l_1 & l_2 \\ d\mu + (\beta_1-\beta_2) & m_1 & m_2 \\ d\nu + (\gamma_1-\gamma_2) & n_1 & n_2 \end{vmatrix} = 0$$

$$\Rightarrow \qquad d\begin{vmatrix} \lambda & l_1 & l_2 \\ \mu & m_1 & m_2 \\ \nu & n_1 & n_2 \end{vmatrix} + \begin{vmatrix} \alpha_1-\alpha_2 & l_1 & l_2 \\ \beta_1-\beta_2 & m_1 & m_2 \\ \gamma_1-\gamma_2 & n_1 & n_2 \end{vmatrix} = 0$$

$$\Rightarrow \qquad d\begin{vmatrix} l_1 & m_1 & n_1 \\ l_2 & m_2 & n_2 \\ \lambda & \mu & \nu \end{vmatrix} = -\begin{vmatrix} \alpha_1-\alpha_2 & \beta_1-\beta_2 & \gamma_1-\gamma_2 \\ l_1 & m_1 & n_1 \\ l_2 & m_2 & n_2 \end{vmatrix}$$

d being the distance between two points, neglecting the negative sign we have the required result.

If d stands for the S.D. between the given lines with dc's λ, μ, ν is perpendicular to both the given lines and as such we have

$$\lambda l_1 + \mu m_1 + \nu n_1 = 0 \text{ and } \lambda l_2 + \mu m_2 + \nu n_2 = 0.$$

Solving these we get

$$\frac{\lambda}{m_1 n_2 - m_2 n_1} = \frac{\mu}{n_1 l_2 - n_2 l_1} = \frac{\nu}{l_1 m_2 - l_2 m_1} = \frac{1}{\sqrt{\Sigma(m_1 n_2 - m_2 n_1)^2}}$$

Also, coefficient of $d = \begin{vmatrix} l_1 & m_1 & n_1 \\ l_2 & m_2 & n_2 \\ \lambda & \mu & \nu \end{vmatrix}$

$$= \lambda(m_1 n_2 - m_2 n_1) + \mu(n_1 l_2 - n_2 l_1) + \nu(l_1 m_2 - l_2 m_1)$$

$$= \frac{\Sigma(m_1 n_2 - m_2 n_1)}{\sqrt{\Sigma(m_1 n_2 - m_2 n_1)^2}} = \sqrt{\Sigma(m_1 n_2 - m_2 n_1)^2}$$

$\therefore$ d the S.D. is given by

$$d = \begin{vmatrix} \alpha_1 - \alpha_2 & \beta_1 - \beta_2 & \gamma_1 - \gamma_2 \\ l_1 & m_1 & n_1 \\ l_2 & m_2 & n_2 \end{vmatrix} \div \sqrt{\Sigma \, (m_1 n_2 - m_2 n_1)^2} \, .$$

6. *A square ABCD of diagonal 2a is folded along the diagonal AC, so that planes DAC, BAC are at right angles. Show that the shortest distance between DC and AB is then $2a / \sqrt{3}$.*

Sol. Let O be the centre of square and OA axis of x. Planes DAC and BAC are mutually at right angles. Take OB and OD as axes of y and z.

Then co-ordinates of A, B, C, D are $(a, 0, 0)$, $(0, a, 0)$, $(-a, 0, 0)$ and $(0, 0, a)$.

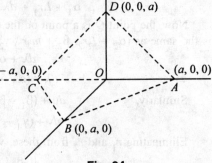

Equations of AB are $(x - a)/a = y/-a = z/0$ and of DC are $x/a = y/0 = (z - a)/a$. Thus, a plane containing DC and parallel to AB is

$$\begin{vmatrix} x & y & z - a \\ a & 0 & a \\ a & -a & 0 \end{vmatrix} = 0$$

$\Rightarrow$ $x + y + z + a = 0$ **Fig. 24**

S.D. = Perpendicular distance of this plane from a point $(a, 0, 0)$ on AB

$$= \frac{a + a}{\sqrt{(1 + 1 + 1)}} = \frac{2a}{\sqrt{3}}.$$

EXERCISES

1. Find the magnitude and the equations of the line of shortest distance between the two lines :

   (i) $\dfrac{x - 3}{2} = \dfrac{y + 15}{-7} = \dfrac{z - 9}{5}; \dfrac{x + 1}{2} = \dfrac{y - 1}{1} = \dfrac{z - 9}{-3}.$ *(Calcutta, 2005; Banglore, 2001)*

   (ii) $\dfrac{x - 3}{-1} = \dfrac{y - 4}{2} = \dfrac{z + 2}{1}; \dfrac{x - 1}{1} = \dfrac{y + 7}{3} = \dfrac{z + 2}{2}.$

            [Ans. (i) $x = y = z$; $4\sqrt{3}$. (ii) $(x - 4) = (y - 2)/3 = -(z + 3)/5$; $\sqrt{35}$**]**

2. Find the length and the equations of the shortest distance line between

$$5x - y - z = 0 \qquad x - 2y + z + 3 = 0;$$
$$7x - 4y - 2z = 0, \qquad x - y + z - 3 = 0.$$

[Hint. Transform the equations to the symmetrical form]

            [Ans. $17x + 20y - 19z - 39 = 0 = 8x + 5y - 31z + 67$; $13/\sqrt{75}$**]**

3. Find the magnitude and the position of the line of shortest distance between the lines

   (i) $2x + y - z = 0, x - y + 2z = 0; x + 2y - 3z = 4, 2x - 3y + 4z = 5$

   (ii) $\dfrac{x}{4} = \dfrac{y + 1}{3} = \dfrac{z - 2}{2}; 5x - 2y - 3z + 6 = 0; x - 3y + 2z - 3 = 0.$ *(Meerut, 2005)*

            [Ans. (i) $3x + z = 0 = 22x - 5y + 4z - 67$, $2\sqrt{14}/7$.

                     (ii) $7x - 2y - 11z + 20 = 0 = 13x - 13z + 24$; $17\sqrt{6/39}$**]**

4. Obtain the co-ordinates of the points where the shortest distance line between the lines

$$\frac{x-23}{-6} = \frac{y-19}{-4} = \frac{z-25}{3}, \frac{x-12}{-9} = \frac{y-1}{4} = \frac{z-5}{2}$$

meets them.   [**Ans.** (11, 11, 31) and (3, 5, 7)]

5. Find the co-ordinates of the point on the join of (− 3, 7, − 13) and (− 6, 1, − 10) which is nearest to the intersection of the planes

$$3x - y - 3z + 32 = 0 \text{ and } 3x + 2y - 15z - 8 = 0. \qquad [\textbf{Ans.} (-7, -1, -9)]$$

6. Show that the shortest distance between the lines

$$x + a = 2y = -12z \text{ and } x = y + 2a = 6z - 6a$$

is 2a.   (*Kumaon, 1999*)

7. Find the shortest distance between the lines

$$\frac{x-1}{2} = \frac{y-2}{3} = \frac{z-3}{4}, \frac{x-2}{3} = \frac{y-3}{4} = \frac{z-4}{5};$$

show also that the lines are coplanar.

(*Garhwal, 2004; Kanpur, 2001, 2003; Avadh, 1998*)

8. Find the length and equations of the line of shortest distance between the lines

$$\frac{x+3}{-4} = \frac{y-6}{3} = \frac{z}{2}; \frac{x+2}{-4} = \frac{y}{1} = \frac{z-7}{1}.$$

(*Garhwal, 2001; Kumaon, 2006*)

[**Ans.** 9; 32x + 34y + 13z − 108 = 0, 12x + 33y + 15z − 81 = 0]

9. Show that the length of the shortest distance between the line $z = x \tan \alpha, y = 0$ and any tangent to the ellipse $x^2 \sin^2 \alpha + y^2 = a^2, z = 0$ is constant.

10. Show that the shortest distance between any two opposite edges of the tetrahedron formed by the planes

$$y + z = 0, z + x = 0, x + y = 0, x + y + z = a,$$

is $2a / \sqrt{6}$ and that the three lines of shortest distance intersect at the point

$$x = y = z = -a. \qquad (Avadh, 1997; Kanpur, 1995)$$

3.7. LENGTH OF THE PERPENDICULAR FROM A POINT TO A LINE

To find the length of the perpendicular from a given point $P(x_1, y_1, z_1)$ to a given line

$$\frac{x-\alpha}{l} = \frac{y-\beta}{m} = \frac{z-\gamma}{n}.$$

Let H be the point (α, β, γ) on the given line and Q the foot of the perpendicular from the point P on it.

We have $PQ^2 = HP^2 - HQ^2$.

Also $HP^2 = (x_1 - \alpha)^2 + (y_1 - \beta)^2 + (z_1 - \gamma)^2$

and HQ = projection of HP on the given line

$$= l(x_1 - \alpha) + m(y_1 - \beta) + n(z_1 - \gamma)$$

provided l, m, n are the actual direction cosines.

It follows that

$$PQ^2 = (x_1 - \alpha)^2 + (y_1 - \beta)^2 + (z_1 - \gamma)^2$$
$$- [l(x_1 - \alpha) + m(y_1 - \beta) + n(z_1 - \gamma)]^2.$$

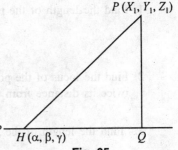

Fig. 25

EXAMPLE

Find the perpendicular distance of $P(1, 2, 3)$ *from the line* $\dfrac{x-6}{3} = \dfrac{y-7}{2} = \dfrac{z-7}{-2}$.

Sol. First Method. $A(6, 7, 7)$ will be a point on the line. Let the perpendicular from P meets the line in N.

Then,

$$AP^2 = (6-1)^2 + (7-2)^2 + (7-3)^2 = 66$$

$$AN = \text{Projection of } AP \text{ on the given line}$$

$$= (6-1)\cdot\frac{3}{\sqrt{17}} + (7-2)\cdot\frac{2}{\sqrt{17}} + (7-3)\left(\frac{-2}{\sqrt{17}}\right)$$

$$= \sqrt{17}$$

$$\therefore \quad PN^2 = AP^2 - AN^2 = 66 - 17 = 49$$

$$\Rightarrow \quad PN = 7.$$

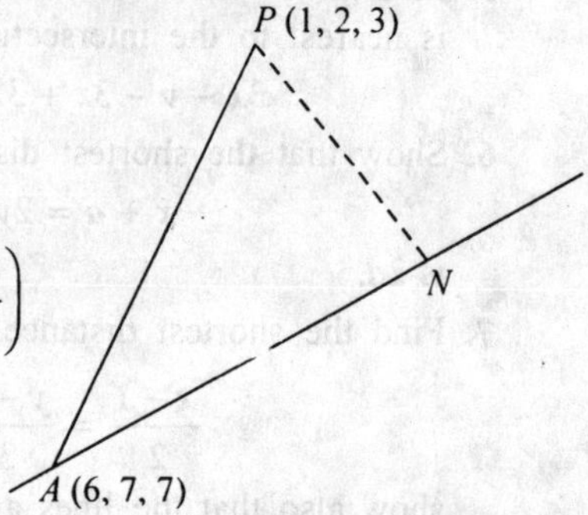

Fig. 26

Second Method. The given line can be written as

$$\frac{x-6}{3/\sqrt{17}} = \frac{y-7}{2/\sqrt{17}} = \frac{z-7}{-2/\sqrt{17}}$$

$$\therefore \quad PN^2 = \left\{\frac{2}{\sqrt{17}}(1-6) - \frac{3}{\sqrt{17}}(2-7)\right\}^2 + \left\{\frac{-2}{\sqrt{17}}(2-7) - \frac{2}{\sqrt{17}}(3-7)\right\}^2$$

$$+ \left\{\frac{3}{\sqrt{17}}(3-7) + \frac{2}{\sqrt{17}}(1-6)\right\}^2 = 49$$

$$\Rightarrow \quad PN = 7.$$

Third Method. Any point N on the line is $(3r + 6, 2r + 7, -2r + 7)$. Let this be the foot of the perpendicular.

Then PN whose dr's are $3r + 5, 2r + 5, -2r + 4$, will be perpendicular to the given line.

$$\therefore \quad\quad\quad 3(3r + 5) + 2(2r + 5) - 2(-2r + 4) = 0$$

$$\Rightarrow \quad\quad\quad\quad\quad r = -1.$$

Thus, the foot of perpendicular N is $(3, 5, 9)$ and hence $PN = 7$.

EXERCISES

1. Find the length of the perpendicular from the point $(4, -5, 3)$ to the line

$$\frac{x-5}{3} = \frac{y+2}{-4} = \frac{z-6}{5}.$$

$$\left[\textbf{Ans. } \frac{\sqrt{457}}{5}\right]$$

2. Find the locus of the point which moves so that its distance from the line $x = y = z$ is twice its distance from the plane $x + y + z = 1$.

$$[\textbf{Ans. } x^2 + y^2 + z^2 + 5xy + 5yz + 5zx - 4x - 4y - 4z + 2 = 0]$$

3. Find the length of the perpendicular from the point $P(5, 4, -1)$ upon the line

$$\frac{1}{2}(x-1) = \frac{1}{9}y = \frac{1}{5}z.$$

$$[\textbf{Ans. } \sqrt{2109/110}]$$

3.8. INTERSECTION OF THREE PLANES

Given three distinct planes such that no two of them are parallel.

We have the following three possibilities in respect of their intersection.

The three planes may :

(*i*) have only one point in common (Fig. 27);

(*ii*) have a line in common so that the three planes are coaxial (Fig. 28);

(*iii*) form a triangular prism (Fig. 29).

We shall in the following find conditions for each of these three possibilities.

Three planes are said to form a triangular prism if the three lines of intersection of the three planes, taken in pairs, are distinct and parallel.

Clearly, the three planes will form a triangular prism if the line of intersection of two of them be parallel to the third.

3.8.1. *To find the condition that the three planes*

$$a_r x + b_r y + c_r z + d_r = 0; (r = 1, 2, 3)$$

should form a prism or intersect in a line.

We assume that the first two planes are *not* parallel.

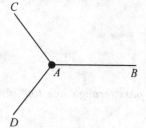

Fig. 27   Fig. 28

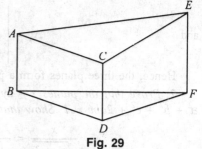

Fig. 29

The line of intersection of the first two planes is

$$\frac{x - (b_1 d_2 - b_2 d_1)/(a_1 b_2 - a_2 b_1)}{b_1 c_2 - b_2 c_1} = \frac{y - (a_2 d_1 - a_1 d_2)/(a_1 b_2 - a_2 b_1)}{a_2 c_1 - a_1 c_2} = \frac{z}{a_1 b_2 - a_2 b_1} \quad ...(i)$$

The three planes will form a triangular prism if this line is parallel to the third plane without lying in the same.

The line (*i*) will be parallel to the third plane, if

$$a_3 (b_1 c_2 - b_2 c_1) + b_3 (c_1 a_2 - c_2 a_1) + c_3 (a_1 b_2 - a_2 b_1) = 0$$

$$\Rightarrow \quad \begin{vmatrix} a_1 & b_1 & c_1 \\ a_2 & b_2 & c_2 \\ a_3 & b_3 & c_3 \end{vmatrix} = 0 \quad ...(ii)$$

Again, the planes will intersect in a line if and only if the line (*i*) lies in the plane

$$a_3 x + b_3 y + c_3 z + d_3 = 0.$$

This requires :

(1) this line is parallel to the third plane *i.e.*, (*ii*) is satisfied, and

(2) the point $\left(\dfrac{b_1 d_2 - b_2 d_1}{a_1 b_2 - a_2 b_1}, \dfrac{a_2 d_1 - a_1 d_2}{a_1 b_2 - a_2 b_1}, 0 \right)$ lies on it implying that

$$a_3 (b_1 d_2 - b_2 d_1) + b_3 (a_2 d_1 - a_1 d_2) + d_3 (a_1 b_2 - a_2 b_1) = 0$$

$$\Rightarrow \quad \begin{vmatrix} a_1 & b_1 & d_1 \\ a_2 & b_2 & d_2 \\ a_3 & b_3 & d_3 \end{vmatrix} = 0 \qquad \ldots(iii)$$

Thus, the three planes will intersect in a line, if the condition

(ii) and (iii) hold

and will form a triangular prism, if

(ii) holds but (iii) does not hold.

The three planes will intersect in a unique finite point if the condition *(ii)* does not hold.

EXAMPLES

1. *Examine the nature of intersection of the planes*

$$2x - 5y + z = 3, \quad x + y + 4z = 5, \quad x + 3y + 6z = 1.$$

Sol. We have

$$\Delta = \begin{vmatrix} 2 & -5 & 1 \\ 1 & 1 & 4 \\ 1 & 3 & 6 \end{vmatrix} = 0$$

and

$$\Delta_1 = \begin{vmatrix} 2 & -5 & -3 \\ 1 & 1 & -5 \\ 1 & 3 & -1 \end{vmatrix} = 42 \neq 0$$

Hence, the three planes form a prism.

2. *Prove that the planes $x = cy + bz$, $y = az + cx$, $z = bx + ay$ pass through one line if $a^2 + b^2 + c^2 + 2abc = 1$. Show that the equations of this line are*

$$\frac{x}{\sqrt{1-a^2}} = \frac{y}{\sqrt{1-b^2}} = \frac{z}{\sqrt{1-c^2}}. \qquad \text{(Kanpur, 1995; Avadh, 1994)}$$

Sol. The three planes can be written as

$$x - cy - bz = 0 \qquad \ldots(1)$$
$$cx - y + az = 0 \qquad \ldots(2)$$
$$bx + ay - z = 0 \qquad \ldots(3)$$

Let (l, m, n) be the dc's of the line of intersection of (1) and (2); then

$$l - cm - bn = 0$$
$$cl - m + an = 0$$

$$\Rightarrow \quad \frac{l}{ac+b} = \frac{m}{bc+a} = \frac{n}{1-c^2}$$

Planes (1) and (2) both pass through origin, hence, their line of intersection will also pass through (0, 0, 0). Thus, equation of line of intersection of (1) and (2) is

$$\frac{x}{ac+b} = \frac{y}{bc+a} = \frac{z}{1-c^2} \qquad \ldots(4)$$

Now the three planes will intersect in a line if (4) lies in (3). The point (0, 0, 0) of (4) already satisfies (3). Hence, the required condition is

$$b(ac+b) + a(bc+a) - (1-c^2) = 0$$

$$\Rightarrow \quad a^2 + b^2 + c^2 + 2abc = 1 \qquad \ldots(5)$$

We have

$$ac + b = \sqrt{(ac+b)^2} = \sqrt{a^2c^2 + b^2 + 2abc} = \sqrt{a^2c^2 + (1 - a^2 - c^2)} \quad \text{[From (5)]}$$
$$= \sqrt{(1-a^2)(1-c^2)}.$$

Similarly, $bc + a = \sqrt{(1-b^2)(1-c^2)}$.

Putting these in (4), we get

$$\frac{x}{\sqrt{1-a^2}} = \frac{y}{\sqrt{1-b^2}} = \frac{z}{\sqrt{1-c^2}}.$$

3. *The plane $x/a + y/b + z/c = 1$ meets the axes OX, OY, OZ which are rectangular, in A, B, C. Prove that the plane through the axes and the internal bisector of the angles of the triangle ABC pass through the line*

$$\frac{x}{a\sqrt{b^2+c^2}} = \frac{y}{b\sqrt{c^2+a^2}} = \frac{z}{c\sqrt{a^2+b^2}}.$$

Sol. We know that bisector of any angle of a triangle meets the opposite side at a point which divides it in the ratio of other two sides. Hence, if CF is the internal bisector of angle ABC, then

$$\frac{AF}{BF} = \frac{AC}{BC} = \frac{\sqrt{(a^2+c^2)}}{\sqrt{(b^2+c^2)}}.$$

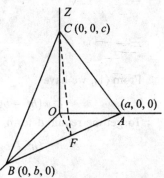

Z
C (0, 0, c)
(a, 0, 0)
A
O
F
B (0, b, 0)
Fig. 30

Thus, co-ordinates of F will become

$$\left(\frac{a\sqrt{(b^2+c^2)}}{\sqrt{(a^2+c^2)} + \sqrt{(b^2+c^2)}} , \; \frac{b\sqrt{a^2+c^2}}{\sqrt{(a^2+c^2)} + \sqrt{(b^2+c^2)}} , \; 0 \right)$$

Plane through z-axis is

$$x + \lambda y = 0$$

If it passes through F, then

$$\lambda = -\frac{a\sqrt{(b^2+c^2)}}{b\sqrt{(a^2+c^2)}}$$

Hence, equation of plane OCF is

$$x - \frac{a\sqrt{(b^2+c^2)}}{b\sqrt{(a^2+c^2)}}\, y = 0$$

i.e.,

$$\frac{x}{a\sqrt{(b^2+c^2)}} = \frac{y}{b\sqrt{(a^2+c^2)}}.$$

Similarly, other planes through axes and lines bisecting the angles A and B are

$$\frac{y}{b\sqrt{a^2+c^2}} = \frac{z}{c\sqrt{(a^2+b^2)}} \quad \text{and} \quad \frac{x}{a\sqrt{(b^2+c^2)}} = \frac{z}{c\sqrt{(a^2+b^2)}}$$

The planes clearly pass through the line

$$\frac{x}{a\sqrt{(b^2+c^2)}} = \frac{y}{b\sqrt{(a^2+c^2)}} = \frac{z}{c\sqrt{(a^2+b^2)}}.$$

4. *Show that the planes* $ax + hy + gz = 0$, $hx + by + fz = 0$, $gx + fy + cz = 0$ *have a common line of intersection if*

$$\Delta = \begin{vmatrix} a & h & g \\ h & b & f \\ g & f & c \end{vmatrix} = 0$$

and the direction ratios of the line satisfy the equations

$$\frac{l^2}{\partial\Delta/\partial a} = \frac{m^2}{\partial\Delta/\partial b} = \frac{n^2}{\partial\Delta/\partial c}.$$

Sol. Let l, m, n be the dc's of the line of intersection of first two planes, then

$$al + hm + gn = 0 \text{ and } hl + bm + fn = 0$$

$$\Rightarrow \qquad \frac{l}{hf - bg} = \frac{m}{gl - af} = \frac{n}{ab - h^2} \qquad \qquad ...(1)$$

But the three planes pass through a common point $(0, 0, 0)$; hence, the line of intersection of first two planes will be in the third plane, if

$$\Rightarrow \qquad g\,(hf - bg) + f\,(gh - af) + c\,(ab - h^2) = 0$$

$$abc + 2fgh - af^2 - bg^2 - ch^2 = 0$$

$$\Rightarrow \qquad \begin{vmatrix} a & h & g \\ h & b & f \\ g & f & c \end{vmatrix} = \Delta = 0.$$

From (1), we have

$$l^2 / (hf - bg)^2 = m^2 / (gh - af)^2 = n^2 / (ab - h^2)^2 \qquad \qquad ...(2)$$

To get the required form, we have

$$(hf - bg)^2 = h^2 f^2 + b^2 g^2 - 2hfbg$$

$$= h^2 f^2 + b^2 g^2 - b\,(af^2 + bg^2 + ch^2 - abc) \qquad \text{[From (2)]}$$

$$= (ab - h^2)\,(bc - f^2)$$

and $$\qquad (gh - af) = (ab - h^2)\,(ca - g^2)$$

Putting these values in (2), we get

$$\frac{l^2}{(ab - h^2)\,(bc - f^2)} = \frac{m^2}{(ab - h^2)\,(ca - g^2)} = \frac{n^2}{(ab - h^2)^2}$$

$$\Rightarrow \qquad \frac{l^2}{bc - f^2} = \frac{m^2}{ca - g^2} = \frac{n^2}{ab - h^2}$$

$$\Rightarrow \qquad \frac{l^2}{\partial\Delta/\partial a} = \frac{m^2}{\partial\Delta/\partial b} = \frac{n^2}{\partial\Delta/\partial c}$$

as $\Delta = abc + 2fgh - af^2 - bg^2 - ch^2$ and $\dfrac{\partial\Delta}{\partial a} = bc - f^2$, etc.

EXERCISES

1. Show that the following sets of planes intersect in lines :

(i) $4x + 3y + 2z + 7 = 0$, $2x + y - 4z + 1 = 0$, $x - 7z - 7 = 0$.

(ii) $2x + y + z + 4 = 0$, $y - z + 4 = 0$, $3x + 2y + z + 8 = 0$.

2. Show that the following sets of planes form triangular prisms :

  (i) $x + y + z + 3 = 0$, $3x + y - 2z + 2 = 0$, $2x + 4y + 7z - 7 = 0$.

  (ii) $x - z - 1 = 0$, $x + y - 2z - 3 = 0$, $x - 2y + z - 3 = 0$.

3. Examine the nature of intersection of the following sets of planes :

  (i) $4x - 5y - 2z - 2 = 0$, $5x - 4y + 2z + 2 = 0$, $2x + 2y + 8z - 1 = 0$.

  (ii) $2x + 3y - z - 2 = 0$, $3x + 3y + z - 4 = 0$, $x - y + 2z - 5 = 0$.

  (iii) $5x + 3y + 7z - 4 = 0$, $3x + 26y + 2z - 9 = 0$, $7x + 2y + 10z - 5 = 0$.

  (iv) $2x + 6y + 11 = 0$, $6x + 20y - 6z + 3 = 0$, $6y - 18z + 1 = 0$.

  [Ans. (i) prism, (ii) point, (iii) line, (iv) prism]

4. Show that the planes

$$bx - ay = n, \ cy - bz = l, \ az - cx = m,$$

will intersect in a line if

$$al + bm + cn = 0,$$

and the direction ratios of the line, then, are a, b, c.

5. Prove that the three planes

$$bz - cy = b - c, \ cx - az = c - a, \ ay - bx = a - b,$$

pass through one line (say l), and the three planes

$$(c - a) z - (a - b) y = b + c,$$
$$(a - b) x - (b - c) z = c + a,$$
$$(b - c) y - (c - a) z = a + b,$$

pass through another line (say l'). Show that the lines l and l' are at right angles to each other.

6. If the planes $x = y + z$, $y = az + x$, $z = x + ay$ pass through one line, find the value of a.

  [Ans. $a = -1$]

7. Prove that the planes $ny - mz = \lambda$, $lz - nx = \mu$ and $mx - ly = \nu$ have a common line if $l\lambda + m\mu + n\nu = 0$. Show also that the distance of the line from the origin is

$$\left(\frac{\lambda^2 + \mu^2 + \nu^2}{l^2 + m^2 + n^2} \right)^{1/2}$$

  (Kanpur, 1996)

OBJECTIVE QUESTIONS

I. Multiple Choice Questions

  Note : *For each of the following questions, four alternatives are given for the answer. Only one of them is correct. Choose the correct alternative.*

1. Any point on the line $\dfrac{x - \alpha}{l} = \dfrac{y - \beta}{m} = \dfrac{z - \gamma}{n}$ is given by :

  (a) (α, β, γ) (b) $(l\alpha, m\beta, n\gamma)$

  (c) $(\alpha + lr, \beta + mr, \gamma + nr)$ (d) None of these.

2. The equations to the x-axis are :

  (a) $\dfrac{x}{0} = \dfrac{y}{1} = \dfrac{z}{1}$ (b) $\dfrac{x}{2} = \dfrac{y}{0} = \dfrac{z}{1}$ (c) $\dfrac{x}{1} = \dfrac{y}{1} = \dfrac{z}{0}$ (d) $\dfrac{x}{1} = \dfrac{y}{0} = \dfrac{z}{0}$.

3. The number of arbitrary constants in the equations of a straight line is :

  (a) 6   (b) 4   (c) 2   (d) 0.

4. The value of λ for which the lines $\dfrac{x-1}{1} = \dfrac{y-2}{\lambda} = \dfrac{z+1}{-1}$ and $\dfrac{x+1}{-\lambda} = \dfrac{y+1}{2} = \dfrac{z-2}{1}$ are perpendicular to each other is :

(a) -1 (b) 1   (c) 0   (d) 2.

5. Equations of the line passing through $(-1, 2, -3)$ and perpendicular to the plane $2x + 3y + z + 5 = 0$ are :

(a) $\dfrac{x-1}{-1} = \dfrac{y+2}{1} = \dfrac{z-3}{-1}$ (b) $\dfrac{x+1}{-1} = \dfrac{y-2}{1} = \dfrac{z+3}{1}$

(c) $\dfrac{x+1}{2} = \dfrac{y-2}{3} = \dfrac{z+3}{1}$ (d) None of these.

6. The co-ordinates of the point of intersection of the line $\dfrac{x+1}{1} = \dfrac{y+3}{3} = \dfrac{z-2}{-2}$ with the plane $3x + 4y + 5z = 5$ are :

(a) $(-1, 2, -3)$ (b) $(1, 3, -2)$ (c) $(-1, -2, 3)$ (d) $(1, -3, 2)$.

7. Two lines, which do not lie in the same plane, are called :

(a) parallel   (b) intersecting   (c) coincident   (d) skew.

(Avadh, 2003)

8. The lines L_1 and L_2 intersect. The shortest distance between them is :

(a) positive   (b) negative   (c) zero   (d) infinity.

9. The direction cosines of two lines at right angles are l_1, m_1, n_1 and l_2, m_2, n_2. Then the dc's of a line perpendicular to both the given lines are :

(a) $m_1 n_2 - m_2 n_1,\ n_1 l_2 - n_2 l_1,\ l_1 m_2 - l_2 m_1$ (b) $l_1 + l_2,\ m_1 + m_2,\ n_1 + n_2$

(c) $l_1 - l_2,\ m_1 - m_2,\ n_1 - n_2$ (d) None of these.

10. The line $\dfrac{x-2}{3} = \dfrac{y-3}{4} = \dfrac{z-4}{5}$ is parallel to the plane :

(a) $2x + y - 2z = 0$ (b) $3x + 4y + 5z = 7$ (c) $x + y + z = 2$ (d) $2x + 3y + 4z = 0$.

11. The equations of line through the point $(1, 2, 3)$ parallel to line $\dfrac{x-4}{2} = \dfrac{y+1}{-3} = \dfrac{z+10}{8}$ are :

(a) $\dfrac{x-1}{2} = \dfrac{y-2}{-3} = \dfrac{z-3}{8}$ (b) $\dfrac{x-1}{1} = \dfrac{y-2}{2} = \dfrac{z-3}{3}$

(c) $\dfrac{x-4}{1} = \dfrac{y+1}{2} = \dfrac{z+10}{3}$ (d) None of these.

12. The equations of the line joining the points $(-2, 4, 2)$ and $(7, -2, 5)$ are :

(a) $\dfrac{x}{-2} = \dfrac{y}{4} = \dfrac{3}{2}$ (b) $\dfrac{x}{7} = \dfrac{y}{-2} = \dfrac{a}{5}$

(c) $\dfrac{x+2}{3} = \dfrac{x-4}{-2} = \dfrac{z-2}{1}$ (d) None of these.

13. The value of k so that the lines $\dfrac{x-1}{-3} = \dfrac{y-2}{2k} = \dfrac{z-3}{2},\ \dfrac{x-1}{3k} = \dfrac{y-5}{1} = \dfrac{z-6}{-5}$ are perpendicular to each other, is :

(a) $-10/7$ (b) $-8/7$ (c) $-6/7$ (d) 1.

14. The equations of the line through the point $(2, 3, -5)$ and equally inclined to the axes are :

(a) $x - 2 = y - 3 = z + 5$

(b) $\dfrac{x-1}{2} = \dfrac{y-1}{3} = \dfrac{z-1}{-5}$

(c) $\dfrac{x}{2} = \dfrac{y}{3} = \dfrac{z}{-5}$

(d) None of these.

15. The lines $\dfrac{x-1}{1} = \dfrac{y-2}{2} = \dfrac{z-3}{3}$ and $\dfrac{x}{2} = \dfrac{y+2}{2} = \dfrac{z-3}{-2}$ are :

(a) parallel　　　(b) skew　　　(c) intersecting　　　(d) at right angles.

16. The lines $\dfrac{x-1}{2} = \dfrac{y-1}{3} = \dfrac{z-3}{0}$ and $\dfrac{x-2}{0} = \dfrac{y-3}{0} = \dfrac{z-4}{1}$ are :

(a) parallel　　　(b) skew　　　(c) coincident　　　(d) perpendicular.

17. The length of the perpendicular drawn from the point $(5, 4, -1)$ on the line $\dfrac{x-1}{2} = \dfrac{y}{9} = \dfrac{z}{5}$ is :

(a) $\sqrt{110/2109}$　　　(b) $(2109/110)$　　　(c) $\sqrt{2109/110}$　　　(d) 54.

18. The points on the line $\dfrac{x+1}{1} = \dfrac{y+3}{3} = \dfrac{z-2}{-2}$ distant $\sqrt{14}$ from the point in which the line meets the plane $3x + 4y + 5z - 5 = 0$ are :

(a) $(0, 0, 0), (2, -4, 6)$

(b) $(0, 0, 0), (3, -4, -5)$

(c) $(0, 0, 0), (2, 6, -4)$

(d) $(2, 6, -4), (3, -4, -5)$.

19. The co-ordinates of the foot of the perpendicular from the point $(1, 3, 4)$ upon the plane $2x - y + z = 0$ are :

(a) $(1, 1, -4)$　　　(b) $(4, -3, 1)$　　　(c) $(1, -3, 4)$　　　(d) $(-1, 4, 3)$.

20. The distance of the point $(-1, -5, 10)$ from the point of intersection of the line $\dfrac{1}{3}(x - 2) = \dfrac{1}{4}(y + 1) = \dfrac{1}{12}(z - 2)$ and the plane $x - y + z = 5$ is :

(a) $(14/5)$　　　(b) 11　　　(c) 13　　　(d) 15.

21. The angle between the line $\dfrac{x+1}{3} = \dfrac{y-1}{2} = \dfrac{z-2}{4}$ and the plane $2x = y - 3z - 4 = 0$ is :

(a) $\cos^{-1}(-4/\sqrt{406})$

(b) $\sin^{-1}(-4/\sqrt{406})$

(c) $30°$

(d) None of these.

22. The line $\dfrac{x+1}{-1} = \dfrac{y-12}{5} = \dfrac{z-7}{2}$ cuts the surface $11x^2 - 5y^2 + z^2 = 0$ in the points :

(a) $(1, 1, 1)$ and $(1, 2, 3)$

(b) $(1, -1, 2)$ and $(1, 2, 4)$

(c) $(1, 2, 3)$ and $(2, -3, 1)$

(d) None of these.

23. The angle between the lines $x = 1, y = 2$ and $y = -1$ and $z = 0$ is :

(a) $90°$　　　(b) $30°$　　　(c) $60°$　　　(d) $0°$.

(Avadh, 2005)

24. The plane $x - 2y + z - 6 = 0$ and the line $\dfrac{x}{1} = \dfrac{y}{2} = \dfrac{z}{3}$ are related as :

(a) parallel to the plane

(b) normal to the plane

(c) lies in the plane

(d) None of these.

25. The straight line passing through (a, b, c) and parallel to the z-axis is :

(a) $\dfrac{x-a}{1} = \dfrac{y-b}{0} = \dfrac{z-c}{0}$ (b) $\dfrac{x-a}{0} = \dfrac{y-b}{0} = \dfrac{z-c}{1}$

(c) $\dfrac{x-a}{0} = \dfrac{y-b}{1} = \dfrac{z-c}{1}$ (d) $\dfrac{x-a}{1} = \dfrac{y-b}{1} = \dfrac{z-c}{0}$.

26. The angle between the lines $\dfrac{x-2}{3} = \dfrac{y+1}{-2}, z = 2$ and $\dfrac{x-1}{1} = \dfrac{2y+3}{3} = \dfrac{z+5}{5}$ is :

(a) $\pi/2$ (b) $\pi/3$ (c) $\pi/6$ (d) None of these.

(*Kanpur, 2001*)

27. The lines $\dfrac{x-1}{2} = \dfrac{y-2}{4} = \dfrac{z-2}{7}$ and $\dfrac{x-1}{4} = \dfrac{y-2}{5} = \dfrac{z-3}{7}$ are :

(a) parallel   (b) intersecting   (c) skew   (d) perpendicular.

28. The line $\dfrac{x-2}{1} = \dfrac{y-3}{2} = \dfrac{z-4}{0}$ is :

(a) parallel to x-axis   (b) parallel to y-axis

(c) parallel to z-axis   (d) lies in a plane parallel to xy-plane.

29. The lines $\dfrac{x}{1} = \dfrac{y}{2} = \dfrac{z}{3}$ and $\dfrac{x-1}{-2} = \dfrac{y-2}{-4} = \dfrac{z-3}{-6}$ are :

(a) parallel   (b) intersecting   (c) skew   (d) coincident.

(*Avadh, 2005*)

30. The equations of the projection of the line $\dfrac{x-1}{2} = \dfrac{y-2}{1} = \dfrac{z-3}{3}$ on the plane $x + y + z - 1 = 0$ are :

(a) $x + y + z - 1 = 0 = 2x - y - z + 3$ (b) $x + y - z - 1 = 0 = x + 2y - z - 3$

(c) $2x - y + 3z - 1 = 0 = x + y + z + 1$ (d) $x + 2y - 3z = 0 = x + y + z + 1$.

31. The condition that the two straight lines $x = mz + a$, $y = nz + b$ and $x = m'z + a'$, $y = n'z + b'$ should intersect is :

(a) $(a - a')(m - m') + (b - b')(n - n') = 0$

(b) $(a - a')(m - m') - (b - b')(n - n') = 0$

(c) $(a - a')(n - n') + (b - b')(m - m') = 0$

(d) $(a - a')(n - n') - (b - b')(m - m') = 0$.

32. The distance of the point $(3, 8, 2)$ from the line $\dfrac{x-1}{2} = \dfrac{y-3}{4} = \dfrac{z-2}{3}$ measured parallel to the plane $3x + 2y - 2z + 5 = 0$ is :

(a) 2   (b) 3   (c) 5   (d) None of these.

33. The straight line through (a, b, c) and parallel to x-axis is :

(a) $\dfrac{x-a}{1} = \dfrac{y-b}{0} = \dfrac{z-c}{0}$ (b) $\dfrac{x-a}{0} = \dfrac{y-b}{1} = \dfrac{z-c}{0}$

(c) $\dfrac{x-a}{0} = \dfrac{y-b}{0} = \dfrac{z-c}{1}$ (d) $\dfrac{x-a}{1} = \dfrac{y-b}{1} = \dfrac{z-c}{1}$.

(*Garhwal, 2004; Avadh, 2004*)

34. The angle between the lines in which the plane $8x - 11y + 2z = 0$ meets the planes $5x - 13y + 3z + 2 = 0$, $3x - 7y - 5z - 1 = 0$ is :

(a) $\cos^{-1}(8/\sqrt{17})$ (b) $\cos^{-1}(2/3)$ (c) $\cos^{-1}(1/3)$ (d) $\pi/2$.

35. The line $\dfrac{x+3}{3} = \dfrac{y-2}{-2} = \dfrac{z+1}{1}$ and the plane $4x + 5y + 3z - 5 = 0$ intersect at a point :

   (a) $(3, 1, -2)$ (b) $(3, -2, 1)$ (c) $(2, -1, 3)$ (d) $(-1, -2, -3)$.

36. For every point (x, y, z) on x-axis :

   (a) $y = 0, z = 0$ (b) $x = 0, z = 0$ (c) $x = 0, y = 0$ (d) $x = 0$.

37. The shortest distance between the line

$$\frac{x-1}{2} = \frac{y-2}{3} = \frac{z-3}{4} \text{ and } \frac{x-2}{3} = \frac{y-4}{4} = \frac{z-5}{4}$$

is :

   (a) $1/6$ (b) $(1/\sqrt{6})$ (c) $(1/\sqrt{3})$ (d) $1/3$.

   (Avadh, 2003)

38. Equation of the straight line $3x + 2y - z - 4 = 0$; $4x + y - 2z + 3 = 0$ in the symmetrical form is :

   (a) $\dfrac{x-2}{3} = \dfrac{y-5}{2} = \dfrac{z}{5}$ (b) $\dfrac{x+2}{3} = \dfrac{y-5}{-2} = \dfrac{z}{5}$

   (c) $\dfrac{x+2}{3} = \dfrac{y-5}{2} = \dfrac{z}{5}$ (d) None of these.

39. Length of the shortest distance between the lines

$$\frac{x-3}{3} = \frac{y-8}{-1} = \frac{z-3}{1} \text{ and } \frac{x+3}{-3} = \frac{y+7}{2} = \frac{z-6}{4}$$

is :

   (a) $3\sqrt{30}$ (b) $3/\sqrt{30}$ (c) $\sqrt{30}$ (d) None of these.

40. Equation of the line passing through the point $(1, 2, 3)$ and parallel to the line $\dfrac{x-6}{12} = \dfrac{y-2}{4} = \dfrac{z+7}{5}$ is given by :

   (a) $\dfrac{x+1}{12} = \dfrac{y+2}{4} = \dfrac{z+3}{5}$

   (b) $\dfrac{x-1}{l} = \dfrac{y-2}{m} = \dfrac{z-3}{n}$; where $12l + 4m + 5n = 0$

   (c) $\dfrac{x-1}{12} = \dfrac{y-2}{4} = \dfrac{z-3}{5}$

   (d) None of these.

41. Let G be the centroid of the triangle formed by the points $(1, 2, 0)$, $(2, 1, 1)$ $(0, 0, 2)$. Then equation of the line OG is given by :

   (a) $x = y = z$ (b) $\dfrac{x-1}{1} = \dfrac{y}{1} = \dfrac{z}{1}$

   (c) $\dfrac{x-1}{1} = \dfrac{y-1}{1} = \dfrac{z-1}{0}$ (d) None of these.

42. Distance of the point $(0, 1, 2)$ from the plane $2x - y + z + 3$ measured parallel to the line $\dfrac{x}{1} = \dfrac{y}{-1} = \dfrac{z}{-1}$ is equal to :

   (a) 0 (b) $3\sqrt{3}$ (c) $\sqrt{3}$ (d) None of these.

43. The distance of the point of intersection of the line $\dfrac{x-3}{2} = \dfrac{y-4}{2} = \dfrac{z-5}{2}$ and the

plane $x + y + z = 17$, from the point $(3, 4, 5)$ is given by :

(a) 3   (b) 3/2   (c) $\sqrt{3}$ (d) None of these.

44. The point in which the line $\dfrac{x}{1} = \dfrac{y}{-1} = \dfrac{z}{1}$ cuts the sphere $x^2 + y^2 + z^2 = 3$ in the points :

(a) $(1, -1, 1), (-1, 1, -1)$

(b) $(-1, 1, 1), (1, -1, -1)$

(c) $(1/\sqrt{3}, -1/\sqrt{3}, 1/\sqrt{3}); (-1/\sqrt{3}, 1/\sqrt{3}, -1/\sqrt{3})$

(d) None of these.

45. The image of the point $(1, 3, 4)$ w.r.t. the plane $2x - y + z + 3 = 0$ is :

(a) $(-1, 4, 3)$ (b) $(-3, 5, 2)$ (c) $(1, 3, 4)$ (d) None of these.

(Avadh, 2003)

46. The equation of the plane through the line $3x - 4y + 5z = 10$, $2x + 2y - 3z = 4$ and parallel to the line $x = 2y = 3z$ is :

(a) $x - 20y + 27z = 14$ (b) $x + 4y + 27z = 14$

(c) $x - 20y + 3z = 14$ (d) None of these.

ANSWERS

1. (c)	**2.** (d)	**3.** (b)	**4.** (b)	**5.** (c)	**6.** (b)	**7.** (d)	**8.** (c)
9. (a)	**10.** (b)	**11.** (b)	**12.** (c)	**13.** (a)	**14.** (a)	**15.** (d)	**16.** (d)
17. (c)	**18.** (c)	**19.** (d)	**20.** (c)	**21.** (b)	**22.** (c)	**23.** (a)	**24.** (a)
25. (b)	**26.** (d)	**27.** (b)	**28.** (d)	**29.** (a)	**30.** (a)	**31.** (d)	**32.** (d)
33. (a)	**34.** (c)	**35.** (d)	**36.** (b)	**37.** (a)	**38.** (b)	**39.** (a)	
40. (a)	**41.** (a)	**42.** (a)	**43.** (c)	**44.** (b)	**45.** (c)	**46.** (a)	

II. Fill in the Blanks

Note : *Fill in the blanks "......." so that the following statements are complete and correct.*

1. The equations of the straight line passing through a given point (x_1, y_1, z_1) and having direction cosines l, m, n are ....

2. The equations of the straight line passing through the points (x_1, y_1, z_1) and (x_2, y_2, z_2) are ....   *(Meerut, 2001)*

3. The direction cosines of the straight line $\dfrac{x+1}{2} = \dfrac{y-3}{1} = \dfrac{z-5}{-2}$ are ......

4. The co-ordinates of the two points on the straight line $\dfrac{x-2}{6} = \dfrac{y+3}{2} = \dfrac{z+1}{3}$ which are at a distance .14 from the point $(2, -3, -1)$ are ....

5. The equations of the straight line passing through the point $(2, -5, -3)$ and parallel to the straight line $\dfrac{x-5}{-1} = \dfrac{y+2}{3} = \dfrac{z-4}{5}$ are ....

6. The equations of the straight line parallel to $\dfrac{x-1}{2} = \dfrac{y-2}{3} = \dfrac{z}{4}$ are

$$\dfrac{x-2}{\cdots} = \dfrac{y-2}{\cdots} = \dfrac{z}{8}.$$

(Meerut, 2001)

7. The direction cosines of the straight line $y = 0$, $z = 0$ are ..... .

8. The equations of the straight line $x - y = 0$, $z = 1$ in symmetrical form are ..... .

9. The direction cosines l, m, n of the straight line $3x + 2y - 5z = 0 = 4x + 2y - 3z + 3$ satisfy the equations ..... .

10. The straight line $3x + 2y - z - 4 = 0$, $4x + y - 2z + 3 = 0$ meets the xy-plane at the point ..... .

11. The line $\dfrac{x}{l} = \dfrac{y}{m} = \dfrac{z}{n}$ is perpendicular to the plane $ax + by + cz + d = 0$, if ..... .

(Meerut, 2001)

12. The conditions for the line $\dfrac{x - x_1}{l} = \dfrac{y - y_1}{m} = \dfrac{z - z_1}{n}$ to be parallel to the plane $ax + by + cz + d = 0$ but not lying in it are ..... .

13. The angle between the straight line $\dfrac{x - 3}{1} = \dfrac{y + 4}{-1} = \dfrac{z}{0}$ and the plane $y - z + 2 = 0$ is ..... .

14. The foot of perpendicular from $(2, 3, 4)$ to the plane $x + y - z + 4 = 0$ is ..... .

15. The S.D. between the lines $x + a = 2y = -12z$ and $x = y + 2a = 6z - 6a$ is ..... .

16. Prove that the planes $x = cy + bz$, $y = az + cx$, $z = bx + ay$ pass through one line if ..... .

17. The planes $2x - 3y - 7z = 0$, $2x - 14y - 13z = 0$, $8x - 31y - 33z = 0$ pass through one ..... .

18. The distance of the point (a, b, c) from x-axis is ..... .   *(Kanpur, 2001)*

19. The straight lines $\dfrac{x - x_1}{l_1} = \dfrac{y - y_1}{m_1} = \dfrac{z - z_1}{n_1}$ and $\dfrac{x - x_2}{l_2} = \dfrac{y - y_2}{m_2} = \dfrac{z - z_2}{n_2}$ are coplanar if ..... .

20. The shortest distance between two intersecting lines is ..... .

21. Two lines are ..... if the shortest distance between them vanishes.

22. The shortest distance between two skew-lines is ..... to both the lines.

ANSWERS

1. $\dfrac{x - x_1}{l} = \dfrac{y - y_1}{m} = \dfrac{z - z_1}{n}$;   2. $\dfrac{x - x_1}{x_2 - x_1} = \dfrac{y - y_1}{y_2 - y_1} = \dfrac{z - z_1}{z_2 - z_1}$;   3. $\dfrac{2}{3}, \dfrac{1}{3}, \dfrac{-2}{3}$;

4. $(14, 15)$ and $(-10, -7, -7)$;   5. $\dfrac{x - 2}{-1} = \dfrac{y + 5}{3} = \dfrac{z + 3}{5}$;   6. $4, 6$;

7. $1, 0, 0$;   8. $\dfrac{x - 0}{1} = \dfrac{y - 0}{1} = \dfrac{z - 1}{0}$;

9. $3l + 2m - 5n = 0$, $4l + 2m - 3n = 0$;   10. $(-2, 5, 0)$;

11. $\dfrac{a}{l} = \dfrac{b}{m} = \dfrac{c}{n}$;   12. $al + bm + cn = 0$, $ax_1 + by_1 + cz_1 + d \neq 0$;

13. $\pi/6$;   14. $\left(\dfrac{1}{3}, \dfrac{4}{3}, \dfrac{17}{3} \right)$;   15. $2a$;

16. $a^2 + b^2 + c^2 + 2abc = 1$;   17. line;   18. $\sqrt{b^2 + c^2}$;

19. $\begin{vmatrix} x_2 - x_1 & y_2 - y_1 & z_2 - z_1 \\ l_1 & m_1 & n_1 \\ l_2 & m_2 & n_2 \end{vmatrix} = 0;$ 20. zero;

21. coplanar;   22. perpendicular.

III. True/False Statements

Note : *Write 'T' for true and 'F' for false statements.*

1. The symmetric form of the equations of a line given by $x = ay + b$, $z = cy + d$ is
   $$\frac{x+b}{a} = \frac{y}{1} = \frac{z-d}{c}.$$

2. The line $\frac{x-\alpha}{l} = \frac{y-\beta}{m} = \frac{z-\gamma}{n}$ will be parallel to the plane $ax + by + cz + d = 0$ if
   $al + bm + cn = 0$ and $a\alpha + b\beta + c\gamma + d = 0$.

3. The planes $x = cy + bz$, $y = az + cx$, $z = bx + ay$ pass through one line if
   $$a^2 + b^2 + c^2 = 1.$$

4. The locus of a point whose distance from x-axis is twice its distance from the yz-plane
   is $4x^2 = y^2 + z^2$.

5. The S.D. between the lines $x + a = 2y = -12z$ and $x = y + 2a = 6z - 2a$ is $2a$.

6. The straight line $\frac{x+1}{1} = \frac{y-2}{3} = \frac{z+4}{-5}$ is parallel to the plane $6x + 8y + 6z = 7$.

7. The straight line $\frac{x-2}{3} = \frac{y+9}{5} = \frac{z-6}{1}$ is perpendicular to the plane $6x + 10y - 2z = 9$.

8. The straight line $\frac{x-2}{5} = \frac{y-1}{6} = \frac{z+1}{4}$ lies in the plane $2x + 3y - 7z = 5$.

9. The lines $\frac{x+1}{3} = \frac{y+3}{5} = \frac{z+5}{7}$ and $\frac{x-2}{1} = \frac{y-4}{4} = \frac{z-6}{7}$ are coplanar.

10. Two parallel straight lines are always coplanar.

11. If two straight lines intersect, they are always coplanar.

12. Two non-coplanar lines are always intersecting lines.

13. The lines $x = ay + b$, $z = cy + d$ and $x = a'y + b'$, $z = c'y + d'$ are perpendicular if
    $aa' + cc' + 1 = 0$.

14. Straight line which is perpendicular to each of the two skew-lines is called the line of
    shortest distance.

15. The equation of a plane through the lines $(x - \alpha_1)/l_1 = (y - \beta_1)/m_1 = (z - \gamma_1)/n_1$ and
    parallel to the line $(x - \alpha_2)/l_2 = (y - \beta_2)/m_2 = (z - \gamma_2)/n_2$ is
    $$\begin{vmatrix} x - \alpha_1 & y - \beta_1 & z - \gamma_1 \\ l_1 & m_1 & n_1 \\ l_2 & m_2 & n_2 \end{vmatrix} = 0.$$

ANSWERS

1. T	2. F	3. F	4. T	5. T	6. T	7. F	8. F
9. T	10. T	11. T	12. F	13. T	14. T	15. T.	

4

Interpretation of Equations – Loci

4.1. INTRODUCTION

In Chapters 2 and 3, it has been shown that an equation of the first degree in x, y, z represents a plane and two such equations *together* represent a straight line.

We now consider the nature of the geometrical loci represented by equations of any degree.

4.2. EQUATION TO A SURFACE

Locus of a variable point with its current co-ordinates x, y, z connected by a single equation $f(x, y, z) = 0$, is a surface.

Consider *any* point $(\alpha, \beta, 0)$ on the XY plane. The lines through this point drawn parallel to the Z-axis, *viz.*, $x = \alpha$, $y = \beta$ meets the locus in points whose z-co-ordinates are given by the roots of the equation $f(\alpha, \beta, z) = 0$.

As this equation has a *finite* number of roots, the number of points of the locus on *every* such line is also finite. Hence, the locus, which is the set of all such points for different values of α, β, must be a surface and not a solid.

Thus, the equation $f(x, y, z) = 0$ represents a surface.

4.2.1. Equations Free from One Variable. Cylinders

Locus of the equation $f(x, y) = 0$ is a cylinder with its generators parallel to Z-axis.

Consider the curve on the XY plane, whose two-dimensional equation is $f(x, y) = 0$. Let (α, β) be a point on it so that $f(\alpha, \beta) = 0$.

Any point (α, β, z) on the line through this point, drawn parallel to the axis OZ, therefore, satisfies the equation $f(x, y) = 0$ and hence every point on the line lies on its locus.

Thus, the locus is the set of lines, parallel to the axis OZ drawn through the points on the curve and is, therefore, a cylindrical surface.

Similarly, the loci of the equations

$$f(y, z) = 0 \text{ and } f(z, x) = 0$$

are cylinders with generators parallel to the X-axis and the Y-axis respectively.

Ex. What surface are represented by the equation

(i) $x^2 + y^2 = a^2$ (ii) $x^2/a^2 + y^2/b^2 = 1$ (iii) $y^2 = 4ax$

(iv) $xy = c^2$ (v) $x^2/a^2 - y^2/b^2 = 1$ (vi) $x^2 = 4ay$

4.2.2. Equations Containing Only One Variable

Locus of the equation $f(x) = 0$ is a ·system of planes parallel to the YZ plane.

If $\alpha_1, \alpha_2, \alpha_3, \ldots, \alpha_n$ be the roots of the equation

$$f(x) = 0,$$

then this equation is equivalent to

$$(x - \alpha_1) (x - \alpha_2) \ ..... \ (x - \alpha_n) = 0$$

and, therefore, represents the planes

$$x = \alpha_1, \ x = \alpha_2, \ ....., \ x = \alpha_n$$

which are parallel to the *YZ* plane.

Similarly the loci of the equations $f(y) = 0$ and $f(z) = 0$, are systems of planes respectively parallel to the *ZX* and *XY* planes.

4.3. EQUATIONS TO A CURVE

Two equations

$$f(x, y, z) = 0, \ \phi(x, y, z) = 0$$

together represent a curve.

The points, whose co-ordinates satisfy these equations *simultaneously*, are common to the two surfaces separately represented by them and, therefore, lie on their curve of intersection.

Hence, the locus of a point whose current co-ordinates are connected by *two* equations is a curve.

EXERCISES

1. Describe the loci represented by

   (*i*) $x^2/a^2 + y^2/b^2 = 1, z = 0$ (*ii*) $y^2 = ax, z = c$

   (*iii*) $x^2 + y^2 = a^2, z^2 = c^2$ (*iv*) $y^2 = ax, z^2 = c^2$

2. Show that the two curves

   $$f(x, y, z) = 0, \ \varphi(x, y, z) = 0;$$

   $$f(x, y, z) - \lambda\varphi(x, y, z) = 0, f(x, y, z) - \mu\varphi(x, y, z) = 0$$

   are the same.

3. Find the equations to the parabola whose focus is the point $(1, 2, 3)$ and directrix the line $x = y = z$.

   [**Ans.** $x^2 + y^2 + z^2 + 2xy + 2yz + 2xz - 6x - 12y - 18z + 42 = 0 = x - 2y + z$]

4.4. SURFACES GENERATED BY STRAIGHT LINES. RULED SURFACES

A straight line, subjected to *three* conditions only, can take up an infinite number of positions. The locus of these lines is called a *Ruled* surface.

4.4.1. *To determine the ruled surface generated by a straight line intersecting three given lines*

$$u_1 = 0 = v_1; \ u_2 = 0 = v_2; \ u_3 = 0 = v_3,$$

where $u_r \equiv a_r x + b_r y + c_r z + d_r, \ v_r = a'_r x + b'_r y + c'_r z + d'_r.$

The straight line

$$u_1 + \lambda_1 v_1 = 0 = u_2 + \lambda_2 v_2 \qquad \qquad ...(i)$$

intersects the first two lines for all values of λ_1, λ_2.   (Note page 76)

The condition of intersection of the line (*i*) with the third given line is a relation between λ_1, λ_2, say

$$f(\lambda_1 \cdot \lambda_2) = 0. \qquad \qquad ...(ii)$$

The required ruled surface is, then, obtained by eliminating λ_1, λ_2 between (*i*) and (*ii*).

Another method will be indicated in the examples below.

4.4.2. Condition for the Intersection of a Straight Line and a Curve

If a straight line intersects a given curve, the co-ordinates of the points of intersection satisfy the four equations (two of the straight line and two of the curve) so that the four equations are simultaneously valid, *i.e.*, consistent. The condition for consistency is obtained by eliminating x, y, z from the four equations.

EXAMPLES

1. *Find the condition for the line*

$$\frac{x - \alpha}{l} = \frac{y - \beta}{m} = \frac{z - \gamma}{n} \qquad \qquad ...(i)$$

to intersect the curve

$$xy = c^2;\ z = 0. \qquad \qquad ...(ii)$$

Sol. Eliminating x, y, z from (i) and (ii), we obtain

$$\left(\alpha - \frac{l\gamma}{n} \right)\left(\beta - \frac{m\gamma}{n} \right) = c^2$$

which is the required condition.

2. *Find the ruled surface generated by the line which intersects the three lines*

$$y = b,\ z = -c;\ z = c,\ x = -a;\ x = a,\ y = -b.$$

Sol. First Method. The line

$$y - b + \lambda_1 (z + c) = 0,\ z - c + \lambda_2 (x + a) = 0, \qquad \qquad ...(i)$$

which intersects the first two of the given lines, will also intersect the third,

if
$$c - 2a\lambda_2 = \frac{2b}{\lambda_1} - c \ \Leftrightarrow\ c = \frac{b}{\lambda_1} + a\lambda_2 \qquad \qquad ...(ii)$$

Eliminating λ_1, λ_2 from (i) and (ii), we obtain

$$c = -\frac{b(z + c)}{y - b} - a\,\frac{z - c}{x + a},$$

$\Leftrightarrow \qquad c (x + a) (y - b) + a (z - c) (y - b) + b (x + a) (z + c) = 0.$

$\Leftrightarrow \qquad ayz + bzx + cxy + abc = 0,$

which is the required locus.

Second Method. Let (α, β, γ) be a point on the required locus and let the equation of the line which passes through the point (α, β, γ) and which intersects the three given lines be

$$\frac{x - \alpha}{l} = \frac{y - \beta}{m} = \frac{z - \gamma}{n}.$$

This line will intersect the three given lines, if we have

$$\frac{b - \beta}{l} = -\frac{c + \gamma}{n},$$

$$\frac{c - \gamma}{n} = -\frac{a + \alpha}{l}, \qquad \qquad ...(iii)$$

and
$$\frac{a - \alpha}{l} = -\frac{b + \beta}{m}. \qquad \qquad ...(iv)$$

Eliminating l, m, n between (iii) and (iv), we have

$$(a - \alpha) (b - \beta) (c - \gamma) + (a + \alpha) (b + \beta) (c + \gamma) = 0.$$

As (α, β, γ) is any point on the variable line, the required locus is

$$(a - x)(b - y)(c - z) + (a + x)(b + y)(c + z) = 0,$$

$\Rightarrow \qquad ayz + bzx + cxy + abc = 0.$

3. *Two skew lines are given by the equations*

$$ax + by = z + c = 0; \quad ax - by = z - c = 0,$$

show that the lines which are perpendicular to the line with direction cosines proportional to l, m, n, and which meet the given lines generate the surface

$$abz(lx + my + nz) = c(a^2mx + b^2ly + abcn).$$

Sol. Let (α, β, γ) be a point on the locus and let

$$\frac{x - \alpha}{\lambda} = \frac{y - \beta}{\mu} = \frac{z - \gamma}{\nu} \qquad \qquad ...(i)$$

be the line through (α, β, γ) which satisfies the given condition.

This line will be perpendicular to the line with direction cosines proportional to l, m, n if

$$l\lambda + m\mu + n\nu = 0 \qquad \qquad ...(ii)$$

and will intersect the given lines if

$$a\lambda(\gamma + c) + b\mu(\gamma + c) - \nu(a\alpha + b\beta) = 0, \qquad ...(iii)$$

and $\qquad a\lambda(\gamma - c) - b\mu(\gamma - c) - \nu(a\alpha - b\beta) = 0. \qquad ...(iv)$

Eliminating λ, μ, ν from $(ii), (iii)$ and (iv), we have

$$\begin{vmatrix} a(\gamma - c) & -b(\gamma - c) & a\alpha - b\beta \\ a(\gamma + c) & b(\gamma + c) & a\alpha + b\beta \\ l & m & -n \end{vmatrix} = 0,$$

$\Leftrightarrow \qquad l(ab\alpha\gamma - b^2c\beta) - m(ab\beta\gamma - a^2c\alpha) + nab(\gamma^2 - c^2) = 0.$

The required locus, therefore, is,

$$abz(lx + my + nz) = c(a^2mx + b^2ly + abcn).$$

4. *Find the ruled surface generated by the line which moves parallel to the ZX plane and meets the curves*

$$xy = c^2, \ z = 0; \quad y^2 = 4cz, \ x = 0.$$

Verify that the locus contains the curves.

Sol. Let (α, β, γ) be a point on the locus and let

$$\frac{x - \alpha}{l} = \frac{y - \beta}{m} = \frac{z - \gamma}{n} \qquad \qquad ...(i)$$

be the line through (α, β, γ) satisfying the given condition.

The line will intersect the two given curves

if $\qquad \left(\alpha - \frac{l\gamma}{n}\right)\left(\beta - \frac{m\gamma}{n}\right) = c^2 \qquad \qquad ...(ii)$

and $\qquad \left(\beta - \frac{\alpha m}{l}\right)^2 = 4c\left(\gamma - \frac{\alpha n}{l}\right). \qquad \qquad ...(iii)$

The line (i) will be parallel to the ZX plane

if $\qquad\qquad\qquad m = 0. \qquad\qquad\qquad (iv)$

Eliminating l, m, n from (ii), (iii) and (iv), we obtain

$$(c^2 - \alpha\beta)(\beta^2 - 4c\gamma) = 4c\alpha\beta\gamma,$$

$$\Rightarrow \qquad y^2(c^2 - xy) = 4c^2z$$

is the equation of the required ruled surface.

Putting x and z separately equal to zero in this equation we get $y^2 = 4cz$ and $xy = c^2$ and hence the verification.

5. *Find the equation of the surface generated by lines which pass through a fixed point* (α, β, γ) *and intersect the curve*

$$ax^2 + by^2 = 1, z = 0.$$

Sol. Let

$$\frac{x - \alpha}{l} = \frac{y - \beta}{m} = \frac{z - \gamma}{n} \qquad \qquad \text{...(i)}$$

be the line through the given point (α, β, γ) satisfying the given condition.

The line will intersect the given curve

if $\qquad\qquad a\left(\alpha - \dfrac{l\gamma}{n}\right)^2 + b\left(\beta - \dfrac{m\gamma}{n}\right)^2 = 1.$ $\qquad\qquad$ ...(ii)

Eliminating l, m, n between (i) and (ii), we get

$$a\left(\alpha - \gamma\frac{x - \alpha}{z - \gamma}\right)^2 + b\left(\beta - \gamma\frac{y - \beta}{z - \gamma}\right)^2 = 1.$$

$$\Rightarrow \quad a(\alpha z - \gamma x)^2 + b(\beta z - \gamma y)^2 = (z - \gamma)^2,$$

which is the required equation to the surface.

6. *A variable line intersects the x-axis and curve* $x = y$, $y^2 = cz$ *and is parallel to the plane* $x = 0$. *Prove that it generates the paraboloid* $xy = cz$.　　　　　(*Bundelkhand, 1995*)

Sol. The plane parallel to the plane $x = 0$ is

$$x = \lambda, \qquad\qquad \text{...(i)}$$

And the plane containing x-axis, *i.e.*, $y = 0$, $z = 0$ is

$$y = \mu z \qquad\qquad \text{...(ii)}$$

∴　The line which intersects the x-axis and is parallel to the plane $x = 0$ is the line of intersection of (i) and (ii).

If this meets the curve $x = y$, $y^2 = cz$, then with the help of (i) and (ii), we have

$$x = \lambda = y$$

and $\qquad\qquad \mu = \dfrac{y}{z} = \dfrac{cy}{cz} = \dfrac{cy}{y^2}$ $\qquad\qquad$ [from $y^2 = cz$]

or $\qquad\qquad \mu = \dfrac{c}{y} = \dfrac{c}{\lambda} \Rightarrow \lambda\mu = c$ $\qquad\qquad$ ...(iii)

The required locus is obtained by eliminating λ and μ from (i), (ii) and (iii) and is

$$c = \lambda\mu = x\cdot(y/z) \Rightarrow xy = cz.$$

7. *Prove that the locus of a variable line which intersects the three given lines* $y = mx$, $z = c$; $y = -mx$, $z = -c$; $y = z$, $mx = -c$ *is the surface* $y^2 - m^2x^2 = z^2 - c^2$.　　　(*Kanpur, 1997*)

Sol. The equation of the plane through the line $y = mx$, $z = c$ is

$$(y - mx) + \lambda_1(z - c) = 0 \qquad\qquad \text{...(i)}$$

The equation of the plane through the line $y = - mx$, $z = - c$ is,

$$(y + mx) + \lambda_2 (z + c) = 0 \qquad \qquad ...(ii)$$

Now any line intersecting the first two given lines is given by plane (i) and (ii). The above two planes intersect in a line and as it meets the third line $y = z$, $mx = - c$, so putting $mx = - c$ and $z = y$ in (i) and (ii), we get

$$(y + c) + \lambda_1 (y - c) = 0 \text{ and } (y - c) + \lambda_2 (y + c) = 0$$

$$\Rightarrow \qquad \qquad \left(\frac{y + c}{y - c}\right) = - \lambda_1 \text{ and } \left(\frac{y + c}{y - c}\right) = - \frac{1}{\lambda_2}$$

$$\Rightarrow \qquad \qquad - \lambda_1 = -1/\lambda_2$$

$$\Rightarrow \qquad \qquad \lambda_1 \lambda_2 = 1 \qquad \qquad ...(iii)$$

Eliminating λ_1 and λ_2 between (i), (ii) and (iii), we get

$$\left(\frac{y - mx}{z - c}\right)\left(\frac{y + mx}{z + c}\right) = 1 \Rightarrow y^2 - m^2 x^2 = z^2 - c^2.$$

EXERCISES

1. Prove that the lines which intersect the lines

$$y = mx, z = c; \ y = - mx; \ z = - c$$

and are perpendicular to the X-axis lie on the surface

$$mxz = cy. \qquad \qquad (Garhwal \ 2006)$$

2. Find the ruled surface generated by the lines which are parallel to the plane

$$x + y = 0$$

and which intersect the line $x - y = 0 = z$ and the curve

$$x^2 = 2az, y = 0. \qquad \qquad \textbf{[Ans.} \ x^2 - y^2 = 2az]$$

3. Find the ruled surface generated by straight lines which intersect the lines $y = 0$, $z = c$; $x = 0$, $z = - c$; and are parallel to the plane

$$lx + my + nz = 0. \qquad \textbf{[Ans.} \ lx/(z + c) + my/(z - c) + n = 0]$$

4. Show that the equation to the surface generated by straight lines intersecting the three lines

$$x = 4a, y + 2z = 0; \ x + 4a = 0, y = 2z; \ y = 4a, x = 2z,$$

is

$$x^2 + y^2 - 4z^2 = 16a^2.$$

5. Show that the locus of the line intersecting the three lines

$$y - z = 1, x = 0; \ z - x = 1, y = 0; \ x - y = 1, z = 0$$

is

$$x^2 + y^2 + z^2 - 2xy - 2yz - 2zx = 1.$$

6. Obtain the locus of the straight line which intersects the circle

$$x^2 + y^2 = r^2, z = 0$$

and the two straight lines $x = 0 = z + a$; $y = 0 = z - a$.

$$\textbf{[Ans.} \ a^2 \ \{x^2 \ (z - a)^2 + y^2 \ (z + a)^2\} = r^2 \ (z - a)^2]$$

7. Prove that the locus of a line which meets the lines

$$y = \pm mx, z = \pm c$$

and the circle

$$x^2 + y^2 = a^2, z = 0$$

is

$$c^2 m^2 \ (cy - mxz)^2 + c^2 \ (yz - cmx)^2 = a^2 m^2 \ (z^2 - c^2)^2. \qquad (Kanpur, \ 1995)$$

8. Find the surface generated by the lines which intersect the lines

$$y = mx, z = c; y = - mx, z = - c \text{ and } x\text{-axis.} \quad (Meerut, 1997; Garhwal, 1994)$$

$$[\textbf{Ans. } cy = mzx]$$

9. A straight line is drawn through a variable point on the ellipse $x^2/a^2 + y^2/b^2 = 1, z = 0$
to meet two fixed lines

$$y = mx, z = c; y = - mx, z = - c.$$

Find the equation to the surface generated. *(Bundelkhand, 1995)*

$$[\textbf{Ans. } a^2c^2m^2 (cy - mxz)^2 + b^2c^2 (mcx - yz)^2 = a^2b^2m^2 (c^2 - z^2)^2]$$

4.5. EQUATIONS OF TWO SKEW LINES IN A SIMPLIFIED FORM

We shall see how with a suitable choice of co-ordinate axes relative to a given pair of skew lines, we can find their equations in a simplified form.

Let the shortest distance between the two given lines AB and CD meet them at L and M and let the shortest distance between the lines be of length $2c$.

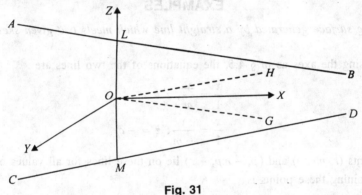

Fig. 31

Through O, the mid-point of LM, draw OG and OH parallel to the given lines AB and CD respectively.

Take the bisectors of the angles between the lines OG and OH as the X-axis and Y-axis and LM as Z-axis. These three lines are mutually at right angles.

Let the angle between the given lines AB, CD be 2θ so that 2θ is also the angle between the lines OG, OH respectively parallel to AB, CD; the line OG makes angles

$$\theta, \frac{1}{2}\pi - \theta, \frac{1}{2}\pi$$

with the axes

$$OX, OY, OZ$$

so that the direction cosines of the line AB which is parallel to the line OG are

$$\cos\theta, \sin\theta, 0$$

Also since OH makes angles

$$-\theta, \frac{1}{2}\pi + \theta, \frac{1}{2}\pi$$

with the axes, the direction cosines of the line CD which is parallel to the line OH are

$$\cos\theta, -\sin\theta, 0.$$

Finally, the co-ordinates of the points L, M are

$$(0, 0, c) \text{ and } (0, 0, -c)$$

respectively for $LM = 2c$.

Thus, the equations of the lines AB, CD are

$$\frac{x}{\cos \theta} = \frac{y}{\sin \theta}, \; z = c \;\; \Leftrightarrow \;\; y = x \tan \theta, \; z = c$$

and

$$\frac{x}{\cos \theta} = \frac{y}{-\sin \theta}, \; z = -c \;\; \Leftrightarrow \;\; y = -x \tan \theta, \; z = -c$$

respectively.

Note 1. $(r, r \tan \theta, c)$ and $(p, -p \tan \theta, -c)$ are the general co-ordinates of points on the two lines; r and p being the parameters.

Note 2. Solutions to certain problems relating to the two non-intersecting straight lines are often simplified by taking the equations of the lines in the form obtained above.

EXAMPLES

1. *Find the surface generated by a straight line which meets two given skew lines at the same angle.*

Sol. Choosing the axes as in § 4.5, the equations of the two lines are

$$\frac{x}{1} = \frac{y}{m}, \; z = c \qquad \qquad \qquad \dots(i)$$

and

$$\frac{x}{1} = \frac{y}{-m}, \; z = -c \qquad \qquad \qquad \dots(ii)$$

so that the points (r, mr, c) and $(p, -mp, -c)$ lie on these lines for all values of r and p.

The line joining these points is

$$\frac{x - r}{r - p} = \frac{y - mr}{m(r + p)} = \frac{z - c}{2c}. \qquad \qquad \dots(iii)$$

As this line makes the same angle with both the lines (i) and (ii), we have

$$r - p + m^2(r + p) = r - p - m^2(r + p) \qquad \qquad \dots(iv)$$

$$\Leftrightarrow \qquad \qquad r + p = 0.$$

From (iii) and (iv), we have

$$\frac{x - r}{2r} = \frac{z - c}{2c}, \; y - mr = 0,$$

so that eliminating r, we obtain

$$mcx = yz,$$

as the required locus.

2. *A point moves so that the lines joining the feet of the perpendiculars from it to two given straight lines subtends a right angle at mid-point of their S.D. Prove its locus is hyperbolic cylinder.*

Sol. Let O, the mid-point of the S.D. between given lines AB and CD, be taken as origin and let the equations of AB and CD (Fig. 31) be

$$\frac{x}{1} = \frac{y}{m} = \frac{z - c}{0} = r \qquad \qquad \qquad \dots(i)$$

and
$$\frac{x}{1} = \frac{y}{-m} = \frac{z+c}{0} = r' \qquad \qquad ...(ii)$$

respectively.

Let the moving point P be (x_1, y_1, z_1) and feet of perpendicular from P to AB and CD be Q and Q'.

Then from (i) and (ii), Q is (r, mr, c) and Q' is $(r', mr', -c)$.

∴   The direction ratios of PQ and PQ' are
$$x_1 - r, \; y_1 - mr, \; z_1 - c \text{ and } x_1 - r', \; y_1 - mr', \; z_1 + c$$

respectively.

Now, PQ is perpendicular to AB and PQ' is perpendicular to CD, so we have
$$1 \cdot (x_1 - r) + m (y_1 - mr) + 0 \cdot (z_1 - c) = 0$$
and
$$1 \cdot (x_1 - r') + m (y_1 + mr') + 0 \cdot (z_1 + c) = 0$$
i.e.,
$$r = (x_1 + my_1)/(1 + m^2) \text{ and } r' = (x_1 - my_1)/(1 + m^2) \qquad ...(iii)$$

Also, QQ' subtends a right angle at O, i.e., OQ is perpendicular to OQ.

∴ $r \cdot r' + mr (-mr') + c(-c) = 0$, since the dr's of OQ are r, mr, c etc.

$\Rightarrow$ $rr'(1 - m^2) = c^2$

$\Rightarrow$ $\left(\dfrac{x_1 + my_1}{1 + m^2} \right) \left(\dfrac{x_1 - my_1}{1 + m^2} \right)(1 - m^2) = c^2$ [from (iii)]

$\Rightarrow$ $x_1^2 - m^2 y_1^2 = [c^2 (1 + m^2)^2 / (1 - m^2)]$

∴   The required locus of $P(x_1, y_1, z_1)$ is $x^2 - m^2 y^2 = \dfrac{c^2 (1 + m^2)^2}{(1 - m^2)}$, which represents a

hyperbolic cylinder.

3. *Find the locus of the mid-points of the line whose extremities are on two given lines and which are parallel to a given plane.*

Sol. Let the equations of the two lines be taken as
$$\frac{x}{1} = \frac{y}{m} = \frac{z-c}{0} = r \qquad \qquad ...(i)$$
and
$$\frac{x}{1} = \frac{y}{-m} = \frac{z+c}{0} = r' \qquad \qquad ...(ii)$$

The co-ordinates of any two points on these are
$$A(r, mr, c) \text{ and } B(r', -mr', -c) \qquad \qquad ...(iii)$$

∴   The direction ratios of the variable line AB are
$$r - r', \; mr + mr', \; c + c \Rightarrow r - r', \; m(r + r'), \; 2c$$

Let this line AB be parallel to a given plane
$$Ax + By + Cz + D = 0 \qquad \qquad ...(iv)$$

Then
$$A(r - r') + Bm(r + r') + C \cdot 2c = 0 \qquad \qquad ...(v)$$

Let $P(x_1, y_1, z_1)$ be the mid-point of AB, then from (iii), we get
$$x_1 = \frac{1}{2}(r + r'); \; y_1 = \frac{1}{2}(mr - mr'); \; z = \frac{1}{2}(c - c) = 0.$$

Eliminating r and r' from (v) with its help, we get
$$A(2y_1/m) + Bm(2x_1) + 2c \cdot C = 0; z_1 = 0$$
∴ The required locus of $P(x_1, y_1, z_1)$ is :
$$Bm^2x + Ay + mcC = 0, z = 0$$
which represents a line in the plane $z = 0$.

4. *AB is the S.D. between two given lines and A', B' are variable points on them, such that the volume of tetrahedron ABA'B' is constant. Prove that the locus of the mid-point of A'B' is a hyperbola whose asymptotes are parallel to the line.*

Sol. Let the given lines be
$$\frac{x}{1} = \frac{y}{m} = \frac{z-c}{0} = r \qquad \qquad ...(i)$$
and
$$\frac{x}{1} = \frac{y}{-m} = \frac{z+c}{0} = r' \qquad \qquad ...(ii)$$

Let $AB = 2c$, so that A is $(0, 0, c)$ and B is $(0, 0, -c)$.

Also, any point A' on (i) is (r, mr, c) and B' on (ii) is $(r', -mr', -c)$.

∴ Volume of the tetrahedron $ABA'B'$

$$= \frac{1}{6} \begin{vmatrix} 0 & 0 & c & 1 \\ 0 & 0 & -c & 1 \\ r & mr & c & 1 \\ r' & -mr' & -c & 1 \end{vmatrix} = \frac{1}{6} \begin{vmatrix} 0 & 0 & c & 1 \\ 0 & 0 & -2c & 0 \\ r & mr & 0 & 0 \\ r' & -mr' & -2c & 0 \end{vmatrix}$$

[subtracting first row from the rest]

$$= -\frac{1}{6} \begin{vmatrix} 0 & 0 & -2c \\ r & mr & 0 \\ r' & -mr' & -2c \end{vmatrix} = -\frac{2}{3} mcrr' = \lambda \text{ (say)}$$

$$\Rightarrow \qquad\qquad rr' = -(3\lambda/2mc) \qquad\qquad ...(iii)$$

Now, let $P(x_1, y_1, z_1)$ be the mid-point of $A'B'$.

Then
$$x_1 = \frac{(r+r')}{2}, y_1 = \frac{(mr - mr')}{2}, z_1 = \frac{1}{2}(c-c)$$
$$\Rightarrow \qquad r + r' = 2x_1, r - r' = 2y_1/m, z_1 = 0 \qquad\qquad ...(iv)$$

Now the required locus of P is obtained by eliminating r and r' from (iii) and (iv). For this, we have
$$4rr' = (r+r')^2 - (r-r')^2$$
$$\Rightarrow \qquad 4\left(\frac{-3\lambda}{2mc}\right) = (2x_1)^2 - \left(\frac{2y_1}{m}\right)^2 ; z_1 = 0$$

∴ Locus of $P(x_1, y_1, z_1)$ is
$$\left(\frac{y}{m}\right)^2 - x^2 = \frac{3\lambda}{2mc}, z = 0$$
$$\Rightarrow \qquad y^2 - m^2x^2 = (3m\lambda)/(2c), z = 0.$$

These equations represent a hyperbola on the *xy*-plane and its asymptotes are parallel to the line $y = \pm mx$. $z = 0$, *i.e.*, parallel to the given lines (i) and (ii).

5. *Show that the locus of lines which meet the lines*

$$\frac{x+a}{0} = \frac{y}{\sin \alpha} = \frac{z}{-\cos \alpha}, \quad \frac{x-a}{0} = \frac{y}{\sin \alpha} = \frac{z}{\cos \alpha}$$

at the same angle is $(xy \cos \alpha - az \sin \alpha)(zx \sin \alpha - ay \cos \alpha) = 0$.   *(Kanpur, 1996)*

Sol. Let a line meets the given lines in the points

$$(- a, r \sin \alpha, - r \cos \alpha) \text{ and } (a, r' \sin \alpha, r' \cos \alpha).$$

Then the direction ratios of this line are

$$a + a, r' \sin \alpha - r \sin \alpha, r' \cos \alpha + r \cos \alpha$$

Equations of this line are

$$\frac{x+a}{2a} = \frac{y - r \sin \alpha}{(r' - r) \sin \alpha} = \frac{z + r \cos \alpha}{r + r' \cos \alpha} \qquad \qquad ...(i)$$

This line meets the given line at the same angle and so on equating the cosine of the angles which this line subtends with the given line, we have

$$2a \cdot 0 + (r' - r) \sin \alpha \cdot \sin \alpha + (r' + r) \cos \alpha \, (- \cos \alpha)$$
$$= \pm \, [2a \cdot 0 + (r' - r) \sin \alpha \cdot \sin \alpha + (r' + r) \cos \alpha \cdot \cos \alpha]$$

$\Rightarrow \qquad (r' + r) \cos^2 \alpha = 0$, if +ve sign is taken

and $\qquad \quad (r' - r) \sin^2 \alpha = 0$ if $-$ve sign is taken

$\Rightarrow \qquad r' = \pm \, r.$

Now, if $r = r'$, then (i) becomes

$$\frac{x+a}{2a} = \frac{y - r \sin \alpha}{0} = \frac{z + r \cos \alpha}{2r \cos \alpha}$$

whence $y = r \sin \alpha$ and $(z + r \cos \alpha) \, 2a = (2r \cos \alpha) \, (x + a)$

$\Rightarrow \qquad y = r \sin \alpha$ and $az = xr \cos \alpha.$

Eliminating r we get,

$$xy \cos \alpha - az \sin \alpha = 0 \qquad \qquad ...(ii)$$

If $r' = - r$, then from (i) eliminating r as above, we get

$$zx \sin \alpha - ay \cos \alpha = 0 \qquad \qquad ...(iii)$$

From (ii) and (iii) we get the required result.

EXERCISES

1. A line intersects each of two fixed perpendicular non-intersecting lines so that the length intercepted is constant; show that the locus of the middle point of the intercept is a circle.

2. A line of constant length has its extremities on two fixed straight lines; find the locus of its middle point.

3. Find the locus of a point which moves so that the perpendiculars drawn from to two given skew lines are at right angles.

4. Two skew lines AP, BQ, inclined to one another at an angle of $60°$, are intersected by the shortest distance between them at A, B, respectively, and P, Q are points on the lines such that AQ is at right angles to BP; prove that $AP \cdot BQ = 2AB^2$.

5. Two skew lines AP, BQ are met by the shortest distance between them at A, B and P, Q are points on them such that $AP = r$, $BQ = p$. If the planes APQ and BPQ are perpendiculars show that, pr, is constant.

6. *AB* and *CD* are two fixed skew lines. Planes are drawn through them at right angles to each other. Find the locus of their line of intersection. Show that the locus degenerates into two planes if *AB* is perpendicular to *CD*.

7. *AB*, *CD* are perpendicular skew lines and the shortest distance between them meets the same at *L* and *M*; *O* is the mid-point of *LM*; *P* and *P'* are variable points on *AB* and *CD* such that $OP^2 + OP'^2$ is constant. Find the locus of the line *PP'*.

8. Prove that the locus of the point which is equidistant from the lines
$$y - mx = 0 = z - c, \; y + mx = 0 = z + c$$
is the surface
$$mxy + (1 + m^2) \, cz = 0.$$

9. One edge of a tetrahedron is fixed in magnitude as well as position and the opposite edge is of given length and lies along a fixed straight line. Show that the locus of the centroid of the tetrahedron is a straight line.

10. The length of two opposite edges of a tetrahedron are *a*, *b*; the shortest distance between them is *2c* and the angle between them is α; prove that its volume is $(abc \sin \alpha)/3$.

11. *A*, *B*, *C* and *A'*, *B'*, *C'* are two sets of points on two skew lines. Prove that if
$$AB : BC = A'B' : B'C'$$
the middle points of *AA'*, *BB'*, *CC'* are collinear.

12. Lines are drawn to intersect the lines
$$y - mx = 0 = z - c, \; y + mx = 0 = z + c$$
and to make a constant angle with Z-axis. Show that the locus of their mid-points in an ellipse whose eccentricity is
$$(1 - m^4)^{1/2} \text{ or } (m^4 - 1)^{1/2} \div m^2.$$
according as $m^2 < 1$ or > 1.

13. *AA'* is the common perpendicular of two skew lines *PQA*, *P'Q'A'*; *P*, *Q* being any two points on the first line and *P'*, *Q'* any two points on the second. Prove that the common perpendicular of *AA'* and the line joining the mid-points of *PP'*, *QQ'* bisects *AA'*.

14. *A* and *B* are variable points on two given non-intersecting lines *CD* and *EF*. Find the locus of a point *P* such that *PA*, *PB* are perpendicular to one another and perpendicular to *CD* and *EF* respectively.   **[Ans.** $(1 - m^2) \, (y^2 - m^2 x^2) + (z^2 - c^2) \, (1 + m^2)^2 = 0$**]**

15. Find the locus of a point which moves so that the ratio of its distance from the given line is constant.

5
Transformation of Co-ordinates

5.1. INTRODUCTION

The co-ordinates of a point in space are determined *relatively* to an assigned system of axes, called the *frame of reference* so that the co-ordinates of a point change with the change in the frame of reference. We shall now obtain relations between the co-ordinates of a point relatively to two different frames of reference.

Let OX, OY, OZ; $O'X'$, $O'Y'$, $O'Z'$ be two frames of reference. Through the point O' draw lines $O'X''$, $O'Y''$, $O'Z''$ parallel to the lines OX, OY, OZ respectively.

Let (x, y, z), (x'', y'', z''), (x', y', z') be the co-ordinates of the same point P relatively to the frames of reference

$$OX, OY, OZ; O'X'', O'Y'', O'Z''; O'X', O'Y', O'Z'$$

We have to find a relation between

$$(x, y, z) \text{ and } (x', y', z')$$

This we shall do in two stages via (x'', y'', z'').

The axes

$$O'X'', O'Y'', O'Z'' \text{ and } OX, OY, OZ$$

are so related that the origin changes from O to O', but the directions of the axes remain unaltered. This situation is discussed in the following § 5.1.1.

The axes

$$O'X', O'Y', O'Z' \text{ and } O'X'', O'Y'', O'Z''$$

are so related that the origin does not change but we have a change in the direction of axes. This situation is discussed in the § 5.1.2.

5.1.1. Change of Origin

To change the origin of co-ordinates without changing the direction of axes.

Let OX, OY, OZ be the original axes and $O'X'$, $O'Y'$, $O'Z'$ the new axes respectively parallel to the original axes. Let the co-ordinates of the new origin O' referred to the original axes be (f, g, h).

Let the co-ordinates of a point P be (x, y, z) and (x', y', z') referred to the original and the new axes respectively.

Draw PL perpendicular to the parallel planes YOZ and $Y'O'Z'$ meeting them at L and L' so that

$$LP = x \text{ and } L'P = x'.$$

Now, LL' is equal to the length of the perpendicular from the new origin O' to the YOZ plane and is, therefore $= f$.

Also $LP = LL' + L'P \Rightarrow x = x' + f.$

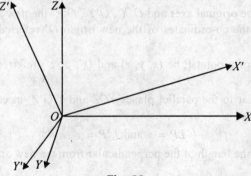

Fig. 32

Similarly

$$y = y' + g \text{ and } z = z' + h.$$

Hence, if in the equation to any surface, we change

$$x, y, z$$

to $x + f, y + g, z + h$

respectively, we obtain the equation to the same surface referred to the point (f, g, h) as origin.

Ex. Find the equations of the plane $2x + 3y + 4z = 7$ referred to the point $(2, -3, 4)$ as origin; directions of the axes remaining the same.   **[Ans.** $2x + 3y + 4z + 4 = 0$**]**

5.1.2. Change of the Directions of Axes

To change the directions of axes without changing the origin.

Let

$$l_1, m_1, n_1; l_2, m_2, n_2; l_3, m_3, n_3$$

be the respective direction cosines of the new axes OX', OY', OZ' with respect to the original axes, OX, OY, OZ.

Let

$$x, y, z \text{ and } x', y', z'$$

be the co-ordinates of a point P referred to the two systems of axes.

Draw $PN' \perp X'OY'$ plane meeting it in N' and also $N'L' \perp OX'$ meeting it in L' so that

$$OL' = x'; L'N' = y'; N'P = z'.$$

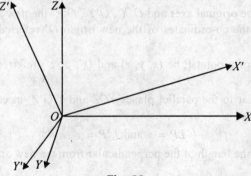

Fig. 33

Now, the projection of OP being equal to the sum of the projections of OL', $L'N'$, $N'P$ on OX', we have

$$x = l_1 x' + l_2 y' + l_3 z'$$

Similarly
$$y = m_1 x' + m_2 y' + m_3 z'$$ ...(A)

and
$$z = n_1 x' + n_2 y' + n_3 z'.$$

By a method similar to the one adopted, we can show that

$$x' = l_1 x + m_1 y + n_1 z$$
$$y' = l_2 x + m_2 y + n_2 z$$ ...(B)
$$z' = l_3 x + m_3 y + n_3 z.$$

The results (A) and (B) can easily be written down with the help of the following table :

	x	y	z
x'	l_1	m_1	n_1
y'	l_2	m_2	n_2
z'	l_3	m_3	n_3

Fig. 34

EXERCISES

1. Find the equation of the surface
$$3x^2 + 5y^2 + 3z^2 + 2yz + 2zx + 2xy = 1$$

with reference to axes through the same origin and with direction cosines proportional to $(-1, 0, 1)$, $(1, -1, 1)$, $(1, 2, 1)$.   [**Ans.** $2x^2 + 3y^2 + 6z^2 = 1$]

2. Show that the equation $lx + my + nz = 0$ becomes $z = 0$, when referred to new axes through the same origin with direction cosines

$$\frac{-m}{\sqrt{l^2 + m^2}}, \frac{l}{\sqrt{l^2 + m^2}}, 0; \frac{-ln}{\sqrt{l^2 + m^2}}, \frac{-mn}{\sqrt{l^2 + m^2}}, \sqrt{l^2 + m^2}; l, m, n.$$

Hence, show that the curve $ax^2 + by^2 = 2z$, $lx + my + nz = 0$ is a rectangular hyperbola if $(a + b) n^2 + am^2 + bl^2 = 0$.

5.1.3. *The degree of an equation is unaltered by any transformation of axes.*

Since, we replace x, y, z by expressions of the first degree, the degree cannot increase.

Also, it cannot decrease for, otherwise, on retransforming the degree must increase.

5.2. RELATIONS BETWEEN THE DIRECTION COSINES OF THREE MUTUALLY PERPENDICULAR LINES

l_1, m_1, n_1; l_2, m_2, n_2; l_3, m_3, n_3 being the direction cosines of three mutually perpendicular lines OX, OY, OZ, we have the relations

$$l_1^2 + m_1^2 + n_1^2 = 1;$$
$$l_2^2 + m_2^2 + n_2^2 = 1;$$ ...(A)
$$l_3^2 + m_3^2 + n_3^2 = 1.$$

and
$$l_1 l_2 + m_1 m_2 + n_1 n_2 = 0;$$
$$l_2 l_3 + m_2 m_3 + n_2 n_3 = 0;$$
$$l_3 l_1 + m_3 m_1 + n_3 n_1 = 0.$$
...(B)

(Cor. 3, page ???)

Thus, these six relations exist between the nine direction cosines. They can also be expressed in another form as shown below.

Now, $l_1, l_2, l_3; m_1, m_2, m_3; n_1, n_2, n_3$ are clearly the direction cosines of the original axes OX, OY, OZ referred to the new axes. Therefore, we have the relations

$$l_1^2 + l_2^2 + l_3^2 = 1;$$
$$m_1^2 + m_2^2 + m_3^2 = 1;$$
$$n_1^2 + n_2^2 + n_3^2 = 1.$$
...(C)

and
$$l_1 m_1 + l_2 m_2 + l_3 m_3 = 0;$$
$$m_1 n_1 + m_2 n_2 + m_3 n_3 = 0;$$
$$n_1 l_1 + n_2 l_2 + n_3 l_3 = 0.$$
...(D)

The relations A, B, C, D are not independent.

In fact the relations C, D can be algebraically deduced from the relations A, B and *vice-versa*, without any geometrical considerations at all.

Cor. *If $l_1, m_1, n_1; l_2, m_2, n_2; l_3, m_3, n_3$ be the direction cosines of three mutually perpendicular straight lines, then*

$$\begin{vmatrix} l_1 & m_1 & n_1 \\ l_2 & m_2 & n_2 \\ l_3 & m_3 & n_3 \end{vmatrix} = \pm 1.$$

For, if D be the given determinant, we have

$$D^2 = \begin{vmatrix} l_1 & m_1 & n_1 \\ l_2 & m_2 & n_2 \\ l_3 & m_3 & n_3 \end{vmatrix} \times \begin{vmatrix} l_1 & m_1 & n_1 \\ l_2 & m_2 & n_2 \\ l_3 & m_3 & n_3 \end{vmatrix}$$

$$= \begin{vmatrix} l_1^2 + m_1^2 + n_1^2 & l_1 l_2 + m_1 m_2 + n_1 n_2 & l_1 l_3 + m_1 m_3 + n_1 n_3 \\ l_1 l_2 + m_1 m_2 + n_1 n_2 & l_2^2 + m_2^2 + n_2^2 & l_2 l_3 + m_2 m_3 + n_2 n_3 \\ l_1 l_3 + m_1 m_3 + n_1 n_3 & l_3 l_2 + m_3 m_2 + n_3 n_2 & l_3^2 + m_3^2 + n_3^2 \end{vmatrix}$$

$$= \begin{vmatrix} 1 & 0 & 0 \\ 0 & 1 & 0 \\ 0 & 0 & 1 \end{vmatrix} = 1 \Rightarrow D = \pm 1.$$

5.3. INVARIANTS

If, by a change of rectangular axes without change of origin, the expression
$$ax^2 + by^2 + cz^2 + 2fyz + 2gzx + 2hxy$$
becomes
$$a'x^2 + b'y^2 + c'z^2 + 2f'yz + 2g'zx + 2h'xy$$

then

(i) $a + b + c = a' + b' + c'$,

(ii) $ab + bc + ca - f^2 - g^2 - h^2 = a'b' + b'c' + c'a' - f'^2 - g'^2 - h'^2$

(iii) $\begin{vmatrix} a & h & g \\ h & b & f \\ g & f & c \end{vmatrix} = \begin{vmatrix} a' & h' & g' \\ h' & b' & f' \\ g' & f' & c' \end{vmatrix}$

Consider two sets of rectangular axes

$$Ox, Oy, Oz; \, OX, OY, OZ$$

through the same origin O. Let P be a point so that if (x, y, z), (X, Y, Z) be the co-ordinates of the same relative to the two systems of axes, we have

$$x^2 + y^2 + z^2 = OP^2 = X^2 + Y^2 + Z^2$$

Thus, we see that

$$x^2 + y^2 + z^2$$

becomes

$$X^2 + Y^2 + Z^2.$$

Also, as given

$$ax^2 + by^2 + cz^2 + 2fyz + 2gzx + 2hxy$$

becomes

$$a'X^2 + b'Y^2 + c'Z^2 + 2f'YZ + 2g'ZX + 2h'XY.$$

Thus, if λ be a constant, the expression

$$ax^2 + by^2 + cz^2 + 2fyz + 2gzx + 2hxy + \lambda (x^2 + y^2 + z^2)$$
$$= (a + \lambda) x^2 + (b + \lambda) y^2 + (c + \lambda) z^2 + 2fyz + 2gzx + 2hxy \qquad ...(1)$$

becomes

$$a'X^2 + b'Y^2 + c'Z^2 + 2f'YZ + 2g'ZX + 2h'XY + \lambda (X^2 + Y^2 + Z^2)$$
$$= (a' + \lambda) X^2 + (b' + \lambda) Y^2 + (c' + \lambda) Z^2 + 2f'YZ + 2g'ZX + 2h'XY \qquad ...(2)$$

If now, for any value of λ, the expression (1) becomes a product of two linear factors, then, for the same value of λ, the expression (2) must also become a product of two linear factors. This follows from the fact that the degree of an expression does not change as a result of the change of axes so that the linear factors of (1) will become the two linear factors of (2).

Now, by § 2.8, the values of λ for which the expressions (1) and (2) are the products of linear factors are respectively the roots of the cubic equations

$$\begin{vmatrix} a + \lambda & h & g \\ h & b + \lambda & f \\ g & f & c + \lambda \end{vmatrix} = 0, \quad \begin{vmatrix} a' + \lambda & h' & g' \\ h' & b' + \lambda & f' \\ g' & f' & c' + \lambda \end{vmatrix} = 0$$

$\Rightarrow$

$$\lambda^3 + \lambda^2 (a + b + c) + \lambda (bc + ca + ab - f^2 - g^2 - h^2) + D = 0 \qquad ...(3)$$
$$\lambda^3 + \lambda^2 (a' + b' + c') + \lambda (b'c' + c'a' + a'b' - f'^2 - g'^2 - h'^2) + D' = 0 \qquad ...(4)$$

where

$$D = \begin{vmatrix} a & h & g \\ h & b & f \\ g & f & c \end{vmatrix}, \quad D' = \begin{vmatrix} a' & h' & g' \\ h' & b' & f' \\ g' & f' & c' \end{vmatrix}$$

As the equations (3) and (4) have the same roots, we have

$$\frac{1}{1} = \frac{a+b+c}{a'+b'+c'} = \frac{bc+ca+ab-f^2-g^2-h^2}{b'c'+c'a'+a'b'-f'^2-g'^2-h'^2} = \frac{D}{D'}$$

$$\Rightarrow \begin{cases} a+b+c.=a'+b'+c', \\ bc+ca+ab-f^2-g^2-h^2 = b'c'+c'a'+a'b'-f'^2-g'^2-h'^2 \\ D = D' \end{cases}$$

Note 1. The result obtained above shows that if in relation to any second degree homogeneous expression

$$ax^2 + by^2 + cz^2 + 2fyz + 2gzx + 2hxy,$$

x, y, z be subjected to a change of rectangular axes without change of origin, then

$$a+b+c, \ bc+ca+ab-f^2-g^2-h^2, \ D$$

are *invariants*.

Note 2. It may be seen that

$$bc + ca + ab - f^2 - g^2 - h^2 = A + B + C,$$

where A, B, C are the co-factors of a, b, c in the determinant D.

Ex. Show directly by changing

$$x, y, z \text{ to } x + p, y + q, z + r$$

respectively that

$$a + b + c, \ A + B + C, \ D$$

are also invariants for a change of origin.

[In fact, as may easily be seen, the coefficients a, b, c, f, g, h are themselves separately invariants for a change of origin without change in the direction of axes.]

EXAMPLE

OA, OB, OC are three mutually perpendicular lines through the origin, and their direction cosines are

$$l_1, m_1, n_1; \ l_2, m_2, n_2; \ l_3, m_3, n_3.$$

If $OA = OB = OC = a$, prove that the equation to the plane ABC is

$$(l_1 + l_2 + l_3) x + (m_1 + m_2 + m_3) y + (n_1 + n_2 + n_3) z = a.$$

Sol. Let the required equation be

$$lx + my + nz + p = 0. \qquad \qquad ...(i)$$

The co-ordinates of the point A are (al_1, am_1, an_1).

The plane (i) passes through the point A. Therefore, we have

$$a(ll_1 + mm_1 + nn_1) + p = 0. \qquad \qquad ...(ii)$$

Similarly, we have

$$a(ll_2 + mm_2 + nn_2) + p = 0, \qquad \qquad ...(iii)$$

$$a(ll_3 + mm_3 + nn_3) + p = 0. \qquad \qquad ...(iv)$$

Multiplying (ii), (iii), (iv) by l_1, l_2, l_3 respectively, and adding, we get

$$al + p(l_1 + l_2 + l_3) = 0. \qquad \text{[From relations (D), page ???]}$$

$$\Rightarrow \qquad \frac{l}{p} = -\frac{l_1 + l_2 + l_3}{a}.$$

Similarly

$$\frac{m}{p} = -\frac{m_1 + m_2 + m_3}{a}, \frac{n}{p} = -\frac{n_1 + n_2 + n_3}{a}.$$

Making substitutions, in (i), we get the required result.

EXERCISES

1. $l_r, m_r, n_r; (r = 1, 2, 3)$ are direction cosines of three mutually perpendicular straight lines and

$$a/l_1 + b/m_1 + c/n_1 = 0, \; a/l_2 + b/m_2 + c/n_2 = 0$$

Prove that

$$a/l_3 + b/m_3 + c/n_3 = 0 \text{ and } a : b : c = l_1l_2l_3 : m_1m_2m_3 : n_1n_2n_3.$$

2. If three rectangular axes be rotated about the line given by

$$x/l = y/m = z/n$$

into new positions and the direction cosines of the new axes referred to the old are $l_1, m_1, n_1; l_2, m_2, n_2; l_3, m_3, n_3;$ and if

$$l_1 = \pm (m_2 n_3 - m_3 n_2),$$

then $l (m_3 \pm n_2) = m (n_1 + l_3) = n (l_2 + m_1).$

EXAMPLES

1. *Show that the planes*

$$3x - 6y - 5z + 3 = 0, \qquad\qquad ...(i)$$

$$6x - 9y - 8z + 3 = 0, \qquad\qquad ...(ii)$$

$$x - y - z + 2 = 0 \qquad\qquad ...(iii)$$

form a triangular prism. Find the area and the lengths of the edges of its normal section.

Sol. Symmetrical form of the equation of the lines of intersection of the first two planes is

$$\frac{x-1}{1} = \frac{y-1}{-2} = \frac{z}{3},$$

and, as may be easily shown, this line is parallel to the third plane but does not lie in it. Hence, the planes form a prism.

Normal sections of the prism are congruent triangles.

We consider the normal section through the origin. Equation of the plane of this normal section is

$$x - 2y + 3z = 0 \qquad\qquad ...(iv)$$

Co-ordinates of the three vertices of the triangular section are obtained by solving simultaneously each of three pairs of the given equations with the equation (iv).

Thus, the vertices are

$$A\left(-\frac{41}{14}, -\frac{16}{14}, \frac{3}{4}\right), \; B\left(-\frac{71}{14}, -\frac{40}{14}, -\frac{3}{14}\right), \; C\left(\frac{15}{14}, \frac{12}{14}, \frac{3}{14}\right)$$

Therefore, the lengths of the edges AB, BC, CA are

$$\frac{\sqrt{1512}}{14}, \frac{\sqrt{10136}}{14}, \frac{\sqrt{3920}}{14}.$$

Let Δ denote the area of the triangle ABC. The co-ordinates of the projections A', B', C' of the points A, B, C on the XY plane are

$$\left(-\frac{41}{14}, -\frac{16}{14}, 0\right); \left(-\frac{71}{14}, -\frac{40}{14}, 0\right), \left(\frac{15}{12}, \frac{12}{14}, 0\right).$$

Let Δ_z denote the area of the triangle $A'B'C'$. We have

$$\Delta_z = \frac{1}{2} \begin{vmatrix} -41/14 & -16/14 & 1 \\ -71/14 & -40/14 & 1 \\ 15/14 & 12/14 & 1 \end{vmatrix} = \frac{9}{7}.$$

If, θ, denotes the angle between the plane (iv) and the XOY plane, we have

$$\cos \theta = \frac{3}{\sqrt{14}}.$$

Also $\Delta_z = \Delta \cos \theta$

$\Rightarrow$

$$\Delta = \frac{\Delta_z}{\cos \theta} = \frac{9}{7} \cdot \frac{\sqrt{14}}{3} = \frac{3}{7}\sqrt{14}.$$

2. *Find the equations of the line of greatest slope on the plane*

$$3x - 4y + 5z - 5 = 0$$

drawn through the point $(3, -4, -4)$ *given that the plane*

$$4x - 5y + 6z = 0$$

is horizontal.

Sol. Line of greatest slope on a given plane, drawn through a given point on the plane, is the line through the point perpendicular to the line of intersection of the given plane with a horizontal plane.

We have, thus, to find the line through the point A $(3, -4, -4)$ perpendicular to the line of intersection of the planes

$$3x - 4y + 5z - 5 = 0, \quad 4x - 5y + 6z - 6 = 0.$$

Equations of this line in the symmetrical form are

$$\frac{x+1}{1} = \frac{y+2}{2} = \frac{z}{1}, \qquad \qquad \qquad \dots(i)$$

so that the general co-ordinates of any point P on the line are

$$(r - 1, 2r - 2, r),$$

r is the parameter.

The line AP will be perpendicular to the line (i), if

$$1(r - 4) + 2(2r + 2) + 1(r + 4) = 0 \Leftrightarrow r = -\frac{2}{3}.$$

Thus, the co-ordinates of P are

$$\left(-\frac{5}{3}, -\frac{10}{3}, -\frac{2}{3}\right).$$

Hence, the required line, AP, of greatest slope is

$$\frac{x-3}{-7} = \frac{y+4}{1} = \frac{z+4}{5}.$$

3. *CP, CQ are conjugate diameters of the ellipse*
$$x^2/a^2 + y^2/b^2 = 1, z = -c;$$
C'P', C'Q' are conjugate diameters of the ellipse
$$x^2/a^2 + y^2/b^2 = 1, z = -c;$$
drawn in the same direction as CP and CQ. Find the locus of the lines PQ' or P'Q.

Sol. Let P be ($a \cos \theta$, $b \sin \theta$, c). Therefore, the points Q, P', Q' are
$$(-a \sin \theta, b \cos \theta, c), (a \cos \theta, b \sin \theta, -c), (-a \sin \theta, b \cos \theta, -c)$$
respectively.

Equations of the line PQ' are
$$\frac{x - a \cos \theta}{a (\cos \theta + \sin \theta)} = \frac{y - b \sin \theta}{b (\sin \theta - \cos \theta)} = \frac{z - c}{2c}. \qquad \qquad ...(i)$$

The locus will be obtained on eliminating θ from the equations (i).

The equations (i) can be written as
$$\frac{x}{a} = \frac{z+c}{2c} \cos \theta + \frac{z-c}{2c} \sin \theta,$$
$$\frac{y}{b} = -\frac{z-c}{2c} \cos \theta + \frac{z+c}{2c} \sin \theta.$$

Squaring and adding, we obtain
$$\frac{x^2}{a^2} + \frac{y^2}{b^2} = \left(\frac{z+c}{2c}\right)^2 + \left(\frac{z-c}{2c}\right)^2$$
$$\Rightarrow \qquad \frac{2x^2}{a^2} + \frac{2y^2}{b^2} - \frac{z^2}{c^2} = 1,$$

as the required locus.

It may be shown that the locus of the line $P'Q$ is the same surface.

4. *Show that the equations of the planes through the lines which bisect the angles between the lines*
$$\frac{x}{l} = \frac{y}{m} = \frac{z}{n} \text{ and } \frac{x}{l'} = \frac{y}{m'} = \frac{z}{n'}$$
and perpendicular to the plane containing them, are
$$(l \pm l') x + (m \pm m') y + (n \pm n') z = 0.$$

Sol. Let OA, OB be the given lines. Take points A and B on the lines such that
$$OA = OB = r.$$

Take another point A' on the line OA produced such that O is the mid-point of AA'.

The co-ordinates of the points A, B, A' are
$$(lr, mr, nr), (l'r, m'r, n'r), (-lr, -mr, -nr)$$
respectively.

Let P, Q be the mid-points of AB and $A'B$ respectively so that OP, OQ are the bisectors of the angles between OA and OB.

The co-ordinates of the points P, Q are
$$\left[\frac{1}{2}(l+l')r, \frac{1}{2}(m+m')r, \frac{1}{2}(n+n')r\right], \left[\frac{1}{2}(l'-l)r, \frac{1}{2}(m'-m)r, \frac{1}{2}(n'-n)r\right]$$
respectively.

Thus, the lines OP, OQ are

$$\frac{x}{l+l'} = \frac{y}{m+m'} = \frac{z}{n+n'}, \frac{x}{l'-l} = \frac{y}{m'-m} = \frac{z}{n'-n} \qquad ...(4)$$

The lines OA, OB, OP, PQ are all coplanar.

Let OR be normal to this plane.

The lines OP, OQ and OR are mutually perpendicular to the planes POQ (*i.e.*, the plane AOB); QOR, ROP are also mutually perpendicular.

The plane QOR passes through a bisector OQ and is perpendicular to the plane AOB so that it is one of the required planes. Being perpendicular to the line OP, its equation is

$$(l - l')\, x + (m - m')\, y + (n - n')\, z = 0.$$

Similarly POR is the other required plane. Being perpendicular to the line OQ, its equation is

$$(l - l')\, x + (m - m')\, y + (n - n')\, z = 0.$$

REVISION EXERCISES I

1. Show that the straight lines

$$\frac{x}{\alpha} = \frac{y}{\beta} = \frac{z}{\gamma}, \frac{x}{a\alpha} = \frac{y}{b\beta} = \frac{z}{c\gamma}, \frac{x}{l} = \frac{y}{m} = \frac{z}{n},$$

will lie in one plane, if

$$l\,(b - c)/\alpha + m\,(c - a)/\beta + n\,(a - b)/\gamma = 0.$$

[**Hint.** The three lines have a point in common, *viz.*, the origin. They will be coplanar, if there exists a line through the origin, perpendicular to each of them. If λ, μ, ν be the direction cosines of this line, we have

$$\lambda\alpha + \mu\beta + \nu\gamma = 0, \ a\alpha\lambda + b\beta\mu + c\gamma\nu = 0, \ l\lambda + m\mu + n\nu = 0.$$

Eliminating λ, μ, ν we have the given condition.]

2. Show that the lines

$$\frac{x}{\alpha/a} = \frac{y}{\beta/b} = \frac{z}{\gamma/c}; \frac{x}{\alpha} = \frac{y}{\beta} = \frac{z}{\gamma}; \frac{x}{a\alpha} = \frac{y}{b\beta} = \frac{z}{c\gamma}$$

are coplanar if $(a - b)\,(b - c)\,(c - a) = 0$.

3. Show that the triangle with vertices (a, b, c), (b, c, a) and (c, a, b) is equilateral. Find the co-ordinates of the vertices of the two regular tetrahedra described on the above equilateral triangle as base. [**Ans.** (f, f, f) where $f = (\Sigma a + 2\sqrt{\Sigma a^2 - \Sigma bc})/3$]

4. If two opposite edges of a tetrahedron are equal in length and are at right angle to the line joining their middle points show that the other two pairs of opposite edges have the same property.

5. Two edges AB, CD of a tetrahedron $ABCD$ are perpendicular; show that the distance between the mid-points of AD and BC is equal to the distance between the mid-points of AC and BD.

6. Planes are drawn so as to make an angle of $60°$ with the line $x = y = z$ and an angle of $45°$ with the line $x = 0 = y - z$. Show that all these planes make an angle of $60°$ with the plane $x = 0$.

Find the equations of the planes of this family which are 3 units distant from the point $(2, 1, 1)$. [**Ans.** $2x + (2 \pm \sqrt{2})\, y + 2\,(2 \pm \sqrt{2})\, z = 20$ or $- 4$]

7. Show that there are two lines which intersect the lines

$$x - 5 = \frac{1}{5}(y - 8) = \frac{1}{3}(z - 14), \quad \frac{1}{2}x = \frac{1}{4}(y + 1) = \frac{1}{3}(z - 10).$$

and also intersect the X-axis perpendicularly. Find the points in which they meet the X-axis. **[Ans. $(2, 0, 0)$, $(74/17, 0, 0)$]**

8. Taking the axis OZ to be vertical, find the equations of the line of greatest slope through the point $P(2, -1, 0)$ on the plane $2x + 3y - 4z - 1 = 0$.

$$\left[\textbf{Ans. } \frac{1}{8}(x - 2) = \frac{1}{12}(y + 1) = \frac{1}{12}z \right]$$

9. The plane $3x + 4y + 5z = 0$ is horizontal. Show that the equations of the line of greatest slope on the plane $x + 2y + 3z = 4$ through the point $(2, -5, 4)$ are

$$(x - 2) = (y + 5) = \frac{1}{2}(z - 4).$$

10. Find the equation of the plane which passes through the points $(0, 1, 1)$ and $(2, 0, -1)$, and is parallel to the line joining $(-1, 1, -2)$, $(3, -2, 4)$. Find also the distance between the lines and the plane. **[Ans. $6x + 10y + z - 11 = 0$; $9/\sqrt{137}$]**

11. A straight line is drawn through the point (α, β, γ) perpendicular to each of two given straight lines which pass through (α, β, γ) and whose direction cosines are l_1, m_1, n_1; l_2, m_2, n_2. Show that the volume of the tetrahedron formed by the point (α, β, γ) and the points where the three lines cut $x = 0$ is

$$\alpha^3 \sin^2 \theta / 6 l_1 l_2 (m_1 n_2 - m_2 n_1)$$

where θ is the angle between the lines.

12. A point P moves so that three mutually perpendicular lines PA, PB, PC may be drawn cutting the axes OX, OY, OZ at A, B, C and the volume of the tetrahedron $OABC$ is constant and equal to $a^3/6$. Show that the point P lies on the surface

$$(x^2 + y^2 + z^2)^3 = 8a^3 xyz.$$

13. Find the angle between the common line of the planes

$$x + y - z = 1, \quad 2x - 3y + z = 2$$

and the line joining the points $(3, -1, 2)$, $(4, 0, -1)$. Find also the equations of the line through the origin which is perpendicular to both the above lines.

[Ans. $\cos^{-1}(10/\sqrt{418})$, $x/14 = -y/11 = z$]

14. Show that the image of the line $x - 1 = -9(y - 2) = -3(z + 3)$ in the plane

$$3x - 3y + 10z = 26$$

is the line $\quad \frac{1}{9}(x - 4) = -(y + 1) = -\frac{1}{3}(z - 7).$

15. The plane $x/a + y/b + z/c = 1$ meets the axes at A, B, C respectively and planes are drawn through OX, OY and OZ meeting BC, CA and AB respectively at right angles. Show that these planes are coaxial.

If the common axis meets the plane ABC in the point P and perpendiculars are drawn from P to the co-ordinate planes, show that the equation of the plane through the feet of the perpendicular is

$$\frac{x}{bc} + \frac{y}{ca} + \frac{z}{ab} = \frac{2abc}{b^2c^2 + c^2a^2 + a^2b^2}.$$

16. From a point P whose co-ordinates are (x, y, z) a perpendicular PM is drawn to the straight line through the origin whose direction cosines are l, m, n and is produced to P' such that $PM = P'M$.

    If the co-ordinates of P' are (x', y', z'), show that

    $$\frac{x + x'}{l} = \frac{y + y'}{m} = \frac{z + z'}{n} = 2(lx + my + nz).$$

17. Show that the reflection of the plane $2x + 3y + z = 1$ in the line

    $$x = y/2 = z/3$$

    is the plane $3x - y - 26z + 7 = 0$.

18. Prove that the reflection of the plane $a'x + b'y + c'z + d' = 0$ in the plane

    $$ax + by + cz + d = 0$$

    is the plane $2(aa' + bb' + cc')(ax + by + cz + d) = (a^2 + b^2 + c^2)(a'x + b'y + c'z + d')$.

19. Find the equations of the straight line through the point $(3, 1, 2)$ to intersect the straight line $x + 4 = (y + 1) = 2(z - 2)$ and parallel to the plane $4x + y + 5z = 0$.

    $$\left[\textbf{Ans. } -\frac{1}{3}(x - 3) = \frac{1}{2}(y - 1) = -\frac{1}{2}(z - 2) \right]$$

20. The line $\dfrac{1}{3}(x + 6) = \dfrac{1}{3}(y + 10) = \dfrac{1}{8}(z + 14)$ is the hypotenuse of an isosceles right-angled triangle whose opposite vertex is $(7, 2, 4)$. Find the equations of the remaining sides.

    $$\left[\textbf{Ans. } \frac{1}{3}(x - 7) = \frac{1}{6}(y - 2) = \frac{1}{2}(z - 4); \frac{1}{2}(x - 7) = -\frac{1}{8}(y - 2) = \frac{1}{6}(z - 4) \right]$$

21. A straight line AB is drawn through a point $(4, 1, 7)$ and perpendicular to the plane $2x + 3y - 4z = 8$. Find the points in which AB and the axis OX are intersected by their common normal.   [**Ans.** $(6, 4, 3), (6, 0, 0)$]

22. Find the equations of the two straight lines through the origin, each of which intersect the straight line $\dfrac{1}{2}(x - 3) = (y - 3) = z$ and is inclined at angle of $60°$ to it.

    $$\left[\textbf{Ans. } \frac{1}{2}x = y = -z; x = -y = \frac{1}{2}z \right]$$

23. Find the direction cosines of the projection of the line $\dfrac{1}{2}(x - 1) = -y = (z + 2)$ upon the plane $2x + y - 3z = 4$.   [**Ans.** $2/\sqrt{6}, -1/\sqrt{6}, 1/\sqrt{6}$]

24. Find the equations of the straight line which is the projection on the plane

    $$3x + 2y + z = 0,$$

    of the line of intersection of the planes $3x - y + 2z = 1$, $x + 2y - z = 2$.

             [**Ans.** $-(x + 1)/11 = (y - 1)/9 = (z - 1)/15$]

25. QP, RP are two lines through a point P with direction cosines proportional to $1, 1, -2$ and $1, -1, 1$ respectively. Find the equation of the plane through the origin which is perpendicular to the plane PQR and parallel to the line QP.

    If P is the point $(-1, 1, 1)$. find the co-ordinates of the foot of the perpendicular from

    P on this plane. $\left[\textbf{Ans. } 4x - 2y + z = 0, \left(-\frac{1}{21}, \frac{11}{21}, \frac{28}{21} \right) \right]$

26. Show that the shortest distance between any two opposite edges of the tetrahedron formed by the planes $x + y = 0$, $y + z = 0$, $z + x = 0$, $x + y + z = a$ is $2a / \sqrt{6}$ and that the three lines of shortest distance meet at the point $(-a, -a, -a)$.

27. Prove that the co-ordinates of the points where the shortest distance lies between the lines

$$\frac{x - a}{l} = \frac{y - b}{m} = \frac{z - c}{n} \quad \text{and} \quad \frac{x - a'}{l'} = \frac{y - b'}{m'} = \frac{z - c'}{n'}$$

meets the first line are

$$a + l \cosec^2 \theta \ (u' \cos \theta - u), \ b + m \cosec^2 \theta \ (u' \cos \theta - u),$$
$$c + n \cosec^2 \theta \ (u' \cos \theta - u),$$

where θ is the angle between the given straight lines and

$$u = l \ (a - a') + m \ (b - b') + n \ (c - c'), \ u' = l' \ (a - a') + m' \ (b - b') + n' \ (c - c').$$

28. Prove that the shortest distance between the axis of z and the line

$$\frac{x}{a} + \frac{z}{c} = \lambda \left(1 + \frac{y}{b}\right), \ \frac{x}{a} + \frac{z}{c} = \frac{1}{\lambda} \left(1 - \frac{y}{b}\right)$$

for varying, λ, generates the surface

$$abz \ (x^2 + y^2) = (a^2 - b^2) \ cxy.$$

29. Prove that through the point (X, Y, Z) a line can be drawn which intersects the lines $y = x \tan \alpha$, $z = c$; $y = -x \tan \alpha$, $z = -c$ and that it meets the plane XY at the point

$$x = (cYZ \cot \alpha - c^2 X)/(Z^2 - c^2), \ y = (cXZ \tan \alpha - c^2 Y)/(Z^2 - c^2), \ z = 0.$$

30. Show that the surface generated by a straight line which intersects the lines $y = 0$, $z = c$; $x = 0$, $z = -c$ and the hyperboloid $z = 0$, $xy + c^2 = 0$ is the surface $z^2 - xy = c^2$.

31. A straight line intersects the three lines

$$x = 0, \ \beta y + \gamma z = \beta \gamma; \ y = 0, \ \gamma z + \alpha x = \gamma \alpha; \ z = 0, \ \alpha x + \beta y = \alpha \beta.$$

Prove that it is parallel to the plane $x + y + z = 0$ and its locus is the surface

$$\Sigma \alpha x^2 + \Sigma \ (\alpha + \beta) \ zy - \Sigma \alpha \ (\beta + \gamma) \ x + \alpha \beta \gamma = 0.$$

32. Show that the planes

$$x = y \sin \psi + z \sin \varphi, \ y = z \sin \theta + x \sin \psi, \ z = x \sin \varphi + y \sin \theta,$$

intersect in the line

$$\frac{x}{\cos \theta} = \frac{y}{\cos \varphi} = \frac{z}{\cos \psi}, \ \text{if} \ \theta + \varphi + \psi = \frac{1}{2} \pi.$$

33. Points P and Q are taken on two given skew lines so that the line PQ is always parallel to a given plane.

If the point R divides the segment PQ in a given ratio, prove that the locus of the point R is a straight line.

34. Find the locus of a point whose distance from a fixed point is in a constant ratio to its distance measured parallel to a given plane, from a given line.

[**Hint.** Take the given plane as the XY plane and its intersection with the given line as origin.]

35. Show that the planes

$$2x + 3y + 4z = 6, \ 3x + 4y + 5z = 2, \ x + 2y + 3z = 2$$

form a prism and find the area of its normal section.   [**Ans.** $8\sqrt{6}/3$]

36. A straight line meets the co-ordinate planes YOZ, ZOX, XOY in the points A, B, C respectively. If α, β, γ denote the angles BOC, COA, AOB respectively, and if the equation of the plane joining the line to O is

$$lx + my + nz = 0,$$

show that

$$l^4 \cot^2 \alpha = m^4 \cot^2 \beta = n^4 \cot^2 \gamma.$$

37. G is the centroid of the triangle whose vertices are the points in which the co-ordinate axes meet a plane. The perpendicular from G to this plane meets the co-ordinate planes A, B, C. Prove that

$$\frac{1}{GA} + \frac{1}{GB} + \frac{1}{GC} = \frac{3}{OK},$$

where K is the foot of the perpendicular from the origin O to the plane.

38. Assuming that the equation

$$ax^2 + by^2 + cz^2 + 2fyz + 2gzx + 2hxy = 0$$

represents two planes, show that their line of intersection is

$$Fx = Gy = Hz,$$

where F, G, H are the minors of f, g, h in the determinant

$$\begin{vmatrix} a & h & g \\ h & b & f \\ g & f & c \end{vmatrix}.$$

39. Three straight lines mutually at right angles meet in a point P and two of them intersect the axes of x and y respectively, while the third passes through a fixed point, $(0, 0, c)$ on the axis of z. Show that the equation of the locus of P is

$$x^2 + y^2 + z^2 = 2cz.$$

40. The triangle with vertices $(5, -4, 3)$, $(4, -1, -2)$ and $(10, -5, 2)$ is projected orthogonally onto the plane whose equation is $x - y = 3$. Find the co-ordinates of the vertices and the area of the new triangle. **[Ans.** $(2, -1, 3)$, $(3, 0, -2)$, $(4, 1, 2)$, $9/\sqrt{2}]$

6

The Sphere

6.1. DEFINITION

A **sphere** *is the locus of a point which remains at a constant distance from a fixed point.*
                                    (*Kanpur, 1994; Poorvanchal, 1996; Avadh, 2005*)

The constant distance is called the *Radius* and the fixed point the *Centre* of the sphere.

6.1.1. Equation of a Sphere

Let (a, b, c) be the centre and r the radius of a given sphere.

Equating the radius r to the distance of any point (x, y, z) on the sphere from its centre (a, b, c), we have

$$(x - a)^2 + (y - b)^2 + (z - c)^2 = r^2$$

$$\Leftrightarrow \quad x^2 + y^2 + z^2 - 2ax - 2by - 2cz + (a^2 + b^2 + c^2 - r^2) = 0 \qquad \dots\text{(A)}$$

which is the required equation of the given sphere.

Thus, the sphere whose centre is the point (a, b, c) and whose radius is r is the set

$$\{(x, y, z) : x^2 + y^2 + z^2 - 2ax - 2by - 2cz + (a^2 + b^2 + c^2 - r^2) = 0\}$$

We note the following *characteristics* of the equation (A) of the sphere :

1. It is of the second degree in x, y, z;

2. The coefficient of x^2, y^2, z^2 are all equal;

3. The product terms xy, yz, zx are absent.

Conversely, we consider the equation

$$ax^2 + ay^2 + az^2 + 2ux + 2vy + 2wz + d = 0, \, a \neq 0 \qquad \dots\text{(B)}$$

having the above three characteristics; a, u, v, w, d being given constants and $a \neq 0$.

The equation (B) can be rewritten as

$$\left(x + \frac{u}{a}\right)^2 + \left(y + \frac{v}{a}\right)^2 + \left(z + \frac{w}{a}\right)^2 = \frac{u^2 + v^2 + w^2 - ad}{a^2}.$$

This manner of rewriting shows that the distance between the variable point (x, y, z) and the fixed point

$$\left(-\frac{u}{a}, \, -\frac{v}{a}, \, -\frac{w}{a}\right)$$

is

$$\frac{\sqrt{u^2 + v^2 + w^2 - ad}}{|a|}, \, u^2 + v^2 + w^2 - ad \geq 0$$

and is, therefore, constant.

The locus of the equation (B) is thus a sphere, if

$$u^2 + v^2 + w^2 - ad \geq 0.$$

6.1.2. General Equation of a Sphere

We write the equation (B) in the form

$$x^2 + y^2 + z^2 + \frac{2u}{a}x + \frac{2v}{a}y + \frac{2w}{a}z + \frac{d}{a} = 0, a \neq 0$$

$$\Leftrightarrow \qquad x^2 + y^2 + z^2 + 2u'x + 2v'y + 2w'z + d' = 0$$

which is taken as the *general equation of a sphere*.

The family of spheres is thus given by the equation

$$x^2 + y^2 + z^2 + 2ux + 2vy + 2wz + d = 0$$

where u, v, w, d are parameters such that $u^2 + v^2 + w^2 - d \geq 0$.

The radius of the sphere is '0' if

$$u^2 + v^2 + w^2 - d = 0$$

In this case, the sphere is what we may call a *Point sphere*.

6.1.3. *Equation to a sphere on line joining* (x_1, y_1, z_1), (x_2, y_2, z_2) *as diameter*.

(Patna, 2003)

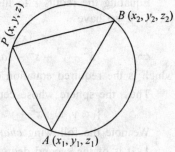

Let $P(x, y, z)$ be a point on the sphere. Then APB is a right-angled triangle right-angled at P.

Now direction cosines of AP are proportional to $x - x_1$, $y - y_1$, $z - z_1$ and direction cosines of BP are proportional to $x - x_2$, $y - y_2$, $z - z_2$.

But AP and BP are at right angles to each other

$$\therefore \quad (x - x_1)(x - x_2) + (y - y_1)(y - y_2)$$
$$+ (z - z_1)(z - z_2) = 0$$

is the required equation of the sphere.

Fig. 35

EXAMPLES

1. *Find the radius and centre of the sphere*

$$x^2 + y^2 + z^2 - 2x + 4y - 6z = 2.$$

Sol. Comparing with the general equation of sphere, we have

$$u = -1, v = 2, w = -3, d = -2.$$

Hence, centre is $(-u, -v, -w) \Rightarrow (1, -2, 3)$

$$\text{radius} = \sqrt{u^2 + v^2 + w^2 - d} = \sqrt{1 + 4 + 9 + 2} = 4.$$

2. *A plane passes through a fixed point (a, b, c); show that the locus of the foot of the perpendicular to it from the origin is the sphere* $x^2 + y^2 + z^2 - ax - by - cz = 0$.

(Rohelkhand 2006)

Sol. Any plane through (a, b, c) is

$$l(x - a) + m(y - b) + n(z - c) = 0 \qquad \qquad ...(1)$$

and the line perpendicular to it from the origin is

$$x/l = y/m = z/n. \qquad \qquad ...(2)$$

The foot of the perpendicular is the point of intersection of (1) and (2). Thus, to find the locus of the foot of perpendicular, one should eliminate l, m, n between (1) and (2), *i.e.*,

$$x(x - a) + y(y - b) + z(z - c) = 0.$$
$$\Rightarrow \qquad x^2 + y^2 + z^2 - ax - by - cz = 0.$$

3. *A point moves so that the sum of the squares of its distances from the six faces of a cube is constant; show that its locus is a sphere.* (*Garhwal 2006, Kumaon, 2003*)

Sol. Take the centre of the cube as the origin and the planes through the centre parallel to its faces as co-ordinate planes.

Let each of the edge of the cube be equal to $2a$.

Then the equations of the faces of the cube are

$$x = a, x = - a; y = a, y = - a; z = a, z = - a.$$

If (f, g, h) be a point of the locus, we have

$$(f - a)^2 + (f + a)^2 + (g - a)^2 + (g + a)^2 + (h - a)^2 + (h + a)^2 = k^2$$

(k, a constant)

$$\Leftrightarrow \qquad 2 (f^2 + g^2 + h^2 + 3a^2) = k^2$$

so that the locus is

$$2 (x^2 + y^2 + z^2 + 3a^2) = k^2,$$

which is a sphere.

EXERCISES

1. Find the centres and the radii of the following spheres :

(i) $x^2 + y^2 + z^2 - 6x + 8y - 10z + 1 = 0$,

(ii) $x^2 + y^2 + z^2 + 2x - 4y - 6z + 5 = 0$,

(iii) $2x^2 + 2y^2 + 2z^2 - 2x + 4y + 2z + 3 = 0$.

$$\left[\textbf{Ans.} \ (i) \ (3, - 4, 5); \ 7 \ (ii) \ (- 1, 2, 3); \ 3 \ (iii) \ \left(\frac{1}{2}, -1, -\frac{1}{2} \right); \ 0 \right]$$

2. Obtain the equation of the sphere described on the join of the points

$$A (2, - 3, 4) \ B (- 5, 6, - 7)$$

as diameter. $\qquad$ [**Ans.** $x^2 + y^2 + z^2 + 3 (x - y + z) - 56 = 0$]

3. Prove that the equation $ax^2 + ay^2 + az^2 + 2ux + 2vy + 2wz + d = 0$ represents a sphere.

Find its radius and centre. $\qquad \left[\textbf{Ans.} \ \frac{\sqrt{\Sigma u^2 - ad}}{a}; \left(-\frac{u}{a}, -\frac{v}{a}, -\frac{w}{a} \right) \right]$

4. Through a point P three mutually perpendicular straight lines are drawn; one passes through a fixed point C on the z-axis, while the others intersect the x-axis and y-axis, respectively; show that the locus of P is a sphere of which C is the centre.

6.2. THE SPHERE THROUGH FOUR GIVEN POINTS

The general equation of a sphere contains *four* parameters and, as such a sphere can be uniquely determined so as to satisfy four conditions, each of which is such that it gives rise to one linear relation between the constants.

In particular, we can find a sphere through four non-coplanar points

$$(x_1, y_1, z_1), (x_2, y_2, z_2), (x_3, y_3, z_3), (x_4, y_4, z_4).$$

Let

$$x^2 + y^2 + z^2 + 2ux + 2vy + 2wz + d = 0 \qquad \qquad ...(i)$$

be the equation of the sphere through the four given points.

We have then the linear equation

$$x_1^2 + y_1^2 + z_1^2 + 2ux_1 + 2vy_1 + 2wz_1 + d = 0, \qquad \ldots(ii)$$

and three more similar equations corresponding to the remaining three points so that we obtain a system of four linear equations in four unknowns u, v, w, d. We solve these equations and substituting the values thus obtained for u, v, w, d in (i), we get the required equation.

(Kanpur, 1998)

EXAMPLES

1. *Find the equation to the sphere through the points* $(0, 0, 0), (0, 1, -1), (-1, 2, 0), (1, 2, 3)$.

(Rohilkhand, 1997)

Sol. Let the equation of the sphere be

$$x^2 + y^2 + z^2 + 2ux + 2vy + 2wz + d = 0 \qquad \ldots(1)$$

As it passes through given points, we have

$$d = 0;$$
$$2 + 2v - 2w + d = 0;$$
$$5 - 2u + 4v + d = 0;$$
$$14 + 2u + 4v + 6w + d = 0$$

yielding $u = -15/14, v = -25/14, w = -11/14$ and $d = 0$.

Hence, the equation of sphere becomes

$$x^2 + y^2 + z^2 - \frac{15}{7}x - \frac{25}{7}y - \frac{11}{7}z = 0$$

or $7(x^2 + y^2 + z^2) - 15x - 25y - 11z = 0.$

2. *OA, OB, OC are three mutually perpendicular lines through the origin and their direction cosines are* $l_1, m_1, n_1; l_2, m_2, n_2; l_3, m_3, n_3$. *If* $OA = a, OB = b,$ *and* $OC = c$, *prove that equation of the sphere through OABC is*

$$x^2 + y^2 + z^2 - x(al_1 + bl_2 + cl_3) - y(am_1 + bm_2 + cm_3) - z(an_1 + bn_2 + cn_3) = 0.$$

Sol. Co-ordinates of points A, B, C respectively are   *(Kumaon 2006)*

$$(l_1a, m_1a, n_1a); (l_2b, m_2b, n_2b); (l_3c, m_3c, n_3c).$$

Let the equation of the sphere be

$$x^2 + y^2 + z^2 + 2ux + 2vy + 2wz + d = 0$$

as it passes through origin, hence, $d = 0$.

It passes through $A(l_1a, m_1a, n_1a)$

$$\therefore \qquad l_1^2a^2 + m_1^2a^2 + n_1^2a^2 + 2ul_1a + 2vm_1a + 2wn_1a = 0$$

or $a + 2ul_1 + 2vm_1 + 2wn_1 = 0.$ ...(1)

Similarly for B and C

$$b + 2ul_2 + 2vm_2 + 2wn_2 = 0 \qquad \ldots(2)$$

and $c + 2ul_3 + 2vm_3 + 2wn_3 = 0$ ...(3)

Now, lines OA, OB, OC are mutually perpendicular, hence $l_1, l_2, l_3; m_1, m_2, m_3; n_1, n_2, n_3$ are the direction cosines of OX, OY, OZ referred to OA, OB, OC as axes (See § 5.2).

Now multiplying (1) by l_1, (2) by l_2, (3) by l_3 and adding, we get

$$al_1 + bl_2 + cl_3 + 2u = 0 \implies u = -\frac{1}{2}(al_1 + bl_2 + cl_3)$$

Similarly,

$$v = -\frac{1}{2}(am_1 + bm_2 + cm_3) \text{ and } w = -\frac{1}{2}(an_1 + bn_2 + cn_3).$$

Substituting the values of u, v, w, the required sphere is obtained.

3. *Prove that the centres of the spheres which touch the lines* $y = mx$, $z = c$; $y = -mx$, $z = -c$; *lie upon the conicoid* $mxy + cz (1 + m^2) = 0$. *(Avadh, 2004)*

Sol. Let the equation of the sphere be

$$x^2 + y^2 + z^2 + 2ux + 2vy + 2wz + d = 0.$$

Line $y = mx$, $z = c$ meets it, where

$$x^2 + m^2x^2 + c^2 + 2ux + 2vmx + 2wc + d = 0$$

or

$$(1 + m^2) x^2 + 2 (u + vm) x + (c^2 + 2wc + d) = 0$$

The line is given to be tangent to the sphere; hence the two values of x given by above equation must be coincident, which gives

$$(u + vm)^2 = (1 + m^2) (c^2 + 2wc + d) \qquad \qquad \text{...(1)}$$

In the same way, line $y = -mx$, $z = -c$ will touch the sphere, if

$$(u - vm)^2 = (1 + m^2) (c^2 - 2wc + d) \qquad \qquad \text{...(2)}$$

Subtracting (2) from (1), we have

$$4uvm = 4wc (1 + m^2)$$

or

$$uvm - wc (1 + m^2) = 0$$

Hence, the locus of centre $(-u, -v, -w)$ will be

$$xym + zc (1 + m^2) = 0.$$

4. *A variable plane through a fixed point* (a, b, c) *cuts the co-ordinate axes in the point* A, B, C. *Show that the locus of the centres of the sphere OABC is*

$$a/x + b/y + c/z = 2.$$

(Avadh, 2005; Meerut, 1998; Poorvanchal, 1995, 96, 97; Kanpur, 1995; Ajmer, 1994, 95; Garhwal, 1994, 99; Kumaon, 1998; Gorakhpur, 1998, 2002; Rohilkhand, 2005)

Sol. Let the sphere $OABC$ be

$$x^2 + y^2 + z^2 + 2ux + 2vy + 2wz = 0,$$

so that u, v, w are different for different spheres. The points A, B, C where it cuts the three axes are $(-2u, 0, 0)$, $(0, -2v, 0)$, $(0, 0, -2w)$. The equation of the plane ABC is

$$\frac{x}{-2u} + \frac{y}{-2v} + \frac{z}{-2w} = 1.$$

Since this plane passes through (a, b, c), we have

$$\frac{a}{-2u} + \frac{b}{-2v} + \frac{c}{-2w} = 1. \qquad \qquad \text{...(2)}$$

If x, y, z be the centre of the sphere (1), then

$$x = -u, \ y = -v, \ z = -w. \qquad \qquad \text{...(3)}$$

From (2) and (3), we obtain

$$\frac{a}{x} + \frac{b}{y} + \frac{c}{z} = 2$$

as the required locus.

5. *A sphere of constant radius 2k passes through the origin and meets the axes in A, B, C. Find the locus of the centroid of the tetrahedron OABC.*   (*U.P.P.C.S, 1999, Avadh, 2000*)

Sol. Let co-ordinates of the points A, B, C be $(a, 0, 0)$, $(0, b, 0)$ and $(0, 0, c)$ respectively.

The equation of the sphere *OABC* is

$$x^2 + y^2 + z^2 - ax - by - cz = 0.$$

Radius of this sphere is given equal to $2k$.

$\therefore$ $a^2 + b^2 + c^2 = 4 (2k)^2 = 16k^2$ ...(1)

Let (x, y, z) be the co-ordinates of the centroid of the tetrahedron *OABC*; then

$$x = a/4, \ y = b/4, \ z = c/4$$

$\Rightarrow$ $a = 4x, \ b = 4y, \ c = 4z.$

Eliminating a, b, c from (1), the required locus is

$$x^2 + y^2 + z^2 = k^2.$$

6. *A sphere whose centre lies in the positive octant passes through the origin and cuts the planes $x = 0$, $y = 0$, $z = 0$ in circles of radii $a\sqrt{2}$, $b\sqrt{2}$, $c\sqrt{2}$, respectively; show that its equation is*

$$x^2 + y^2 + z^2 - 2x \sqrt{b^2 + c^2 - a^2} - 2y \sqrt{c^2 + a^2 - b^2} - 2z \sqrt{a^2 + b^2 - c^2} = 0.$$

Sol. Since the sphere passes through the origin, let its equation be

$$x^2 + y^2 + z^2 + 2ux + 2vy + 2wz = 0$$ ...(1)

Plane $x = 0$ cuts it in

$$y^2 + z^2 + 2vy + 2wz = 0$$

The radius of this circle is $a\sqrt{2}$

$\therefore$ $v^2 + w^2 = 2a^2$

Similarly $w^2 + u^2 = 2b^2$

and $u^2 + v^2 = 2c^2$

These give $u^2 = b^2 + c^2 - a^2$, $v^2 = c^2 + a^2 - b^2$, $w^2 = a^2 + b^2 - c^2$.

Substituting the values of u, v and w in (1), we get the required equation.

7. *A sphere of constant radius k passes through the origin and cuts the axes in A, B and C. Find the locus of the centroid of the triangle ABC.*

                          (*Kanpur, 1996; Poorvanchal, 1994; Ajmer, 1998; Rohilkhand, 2000*)

Sol. Let the co-ordinates of A, B and C be $(a, 0, 0)$, $(0, b, 0)$ and $(0, 0, c)$ respectively. The sphere also passes through the origin $(0, 0, 0)$.

Let the equation of the sphere be

$$x^2 + y^2 + z^2 + 2ux + 2vy + 2wz + d = 0$$

As it passes through $(0, 0, 0)$, $(a, 0, 0)$, $(0, b, 0)$ and $(0, 0, c)$, we have $d = 0$,

$$a^2 + 2ua + d = 0 \ \Rightarrow \ u = -\frac{1}{2}a, \ v = -\frac{1}{2}b, \ w = -\frac{1}{2}c$$

$\therefore$ Required equation of sphere is

$$x^2 + y^2 + z^2 - ax - by - cz = 0$$ ...(i)

Its radius $= \sqrt{\left(\frac{1}{2}a\right)^2 + \left(\frac{1}{2}b\right)^2 + \left(\frac{1}{2}c\right)^2} = k$

$\Rightarrow$ $a^2 + b^2 + c^2 = 4k^2$ ...(ii)

If (x_1, y_1, z_1) be the co-ordinates of the centroid of $\triangle ABC$, then

$$x_1 = \frac{1}{3}a, \; y_1 = \frac{1}{3}b, \; z_1 = \frac{1}{3}c \; \Rightarrow \; a = 3x_1, \; b = 3y_1, \; c = 3z_1.$$

Substituting these values in (ii) and generalizing, the required locus is

$$9(x^2 + y^2 + z^2) = 4k^2.$$

EXERCISES

1. Find the equation of the sphere through the four points

   $(4, -1, 2), (0, -2, 3), (1, -5, -1), (2, 0, 1).$ (Avadh, 2002; Kumaon, 2001)

   [**Ans.** $x^2 + y^2 + z^2 - 4x + 6y - 2z + 5 = 0$]

2. Find the equation of the sphere through the four points

   $(0, 0, 0), (-a, \dot{b}, c), (a, -b, c), (a, b, -c)$

   and determine its radius.   (Garhwal, 1996)

   $$\left[\mathbf{Ans.} \; \frac{x^2 + y^2 + z^2}{a^2 + b^2 + c^2} - \frac{x}{a} - \frac{y}{b} - \frac{z}{c} = 0; \; \frac{1}{2}(a^2 + b^2 + c^2)\sqrt{a^{-2} + b^{-2} + c^{-2}} \right]$$

3. Find the equation of the sphere passing through the origin and the points $(1, 0, 0)$, $(0, 2, 0)$ and $(0, 0, 3)$.   (Kanpur, 2003) [**Ans.** $x^2 + y^2 + z^2 - x - 2y - 3z = 0$]

4. Obtain the equation of the sphere circumscribing the tetrahedron whose faces are

   $x = 0, \; y = 0, \; z = 0, \; x/a + y/b + z/c = 1.$ (Kumaon, 1997, 2002)

5. Obtain the equation of the sphere which passes through the three points

   $(1, 0, 0), (0, 1, 0), (0, 0, 1),$

   and has its radius as small as possible.   (Agra, 1994; Garhwal, 2000)

   [**Ans.** $3(x^2 + y^2 + z^2) - 2(x + y + z) - 1 = 0$]

6. Show that the equation of the sphere passing through the three points $(3, 0, 2), (-1, 1, 1)$, $(2, -5, 4)$ and having its centre on the plane $2x + 3y + 4z = 6$ is

   $$x^2 + y^2 + z^2 + 4y - 6z = 1.$$

   (M.D.U. Rohtak, 1997; Rohilkhand, 2001)

7. Obtain the sphere having its centre on the line $5y + 2z = 0 = 2x - 3y$ and passing through the two points $(0, -2, -4), (2, -1, -1).$

   (Garhwal, 1995; Bundelkhand, 1998; Gorakhpur, 2003)

   [**Ans.** $x^2 + y^2 + z^2 - 6x - 4y + 10z + 12 = 0$]

8. Find the equation to a sphere passing through the points $(1, -3, 4), (1, -5, 2), (1, -3, 0)$ and having centre on the plane $x + y + z = 0.$ (Kanpur, 1999)

   [**Ans.** $x^2 + y^2 + z^2 - 2x + 6y - 4z + 10 = 0$]

9. A sphere of constant radius r passes through the origin $\dot{O}$ and cuts the axes in A, B, C. Find the locus of the foot of the perpendicular from O to the plane ABC.

   (Bundelkhand, 1996; Poorvanchal, 1998; Ajmer, 1997; Agra, 1995; Garhwal, 1998; Rohilkhand, 2000; Kumaon, 1994, 96, 2000)

   [**Ans.** $(x^2 + y^2 + z^2)^2 (x^{-2} + y^{-2} + z^{-2}) = 4r^2$]

10. If O be the centre of a sphere of radius unity and A, B be two points in a line with O such that $OA \cdot OB = 1$, and if P be a variable point on the sphere, show that

    $$PA : PB = \text{constant}.$$

6.3.1. Plane Section of a Sphere

Consider a sphere and a plane. We suppose that the sphere and the plane have points in common, *i.e.*, intersect. The set of points common to a sphere and a plane, assuming that the sphere and the plane intersect, is called a *Plane Section* of a sphere. We show that *the locus of points common to a sphere and a plane is a circle, i.e., a plane section of a sphere is a circle.*

Let O be the centre of the sphere and P, a point on the plane section. Let ON be perpendicular to the given plane; N being the foot of the perpendicular.

As ON is perpendicular to the plane which contains the line NP, we have

$$ON \perp NP \implies NP^2 = OP^2 - ON^2.$$

Now, O and N being fixed points, this relation shows that NP is constant for all positions of P on the section.

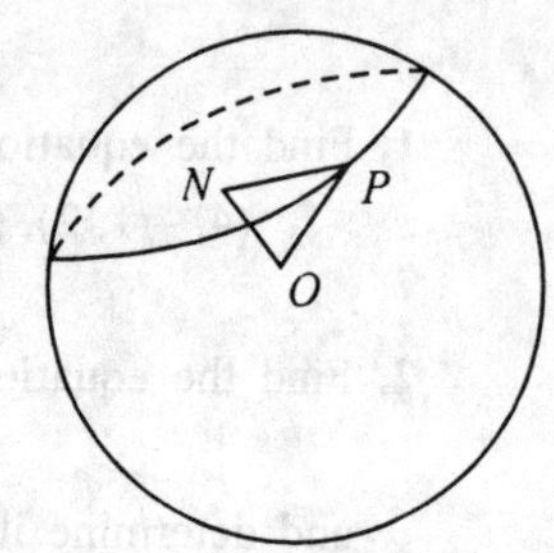

Hence, the locus of P is a circle whose centre is the point N, *viz.*, the foot of the perpendicular from the centre of the sphere to the plane.

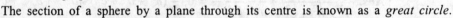

Fig. 36

The section of a sphere by a plane through its centre is known as a *great circle*.

The centre and radius of a great circle are the same as those of the sphere.

There exist points of intersection of a sphere and a plane if and only if the distance of the centre of the sphere from the plane is less than or equal to the radius of the sphere.

Thus, the sphere

$$x^2 + y^2 + z^2 + 2ux + 2vy + 2wz + d = 0$$

will intersect the plane

$$lx + my + nz = p$$

if and only if

$$(ul + vm + wn + p)^2 \le (l^2 + m^2 + n^2)(u^2 + v^2 + w^2 - d).$$

Cor. *The circle through three given points lies entirely on any sphere through the same three points.*

Thus, the condition of a sphere containing a given circle is equivalent to that of its passing through any three of its points.

6.3.2. Intersection of Two Spheres

We now consider two spheres and assume that the given spheres have points in common, *i.e.*, intersect. Assuming that two given spheres intersect, we show that *the locus of the points of intersection of two spheres is a circle.*

The co-ordinates of points, if any, common to the two spheres

$$S_1 = x^2 + y^2 + z^2 + 2u_1x + 2v_1y + 2w_1z + d_1 = 0,$$
$$S_2 = x^2 + y^2 + z^2 + 2u_2x + 2v_2y + 2w_2z + d_2 = 0$$

satisfy both these equations and, therefore, they also satisfy the equation

$$S_1 - S_2 = 2x(u_1 - u_2) + 2y(v_1 - v_2) + 2z(w_1 - w_2) + (d_1 - d_2) = 0$$

which, being of the first degree, represents a plane.

Thus, the points of intersection of the two spheres are the same as those of any one of them and this plane and, therefore, they lie on a circle. [See § 6.3.1].

6.3.3. Sphere With a Given Diameter

To find the equation of the sphere described on the segment joining the points

$$A(x_1, y_1, z_1), B(x_2, y_2, z_2)$$

as a diameter.

Let $P(x, y, z)$ be a point on the sphere described on the segment AB as diameter.

Since the section of the required sphere by the plane through the three points P, A, B, is a great circle having AB as diameter, the point P lies on a semi-circle and, therefore

$$PA \perp PB.$$

The direction cosines of PA, PB being proportional to

$$x - x_1, y - y_1, z - z_1 \text{ and } x - x_2, y - y_2, z - z_2$$

they will be perpendicular, if

$$(x - x_1)(x - x_2) + (y - y_1)(y - y_2) + (z - z_1)(z - z_2) = 0,$$

which is the required equation of the sphere.

6.4. EQUATIONS OF A CIRCLE

A circle is the intersection of its plane with some sphere through it. As such, a circle can be represented by *two* equations, representing a sphere and the other a plane.

Thus, the two equations

$$x^2 + y^2 + z^2 + 2ux + 2vy + 2wz + d = 0, \; lx + my + nz = p$$

taken together represent a circle.

A circle can also be represented by the equations of any two spheres through it.

Note. The reader may note that the equations

$$x^2 + y^2 + z^2 + 2fy + c = 0, \; z = 0$$

also represent a circle which is the intersection of the cylinder

$$x^2 + y^2 + z^2 + 2fy + c = 0$$

with the plane

$$z = 0.$$

EXAMPLES

1. *Find the equations of the circle circumscribing the triangle formed by the three points*
$$(a, 0, 0), (0, b, 0), (0, 0, c).$$

Obtain also the co-ordinates of the centre of this circle.

Sol. The equation of the plane passing through these three points is

$$x/a + y/b + z/c = 1.$$

The required circle is the curve of intersection of this plane with *any* sphere through the three points.

To find the equation of this sphere, a fourth point is necessary which for the sake of convenience, we take as origin.

If

$$x^2 + y^2 + z^2 + 2ux + 2vy + 2wz + d = 0$$

be the sphere through these four points, we have

$$a^2 + 2ua + d = 0; \; b^2 + 2vb + d = 0; \; c^2 + 2wc + d = 0;$$
$$d = 0.$$

These give

$$d = 0, \; u = -\frac{1}{2}a, \; v = -\frac{1}{2}b, \; w = -\frac{1}{2}c.$$

Thus, the equation of the sphere is

$$x^2 + y^2 + z^2 - ax - by - cz = 0$$

Hence

$$x^2 + y^2 + z^2 - ax - by - cz = 0, \quad \frac{x}{a} + \frac{y}{b} + \frac{z}{c} = 1$$

are the equations of the circle.

The centre of this circle, is the foot of the perpendicular from the centre $\left(\frac{1}{2} a, \frac{1}{2} b, \frac{1}{2} c \right)$ of the sphere to the plane

$$\frac{x}{a} + \frac{y}{b} + \frac{z}{c} = 1.$$

The equations of the perpendicular are

$$\frac{x - \dfrac{1}{2} a}{1/a} = \frac{y - \dfrac{1}{2} b}{1/b} = \frac{z - \dfrac{1}{2} c}{1/c} = r, \text{ say}$$

$$\Rightarrow \qquad \left(\frac{r}{a} + \frac{a}{2}, \frac{r}{b} + \frac{b}{2}, \frac{r}{c} + \frac{c}{2} \right),$$

is any point on the line. Its intersection with the plane is given by

$$r \left(\frac{1}{a^2} + \frac{1}{b^2} + \frac{1}{c^2} \right) + \frac{1}{2} = 0 \Rightarrow r = -\frac{1}{(2 \Sigma a^{-2})}.$$

Thus, the centre is

$$\left[\frac{a (b^{-2} + c^{-2})}{2 \Sigma a^{-2}}, \frac{b (c^{-2} + a^{-2})}{2 \Sigma a^{-2}}, \frac{c (a^{-2} + b^{-2})}{2 \Sigma a^{-2}} \right].$$

2. *Show that the centres of all sections of the sphere*

$$x^2 + y^2 + z^2 = r^2$$

by planes through a point (x', y', z') *lie on the sphere*

$$x (x - x') + y (y - y') + z (z - z') = 0.$$

Sol. The plane which cuts the sphere in a circle with centre (f, g, h) is

$$f (x - f) + g (y - g) + h (z - h) = 0.$$

It will pass through (x', y', z'), if

$$f (x' - f) + g (y' - g) + h (z' - h) = 0,$$

and accordingly the locus of (f, g, h) is the sphere

$$x (x' - x) + y (y' - y) + z (z' - z) = 0.$$

3. *A variable plane is parallel to the given plane* $x/a + y/b + z/c = 0$ *and meets the axes in A, B, C. Prove that the circle ABC lies on the cone*

$$yz (b/c + c/b) + zx (c/a + a/c) + xy (a/b + b/a) = 0.$$

(Ajmer, 1996; Lucknow, 1994, 96; Rohilkhand, 1998; Garhwal, 1995; Kanpur, 1997)

Sol. Let the variable plane, which is parallel to the given plane, be

$$x/a + y/b + z/c = k \qquad \qquad ...(1)$$

This meets the axes in $A\ (ak, 0, 0)$, $B\ (0, bk, 0)$ and $C\ (0, 0, ck)$. Hence, equation of the sphere $OABC$ is

$$x^2 + y^2 + z^2 - akx - bky - ckz = 0$$

or

$$x^2 + y^2 + z^2 - k\ (ax + by + cz) = 0 \qquad \text{...(2)}$$

The circle ABC lies on both, the plane (1) and the sphere (2). Hence, (1) and (2) together represent the circle ABC and the locus of the circle ABC will be obtained by eliminating k from (1) and (2). Thus, the locus of circle ABC is

$$(x^2 + y^2 + z^2) - (x/a + y/b + z/c)\ (ax + by + cz) = 0$$

or

$$yz\ (b/c + c/b) + zx\ (c/a + a/c) + xy\ (a/b + b/a) = 0.$$

4. *If r be the radius of the circle*

$$x^2 + y^2 + z^2 + 2ux + 2vy + 2wz + d = 0,\ lx + my + nz = 0,$$

prove that

$$(r^2 + d)\ (l^2 + m^2 + n^2) = (mw - nv)^2 + (nu - lw)^2 + (lv - mu)^2.\quad \textit{(Rohilkhand, 1998)}$$

Sol. The equation of the given sphere is

$$x^2 + y^2 + z^2 + 2ux + 2vy + 2wz + d = 0 \qquad \text{...(1)}$$

having centre at $(-u, -v, -w)$ and radius $CP = \sqrt{u^2 + v^2 + w^2 - d}$.

Now distance CN of centre of sphere from the plane is length of perpendicular from centre of sphere on the plane

$$lx + my + nz = 0.$$

Hence,

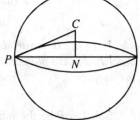

$$CN = \frac{lu + mv + nw}{\sqrt{l^2 + m^2 + n^2}}$$

$$CP = \sqrt{u^2 + v^2 + w^2 - d},\ NP = r$$

$$r^2 = CP^2 - CN^2 = u^2 + v^2 + w^2 - d - \frac{(lu + mv + nw)^2}{l^2 + m^2 + n^2}$$

Fig. 37

$$\Rightarrow (r^2 + d)\ (l^2 + m^2 + n^2) = (u^2 + v^2 + w^2)\ (l^2 + m^2 + n^2) - (lu + mv + nw)^2$$

$$\Rightarrow (r^2 + d)\ (l^2 + m^2 + n^2) = (mw - nv)^2 + (nu - lw)^2 + (lv - mu)^2,$$

by Lagrange's identity.

5. *A is a point OX and B on OY so that the angle OAB is constant (= α). On AB as diameter a circle is described whose plane is parallel to OZ. Prove that as AB varies, the circle generates the cone $2xy - z^2 \sin 2\alpha = 0$.* *(Agra, 1996; Kanpur, 1996; Garhwal, 2001)*

Sol. Let A be the point $(a, 0, 0)$ and $B\ (0, b, 0)$.

Then since $\angle OAB = \alpha$, we have

$$\tan \alpha = b/a \qquad \text{...(1)}$$

Now, a sphere on AB as diameter is

$$(x - a)\ x + (y - b)\ y + z^2 = 0$$

$$\Rightarrow \qquad x^2 + y^2 + z^2 = ax + by \qquad \text{...(2)}$$

A plane through AB parallel to OZ is

$$x/a + y/b = 1 \qquad \text{...(3)}$$

The required circle is given by intersection of (2) and (3). Now to determine the locus of the circle, we will eliminate a and b from (2), with the help of (1) and (3). So, we have

$$x^2 + y^2 + z^2 = (ax + by)\ (x/a + y/b)$$

$\Rightarrow \qquad\qquad x^2 + y^2 + z^2 = x^2 + y^2 + xy\,(a/b + b/a)$

$\Rightarrow \qquad\qquad\qquad\qquad z^2 = xy\,(\tan\alpha + \cot\alpha)$

$\Rightarrow \qquad\qquad\qquad\qquad z^2 = 2xy/\sin 2\alpha$

$\Rightarrow \qquad\qquad\qquad\qquad 2xy - z^2\sin 2\alpha = 0.$

6. *Show that the sphere*

$$S_1 \equiv x^2 + y^2 + z^2 + 2u_1 x + 2v_1 y + 2w_1 z + d_1 = 0$$

cuts $\qquad\qquad S_2 \equiv x^2 + y^2 + z^2 + 2u_2 x + 2v_2 y + 2w_2 z + d_2 = 0$

in a great circle if

$$2\,(u_2^{\,2} + v_2^{\,2} + w_2^{\,2}) - d_2 = 2\,(u_1 u_2 + v_1 v_2 + w_1 w_2) - d_1$$

or $\qquad\qquad 2\,(u_1 u_2 + v_1 v_2 + w_1 w_2) = 2r_2^{\,2} + d_1 + d_2,$

where r_2 *is the radius of the second sphere.*

Sol. The plane of the circle, *i.e.*, the plane in which their circle of intersection lies, is $S_1 - S_2 = 0,$

or $\qquad 2\,(u_1 - u_2)\,x + 2\,(v_1 - v_2)\,y + 2\,(w_1 - w_2)\,z + d_1 - d_2 = 0.$ ...(1)

The circle of intersection will be the great circle of the sphere S_2 only when the above plane passes through the centre of the sphere S_2, *i.e.*, passes through the point $(-u_2, -v_2, -w_2)$. Hence,

$$2\,(u_1 - u_2)\,(-u_2) + 2\,(v_1 - v_2)\,(-v_2) + 2\,(w_1 - w_2)\,(-w_2) + d_1 - d_2 = 0$$

or $\qquad\qquad 2\,(u_2^{\,2} + v_2^{\,2} + w_2^{\,2}) - d_2 = 2\,(u_1 u_2 + v_1 v_2 + w_1 w_2) - d_1$

$\Rightarrow \qquad\qquad 2\,(u_1 u_2 + v_1 v_2 + w_1 w_2) = 2r_2^{\,2} + d_1 + d_2.$

7. *POP' is a variable diameter of the ellipse* $z = 0$, $x^2/a^2 + y^2/b^2 = 1$, *and a circle is described in the plane PP'ZZ' on PP' as diameter. Prove that as PP' varies, the circle generates the surface*

$$(x^2 + y^2 + z^2)\,(x^2/a^2 + y^2/b^2) = x^2 + y^2.$$

Sol. Let P be the point $(a\cos\phi,\ b\sin\phi,\ 0)$; then P' is the point $(-a\cos\phi,\ -b\sin\phi,\ 0)$ where ϕ varies as POP' varies.

Equation of the sphere on PP' as diameter is

$$(x - a\cos\phi)\,(x + a\cos\phi) + (y - b\sin\phi)\,(y + b\sin\phi) + z^2 = 0$$

or $\qquad\qquad x^2 + y^2 + z^2 = a^2\cos^2\phi + b^2\sin\phi$ ...(1)

The equation of $PP'ZZ'$, *i.e.*, the plane through PP' parallel to z-axis, is

$$x/a\cos\phi = y/b\sin\phi$$ ...(2)

The required circle is given by the intersection of (1) and (2). The locus of the circle will be obtained by eliminating ϕ from (1) and (2).

From (2), we have

$$\frac{x/a}{\cos\phi} = \frac{y/a}{\sin\phi} = \frac{\sqrt{x^2/a^2 + y^2/b^2}}{1}$$

$\therefore \qquad a\cos\phi = x/\sqrt{x^2/a^2 + y^2/b^2}$ and $b\sin\phi = y/\sqrt{x^2/a^2 + y^2/b^2}$

Putting these values in (1), we get

$$x^2 + y^2 + z^2 = \frac{x^2}{(x^2/a^2 + y^2/b^2)} - \frac{y^2}{(x^2/a^2 + y^2/b^2)}$$

or $\qquad\qquad (x^2 + y^2 + z^2)\,(x^2/a^2 + y^2/b^2) = x^2 + y^2.$

EXERCISES

1. Find the centre and the radius of the circle
$$x + 2y + 2z = 15, \; x^2 + y^2 + z^2 - 2y - 4z = 11. \qquad (Gorakhpur, \; 2001)$$
[**Ans.** $(1, 3, 4), \sqrt{7}$]

2. Find the equations of that section of the sphere
$$x^2 + y^2 + z^2 = a^2$$
of which a given internal point (x_1, y_1, z_1) is the centre.

[**Hint**. The plane through (x_1, y_1, z_1) drawn perpendicular to the line joining this point to the centre $(0, 0, 0)$ of the sphere determines the required section.]
[**Ans.** $x^2 + y^2 + z^2 = a^2, \; xx_1 + yy_1 + zz_1 = x_1^2 + y_1^2 + z_1^2$]

3. Obtain the equations of the circle lying on the sphere
$$x^2 + y^2 + z^2 - 2x + 4y - 6z + 3 = 0$$
and having its centre at $(2, 3, -4)$.
[**Ans.** $x^2 + y^2 + z^2 - 2x + 4y - 6z + 3 = 0 = x + 5y - 7z - 45$]

4. O is the origin and A, B, C are the points
$$(4a, 4b, 4c), \; (4b, 4c, 4a), \; (4c, 4a, 4b).$$
Show that the sphere
$$x^2 + y^2 + z^2 - 2 \, (x + y + z) \, (a + b + c) + 8 \, (bc + ca + ab) = 0$$
passes through the nine point circles of the faces of the tetrahedron $OABC$.

5. Find the equation of the diameter of the sphere $x^2 + y^2 + z^2 = 29$ such that a rotation about it will transfer the point $(4, -3, 2)$ to the point $(5, 0, -2)$ along a great circle of the sphere. Find also the angle through which the sphere must be so rotated.

[**Ans.** $x/2 = y/6 = z/6 = \dfrac{1}{6} z, \; \cos^{-1} (16/29)$]

6. Show that the following sets of points are concyclic :
   (i) $(5, 0, 2), (2, -6, 0), (7, -3, 8), (4, -9, 6)$.
   (ii) $(-8, 5, 2), (-5, 2, 2), (-7, 6, 6), (-4, 3, 6)$.

6.4.1. Sphere Through a Given Circle

The equation
$$S + kU = 0$$
represents a sphere through the circle with equations
$$S = 0, \; U = 0,$$
where
$$S \equiv x^2 + y^2 + z^2 + 2ux + 2vy + 2wz + d,$$
$$U \equiv lx + my + nz - p$$

Thus, the set of spheres through the circle
$$S = 0, \; U = 0,$$
is
$$\{S + kU = 0; \; k \text{ is the parameter}\}.$$

Also the equation
$$S + kS' = 0,$$
represents a sphere through the circle with equations
$$S = 0, \; S' = 0,$$

where

$$S \equiv x^2 + y^2 + z^2 + 2ux + 2vy + 2wz + d$$
$$S' \equiv x^2 + y^2 + z^2 + 2u'x + 2v'y + 2w'z + d'$$

for all values of k.

The set of spheres through the circle

$$S = 0, \ S' = 0$$

is thus

$$\{S + kS' = 0; \ k \text{ is the parameter}\}.$$

Here k is a parameter which may be so chosen that these equations fulfil one more condition.

Note 1. We notice that the equation of the plane of the circle through the two given spheres

$$S = 0, \ S' = 0$$

is

$$S - S' = 2 \ (u - u') \ x + 2 \ (v - v') \ y + 2 \ (w - w') \ z + d - d' = 0.$$

From this we see that the equation of any sphere through the circle

$$S = 0, \ S' = 0$$

is also of the form

$$S + k \ (S - S') = 0;$$

k, being the parameter.

This form sometimes proves comparatively more convenient.

Note 2. It is important to remember that the general equation of a sphere through the circle

$$x^2 + y^2 + 2gx + 2fy + c = 0, \ z = 0$$

is

$$x^2 + y^2 + z^2 + 2gx + 2fy + 2kz + c = 0,$$

where k is the parameter.

EXAMPLES

1. *Find the equation of the sphere through the circle*

$$x^2 + y^2 + z^2 = 9, \ 2x + 3y + 4z = 5$$

and the point $(1, 2, 3)$.   (*M.D.U. Rohtak, 2001; Rohilkhand, 1994; Agra, 1996; Gorakhpur, 1997, 2000; Poorvanchal, 1994*)

Sol. The sphere

$$x^2 + y^2 + z^2 - 9 + k \ (2x + 3y + 4z - 5) = 0$$

passes through the given circle for all values of k.

It will pass through $(1, 2, 3)$ if

$$5 + 15k = 0 \ \Rightarrow \ k = -\frac{1}{3}.$$

The required equation of the sphere, therefore, is

$$3 \ (x^2 + y^2 + z^2) - 2x - 3y - 4z - 22 = 0.$$

2. *Show that the two circles*

$$x^2 + y^2 + z^2 - y + 2z = 0, \ x - y + z - 2 = 0;$$
$$x^2 + y^2 + z^2 + x - 3y + z - 5 = 0, \ 2x - y + 4z - 1 = 0;$$

lie on the same sphere and find its equation.   (*Avadh, 2000; Garhwal, 1999*)

Sol. The equations of *any* sphere through the first circle is

$$x^2 + y^2 + z^2 - y + 2z + k (x - y + z - 2) = 0, \qquad ...(i)$$

and that of *any* sphere through the second circle is

$$x^2 + y^2 + z^2 + x - 3y + z - 5 + k' (2x - y + 4z - 1) = 0 \qquad ...(ii)$$

The equations (*i*) and (*ii*) will represent the same sphere, if k, k' can be chosen so as to satisfy the four linear equations.

$$k = 2k' + 1, \quad -1 - k = -k' - 3,$$

$$2 + k = 4k' + 1, \quad -2k = -k' - 5$$

The first two of these equations give $k = 3$, $k' = 1$, and these values clearly satisfy the remaining two equations also. These four equations in k, k' being consistent, the two circles lie on the same sphere, viz.,

$$x^2 + y^2 + z^2 - y + 2z + 3 (x - y + z - 2) = 0$$

$$\Rightarrow \qquad x^2 + y^2 + z^2 + 3x - 4y + 5z - 6 = 0.$$

3. *Prove that the plane $x + 2y - z = 4$ cuts the sphere $x^2 + y^2 + z^2 - x + z - 2 = 0$ in a circle of radius unity and find the equation of sphere which has this circle for one of its great circle.*

(*Meerut, 1997; Rohilkhand, 1999; Avadh, 1999, 2001; Garhwal, 1994*)

Sol. The centre of the given sphere is $(1/2, 0, -1/2)$ and its radius

$$= \sqrt{(1/2)^2 + 0^2 + (-1/2)^2 - (-1)} = \sqrt{5/2} = r.$$

Length of perpendicular from $(1/2, 0, -1/2)$ to the plane is

$$\frac{1}{2}\sqrt{6} = p \text{ (say)}$$

∴   Radius of circle $= \sqrt{r^2 - p^2} = \sqrt{5/2 - 6/4} = 1.$

Now, equation of a sphere through given circle is

$$x^2 + y^2 + z^2 - x + z - 2 + \lambda (x + 2y - z - 4) = 0$$

or $\qquad x^2 + y^2 + z^2 + (\lambda - 1) x + 2\lambda y + (1 - \lambda) z - (2 + 4\lambda) = 0 \qquad ...(1)$

Its centre is $[-(\lambda - 1)/2, -\lambda, -(1 - \lambda)/2]$.

If the circle is a great circle of the sphere (1), then its centre should lie on the plane

$$x + 2y - z - 4 = 0$$

of the circle.

∴ $\qquad -\frac{1}{2}(\lambda - 1) + 2(-\lambda) + \frac{1}{2}(1 - \lambda) - 4 = 0$

or $\qquad -3\lambda - 3 = 0$ or $\lambda = -1$

From (1), the equation of required sphere is

$$x^2 + y^2 + z^2 - 2x - 2y + 2z + 2 = 0.$$

EXERCISES

1. Find the equation of the sphere through the circle

$$x^2 + y^2 + z^2 + 2x + 3y + 6 = 0, \quad x - 2y + 4z - 9 = 0,$$

and the centre of the sphere

$$x^2 + y^2 + z^2 - 2x + 4y - 6z + 5 = 0.$$

[**Ans.** $x^2 + y^2 + z^2 + 7y - 8z + 24 = 0$]

2. Find the equation to the sphere which passes through point (α, β, γ) and the circle $x^2 + y^2 = a^2$, $z = 0$.   (*Avadh, 1997; Kanpur, 1998*)

[**Ans.** $(x^2 + y^2 + z^2 - a^2) \gamma + (a^2 - \alpha^2 - \beta^2 - \gamma^2) z = 0$]

3. Show that the equation of the sphere having its centre on the plane

$$4x - 5y - z = 3$$

and passing through the circle with equations

$$x^2 + y^2 + z^2 - 2x - 3y + 4z + 8 = 0, \; x^2 + y^2 + z^2 + 4x + 5y - 6z + 2 = 0;$$

is $x^2 + y^2 + z^2 + 7x + 9y - 11z - 1 = 0.$

4. Obtain the equation of the sphere having the circle

$$x^2 + y^2 + z^2 + 10y - 4z - 8 = 0, \; x + y + z = 3$$

as the great circle.   (*Gorakhpur, 2000*)

[**Hint.** The centre of the required sphere lies on the plane $x + y + z = 3$]

[**Ans.** $x^2 + y^2 + z^2 - 4x + 6y - 8z + 4 = 0$]

5. A sphere S has points $(0, 1, 0)$, $(3, -5, 2)$ at opposite ends of a diameter. Find the equation of the sphere having the intersection of the sphere S with the plane

$$5x - 2y + 4z + 7 = 0$$

as a great circle.   (*Delhi 2005*)   [**Ans.** $x^2 + y^2 + z^2 + 2x + 2y + 2z + 2 = 0$]

6. Obtain the equation of the sphere which passes through the circle $x^2 + y^2 = 4, z = 0$ and is cut by the plane $x + 2y + 2z = 0$ in a circle of radius 3.   (*U.P.P.C.S. 2001*)

[**Ans.** $x^2 + y^2 + z^2 = 6z - 4 = 0$]

7. Show that the two circles

$$2 (x^2 + y^2 + z^2) + 8x - 13y + 17z - 17 = 0, \; 2x + y - 3z + 1 = 0;$$
$$x^2 + y^2 + z^2 + 3x - 4y + 3z = 0, \; x - y + 2z - 4 = 0;$$

lie on the same sphere and find its equation.   (*Kanpur, 1995*)

[**Ans.** $x^2 + y^2 + z^2 + 5x - 6y + 7z - 8 = 0$]

8. Prove that the circles

$$x^2 + y^2 + z^2 - 2x + 3y + 4z - 5 = 0, \; 5y + 6z + 1 = 0;$$
$$x^2 + y^2 + z^2 - 3x - 4y + 5z - 6 = 0, \; x + 2y - 7z = 0;$$

lie on the same sphere and find its equation.

(*Kanpur, 1995; Lucknow, 1995; Avadh, 1994, 96; Garhwal, 1993, 2004*)

[**Ans.** $x^2 + y^2 + z^2 - 2x - 2y - 2z - 6 = 0$]

6.5. INTERSECTION OF A SPHERE AND A LINE

Let

$$x^2 + y^2 + z^2 + 2ux + 2vy + 2wz + d = 0 \qquad \qquad ...(1)$$

and

$$\frac{x - \alpha}{l} = \frac{y - \beta}{m} = \frac{z - \gamma}{n}; \qquad \qquad ...(2)$$

be the equations of a sphere and a line respectively.

The point $(lr + \alpha, \, mr + \beta, \, nr + \gamma)$ which lies on the given line (2) for all values of r, will also lie on the given sphere (1), for those of the values of r which satisfy the equation

$$r^2 (l^2 + m^2 + n^2) + 2r [l (\alpha + u) + m (\beta + v) + n (\lambda + w)]$$
$$+ (\alpha^2 + \beta^2 + \gamma^2 + 2u\alpha + 2v\beta + 2w\gamma + d) = 0, \qquad ...(A)$$

and this latter being a quadratic equation in r, gives two values say, r_1, r_2 of r. We suppose that the equation has real roots so that r_1, r_2 are real. Then

$$(lr_1 + \alpha, mr_1 + \beta, nr_1 + \gamma), (lr_2 + \alpha, mr_2 + \beta, nr_2 + \gamma)$$

are the two points of intersection.

Ex. Find the co-ordinates of the points where the line

$$\frac{1}{4}(x + 3) = \frac{1}{3}(y + 4) = -\frac{1}{5}(z - 8)$$

intersects the sphere

$$x^2 + y^2 + z^2 + 2x - 10y = 23 \qquad \textbf{[Ans. } (1, -1, 3); (5, 2, -2)]$$

6.5.1. Power of a Point

Let l, m, n be the direction cosines of the given line (2) in § 6.5, so that $l^2 + m^2 + n^2 = 1$. Then r_1, r_2 are the distances of the point A (α, β, γ) from the points of intersection P and Q and we have

$$AP \cdot AQ = r_1 r_2 = \alpha^2 + \beta^2 + \gamma^2 + 2u\alpha + 2v\beta + 2w\gamma + d$$

which is independent of the direction cosines l, m, n.

Thus, *if from a fixed point A, chords be drawn in any direction to intersect a given sphere in P and Q, then $AP \cdot AQ$ is constant.* This constant is called the *Power* of the point A with respect to the sphere.

EXAMPLE

Show that the sum of the squares of the intercepts made by a given sphere on any three mutually perpendicular straight lines through a fixed point is constant.

Sol. Take the fixed point O as the origin and *any* three mutually perpendicular lines through it as the co-ordinate axes. With this choice of axes, let the equation of the given sphere be

$$x^2 + y^2 + z^2 + 2ux + 2vy + 2wz + d = 0.$$

The X-axis, ($y = 0 = z$) meets the sphere in points given by

$$x^2 + 2ux + d = 0,$$

so that if x_1, x_2 be its roots, the two points of intersection are (x_1, 0, 0), (x_2, 0, 0).

Also we have

$$x_1 + x_2 = -2u, \ x_1 x_2 = d.$$

$\therefore$ (intercept on X-axis)$^2 = (x_1 - x_2)^2 = (x_1 + x_2)^2 - 4x_1 x_2 = 4 (u^2 - d).$

Similarly

(intercept on Y-axis)$^2 = 4 (v^2 - d),$

(intercept on Z-axis)$^2 = 4 (w^2 - d).$

The sum of the squares of the intercepts

$$= 4 (u^2 + v^2 + w^2 - 3d)$$
$$= 4 (u^2 + v^2 + w^2 - d) - 8d = 4r^2 - 8p,$$

where r is the radius of the given sphere and p is the power of the given point with respect to the sphere.

Since the sphere and the point are both given, r and p are both constants.

Hence, the result.

Note. The coefficients u, v, w and d in the equation of the sphere will be different for different sets of mutually perpendicular lines through O as axes.

Since the sphere is fixed and the point O is also fixed, the expression
$$r^2 = u^2 + v^2 + w^2 - d$$
for the square of the radius and
$$p = d,$$
for the power of the point, with respect to the sphere will be invariant.

EXERCISES

1. Find the locus of a point whose powers with respect, to two given spheres are in a constant ratio.

2. Show that the locus of the mid-points of a system of parallel chords of a sphere is a plane through its centre perpendicular to the given chords.

6.6. EQUATION OF A TANGENT PLANE

To find the equation of the tangent plane at any point (α, β, γ) *of the sphere*
$$x^2 + y^2 + z^2 + 2ux + 2vy + 2wz + d = 0.$$

(Agra, 1998; Kanpur, 2002, 03, 04, 05; Patna. 2003)

The point (α, β, γ) lies on the sphere
$$\Rightarrow \qquad \alpha^2 + \beta^2 + \gamma^2 + 2u\alpha + 2v\beta + 2w\gamma + d = 0. \qquad \qquad ...(i)$$
The points of intersection of any line
$$\frac{x - \alpha}{l} = \frac{y - \beta}{m} = \frac{z - \gamma}{n} = r \qquad \qquad ...(ii)$$
through (α, β, γ) with the given sphere are
$$(lr + \alpha, \ mr + \beta, \ nr + \gamma)$$
where the values of r are the roots of the quadratic equation
$$r^2 (l^2 + m^2 + n^2) + 2r [l (\alpha + u) + m (\beta + v) + n (\gamma + w)]$$
$$+ (\alpha^2 + \beta^2 + \gamma^2 + 2u\alpha + 2v\beta + 2w\gamma + d) = 0.$$

By virtue of the condition (i), one root of this quadratic equation is zero so that one of the points of intersection coincides with (α, β, γ).

In order that the second point of intersection may also coincide with (α, β, γ), the second value of r must also vanish and this requires,
$$l (\alpha + u) + m (\beta + v) + n (\gamma + w) = 0. \qquad \qquad ...(iii)$$
Thus, the line
$$\frac{x - \alpha}{l} = \frac{y - \beta}{m} = \frac{z - \gamma}{n}$$
meets the sphere in two coincident points at (α, β, γ) and so is a *tangent line* to it thereat for any set of values l, m, n which satisfy the condition (iii).

The locus of the tangent lines at (α, β, γ), obtained by eliminating l, m, n between the condition (iii) and the equations (ii) of the line is
$$(x - \alpha) (\alpha + u) + (y - \beta) (\beta + v) + (z - \gamma) (\gamma + w) = 0$$
$$\Leftrightarrow \qquad \alpha x + \beta y + \gamma z + u (x + \alpha) + v (y + \beta) + w (z + \gamma) + d$$
$$= \alpha^2 + \beta^2 + \gamma^2 + 2u\alpha + 2v\beta + 2w\gamma + d = 0 \qquad \text{[From } (i)]$$
which is a plane known as the *tangent plane* at (α, β, γ).

It follows that
$$(\alpha + u) x + (\beta + v) y + (\gamma + w) z + (u\alpha + v\beta + w\gamma + d) = 0$$
is the equation of the tangent plane to the given sphere at the given point (α, β, γ).

Cor. 1. *The line joining the centre of a sphere to any point on it is perpendicular to the tangent plane thereat,* for the direction cosines of the line joining the centre $(-u, -v, -w)$ and the point (α, β, γ) on the sphere are proportional to

$$(\alpha + u, \beta + v, \gamma + w)$$

which are also the coefficients of x, y, z in the equation of the tangent plane at (α, β, γ). Hence, the result.

Cor. 2. If a plane or a line touches a sphere, then the length of the perpendicular from its centre to the plane or the line is equal to its radius.

Note. Any line in the tangent plane through its plane of contact touches the section of the sphere by any plane through the line.

EXAMPLES

1. *Show that the plane $lx + my + nz = p$ will touch the sphere*

$$x^2 + y^2 + z^2 + 2ux + 2vy + 2wz + d = 0,$$

if

$$(ul + vm + wn + p)^2 = (l^2 + m^2 + n^2)(u^2 + v^2 + w^2 - d).$$

(Ajmer, 1998; Avadh, 2002; Utkal, 2003)

Sol. Equating the radius $\sqrt{u^2 + v^2 + w^2 - d}$ of the sphere to the length of the perpendicular from the centre $(-u, -v, -w)$ to the plane

$$lx + my + nz = p,$$

we get the required condition.

2. *Find the two tangent planes to the sphere*

$$x^2 + y^2 + z^2 - 4x + 2y - 6z + 5 = 0$$

which are parallel to the plane

$$2x + 2y = z.$$

Sol. The general equation of a plane parallel to the given plane is

$$2x + 2y - z = 0$$

$$2x + 2y - z + \lambda = 0; \ \lambda \text{ is a parameter.}$$

This will be a tangent plane, if its distance from the centre $(2, -1, 3)$ of the sphere is equal to the radius 3 and this requires

$$\frac{-1 + \lambda}{\pm 3} = 3 \implies \lambda = 10 \text{ or } -8.$$

Hence, the required tangent planes are

$$2x + 2y - z + 10 = 0 \text{ and } 2x + 2y - z - 8 = 0.$$

3. *Find the equation of the sphere which touches the sphere*

$$x^2 + y^2 + z^2 - x + 3y + 2z - 3 = 0,$$

at the point $(1, 1, -1)$ and passes through the origin. *(Rohilkhand, 1996, 2003)*

Sol. The tangent plane to the given sphere at $(1, 1, -1)$ is

$$x + 5y - 6 = 0.$$

The equation of the required sphere is, therefore,

$$x^2 + y^2 + z^2 - x + 3y + 2z - 3 + k(x + 5y - 6) = 0$$

where k is a suitably chosen number.

This will pass through the origin if $k = -1/2$.

Thus, the required equation is

$$2(x^2 + y^2 + z^2) - 3x + y + 4z = 0.$$

4. *Find the equations of the sphere through the circle*

$$x^2 + y^2 + z^2 = 1, \ 2x + 4y + 5z = 6$$

and touching the plane

$$z = 0. \hspace{3cm} (Ajmer, \ 1996; \ Avadh, \ 1998)$$

Sol. The sphere

$$x^2 + y^2 + z^2 - 1 + \lambda \ (2x + 4y - 5z - 6) = 0$$

passes through the given circle for all values of λ.

Its centre is $\left(-\lambda, \ -2\lambda, \ -\dfrac{5}{2}\lambda\right)$, and radius is $\left(\lambda^2 + 4\lambda^2 + \dfrac{25}{4}\lambda^2 + 1 + 6\lambda\right)^{1/2}$

Since it touches $z = 0$, we have by Cor. 2,

$$-\frac{5}{2}\lambda = \pm \left(5\lambda^2 + \frac{25}{4}\lambda^2 + 1 + 6\lambda\right)^{1/2}$$

$$\Rightarrow \hspace{3cm} 5\lambda^2 + 6\lambda + 1 = 0.$$

This gives

$$\lambda = -1 \ or \ -\frac{1}{5}.$$

The two required spheres, therefore, are

$$x^2 + y^2 + z^2 - 2x - 4y - 5z + 5 = 0,$$
$$5 \ (x^2 + y^2 + z^2) - 2x - 4y - 5z + 1 = 0.$$

5. *Find the equations of the two tangent planes to the sphere*

$$x^2 + y^2 + z^2 = 9,$$

which pass through the line

$$x + y = 6, \ x - 2z = 3.$$

Sol. Any plane

$$x + y - 6 + \lambda \ (x - 2z - 3) = 0$$

through the given line will touch the given sphere if

$$\frac{-6 - 3\lambda}{\sqrt{(1 + \lambda)^2 + 1 + 4\lambda^2}} = 3,$$

$$\Rightarrow \hspace{2cm} 2\lambda^2 - \lambda - 1 = 0 \ \Rightarrow \ \lambda = 1, \ -\frac{1}{2}$$

The two required planes, therefore, are

$$2x + y - 2z = 9, \ x + 2y + 2z = 9.$$

6. *Find the locus of the centre of the sphere of constant radius which passes through a given point and touches the given line.*

Sol. Let us take x-axis as given line and perpendicular to it from the given point as the axis of z. The given point thus lies on the axis of z. Let its co-ordinates be $(0, 0, c)$.

Let the equation of sphere be

$$x^2 + y^2 + z^2 + 2ux + 2vy + 2wz + d = 0 \hspace{2cm} ...(1)$$

It passes through $(0, 0, c)$

$$\therefore \hspace{3cm} c^2 + 2wc + d = 0 \hspace{2cm} ...(2)$$

The radius of the sphere is constant say λ,
$$u^2 + v^2 + w^2 - d = \lambda^2 \qquad \qquad ...(3)$$
Sphere meets x-axis ($y = 0$, $z = 0$), where
$$x^2 + 2ux + d = 0. \qquad \qquad ...(4)$$
The line, *i.e.*, x-axis will touch (1) if
$$u^2 = d \qquad \qquad ...(5)$$
Eliminating d from (2), (3), (4) and (5), we get
$$u^2 + c^2 + 2wc = 0 \qquad \qquad ...(6)$$
and
$$v^2 + w^2 = \lambda^2 \qquad \qquad ...(7)$$
Hence, locus of centre $(-u, -v, -w)$ will be
$$x^2 + c^2 - 2cz = 0 \text{ and } y^2 + z^2 = \lambda^2.$$
The locus of the centres is, therefore, the curve of intersection of above two surfaces.

7. *Show that the spheres $x^2 + y^2 + z^2 = 64$ and $x^2 + y^2 + z^2 - 12x + 4y - 6z + 48 = 0$ touch internally and find their point of contact.* (*Garhwal, 2001*)

Sol. Note. Two spheres will touch internally if the difference of their radii is equal to the distance between their centres. The distance between two centres *viz.*, $(0, 0, 0)$ and $(6, -2, 3)$ is equal to 7.

$$\text{Radius of first sphere} = \sqrt{64} = 8$$
and
$$\text{radius of second sphere} = \sqrt{36 + 4 + 9 - 48} = 1.$$
$$\therefore \qquad \text{difference of radii} = 8 - 1 = 7 = \text{distance between centres.}$$
Hence, two spheres touch internally.

Let (α, β, γ) be their point of contact. Then tangent planes to two spheres at this point are
$$\alpha x + \beta y + \gamma z = 64$$
and
$$\alpha x + \beta y + \gamma z - 6(x + \alpha) + 2(y + \beta) - 3(z + \gamma) + 48 = 0.$$
Comparing the two, we have
$$\frac{\alpha - 6}{\alpha} = \frac{\beta + 2}{\beta} = \frac{\gamma - z}{\gamma} = \frac{-6\alpha + 2\beta - 3\gamma + 48}{-64} = k \text{ (say)}$$

This gives
$$\alpha - 6 = \alpha k; \ \beta + 2 = \beta k; \ \gamma - 3 = k\gamma; \ -6\alpha + 2\beta - 3\gamma + 48 = -64k$$
or
$$\alpha = \frac{6}{1-k}, \ \beta = \frac{-2}{1-k}, \ \gamma = \frac{3}{1-k}.$$

Substituting these values in the fourth relation, we get $k = 1/8$.
Hence, the point of contact is
$$\left(\frac{48}{7}, -\frac{16}{7}, \frac{24}{7} \right).$$

8. *If the tangent plane to the sphere $x^2 + y^2 + z^2 = r^2$ makes intercepts a, b, c on the co-ordinate axes, show that*
$$\frac{1}{a^2} + \frac{1}{b^2} + \frac{1}{c^2} = \frac{1}{r^2}.$$

(*Ajmer, 1994; Bundelkhund, 1999; Kanpur, 2004*)

Sol. The equation to the tangent plane at (α, β, γ) to the given sphere is
$$x\alpha + y\beta + z\gamma = r^2 \qquad \qquad ...(i)$$

Given that a is the intercept made by the plane (i) on x-axis. So,

$$a\alpha = r^2 \Rightarrow \alpha = \frac{r^2}{a}$$

Similarly,

$$\beta = \frac{r^2}{b} \text{ and } \gamma = \frac{r^2}{c}.$$

Also, as (α, β, γ) is a point on the sphere, so we have

$$\alpha^2 + \beta^2 + \gamma^2 = r^2$$

$\Rightarrow$

$$(r^2/a)^2 + (r^2/b)^2 + (r^2/c)^2 = r^2$$

$\Rightarrow$

$$\frac{1}{a^2} + \frac{1}{b^2} + \frac{1}{c^2} = \frac{1}{r^2}.$$

EXERCISES

1. Find the equation of the tangent plane to the sphere

$$3(x^2 + y^2 + z^2) - 2x - 3y - 4z - 22 = 0$$

and the point $(1, 2, 3)$.   (*Rohilkhand, 2001; Kumaon, 1999, 2001, 2006*)

[**Ans.** $4x + 9y + 14z - 64 = 0$]

2. Find the equation of the tangent line to the circle

$$x^2 + y^2 + z^2 + 5x - 7y + 2z - 8 = 0, \ 3x - 2y + 4z + 3 = 0$$

and the point $(-3, 5, 4)$.   [**Ans.** $(x + 3)/32 = (y - 5)/34 = -(z - 4)/7$]

3. Find the value of a for which the plane

$$x + y + z = a\sqrt{3}$$

touches the sphere

$$x^2 + y^2 + z^2 - 2x - 2y - 2z - 6 = 0.$$ [**Ans.** $\pm\sqrt{3}$]

4. Find the equation of the tangent planes to the sphere

$$x^2 + y^2 + z^2 + 2x - 4y + 6z - 7 = 0,$$

which intersects the line

$$6x - 3y - 2z = 0 = 3z + 2.$$ (*Avadh, 1997; Gorakhpur, 2000*)

[**Ans.** $2x - y + 4z = 5, \ 4x - 2y - z = 16$]

5. Show that the plane $2x - 2y + z + 12 = 0$ touches the sphere

$$x^2 + y^2 + z^2 - 2x - 4y + 2z = 3$$

and find the point of contact.   (*Rohilkhand, 1997; Garhwal, 2004; Meerut, 2005*)

[**Ans.** $(-1, 4, -2)$]

[**Hint.** The point of contact of a tangent plane is the point where the line through the centre perpendicular to the plane meets the sphere.]

6. Find the co-ordinates of the points on the sphere

$$x^2 + y^2 + z^2 - 4x + 2y = 4$$

the tangent planes at which are parallel to the plane

$$2x - y + 2z = 1.$$ (*Kumaon, 2002*)

[**Ans.** $(4, -2, 2), (0, 0, -2)$]

7. Show that the equation of the sphere which touches the sphere

$$4(x^2 + y^2 + z^2) + 10x - 25y - 2z = 0,$$

at the point $(1, 2, -2)$ and passes through the point $(-1, 0, 0)$ is

$$x^2 + y^2 + z^2 + 2x - 6y + 1 = 0.$$

8. Obtain the equations of the tangent planes to the sphere

$$x^2 + y^2 + z^2 + 6x - 2z + 1 = 0,$$

which pass through the line

$$3 (16 - x) = 3z = 2y + 30.$$

[**Ans.** $2x + 2y - z - 2 = 0, x + 2y - 2z + 14 = 0$]

9. Obtain the equations of the sphere which pass through the circle

$$x^2 + y^2 + z^2 - 2x + 2y + 4z - 3 = 0, 2x + y + z = 4$$

and touches the plane $3x + 4y = 14$.

[**Ans.** $x^2 + y^2 + z^2 + 2x + 4y + 6z - 11 = 0, x^2 + y^2 + z^2 - 2x + 2y + 4z - 3 = 0$]

10. Find the equation of the sphere which has its centre at the origin and which touches the line $2 (x + 1) = 2 - y = z + 3$.   [**Ans.** $9 (x^2 + y^2 + z^2) = 5$]

11. Find the equation of the spheres of radius r which touch the three co-ordinate axes. How many such spheres are there ?   (*Garhwal, 2002*)

[**Ans.** $2 (x^2 + y^2 + z^2) + 2 \sqrt{2} (\pm x \pm y \pm z) r + r^2 = 0;$ eight]

12. Prove that the equation of the sphere which lies in the octant *OXYZ* and touches the co-ordinate planes is of the form

$$x^2 + y^2 + z^2 - 2\lambda (x + y + z) + 2\lambda^2 = 0.$$

Show that, in general, two spheres can be drawn through a given point to touch the co-ordinate planes and find for what positions of the point the spheres are (*a*) real, (*b*) coincident.

The distances of the centre from the co-ordinate planes are all equal to the radius so that we may suppose that λ is the radius and $(\lambda, \lambda, \lambda)$ is the centre, λ being the parameter.

13. Show that the spheres

$$x^2 + y^2 + z^2 = 25, x^2 + y^2 + z^2 - 24x - 40y - 18z + 225 = 0$$

touch externally and find the point of the contact.   [**Ans.** 12/5, 20/5, 9/5]

14. Find the centres of the two spheres which touch the plane

$$4x + 3y = 47$$

at the point (8, 5, 4) and the sphere

$$x^2 + y^2 + z^2 = 1.$$ [**Ans.** (4, 2, 4), (64/21, 27/21, 4)]

15. Obtain the equations of spheres that pass through the points (4, 1, 0), (2, – 3, 4), (1, 0, 0) and touch the plane $2x + 2y - z = 11$.   [**Ans.** $x^2 + y^2 + z^2 - 6x + 2y - 4z + 5 = 0;$

$$16 (x^2 + y^2 + z^2) - 102x + 50y - 49z + 86 = 0]$$

16. Find the equation of the sphere inscribed in the tetrahedron whose faces are

(*i*) $x = 0, y = 0, z = 0, x + 2y + 2z = 1$.

(*ii*) $x = 0, y = 0, z = 0, 2x - 6y + 3z + 6 = 0$.

[**Ans.** (*i*) $32 (x^2 + y^2 + z^2) - 8 (x - y + z) + 1 = 0,$

(*ii*) $9 (x^2 + y^2 + z^2) + 6 (x - y + z) + 2 = 0]$

17. Tangent plane at any point of the sphere $x^2 + y^2 + z^2 = r^2$ meets the co-ordinate axes at *A*, *B*, *C*. Show that the locus of the point of intersection of planes drawn parallel to the co-ordinate planes through *A*, *B*, *C* is the surface $x^{-2} + y^{-2} + z^{-2} = r^{-2}$.

6.6.1. Plane of Contact

To find the locus of the points of contact of the tangent planes which pass through a given point (α, β, γ) *and touch the sphere*

$$x^2 + y^2 + z^2 + 2ux + 2vy + 2wz + d = 0.$$

The tangent plane

$$x(x' + u) + y(y' + v) + z(z' + w) + (ux' + vy' + wz' + d) = 0$$

at (x', y', z') will pass through the point (α, β, γ), if

$$\alpha(x' + u) + \beta(y' + v) + \gamma(z' + w) + (ux' + vy' + wz' + d) = 0$$

$$\Leftrightarrow \qquad x'(\alpha + u) + y'(\beta + v) + z'(\gamma + w) + (u\alpha + v\beta + w\gamma + d) = 0$$

which is the condition that the point (x', y', z') should lie on the plane

$$x(\alpha + u) + y(\beta + v) + z(\gamma + w) + (u\alpha + v\beta + w\gamma + d) = 0.$$

It is called the *plane of contact* for the point (α, β, γ).

Thus, the locus of points of contact is the circle in which the plane cuts the sphere.

Ex. 1. Show that the line joining any point P to the centre of a given sphere is perpendicular to the plane of contact of P and if OP meets it in Q, then

$$OP \cdot OQ = (\text{radius})^2.$$

Ex. 2. Show that the planes of contact of all points on the line

$$x/2 = (y - a)/3 = (z + 3a)/4$$

with respect to the sphere $x^2 + y^2 + z^2 = a^2$ pass through the line

$$-(2x + 3a)/13 = (y - a)/3 = z/1.$$

6.6.2. The Polar Plane

If a line drawn through a fixed point A meets a given sphere in points P, Q and a point R is taken on this line such that the segment AR is divided internally and externally by the points P, Q in the same ratio, then **the locus of R is a plane called the Polar Plane** of A w.r.t. the sphere.

Consider the sphere

$$x^2 + y^2 + z^2 = a^2, \qquad\qquad\qquad ...(1)$$

and let A be the point (α, β, γ).

Let $R(x, y, z)$ be the co-ordinates of the point R on any line through A. The co-ordinates of the point dividing AR in the ratio $\lambda : 1$ are

$$\left[\left(\frac{\lambda x + \alpha}{\lambda + 1} \right), \left(\frac{\lambda y + \beta}{\lambda + 1} \right), \left(\frac{\lambda z + \gamma}{\lambda + 1} \right) \right]$$

This point will be on the sphere (1) for values of λ which are roots of the quadratic equation

$$\left(\frac{\lambda x + \alpha}{\lambda + 1} \right)^2 + \left(\frac{\lambda y + \beta}{\lambda + 1} \right)^2 + \left(\frac{\lambda z + \gamma}{\lambda + 1} \right)^2 = a^2,$$

$$\Leftrightarrow \quad \lambda^2 (x^2 + y^2 + z^2 - a^2) + 2\lambda(\alpha x + \beta y + \gamma z - a^2) + (\alpha^2 + \beta^2 + \gamma^2 - a^2) = 0 \qquad ...(2)$$

Its roots λ_1 and λ_2 are the ratios in which the points P, Q divide the segment AR.

Since P, Q divide the segment AR internally and externally in the same ratio, we have

$$\lambda_1 + \lambda_2 = 0.$$

Thus, from (2), we have

$$\alpha x + \beta y + \gamma z - a^2 = 0, \qquad\qquad\qquad ...(3)$$

which is the relation satisfied by the co-ordinates (x, y, z) of R.

Hence, (3) is the locus of R. Clearly it is a plane.

Thus, we have seen here that the equation of the polar plane of the point (α, β, γ) with respect to the sphere

$$x^2 + y^2 + z^2 = a^2,$$

is
$$\alpha x + \beta y + \gamma z = a^2.$$

It may similarly be shown that the polar plane of (α, β, γ) with respect to the sphere

$$x^2 + y^2 + z^2 + 2ux + 2vy + 2wz + d = 0,$$

is the plane

$$(\alpha + u)\, x + (\beta + v)\, y + (\gamma + w)\, z + (u\alpha + v\beta + w\gamma + d) = 0.$$

On comparing the equation of the polar plane with that of the tangent plane (§ 6.6) and the plane of contact (§ 6.6.1), we see that the polar plane of a point lying on the sphere is the tangent plane at the point and that of a point, lying outside it, is its plane of contact.

Pole of a Plane. Def. *If π be the polar plane of a point P, then P is called the pole of the plane π.*

6.6.3. Pole of a Plane

To find the pole of the plane

$$lx + my + nz = p \qquad\qquad ...(i)$$

with respect to the sphere

$$x^2 + y^2 + z^2 = a^2. \qquad (Kumaon,\ 1995,\ 99;\ Agra,\ 1995)$$

If (α, β, γ) be the required pole, then we see that the equation (i) is identical with

$$\alpha x + \beta y + \gamma z = a^2 \qquad\qquad ...(ii)$$

so that, on comparing (i) and (ii), we obtain

$$\frac{\alpha}{l} = \frac{\beta}{m} = \frac{\gamma}{n} = \frac{a^2}{p},$$

$\Rightarrow \qquad\qquad \alpha = a^2 l / p,\ \beta = a^2 m / p,\ \gamma = a^2 n / p.$

Thus, the point

$$(a^2 l/p,\ a^2 m/p,\ a^2 n/p)$$

is the pole of the plane $lx + my + nz = p$, w.r.t. the sphere $x^2 + y^2 + z^2 = a^2$.

6.6.4. Some Results Concerning Poles and Polars

In the following discussion, we shall always take the equation of a sphere in the form

$$x^2 + y^2 + z^2 = a^2.$$

1. *The line joining the centre O of a sphere to any point P is perpendicular to the polar plane of P.*

The direction ratios of the line joining the centre $O\,(0, 0, 0)$ to the point $P\,(\alpha, \beta, \gamma)$ are α, β, γ and these are also the direction ratios of the normal to the polar plane $\alpha x + \beta y + \gamma z = a^2$ of $P\,(\alpha, \beta, \gamma)$.

2. *If the line joining the centre O of a sphere to a point P meets the polar plane of P in Q, then*

$$OP \cdot OQ = a^2,$$

where a is the radius of the sphere.

We have

$$OP = \sqrt{\alpha^2 + \beta^2 + \gamma^2}.$$

Also, OQ, which is the length of the perpendicular from the centre $O\,(0,\,0,\,0)$ to the polar plane $\alpha x + \beta y + \gamma z = a^2$ of P, is given by

$$OQ = \frac{a^2}{\sqrt{\alpha^2 + \beta^2 + \gamma^2}}$$

Hence, the result.

3. *If the polar plane of a point P passes through a point Q, then the polar plane Q passes through P.*

The condition that the polar plane

$$\alpha_1 x + \beta_1 y + \gamma_1 z = a^2,$$

of $P\,(\alpha_1,\,\beta_1,\,\gamma_1)$ passes through $Q\,(\alpha_2,\,\beta_2,\,\gamma_2)$ is

$$\alpha_1\alpha_2 + \beta_1\beta_2 + \gamma_1\gamma_2 = a^2,$$

which is also, by symmetry, or directly, the condition that the polar plane of Q passes through P.

Conjugate Points. *Two points such that the polar plane of either passes through the other are called conjugate points.*

4. *If the pole of a plane π_1 lies on another plane π_2, then the pole of π_2 also lies on π_1.*

The condition that the pole

$$\left(\frac{a^2 l_1}{p_1},\; \frac{a^2 m_1}{p_1},\; \frac{a^2 n_1}{p_1}\right)$$

of the plane π_1

$$l_1 x + m_1 y + n_1 z = p_1$$

lies on the plane π_2

$$l_2 x + m_2 y + n_2 z = p_2$$

is

$$a^2\,(l_1 l_2 + m_1 m_2 + n_1 n_2) = p_1 p_2$$

which is also, clearly, the condition that the pole

$$(a^2 l_2/p_2,\; a^2 m_2/p_2,\; a^2 n_2/p_2)$$

of π_2 lies on π_1.

Conjugate planes. *Two planes such that the pole of either lies on the other are called conjugate planes.*

5. *The polar planes of all the points on a line l pass through another line l'.*

The polar plane of any point,

$$(lr + \alpha,\; mr + \beta,\; nr + \gamma),$$

on the line, l,

$$\frac{x - \alpha}{l} = \frac{y - \beta}{m} = \frac{z - \gamma}{n}$$

is

$$(lr + \alpha)\,x + (mr + \beta)\,y + (nr + \gamma)\,z = a^2,$$

$$\Leftrightarrow \qquad (\alpha x + \beta y + \gamma z - a^2) + r\,(lx + my + nz) = 0,$$

which clearly passes through the line

$$\alpha x + \beta y + \gamma z - a^2 = 0,\; lx + my + nz = 0,$$

whatever value, r, may have. Hence, the result.

Let this line be l'. We shall now prove that the polar plane of every point on l' also passes through the line l.

Now, as the polar plane of any arbitrary point P on l passes through *every* point of l', . therefore, the polar plane of every point of l', passes through the point P on l and as, P is arbitrary, it passes through every point of l, *i.e.*, it passes through l.

Thus, we see that if l' is the line such that the polar planes, of all the points on a line l, pass through it, then the polar planes of all the points on l' pass through l.

Polar Lines. *Two lines such that the polar plane of every point on either passes through the other are called* **Polar Lines.**

EXAMPLE

Find the polar line of $(x - 1)/2 = (y ÷ 2)/3 = (z - 3)/4$ w.r.t. the sphere $x^2 + y^2 + z^2 = 16$.

Sol. Any point on given line is $(2r + 1, 3r + 2, 4r + 3)$. Polar plane of this point with respect to sphere is

$$x(2r + 1) + y(3r + 2) + z(4r + 3) = 16$$

i.e.,
$$(x + 2y + 3z - 16) + r(2x + 3y + 4z) = 0$$

This clearly passes through the line

$$x + 2y + 3z - 16 = 0 = 2x + 3y + 4z$$

which is the required polar line.

EXERCISES

1. Show that the polar line of

$$(x + 1)/2 = (y - 2)/3 = (z + 3),$$

   with respect to the sphere

$$x^2 + y^2 + z^2 = 1,$$

   is the line

$$\frac{7x + 3}{11} = \frac{2 - 7y}{5} = \frac{z}{-1}.$$

2. Show that if a line l is coplanar with the polar line of a line l' then l' is coplanar with the polar line of l.

3. If PA, QB be drawn perpendicular to the polars of Q and P respectively, with respect to a sphere, with centre O, then

$$\frac{PA}{QB} = \frac{OP}{OQ}.$$

4. Show that, for a given sphere, there exist an unlimited number of tetrahedra such that each vertex is the pole of the opposite face with respect to the sphere.

   (Such a tetrahedron is known as a *self-conjugate* or *self-polar* tetrahedron.)

6.7. ANGLE OF INTERSECTION OF TWO SPHERES

Def. *The angle of intersection of two spheres at a common point is the angle between the tangent planes to them at that point* and is, therefore, also equal to the angle between the radii of the spheres to the common point; the radii being perpendicular to the respective tangent planes at the point.

The angle of intersection at every common point of the spheres is the same, for if P, P', be any two common points and C, C' the centres of the spheres, the triangles $CC'P$ and $CC'P'$ are congruent and accordingly

$$\angle CPC' = \angle CP'C'.$$

The spheres are said to be **orthogonal** if the angle of intersection of two spheres is a right angle. In this case

$$CC'^2 = CP^2 + C'P^2.$$

6.7.1. Condition for the Orthogonality of Two Spheres

To find the condition for the two spheres

$$x^2 + y^2 + z^2 + 2u_1x + 2v_1y + 2w_1z + d_1 = 0,$$
$$x^2 + y^2 + z^2 + 2u_2x + 2v_2y + 2w_2z + d_2 = 0,$$

to be orthogonal.   *(Agra, 1998)*

The spheres will be orthogonal if *the square of the distance between their centres is equal to the sum of the squares of their radii* and this requires

$$(u_1 - u_2)^2 + (v_1 - v_2)^2 + (w_1 - w_2)^2 = (u_1^2 + v_1^2 + w_1^2 - d_1) + (u_2^2 + v_2^2 + w_2^2 - d_2)$$

$$\Leftrightarrow \qquad 2u_1u_2 + 2v_1v_2 + 2w_1w_2 = d_1 + d_2.$$

EXAMPLES

1. *If d is the distance between the centres of two spheres of radii r_1 and r_2, prove that the angle between them is $\cos^{-1}\{(r_1^2 + r_2^2 - d^2)/2r_1r_2\}$.*

Sol. The angle of intersection, *i.e.*, the angle between the tangents at P is the angle between the radii of the two spheres joining P. Thus, $\angle C_1PC_2 = \theta$.

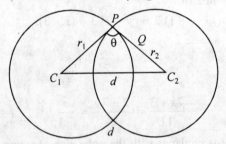

Fig. 38

Applying cosine formula to $\triangle C_1PC_2$, we have

$$d^2 = r_1^2 + r_2^2 - 2r_1r_2 \cos \theta$$

$$\therefore \qquad \cos \theta = (r_1^2 + r_2^2 - d^2)/2r_1r_2.$$

2. *Two spheres of radii r_1 and r_2 cut orthogonally. Prove that the radius of the common circle is $r_1r_2 / \sqrt{r_1^2 + r_2^2}$.*

(Garhwal, 1997, 2000; Ajmer, 1995, 97; Avadh, 1995; Kanpur, 1997; Poorvanchal, 2004)

Sol. Let the common circle be

$$x^2 + y^2 = a^2, \ z = 0.$$

The sphere

$$x^2 + y^2 + z^2 + 2kz - a^2 = 0$$

passes through this circle for all values of k. Let the two given spheres through the circle be

$$x^2 + y^2 + z^2 + 2k_1z - a^2 = 0, \ x^2 + y^2 + z^2 + 2k_2z - a^2 = 0.$$

We have
$$r_1^2 = k_1^2 + a^2, \quad r_2^2 = k_2^2 + a^2 \qquad \qquad ...(i)$$

Since the spheres cut orthogonally, we have
$$2k_1k_2 = a^2 + a^2 = 2a^2 \qquad \qquad ...(ii)$$

From (i) and (ii), eliminating k_1, k_2, we have
$$(r_1^2 - a^2)(r_2^2 - a^2) = a^4 \quad \Leftrightarrow \quad a^2 = r_1^2 r_2^2/(r_1^2 + r_2^2).$$

Hence, the result.

EXERCISES

1. Find the equation of the sphere that passes through the circle
$$x^2 + y^2 + z^2 - 2x + 3y - 4z + 6 = 0, \quad 3x - 4y + 5z - 15 = 0$$
and cuts the sphere
$$x^2 + y^2 + z^2 + 2x + 4y - 6z + 11 = 0$$
orthogonally.   (*Avadh, 2002*) [**Ans.** $5(x^2 + y^2 + z^2) - 13x + 19y - 25z + 45 = 0$]

2. Find the equation of the sphere that passes through the two points
$$(0, 3, 0), (-2, -1, -4)$$
and cuts orthogonally the two spheres
$$x^2 + y^2 + z^2 + x - 3z - 2 = 0, \quad 2(x^2 + y^2 + z^2) + x + 3y + 4 = 0.$$
[**Ans.** $x^2 + y^2 + z^2 + 2x - 2y + 4z - 3 = 0$]

3. Find the equation of the sphere which touches the plane
$$3x + 2y - z + 2 = 0$$
at the point $(1, -2, 1)$ and cuts orthogonally the sphere
$$x^2 + y^2 + z^2 - 4x + 6y + 4 = 0.$$
(*Garhwal, 1998; Rohilkhand, 1995; Kanpur, 1995, 99; Delhi, 2005*)
[**Ans.** $x^2 + y^2 + z^2 + 7x + 10y - 5z + 12 = 0$]

4. Show that every sphere through the circle
$$x^2 + y^2 - 2ax + r^2 = 0, \quad z = 0$$
cuts orthogonally every sphere through the circle
$$x^2 + z^2 = r^2, \quad y = 0. \qquad (Ajmer, 1998)$$

5. Two points P, Q are conjugate with respect to a sphere S; show that the sphere on PQ as diameter cuts S orthogonally.

6. If two spheres S_1 and S_2 are orthogonal, the polar plane of any point on S_1 with respect to S_2 passes through the other end of the diameter of S_1 through P.

6.8. RADICAL PLANE

The locus of a point whose powers with respect to two spheres are equal is a plane perpendicular to the line joining their centres.

The powers of the point $P(x, y, z)$ with respect to the spheres
$$S_1 \equiv x^2 + y^2 + z^2 + 2u_1 x + 2v_1 y + 2w_1 z + d_1 = 0,$$
$$S_2 \equiv x^2 + y^2 + z^2 + 2u_2 x + 2v_2 y + 2w_2 z + d_2 = 0,$$
are
$$x^2 + y^2 + z^2 + 2u_1 x + 2v_1 y + 2w_1 z + d_1,$$
and
$$x^2 + y^2 + z^2 + 2u_2 x + 2v_2 y + 2w_2 z + d_2,$$
respectively.

Equating these, we obtain

$$2x (u_1 - u_2) + 2y (v_1 - v_2) + 2z (w_1 - w_2) + (d_1 - d_2) = 0,$$

as the required locus. This locus being of the first degree in (x, y, z), represents a plane which is obviously perpendicular to the line joining the centres of the two spheres. This plane is called the *Radical plane* of the two spheres.

Thus, *the radical plane of two spheres*

$$S_1 = 0, S_2 = 0,$$

in both of which the coefficients of the second degree terms are equal to unity, is

$$S_1 - S_2 = 0.$$

In case the two spheres intersect, the plane of their common circle is their radical plane (§ 6.3.2).

6.8.1. Radical Line

The three radical planes of three spheres intersect in a line.

If

$$S_1 = 0, S_2 = 0, S_3 = 0$$

be the three spheres, their radical planes

$$S_1 - S_2 = 0, S_2 - S_3 = 0, S_3 - S_1 = 0,$$

clearly meet in the line

$$S_1 = S_2 = S_3$$

$$\Leftrightarrow \qquad S_1 - S_2 = 0, S_2 - S_3 = 0$$

This line is called the *Radical line* of the three spheres.

6.8.2. Radical Centre (U.P.P.C.S. 1998)

The four radical lines of four spheres taken three by three intersect at a point.

The point common to the three planes

$$S_1 = S_2 = S_3 = S_4$$

is clearly common to the radical lines, taken three by three, of the four spheres

$$S_1 = 0, S_2 = 0, S_3 = 0, S_4 = 0.$$

This point is the intersection of the two lines

$$S_1 - S_2 = 0, S_2 - S_3 = 0; S_1 - S_3 = 0, S_2 - S_4 = 0.$$

This point is called the *Radical centre* of the four spheres.

6.8.3. Theorem

If $S_1 = 0, S_2 = 0$, be two spheres, then the equation

$$S_1 + \lambda S_2 = 0,$$

λ *being the parameter, represents a system of spheres such that any two members of the system have the same radical plane.*

Let

$$S_1 + \lambda_1 S_2 = 0 \text{ and } S_1 + \lambda_2 S_2 = 0$$

be any two members of the system.

Making the coefficients of second degree terms unity, we write these equations in the form

$$\frac{S_1 + \lambda_1 S_2}{1 + \lambda_1} = 0, \frac{S_1 + \lambda_2 S_2}{1 + \lambda_2} = 0.$$

The radical plane of these two spheres is

$$\frac{S_1 + \lambda_1 S_2}{1 + \lambda_1} - \frac{S_1 + \lambda_2 S_2}{1 + \lambda_2} = 0,$$

$$\Leftrightarrow \qquad S_1 - S_2 = 0.$$

Since this equation is independent of λ_1 and λ_2, we see that every two members of the system have the same radical plane.

Co-axal Systems. Def. *A system of spheres any two members of which have the same radical plane is called a co-axal system of spheres.*

Thus, the system of spheres

$$S_1 + \lambda S_2 = 0$$

is co-axal and we say that it is determined by the two spheres

$$S_1 = 0, \ S_2 = 0.$$

The common radical plane is

$$S_1 - S_2 = 0.$$

This co-axal system is also given by the equation

$$S_1 + k_2 \, (S_1 - S_2) = 0.$$

Refer Note 1, § 6.4.1.

Note. It can similarly be proved that the system of spheres

$$S + \lambda U = 0$$

is co-axal; $S = 0$ being a sphere and $U = 0$ a plane; the common radical plane is $U = 0$.

Cor. *The locus of the centres of spheres of a co-axal system is a line.*

For, if (x, y, z) be the centre of the sphere

$$S_1 + \lambda S_2 = 0,$$

we have

$$x = -\frac{u_1 + \lambda u_2}{1 + \lambda}, \ y = -\frac{v_1 + \lambda v_2}{1 + \lambda}, \ z = -\frac{w_1 + \lambda w_2}{1 + \lambda}$$

On eliminating λ, we find that it lies on the line

$$\frac{x + u_1}{u_1 - u_2} = \frac{y + v_1}{v_1 - v_2} = \frac{z + w_1}{w_1 - w_2}.$$

This result is also otherwise clear as the line joining the centres of any two spheres is perpendicular to their common radical plane.

6.9. A SIMPLIFIED FORM OF THE EQUATION OF TWO GIVEN SPHERES

By taking the line joining the centres of two given spheres as X-axis, their equations take the form

$$x^2 + y^2 + z^2 + 2u_1 x + d_1 = 0, \ x^2 + y^2 + z^2 + 2u_2 x + d_2 = 0.$$

The radical plane of these spheres is

$$2x \, (u_1 - u_2) + (d_1 - d_2) = 0.$$

Further, if we take this radical plane as the YZ plane, *i.e.*, $x = 0$, we have $d_1 = d_2 = d$ (say).

Thus, by taking the line joining the centres of two given spheres as X-axis and their radical plane as the YZ plane, their equations take the form

$$x^2 + y^2 + z^2 + 2u_1 x + d = 0, \ x^2 + y^2 + z^2 + 2u_2 x + d = 0,$$

where u_1, u_2 are different.

Cor. 1. The equation

$$x^2 + y^2 + z^2 + 2kx + d = 0; \ k, \text{ is a parameter}$$

represents a co-axal system of spheres for different values of k; d being constant. The YZ plane is the common radical plane and X-axis the line of centres.   (*Kanpur, 1997*)

Cor. 2. Limiting Points. The equation

$$x^2 + y^2 + z^2 + 2kx + d = 0$$

can be written as

$$(x + k)^2 + y^2 + z^2 = k^2 - d.$$

For $k = \pm \sqrt{d}$, we get spheres of the system with radius zero and thus the *system includes the two points spheres*

$$(- \sqrt{d}, \ 0, \ 0), \ (\sqrt{d}, \ 0, \ 0).$$

These two points, called the *limiting points*, exist only when d is positive, *i.e.*, when the spheres do not meet the radical plane in a real circle.   (*Kanpur, 1997*)

Def. Limiting points *of a co-axal system of spheres are the point spheres of the system.*

EXAMPLES

1. *Find the limiting points of the co-axal system defined by the spheres*

$$x^2 + y^2 + z^2 + 3x - 3y + 6 = 0, \ x^2 + y^2 + z^2 - 6y - 6z + 6 = 0. \quad (Avadh, 1999)$$

Sol. The equation of the plane of the circle through the two given spheres is

$$3x + 3y + 6z = 0 \ \Leftrightarrow \ x + y + 2z = 0.$$

Then the equation of the co-axal system determined by the given spheres is

$$x^2 + y^2 + z^2 + 3x - 3y + 6 + \lambda \ (x + y + 2z) = 0,$$

$$\Leftrightarrow \qquad x^2 + y^2 + z^2 + (3 + \lambda) \ x + (\lambda - 3) \ y + 2\lambda z + 6 = 0 \qquad \qquad ...(1)$$

λ being a parameter.

The centre of (1) is

$$\left(- \frac{3 + \lambda}{2}, \ - \frac{\lambda - 3}{2}, \ - \lambda \right),$$

and its radius is

$$\left[\left(\frac{3 + \lambda}{2} \right)^2 + \left(\frac{\lambda - 3}{2} \right)^2 + \lambda^2 - 6 \right]^{1/2}$$

Equating this radius to zero, we obtain

$$6\lambda^2 - 6 = 0 \ \Leftrightarrow \ \lambda = \pm 1.$$

The spheres corresponding to these values of λ become point spheres coinciding with their centres and are the limiting points of the given system of spheres.

The limiting points, therefore, are

$$(- 1, \ 2, \ 1) \text{ and } (- 2, \ 1, \ - 1).$$

2. *Show that spheres which cut two given spheres along great circles all pass through two fixed points.*

Sol. With proper choice of axes, the equations of the given spheres take the form

$$x^2 + y^2 + z^2 + 2u_1 x + d = 0. \qquad \qquad ...(i)$$

$$x^2 + y^2 + z^2 + 2u_2 x + d = 0. \qquad \qquad ...(ii)$$

The equation of any other sphere is

$$x^2 + y^2 + z^2 + 2ux + 2vy + 2wz + c = 0 \qquad \text{...(iii)}$$

where u, v, w, c are different for different spheres.

The plane

$$2x(u - u_1) + 2vy + 2wz + (c - d) = 0,$$

of the circle common to the spheres (i) and (iii) will pass through the centre

$$(-u_1, 0, 0)$$

of (i), if

$$-2u_1(u - u_1) + (c - d) = 0, \qquad \text{...(iv)}$$

which is thus the condition for the sphere (iii) to cut the sphere (i) along a great circle.

Similarly $\qquad -2u_1(u - u_2) + (c - d) = 0, \qquad$ ...(v)

is the condition for the sphere (iii) to cut the sphere (ii) along the great circle.

Solving the linear equations (iv) and (v) for u and c, we get

$$u = u_1 + u_2; \; c = 2u_1 u_2 + d,$$

so that u, c are constants, being dependent on u_1, u_2, d only.

The sphere (iii) cuts X-axis at points whose x-co-ordinates are the roots of the equation

$$x^2 + 2ux + c = 0.$$

The roots of this equation are constant, depending as they do upon the constants u and c only.

Thus, every sphere (iii) meets the X-axis at the same two points and hence, the result.

EXERCISES

1. Show that the sphere

$$x^2 + y^2 + z^2 + 2vy + 2wz - d = 0$$

passes through the limiting points of the co-axal system

$$x^2 + y^2 + z^2 + 2kx + d = 0$$

and cuts every member of the system orthogonally, whatever be the values of v, w.

Hence, deduce that every sphere that passes through the limiting points of a co-axal system cuts every sphere of the system orthogonally.

2. Show that the locus of the point spheres of the system

$$x^2 + y^2 + z^2 + 2vy + 2wz - d = 0$$

is the common circle of the system

$$x^2 + y^2 + z^2 + 2ux + d = 0$$

u, v, w being the parameters and d a constant.

3. Show that the sphere which cuts two spheres orthogonally will cut every member of the co-axal system determined by them orthogonally.

4. Find the limiting points of the co-axal system of spheres

$$x^2 + y^2 + z^2 - 20x + 30y - 40z + 29 + \lambda(2x - 3y - 4z) = 0.$$

[**Ans.** $(2, -3, 4), (-2, 3, -4)$]

5. Three spheres of radii r_1, r_2, r_3, have their centres A, B, C at the points $(a, 0, 0)$, $(0, b, 0)$, $(0, 0, c)$ and $r_1^2 + r_2^2 + r_3^2 = a^2 + b^2 + c^2$. A fourth sphere passes through the origin and the points A, B, C. Show that the radical centre of the four spheres lies on the plane $ax + by + cz = 0$.

6. Show that the locus of a point from which equal tangents may be drawn to the three spheres

$$x^2 + y^2 + z^2 + 2x + 2y + 2z + 2 = 0, \quad x^2 + y^2 + z^2 + 4x + 4z + 4 = 0,$$
$$x^2 + y^2 + z^2 + x + 6y - 4z - 2 = 0,$$

is the straight line

$$x/2 = (y - 1)/5 = z/3.$$

7. Show that there are, in general, two spheres of a co-axal system which touch a given plane.

Find the equations to the two spheres of the co-axal system

$$x^2 + y^2 + z^2 - 5 + \lambda (2x + y + 3z - 3) = 0,$$

which touch the plane

$$3x + 4y = 15.$$

[**Ans.** $x^2 + y^2 + z^2 + 4x + 2y + 6z - 11 = 0,\ 5(x^2 + y^2 + z^2) - 8x - 4y - 12z - 13 = 0$]

8. P is a variable point on a given line and A, B, C are its projections on the axes. Show that the sphere $OABC$ passes through a fixed circle.

9. Show that the radical planes of the spheres of a co-axal system and of a given sphere pass through a line.

OBJECTIVE QUESTIONS

I. Multiple Choice Questions

Note : *For each of the following questions, four alternatives are given for the answer. Only one of them is correct. Choose the correct alternative.*

1. Centre of sphere $x^2 + y^2 - z^2 - 4x + 6y - 8z + 8 = 0$ will be :

    (*a*) $(2, -3, 4)$ (*b*) $(2, 3, 4)$ (*c*) $(-2, -3, -4)$ (*d*) $(1, 2, 3)$.

                                                    (*Garhwal, 2004*)

2. Centre of the sphere $x^2 + y^2 + z^2 + 2x + 2y - 2z + 3 = 0$ is :

    (*a*) $(1, 1, 1)$ (*b*) $(-1, 1, 1)$ (*c*) $(-1, -1, 1)$ (*d*) $(1, 1, -1)$.

                                                    (*Kanpur, 2001*)

3. The radius of the sphere $x^2 + y^2 + z^2 - 2x + 4y - 6z + 7 = 0$ is :

    (*a*) 49   (*b*) 5   (*c*) -7 (*d*) $\sqrt{7}$.

                                                    (*Avadh, 2001*)

4. The equation to the sphere on the join of (x_1, y_1, z_1) and (x_2, y_2, z_2) as the diameter is :

    (*a*) $\sqrt{(x - x_1)(x - x_2)} + \sqrt{(y - y_1)(y - y_2)} + \sqrt{(z - z_1)(z - z_2)} = 0$

    (*b*) $(x - x_1)(x - x_2) + (y - y_1)(y - y_2) + (z - z_1)(z - z_2) = 0$

    (*c*) $\dfrac{x - x_1}{x - x_2} + \dfrac{y - y_1}{y - y_2} + \dfrac{z - z_1}{z - z_2} = 0$

    (*d*) None of these.

5. The two equations $x^2 + y^2 + z^2 + 2ux + 2vy + 2wz + d = 0$ and $lx + my + nz = p$ taken together represent a :

    (*a*) sphere   (*b*) plane   (*c*) pair of planes   (*d*) circle.

6. If a straight line from a fixed point A is drawn in any direction meeting a given sphere at P and Q, then $AP \cdot AQ$:

    (a) is independent of the d.c.'s of the straight line

    (b) depends on the d.c.'s of the straight line

    (c) may or may not depend on the d.c.'s of the straight line

    (d) None of these.

7. The two spheres $x^2 + y^2 + z^2 + 2ux + 2vy + 2wz + d = 0$ and $x^2 + y^2 + z^2 + 2u'x + 2v'y + 2w'z + d' = 0$ are orthogonal if :

    (a) $uu' + vv' + ww' = d + d'$ (b) $uu' + vv' + ww' = 2\ (d + d')$

    (c) $2\ (uu' + vv' + ww') = d + d'$ (d) None of these.

8. The equation $ax^2 + ay^2 + az^2 + 2ux + 2vy + 2wz + d = 0$, $a \neq 0$, represents a sphere if :

    (a) $u^2 + v^2 + w^2 + ad \leq 0$ (b) $u^2 + v^2 + w^2 + ad \geq 0$

    (c) $u^2 + v^2 + w^2 - ad \leq 0$ (d) $u^2 + v^2 + w^2 - ad \geq 0$. (Avadh, 2005)

9. A plane passes through a fixed point (a, b, c). The locus of the foot of the perpendicular drawn to it from the origin is :

    (a) $x^2 + y^2 + z^2 + ax + by + cz = 0$ (b) $x^2 + y^2 + z^2 - ax - by - cz = 0$

    (c) $x^2 + y^2 + z^2 + 2ax + 2by + 2cz = 0$ (d) $x^2 + y^2 + z^2 - 2ax - 2by - 2cz = 0$.

10. The radius of the sphere which passes through the point $(3, 0, 2)$, $(-1, 1, 1)$, $(2, -5, 4)$ and whose centre lies on the plane $2x + 3y + 4z - 6 = 0$ is :

    (a) $\sqrt{7}$ (b) $\sqrt{21}$ (c) $\sqrt{14}$ (d) $2\sqrt{7}$.

11. Equation of the sphere with centre $(1, -1, 1)$ and radius equal to that of sphere $2x^2 + 2y^2 + 2z^2 - 2x + 4y - 6z = 1$ is :

    (a) $x^2 + y^2 + z^2 + 2x - 2y + 2z + 1 = 0$ (b) $x^2 + y^2 + z^2 - 2x + 2y - 2z - 1 = 0$

    (c) $x^2 + y^2 + z^2 - 2x + 2y - 3z - 1 = 0$ (d) None of these.

12. Centre of the sphere $(x - x_1)\ (x - x_2) + (y - y_1)\ (y - y_2) + (z - z_1)\ (z - z_2) = 0$ is :

    (a) (x_2, y_2, z_2) (b) $\left(\dfrac{x_1 - x_2}{2}, \dfrac{y_1 - y_2}{2}, \dfrac{z_1 - z_2}{2} \right)$

    (c) $\left(\dfrac{x_1 + x_2}{2}, \dfrac{y_1 + y_2}{2}, \dfrac{z_1 + z_2}{2} \right)$ (d) (x_1, y_1, z_1).

13. The equation of the sphere through the origin and making intercepts a, b, c on co-ordinate axes is :

    (a) $x^2 + y^2 + z^2 + ax + by + cz = 0$ (b) $x^2 + y^2 + z^2 - 2ax - 2by - 2cz = 0$

    (c) $x^2 + y^2 + z^2 = a + b + c$ (d) $x^2 + y^2 + z^2 - ax - by - cz = 0$.

14. The equation of the sphere with centre at $(2, 3, -4)$ and touching the plane
$$2x + 6y - 3z + 15 = 0$$
    is :

    (a) $x^2 + y^2 + z^2 - 4x - 6y + 8z - 20 = 0$ (b) $x^2 + y^2 + z^2 + 4x - 6y - 8z - 20 = 0$

    (c) $x^2 + y^2 + z^2 - 4x - 6y + 8z + 20 = 0$ (d) None of these.

15. The radius of the circle $x^2 + y^2 + z^2 - 2y - 4z - 20 = 0$, $x + 2y + 2z = 15$ is :

    (a) 3   (b) 4   (c) $\sqrt{7}$ (d) $\sqrt{14}$.

(Avadh, 2003, 2005)

16. The equation of the tangent plane at a point (x_1, y_1, z_1) of the sphere
$$x^2 + y^2 + z^2 + 2ux + 2vy + 2wz + d = 0$$
is :

   (a) $xx_1 + yy_1 + zz_1 + ux + vy + wz + d = 0$

   (b) $xx_1 + yy_1 + zz_1 + ux_1 + vy_1 + wz_1 + d = 0$

   (c) $xx_1 + yy_1 + zz_1 + u(x + x_1) + v(y + y_1) + w(z + z_1) + d = 0$

   (d) None of these.

17. The plane $2x - 2y + z + 12 = 0$ touches the sphere $x^2 + y^2 + z^2 - 2x - 4y + 2z - 3 = 0$ at the point :

   (a) $(1, -4, -2)$ (b) $(-1, 4, -2)$ (c) $(-1, -4, 2)$ (d) $(1, 4, -2)$.

18. The equation $x^2 + y^2 + z^2 + 2ux + 2vy + 2wz + d = 0$ represents a sphere if
$$u^2 + v^2 + w^2 - d$$
is :

   (a) zero or negative   (b) negative   (c) zero   (d) positive.

19. The equation of the sphere passing through $(0, 0, 0)$, $(a, 0, 0)$, $(0, b, 0)$ $(0, 0, c)$ is :

   (a) $x^2 + y^2 + z^2 + 2ax + 2by + 2cz = 0$ (b) $x^2 + y^2 + z^2 - 2ax - 2by - 2cz = 0$

   (c) $x^2 + y^2 + z^2 - ax - by - cz = 0$ (d) $x^2 + y^2 + z^2 + ax + by + cz = 0$.

(Rohilkhand, 2003)

20. The equation of the sphere concentric with the sphere
$$x^2 + y^2 + z^2 - 4x - 6y - 8z - 5 = 0$$
and which passes through origin is :

   (a) $x^2 + y^2 + z^2 - 4x - 6y - 8z = 0$ (b) $x^2 + y^2 + z^2 - 6y - 8z = 0$

   (c) $x^2 + y^2 + z^2 = 0$ (d) None of these.   *(Kumaon 2006)*

21. The centre of the sphere which passes through $(a, 0, 0)$, $(0, b, 0)$ $(0, 0, c)$ and $(0, 0, 0)$ is :

   (a) $(a/2, 0, 0)$ (b) $(0, b/2, 0)$ (c) $(0, 0, c/2)$ (d) $(a/2, b/2, c/2)$.

22. The radius of the sphere $x^2 + y^2 + z^2 - 6x + 8y - 10z + 1 = 0$ is :

   (a) 7   (b) 5   (c) 2   (d) 15.

23. The equation of the sphere on the join of $(2, 3, 5)$, $(4, 9, -3)$ as diameter is :

   (a) $x^2 + y^2 + z^2 - 6x - 12y - 2z + 20 = 0$ (b) $(x - 2)(x - 4) + (y - 3)(y - 9) = 0$

   (c) $(x - 2)(x - 4) + (z - 5)(z + 3) = 0$ (d) $(y - 3)(y - 9) + (z - 5)(z + 3) = 0$.

24. If $(2, 3, 5)$ is one end of a diameter of the sphere $x^2 + y^2 + z^2 - 6x - 12y - 2z + 20 = 0$, then co-ordinates of the other end of diameter are :

   (a) $(4, 3, 5)$ (b) $(4, 3, -3)$ (c) $(4, 9, -3)$ (d) None of these.

25. If two spheres of radii r_1 and r_2 cut orthogonally, then the radius of the common circle is :

   (a) $r_1 r_2$ (b) $\sqrt{r_1^2 + r_2^2}$ (c) $r_1 r_2 \sqrt{r_1^2 + r_2^2}$ (d) $\dfrac{r_1 r_2}{\sqrt{r_1^2 + r_2^2}}$.

26. Two spheres of radii 3 and 4 intersect orthogonally; then the radius of common circle is :

   (a) 7   (b) 12/5   (c) 5   (d) 8.

(Avadh, 2001)

27. The point of contact of the spheres
$$x^2 + y^2 + z^2 + 2x - 4y - 4z - 7 = 0, \quad x^2 + y^2 + z^2 + 2x - 4y - 16z + 65 = 0$$
is :

   (a) $(1, 2, 6)$ (b) $(1, 2, -6)$ (c) $(1, -2, 6)$ (d) $(-1, 2, 6)$.

28. The angle of intersection of the spheres $x^2 + y^2 + z^2 - 2x - 4y - 6z + 10 = 0$ and $x^2 + y^2 + z^2 - 6x - 2y + 2z + 2 = 0$ is :

    (a) $\pi/2$ (b) $\cos^{-1} (2/3)$ (c) $\cos^{-1} (1/3)$ (d) $\pi/3$.

                                                                  (Avadh, 2005)

ANSWERS

1. (a)	**2.** (c)	**3.** (d)	**4.** (b)	**5.** (c)	**6.** (a)	**7.** (c)	**8.** (a)
9. (b)	**10.** (c)	**11.** (b)	**12.** (c)	**13.** (d)	**14.** (a)	**15.** (b)	**16.** (c)
17. (b)	**18.** (d)	**19.** (c)	**20.** (a)	**21.** (d)	**22.** (a)	**23.** (a)	**24.** (c)
25. (d)	**26.** (b)	**27.** (d)	**28.** (b)				

II. Fill in the Blanks

Note : *Fill in the blanks "......." so that the following statements are complete and correct.*

1. The equation of a sphere whose centre is the point (x_1, y_1, z_1) and radius r is ......

2. The equation $x^2 + y^2 + z^2 + 2ux + 2vy + 2wz = 0$ represents a sphere passing through the ......

3. The equation of a sphere whose centre is at origin and radius a is ......

4. The equation $ax^2 + by^2 + cz^2 + 2ux + 2vy + 2wz + d = 0$ represents a sphere if ......

5. The equation of the sphere with the end points of its diameter as the points (x_1, y_1, z_1) and (x_2, y_2, z_2) is $(x - x_1)(x - x_2) + (y - y_1)(y - y_2) + ... = 0.$ *(Meerut, 2001)*

6. The co-ordinates of the centre of the sphere $x^2 + y^2 + z^2 + 2ux + 2vy + 2wz + d = 0$ are ..... and its radius is ......

7. The co-ordinates of the centre of the sphere $2x^2 + 2y^2 + 2z^2 - 2x + 4y - 6z = 15$ are ......

                                                                   (Meerut, 2001)

8. The section of a sphere by a plane is a ......

9. A great circle is the section of a sphere by a plane passing through the ..... of the sphere.

10. The radius of the circle $x^2 + y^2 + z^2 = 25$, $2x + 3y - 4z = 0$ is ......

11. The equation of the tangent plane to the sphere $x^2 + y^2 + z^2 = a^2$ at the point (x_1, y_1, z_1) on it is ......

12. The tangent plane at any point of a sphere is perpendicular to the ..... through that point.

13. The pole of the plane $lx + my + nz = p$ with respect to the sphere $x^2 + y^2 + z^2 = a^2$ is ......

14. A sphere of radius k passes through the origin and meets the axes in A, B, C. Then the centroid of the triangle ABC lies on the sphere $9(x^2 + y^2 + z^2) = ...$

15. If the plane $lx + my + nz = p$ touches the sphere $x^2 + y^2 + z^2 + 2ux + 2vy + 2wz + d = 0$, then $(lu + mv + nw + p)^2 = (.....)(u^2 + v^2 + w^2 - d).$

16. The spheres $x^2 + y^2 + z^2 - 2x = 3$ and $x^2 + y^2 + z^2 + 6x + 6y + 9 = 0$ touch ......

17. Two lines which are such that the polar of any point on any one passes through the other, are known as ......

18. The radius of the common circle of two spheres of radii r_1 and r_2 and cutting orthogonally is ......

19. If the distance between the centres of the two spheres is equal to the difference of their radii, then the two spheres touch ......

20. If the distance between the centres of the two spheres is equal to the sum of their radii, then the two spheres touch ......

21. The equation of the radical plane of the spheres $x^2 + y^2 + z^2 - 3x + 4y - 5z - 7 = 0$ and $x^2 + y^2 + z^2 + 2x + 7y + 6z - 8 = 0$ is ......

22. The radical plane of the two spheres is ..... to the line joining their centres.

ANSWERS

1. $(x - x_1)^2 + (y - y_1)^2 + (z - z_1)^2 = r^2$;   **2.** origin;

3. $x^2 + y^2 + z^2 = a^2$;   **4.** $a = b = c$;   **5.** $(z - z_1)(z - z_2)$;

6. $(-u, -v, -w)$, $\sqrt{u^2 + v^2 + w^2 - d}$;   **7.** $\left(\dfrac{1}{2}, -1, \dfrac{3}{2}\right)$;   **8.** circle;

9. centre;   **10.** 5;   **11.** $xx_1 + yy_1 + zz_1 = a^2$;

12. radius;   **13.** $\left(\dfrac{la^2}{p}, \dfrac{ma^2}{p}, \dfrac{na^2}{p}\right)$;   **14.** $4k^2$;   **16.** extremely;

17. polar lines;   **18.** $r_1 r_2 / \sqrt{r_1^2 + r_2^2}$;   **19.** internally;   **20.** externally;

21. $5x + 3y + 11z - 1 = 0$;   **22.** perpendicular.

III. True/False Statements

Note : *Write 'T' for true and 'F' for false statements.*

1. The co-ordinates of the centre of the sphere $x^2 + y^2 + z^2 - ax - by - cz = 0$ are (a, b, c).
2. The equation $2x^2 + 2y^2 - 2z^2 + 3x - 4y + 3z - 9 = 0$ represents a sphere.
3. The equation of any sphere passing through the circle $x^2 + y^2 = a^2$, $z = 0$ is
$$(x^2 + y^2 - a^2) + \lambda z = 0.$$
4. The plane $2x - 3y + 4z = 5$ touches the sphere $x^2 + y^2 + z^2 = 25/29$.
5. The spheres $x^2 + y^2 + z^2 - 2x - 5z + 4 = 0$ and $x^2 + y^2 + z^2 + 6y - 4 = 0$ cut orthogonally.
6. If the polar plane of P passes through Q, then the polar plane of Q will pass through P.
7. The equation of the sphere passing through $(0, 0, 0)$, $(1, 0, 0)$, $(0, 1, 0)$ and $(0, 0, 1)$ is $x^2 + y^2 + z^2 - x - y - z = 0$.
8. A system of spheres every two members of which have the same radical plane is said to be co-axal.
9. A plane passes through a fixed point (p, q, r) and cuts the axes in A, B, C; then the locus of the centre of the sphere $OABC$ is $(x/p) + (y/q) + (z/r) = 2$.
10. The equation of the sphere on the join of $(2, -3, 4)$ and $(-5, 6, -7)$ as diameter is $x^2 + y^2 + z^2 + 3x - 3y + 3z - 56 = 0$.
11. The curve of intersection of two spheres is a circle.   *(Kanpur, 2001)*
12. The general equation of a sphere contains four independent constants.
13. Two spheres touch externally, if the distance between their centres is equal to the sum of their radii.
14. If the line joining the centre of the sphere and point P meets the polar plane of P in Q, then $OP \cdot OQ = (\text{radius})^2$.
15. Radical plane of two spheres is the locus of the point from where the square of the lengths of the tangents to the two spheres are equal.

ANSWERS

1. F	**2.** F	**3.** F	**4.** T	**5.** T
6. T	**7.** T	**8.** T	**9.** F	**10.** T
11. T	**12.** T	**13.** T	**14.** T	**15.** T.

7

Cones, Cylinders

7.1. DEFINITION

A **cone** *is a surface generated by a straight line which passes through a fixed point and satisfies one more condition*; for instance, it may intersect a given curve or touch a given surface.

(Kumaon, 1995; Sagar, 1995)

The fixed point is called the *Vertex* and the given curve the *Guiding curve* of the cone. An individual straight line on the surface of a cone is called its *Generator*.

Thus, a cone is essentially a set of lines called *Generators* through a given point. Also we may say that a cone is a set of points on its generators.

Whereas we can have cones with equations of any degree whatsoever depending upon the condition to be satisfied by its generators, we shall in this book be concerned only with *Quadratic cones*, *i.e.*, cones with second degree equations.

It will be seen that the degree of the equation of a cone whose generators intersect a given conic or touch a given sphere is of the second degree.

7.1.1. Equation of a Cone with a Conic as Guiding Curve

To find the equation of the cone whose vertex is the point

$$(\alpha, \beta, \gamma)$$

are whose generators intersect the conic

$$ax^2 + 2hxy + by^2 + 2gx + 2fy + c = 0, z = 0 \qquad \text{...(i)}$$

(Kumaon, 1995, 97; Kanpur, 1996; Bhopal, 2000, 01; Sagar, 1997; Jiwaji, 1998; Jabalpur, 1998; Bilaspur, 1999)

We have to find the locus of points on lines which pass through the given point (α, β, γ) and intersect the given curve.

The equations to *any* line through (α, β, γ) are

$$\frac{x - \alpha}{l} = \frac{y - \beta}{m} = \frac{z - \gamma}{n} \qquad \text{...(ii)}$$

This line will be a generator of the cone if and only if it intersects the given curve.

This line meets the plane $z = 0$ in the point

$$\left(\alpha - \frac{l\gamma}{n}, \beta - \frac{m\gamma}{n}, 0\right)$$

which will lie on the given conic, if

$$a\left(\alpha - \frac{l\gamma}{n}\right)^2 + 2h\left(\alpha - \frac{l\gamma}{n}\right)\left(\beta - \frac{m\gamma}{n}\right) + b\left(\beta - \frac{m\gamma}{n}\right)^2$$

$$+ 2g\left(\alpha - \frac{l\gamma}{n}\right) + 2f\left(\beta - \frac{m\gamma}{n}\right) + c = 0 \quad \text{...(iii)}$$

This is the condition for the line (*ii*) to intersect the conic (*i*). Eliminating *l*, *m*, *n* between (*ii*) and (*iii*), we get

$$a\left(\alpha - \frac{x-\alpha}{z-\gamma}\gamma\right)^2 + 2h\left(\alpha - \frac{x-\alpha}{z-\gamma}\gamma\right)\left(\beta - \frac{y-\beta}{z-\gamma}\gamma\right) + b\left(\beta - \frac{y-\beta}{z-\gamma}\gamma\right)^2$$

$$+ 2g\left(\alpha - \frac{x-\alpha}{z-\gamma}\gamma\right) + 2f\left(\beta - \frac{y-\beta}{z-\gamma}\gamma\right) + c = 0$$

$$\Rightarrow \quad a(\alpha z - x\gamma)^2 + 2h(\alpha z - x\gamma)(\beta z - y\gamma) + (\beta z - y\gamma)^2$$
$$+ 2g(\alpha z - x\gamma)(z-\gamma) + 2f(\beta z - y\gamma)(z-\gamma) + c(z-\gamma)^2 = 0,$$

which is the required equation of the cone.

EXAMPLES

1. *Find the equation of the cone whose vertex is* (α, β, γ) *and base* $ax^2 + by^2 = 1$, $z = 0$.

(Bilaspur, 1996; Gorakhpur, 2000; Jabalpur, 1995, 2001; Rohilkhand, 1997; Sagar, 1998; Vikram, 1998)

Sol. Any line through (α, β, γ) is

$$\frac{x-\alpha}{l} = \frac{y-\beta}{m} = \frac{z-\gamma}{n} \qquad \qquad ...(i)$$

This cuts $z = 0$, where

$$\frac{x-\alpha}{l} = \frac{y-\beta}{m} = \frac{-\gamma}{n}$$

$$\Rightarrow \qquad \qquad \left(\alpha - \frac{l\gamma}{n}, \beta - \frac{m\gamma}{n}, 0\right)$$

which will lie on the given conic, if

$$a\left(\alpha - \frac{l\gamma}{n}\right)^2 + b\left(\beta - \frac{m\gamma}{n}\right)^2 = 1$$

Eliminating *l*, *m*, *n* with the help of (*i*), we get

$$a\left(\alpha - \frac{x-\alpha}{z-\gamma}\gamma\right) + b\left(\beta - \frac{y-\beta}{z-\gamma}\gamma\right)^2 = 1$$

or $\qquad a(\alpha z - \gamma x)^2 + b(\beta z - z\gamma)^2 = (z - \gamma)^2$

This is the required cone.

2. *Find the equation of a cone whose vertex is* (α, β, γ) *and base* $y^2 = 4ax$, $z = 0$.

(Avadh, 1995, 97; Bundelkhand, 1995; Gorakhpur, 1997, 98, 99, 2002; Jabalpur, 1997; Poorvanchal, 1995, 96; Vikram, 2000)

Sol. Any line through (α, β, γ) is

$$\frac{x-\alpha}{l} = \frac{y-\beta}{m} = \frac{z-\gamma}{n} \qquad \qquad ...(i)$$

It meets the plane $z = 0$ at $\left(\alpha - \frac{l\gamma}{n}, \beta - \frac{m\gamma}{n}, 0\right)$ and if it lies on $y^2 = 4ax$, $z = 0$, then

$$\left(\beta - \frac{m\gamma}{n}\right)^2 = 4a\left(\alpha - \frac{l\gamma}{n}\right) \qquad \qquad ...(ii)$$

Eliminating l, m, n between (i) and (ii), we get

$$\left[\beta - \left(\frac{y-\beta}{z-\gamma}\right)\gamma\right]^2 = 4a\left[\alpha - \left(\frac{x-\alpha}{z-\gamma}\right)\gamma\right]$$

$\Rightarrow \quad (\beta z - y\gamma)^2 = 4a\,(\alpha z - \gamma x)\,(z - \gamma)$.

3. *Find the equation of the cone with vertex* (5, 4, 3) *and* $3x^2 + 2y^2 = 6$, $y + z = 0$ *as base.*

(Bhopal, 1994, 95, 98; Bilaspur, 1995; Indore, 1997;
Jiwaji, 1995; Sagar, 1999; Vikram, 1999)

Sol. Let

$$\frac{x-5}{l} = \frac{y-4}{m} = \frac{z-3}{n}$$

be a generator of the cone.

Any point on this line has the co-ordinates

$$(lr + 5, \; mr + 4, \; nr + 3)$$

This point will lie on the base, if

$$3\,(lr+5)^2 + 2\,(mr+4)^2 = 6 \qquad\qquad\qquad ...(i)$$

and $\qquad\qquad\qquad\qquad mr + 4 + nr + 3 = 0$

$\Rightarrow \qquad\qquad\qquad\qquad r\,(m+n) = -7 \qquad\qquad\qquad ...(ii)$

From (i)

$$3\,[l\,(m+n)\,r + 5\,(m+n)^2]^2 + 2\,[m\,(m+n)\,r + 4\,(m+n)] = (m+n)^2$$

$\Rightarrow \quad 3\,(-7l + 5m + 5n)^2 + 2\,(-7m + 4m + 4n)^2 = 6\,(m+n)^2 \qquad$ [using (iii)]

Hence, the locus of (l, m, n) is

$$3\,[-7\,(x-5) + 5\,(y-4) + 5\,(z-3)]^2 + 2\,[-3\,(y-4) + 4\,(z-3)]^2$$
$$= 6\,(y-4+z-3)^2$$

$\Rightarrow \quad 3\,(-7x + 5y + 5z)^2 + 2\,(-3y + 4z)^2 = 6\,(y+z-7)^2$

$\Rightarrow \quad 147x^2 + 87y^2 + 101z^2 - 210xy + 90yz - 210zx - 294 = 0$.

4. *The section of a cone whose vertex is* P *and guiding curve the ellipse* $x^2/a^2 + y^2/b^2 = 1$, $z = 0$ *by the plane* $z = 0$ *is a rectangular hyperbola. Show that the locus of* P *is*

$$\frac{x^2}{a^2} + \frac{y^2 + z^2}{b^2} = 1. \qquad\qquad (\textit{Indore, 1997, 99})$$

Sol. Let the point P be (α, β, γ). Then proceeding as in Ex. 1 earlier, we get the required cone as

$$\frac{1}{a^2}\,(\alpha z - \gamma x)^2 + \frac{1}{b^2}\,(\beta z - \gamma y)^2 = (z-\gamma)^2$$

This meets $x = 0$ in a curve

$$\frac{\alpha^2 z^2}{a^2} + \frac{(\beta z - \gamma y)^2}{b^2} = (z-\gamma)^2, \; x = 0$$

This will be a rectangular hyperbola, if

$$\text{coeff. of } y^2 + \text{coeff. of } z^2 = 0$$

$$\Rightarrow \qquad\qquad \frac{\alpha^2}{a^2} + \frac{\beta^2}{b^2} + \frac{\gamma^2}{b^2} - 1 = 0$$

$\therefore$ locus of (α, β, γ) is

$$\frac{x^2}{a^2} + \frac{y^2 + z^2}{b^2} = 1.$$

5. *Two cones pass through the curves* $y = 0, z^2 = 4ax$; $x = 0, z^2 = 4by$ *and they have a common vertex. The plane* $z = 0$ *meets them in two conics that intersect in four concyclic points. Show that the vertex lies on the surface*

$$z^2 (x/a + y/b) = 4 (x^2 + y^2).$$

Sol. Let (α, β, γ) be the co-ordinates of the common vertex. Then any lines through vertex is

$$\frac{x - \alpha}{l} = \frac{y - \beta}{m} = \frac{z - \gamma}{n} \qquad \qquad ...(i)$$

This meets $y = 0$ at $\left(\alpha - \dfrac{l\beta}{m}, 0, \gamma - \dfrac{n\beta}{m} \right)$, so (i) will cut the curve $y = 0, z^2 = 4ax$, if

$$\left(\gamma - \frac{n\beta}{m} \right)^2 = 4a \left(\alpha - \frac{l\beta}{m} \right)$$

or $\qquad\qquad\qquad (m\gamma - n\beta)^2 = 4am (\alpha m - l\beta)$

Substituting proportional values of l, m, n from (i), the cone through the curve $y = 0, z^2 = 4ax$ is

$$(\gamma y - \beta z)^2 = 4a (y - \beta) (\alpha y - \beta x) \qquad \qquad ...(ii)$$

Similarly cone through the curve $x = 0, z^2 = 4by$ is

$$(\gamma x - \alpha z)^2 = 4b (x - \alpha) (\beta x - \alpha y) \qquad \qquad ...(iii)$$

These cones cut $z = 0$, where

$$\gamma^2 y^2 = 4a (y - \beta) (\alpha y - \beta x), z = 0 \qquad \qquad ...(iv)$$

and $\qquad\qquad \gamma^2 x^2 = 4b (x - \alpha) (\beta x - \alpha y), z = 0 \qquad \qquad ...(v)$

Any curve in plane $z = 0$ through intersection of curves (iv) and (v) is

$$\gamma^2 y^2 - 4a (y - \beta) (\alpha y - \beta x) + \lambda [\gamma^2 x^2 - 4b (y - \alpha) (\beta x - \alpha y)] = 0.$$

This will be a circle if

$$\text{coeff. of } x^2 = \text{coeff. of } y^2$$

$\Rightarrow \qquad\qquad\qquad \lambda (\gamma - 4b\beta) = \gamma^2 - 4a\alpha$

$$\text{coeff. of } xy = 0$$

$\Rightarrow \qquad\qquad\qquad 4a\beta + 4\lambda b\alpha = 0$

Eliminating λ from these relations, we get

$$- \frac{a\beta}{b\alpha} (\gamma^2 - 4b\beta) = \gamma^2 - 4a\alpha$$

or $\qquad\qquad\qquad \gamma^2 \left(\frac{\alpha}{a} + \frac{\beta}{b} \right) = 4 (\alpha^2 + \beta^2)$

Hence, locus of the vertex (α, β, γ) is

$$z^2 \left(\frac{x}{a} + \frac{y}{b} \right) = 4 (x^2 + y^2).$$

6. *The vertex of cone is* (a, b, c) *and the yz-plane cuts it in the curve* $F(y, z) = 0, x = 0,$
show that xz-plane cuts it in the curve,

$$y = 0, \ F\left[\frac{bx}{x-a}, \ \frac{cx-az}{x-a}\right] = 0$$

(Bhopal, 1996; Ravishankar, 1995, 2001)

Sol. Any line through (a, b, c) is

$$\frac{x-a}{l} = \frac{y-b}{m} = \frac{z-c}{n} \qquad \qquad ...(i)$$

It meets $x = 0$ in the point $\left[0, \ b - \dfrac{am}{l}, \ c - \dfrac{an}{l}\right]$ and if it lies on the given curve $F(y, z) = 0,$
then

$$F\left[b - \frac{am}{l}, \ c - \frac{an}{l}\right] = 0 \qquad \qquad ...(ii)$$

Eliminating l, m, n between (i) and (ii), we get

$$F\left[b - a\left(\frac{y-b}{x-a}\right), \ c - a\left(\frac{z-c}{x-a}\right)\right] = 0$$

$$\Rightarrow \qquad \qquad F\left[\frac{bx-ay}{x-a}, \ \frac{cx-az}{x-a}\right] = 0.$$

It meets zx-plane, *i.e.*, $y = 0$ in the curve

$$F\left[\frac{bx}{x-a}, \ \frac{cx-az}{x-a}\right] = 0, \ y = 0.$$

7. *Find the equation of the cone with vertex at* $(2a, b, c)$ *and passing through the curve*
$x^2 + y^2 = 4a^2$ *and* $z = 0.$ *Find b and c if the cone also passes through the curve* $y^2 = 4a(z + a),$
$x = 0.$ *Also, show that the cone is cut by the plane* $y = 0$ *in two straight lines and the angle*
θ *between them is given by* $\tan \theta = 2.$

Sol. Any line through $(2a, b, c)$ is

$$\frac{x-2a}{l} = \frac{y-b}{m} = \frac{z-c}{n} \qquad \qquad ...(i)$$

It meets $z = 0$ in the point $\left[2a - \dfrac{lc}{n}, b - \dfrac{mc}{n}, 0\right]$ and if it lies on the curve $x^2 + y^2 = 4a^2, z = 0,$
then we get

$$\left(2a - \frac{lc}{n}\right)^2 + \left(b - \frac{mc}{n}\right)^2 = 4a^2 \qquad \qquad ...(ii)$$

Eliminating l, m, n between (i) and (ii) we get the required cone as

$$\left[2a - \left(\frac{x-2a}{z-c}\right)c\right]^2 + \left[b - \left(\frac{y-b}{z-c}\right)c\right]^2 = 4a^2$$

$$\Rightarrow \qquad (2az - cx)^2 + (bz - yc)^2 = 4a^2(z-c)^2 \qquad \qquad ...(iii)$$

If this cone passes through $y^2 = 4a(z + a), x = 0,$ then putting $x = 0$ in (iii), we get

$$(2az)^2 + (bz - yc)^2 = 4a^2(z-c)^2$$

$$\Rightarrow \qquad b^2z^2 + c^2y^2 - 2bcyz - 4a^2c^2 + 8a^2zc = 0 \qquad \qquad ...(iv)$$

If it is same as $y^2 = 4a (z + a)$, then comparing this with (iv), we have

$$b^2 = 0 \Rightarrow b = 0 \text{ which reduces } (iv) \text{ to}$$

$$c^2 y^2 = 4a^2 c^2 - 8a^2 zc$$

$$\Rightarrow \qquad y^2 = -\left(\frac{8a^2}{c}\right)\left(z - \frac{1}{2}c\right)$$

This gives

$$-\frac{8a^2}{c} = 4a \text{ and } -\frac{1}{2}c = a$$

$$\Rightarrow \qquad c = -2a.$$

Hence, $b = 0$, $c = -2a$.

Substituting these values of b and c in (iii), the equation of cone intersecting the given conic reduces to

$$(2ax + 2az)^2 + 4a^2 y^2 = 4a^2 (z + 2a)^2$$

$$\Rightarrow \qquad x^2 + y^2 + 2zx - 4az - 4a^2 = 0 \qquad \qquad \qquad ...(v)$$

The plane $y = 0$ cuts cone (v) in

$$x^2 + 2zx - 4az - 4a^2 = 0, \ y = 0$$

$$\Rightarrow \qquad (x^2 - 4a^2) + 2z (x - 2a) = 0, \ y = 0$$

$$\Rightarrow \qquad (x - 2a) (x + 2a + 2z) = 0, \ y = 0$$

$$\Rightarrow \qquad x - 2a = 0, \ y = 0$$

and

$$x + 2a + 2z = 0, \ y = 0$$

This gives the required lines. These lines lie in the plane $y = 0$ and their combined equation is

$$y = 0, \ x^2 + 2zx - 4az - 4a^2 = 0.$$

If θ be the angle between these lines; then

$$\tan \theta = \frac{2\sqrt{1^2 - 0}}{1 + 0} = 2.$$

EXERCISES

1. Find the equation of the cone whose generators pass through the point (α, β, γ) and have their direction cosines satisfying the relation $al^2 + bm^2 + cn^2 = 0$.

    [**Ans.** $a (x - \alpha)^2 + b (y - \beta)^2 + c (z - \gamma)^2 = 0$]

2. Find the equation of the cone whose vertex is the point $(1, 1, 0)$ and whose guiding curve is $y = 0$, $x^2 + z^2 = 4$. *(Delhi, 2005)*   [**Ans.** $x^2 - 3y^2 + z^2 - 2xy + 8y - 4 = 0$]

3. Obtain the locus of the lines which pass through a point (α, β, γ) and through points of the conic

$$x^2/a^2 + y^2/b^2 = 1, \ z = 0.$$

    (Indore, 1994; Patna, 2003; Poorvanchal, 1999)

$$\left[\textbf{Ans.} \ \left(\frac{\alpha z - x\gamma}{a}\right)^2 + \left(\frac{\beta z - y\gamma}{b}\right)^2 = (z - \gamma)^2\right]$$

4. Show that the equation of the cone whose vertex is the origin and whose base is the circle through the three points $(a, 0, 0)$, $(0, b, 0)$, $(0, 0, c)$ is $\Sigma a (b^2 + c^2) yz = 0$.

5. Find the equation of the cone with vertex at $(1, 2, 3)$ and guiding curve
$$x^2 + y^2 + z^2 = 4, \ x + y + z = 1. \qquad \textit{(Garhwal, 2002)}$$
[**Ans.** $5x^2 + 3y^2 + z^2 - 2xy - 6yz - 4zx + 6x + 8y + 10z - 26 = 0$]

6. Find the equation of the cone whose vertex is at the point $(- 1, 1, 2)$ and whose guiding curve is $3x^2 - y^2 = 1$, $z = 0$. \qquad *(Garhwal, 2004; M.D.U. Rohtak, 1996)*
[**Ans.** $12x^2 - 4y^2 + z^2 - 4yz + 12zx + 4z - 4 = 0$]

7. Find the equation of cone whose vertex is $(1, 2, 3)$ and base is $y^2 = 4ax$, $z = 0$.
(Vikram, 2000) [**Ans.** $(2z - 3y)^2 = 4a (z - 3) (z - 3x)$]

8. Find the equation of the cone with vertex $(2, 3, 1)$ and passing through the curve
$$x^2 + y^2 + z^2 - 2x + 4y - 6z + 7 = 0 \text{ and } x + 2y + 2z = 5. \ \textit{(M.D.U. Rohtak, 2000)}$$

9. The plane $lx + my + nz = 0$ moves in such a way that its intersection with the planes
$$ax + by + cz + d = 0, \ a'x + b'y + c'z + d' = 0$$
are perpendicular. Show that the normal to the plane through the origin describes, in general, a cone of the second degree, and find its equation. Examine the case when $aa' + bb' + cc' = 0$, *i.e.*, when the two given planes are perpendicular.

7.1.2. Enveloping Cone of a Sphere

To find the equation of the cone whose vertex is at the point (α, β, γ) and whose generators touch the sphere
$$x^2 + y^2 + z^2 = a^2. \qquad ...(i)$$
(Kanpur, 1999)

The equations to *any* line through (α, β, γ) are
$$\frac{x - \alpha}{l} = \frac{y - \beta}{m} = \frac{z - \gamma}{n} \qquad ...(ii)$$

This line will be a generator of the given curve if and only if it touches the given sphere. The points of intersection of the line (ii) with the sphere (i) are given by
$$r^2 (l^2 + m^2 + n^2) + 2r (l\alpha + m\beta + n\gamma) + (\alpha^2 + \beta^2 + \gamma^2 - a^2) = 0 \qquad \text{(See § 6.5)}$$
so that the line will touch the sphere, if the two roots of the quadratic equation in r are equal and this requires
$$(l\alpha + m\beta + n\gamma)^2 = (l^2 + m^2 + n^2) (\alpha^2 + \beta^2 + \gamma^2 - a^2). \qquad ...(iii)$$
This is the condition for the line (ii) to touch the sphere (i).

Eliminating l, m, n between (ii) and (iii), we get
$$[\alpha (x - \alpha) + \beta (y - \beta) + \gamma (z - \gamma)]^2$$
$$= [(x - \alpha)^2 + (y - \beta)^2 + (z - \gamma)^2] (\alpha^2 + \beta^2 + \gamma^2 - a^2) \qquad ...(iv)$$
which is the required equation of the cone.

If we write
$$S \equiv x^2 + y^2 + z^2 - a^2, \ S_1 \equiv \alpha^2 + \beta^2 + \gamma^2 - a^2, \ T \equiv \alpha x + \beta y + \gamma z - a^2$$
the equation (iv) can be rewritten as
$$(T - S_1)^2 = (S - 2T + S_1) S$$
$$\Leftrightarrow \qquad SS_1 = T^2$$
$$\Leftrightarrow (x^2 + y^2 + z^2 - a^2) (\alpha^2 + \beta^2 + \gamma^2 - a^2) = (\alpha x + \beta y + \gamma z - a^2)^2.$$

Def. Enveloping cone. *The cone formed by the tangent lines to a surface, drawn from a given point is called the Enveloping Cone of the surface with given point as its vertex.*
(Garhwal, 2001; Utkal, 2003)

EXERCISES

1. Find the enveloping cone of the sphere

$$x^2 + y^2 + z^2 - 2x + 4z = 1$$

with its vertex at $(1, 1, 1)$.

(*Avadh, 2002; Kumaon, 1999*)

[**Ans.** $4x^2 + 3y^2 - 5z^2 - 6yz - 8x + 16z - 4 = 0$]

2. Show that the plane $z = 0$ cuts the enveloping cone of the sphere $x^2 + y^2 + z^2 = 11$ which has its vertex at $(2, 4, 1)$ in a rectangular hyperbola.

7.1.3. Quadratic Cones with Vertex at Origin

The equation of a cone whose vertex is the origin is homogeneous and conversely.

(*Ajmer, 1996; Bilaspur, 2000; Indore, 2000; Agra, 1996; Kanpur, 1997; Jabalpur, 1999; Ravishankar, 1997; Vikram, 1994*)

We take up the general equation

$$ax^2 + by^2 + cz^2 + 2fyz + 2gzx + 2hxy + 2ux + 2vy + 2wz + d = 0 \qquad ...(1)$$

of the second degree and show that it represents a cone with its vertex at the origin, if and only if

$$u = v = w = d = 0.$$

Let the equation represent a cone with its vertex at the origin.

Let $P(x', y', z')$ be a point on the cone represented by equation (1). Then

$$(rx', ry', rz')$$

are the general co-ordinates of a point on the line OP joining the point P to the origin O.

Since the line OP is a generator of the cone (i), the point

$$(rx', ry', rz')$$

lies on it for every value of r implying that the equation

$$r^2(ax'^2 + by'^2 + cz'^2 + 2fy'z' + 2gz'x' + 2hx'y') + 2r(ux' + vy' + wz') + d = 0$$

is true for every value of r.

This implies that we have

$$ax'^2 + by'^2 + cz'^2 + 2fy'z' + 2gz'x' + 2hx'y' = 0 \qquad ...(i)$$

$$ux' + vy' + wz' = 0 \qquad ...(ii)$$

$$d = 0. \qquad ...(iii)$$

From (ii), we see that if u, v, w, be not all zero, then the co-ordinates x', y', z' of any point on the cone satisfy an equation of the first degree viz.,

$$ux + vy + wz = 0$$

so that the surface is a plane and we have a contradiction. Thus,

$$u = v = w = 0; \, d = 0$$

so that the equation of a cone with its vertex at the origin is necessarily homogeneous.

Conversely. *We show that every homogeneous equation of the second degree represents a cone with its vertex at the origin.*

It is clear from the nature of the equation that if the co-ordinates x', y', z' satisfy it, then so do also rx', ry', rz' for all values of r.

Hence, if any point P lies on the surface, then every point on the line OP lies on it.

Thus, the surface is generated by lines through the origin O and hence, by definition is a cone with its vertex at O.

Note. A homogeneous equation of the second degree will represent a pair of planes, if the homogeneous expression can be factorized into linear factors. The condition for this has already been obtained in Chapter 2. A pair of intersecting planes can thus be thought of as a cone with any point on the line of intersection as a vertex thereof.

Cor. 1. If l, m, n be the direction ratios of any generator of the cone

$$ax^2 + by^2 + cz^2 + 2fyz + 2gzx + 2hxy = 0 \qquad \qquad ...(1)$$

so that the point (lr, mr, nr) lies on it for every value of r, we have

$$al^2 + bm^2 + cn^2 + 2fmn + 2gnl + 2hlm = 0. \qquad \qquad ...(2)$$

Conversely, it is obvious that if the result (2) be true then the line with direction ratios l, m, n is a generator of the cone whose equation is (1). The proof of this statement is straightforward.

Cor. 2. The general equation of a cone with its vertex at the point (α, β, γ) is

$$a(x - \alpha)^2 + b(y - \beta)^2 + c(z - \gamma)^2$$
$$+ 2f(z - \gamma)(y - \beta) + 2g(x - \alpha)(z - \gamma) + 2h(x - \alpha)(y - \beta) = 0,$$

as can easily be verified by transferring the origin to the point (α, β, γ).

EXAMPLES

1. *Find the equation of the cone whose vertex is at the origin and which passes through the curve given by the equations*

$$ax^2 + by^2 + cz^2 = 1, \ lx + my + nz = p.$$

(Avadh, 1996; Jabalpur, 1999, 2001; Poorvanchal, 1998;
Rohilkhand, 2000; Sagar, 1998)

Sol. The required equation is the homogeneous equation of the second degree satisfied by points satisfying the two given equations.

We have $\qquad \qquad lx + my + nz = p \ \Leftrightarrow \ \dfrac{lx + my + nz}{p} = 1.$

Thus, the required equation is

$$ax^2 + by^2 + cz^2 = \left(\frac{lx + my + nz}{p} \right)^2,$$

$\Leftrightarrow \ \Sigma (ap^2 - l^2) x^2 - 2\Sigma lmxy = 0.$

2. *Show that the equation of the cone whose vertex is the origin and base curve* $z = k$, $f(x, y) = 0$ *is*

$$f\left(\frac{xk}{z}, \frac{yk}{z} \right) = 0. \qquad \qquad (Ajmer, 1998; Bilaspur, 2001)$$

Sol. Let $\qquad \qquad f(x, y) = ax^2 + by^2 + 2hxy + 2gx + 2fy + c = 0 \qquad \qquad ...(i)$

By making (i) homogeneous with the help of $z = k$, we get the equation of required cone as

$$ax^2 + by^2 + 2hxy + 2gx \left(\frac{z}{k} \right) + 2fy \left(\frac{z}{k} \right) + c \left(\frac{z}{k} \right)^2 = 0$$

Multiplying by $\dfrac{k^2}{z^2}$, we get

$$a \left(\frac{xk}{z} \right)^2 + b \left(\frac{yk}{z} \right)^2 + 2h \left(\frac{xk}{z} \right) \left(\frac{yk}{z} \right) + 2g \left(\frac{xk}{z} \right) + 2f \left(\frac{yk}{z} \right) + c = 0$$

$$\Rightarrow \qquad f\left(\frac{xk}{z}, \frac{yk}{z} \right) = 0.$$

EXERCISES

1. Find the equation of the cone whose vertex is at the origin and the direction cosines of whose generators satisfy the relation

$$3l^2 - 4m^2 + 5n^2 = 0. \quad (Utkal, 2003) \text{ [Ans. } 3x^2 - 4y^2 + 5z^2 = 0]$$

2. Find the equations to the cones with vertex at the origin and which pass through the curves given by the equations

(i) $z = 2$, $x^2 + y^2 = 4$. (ii) $ax^2 + by^2 = 2z$, $lx + my + nz = p$.

(Kumaon, 2004; M.D.U. Rohtak, 1998; Kanpur, 2004)

(iii) $ax^2 + by^2 + cz^2 = 1$, $\alpha x^2 + \beta y^2 = 2z$ (Avadh 2006, Gorakhpur, 2003)

(iv) $x^2 + y^2 + z^2 + x - 2y + 3z = 4$; $x^2 + y^2 + z^2 + 2x - 3y + 4z = 5$.

[**Ans.** (i) $x^2 + y^2 + z^2 = 0$, (ii) $p(ax^2 + by^2) = 2z(lx + my + nz)$,

(iii) $(ax^2 + by^2 + cz^2) 4z^2 = (\alpha x^2 + \beta y^2)^2$, (iv) $2x^2 + y^2 - 5xy - 3yz + 4zx = 0$]

3. A sphere S and a plane α have, respectively, the equations

$$\varphi + u + c = 0; \ v = 1$$

where $\varphi = x^2 + y^2 + z^2$, u and v are homogeneous linear functions of x, y, z and c is a constant. Find the equation of the cone whose generators join the origin O to the points of intersection of S and α.

Show that this cone meets S again in points lying on a plane β and find the equation of β in terms of u, v and c.

If the radius of S varies, while its centre, the plane α, at the point O remains fixed, prove that β passes through a fixed line.

[The required cone, C, is given by

$$C \equiv \varphi + uv + cv^2.$$

Now $C - S \equiv (\varphi + uv + cv^2) - (\varphi + u + c) = (v - 1)(u + cv + c)$

so that we see that the cone C meets the sphere S again in points lying on the plane $\beta \equiv u + cv + c = 0$.

Since the radius of S varies and its centre remains fixed, we see that u is constant while c varies. Also v is constant. This shows that the plane $\beta \equiv u + c(v + 1)$ passes through the line of intersection of the fixed planes $u = 0$, $v + 1 = 0$.]

7.1.4. Determination of Quadratic Cones Under Given Conditions

As a general equation of quadratic cone with a given vertex contains *five arbitrary constants*, it follows that five conditions determine such a cone provided each condition gives rise to a single linear relation between the constants. For instance, *a cone can be determined so as to have any given five concurrent lines as generators*, no three of them being coplanar.

EXAMPLES

1. *Show that the general equation to a cone which passes through the three axes is*

$$fyz + gzx + hxy = 0,$$

f, g, h being parameters. (Ajmer, 1998; Bilaspur, 1995, 98; Bhuj, 1999; Bundelkhand, 1994, 97; Gorakhpur, 1998; Indore, 2001; Jabalpur, 1995, 97; Jiwaji, 1994, 2000; Poorvanchal, 1995; Rewa, 2000; Rohilkhand, 1999; Sagar, 2000)

Sol. The general equation of a cone with its vertex at the origin is

$$ax^2 + by^2 + cz^2 + 2fyz + 2gzx + 2hxy = 0 \qquad ...(i)$$

Now X-axis is a generator.

$\Rightarrow$ its direction cosines (1, 0, 0) satisfy (i) $\Rightarrow$ $a = 0$.

Similarly $b = c = 0$.

2. *Show that a cone can be found so as to contain any two given sets of three mutually perpendicular concurrent lines as generators.*   (*Kanpur, 1996*)

Sol. Take the three lines of one set as co-ordinate axes.

Let the lines OP, OQ, OR of the second set be

$$\frac{x}{l_1} = \frac{y}{m_1} = \frac{z}{n_1}, \frac{x}{l_2} = \frac{y}{m_2} = \frac{z}{n_2}, \frac{x}{l_3} = \frac{y}{m_3} = \frac{z}{n_3},$$

respectively.

The general equation of a cone through the three axes is

$$fyz + gzx + hxy = 0; f, g, h \text{ are parameters.}$$

It will contain the lines OP and OQ as generators, if

$$fm_1n_1 + gn_1l_1 + hl_1m_1 = 0, \qquad \qquad ...(i)$$

$$fm_2n_2 + gn_2l_2 + hl_2m_2 = 0. \qquad \qquad ...(ii)$$

The lines of the set being mutually perpendicular, we have

$$\left. \begin{array}{c} m_1n_1 + m_2n_2 + m_3n_3 = 0, \\ n_1l_1 + n_2l_2 + n_3l_3 = 0, \\ l_1m_1 + l_2m_2 + l_3m_3 = 0. \end{array} \right\} \qquad ...(A)$$

Adding (i), (ii) and employing the relation (A), we deduce the condition

$$fm_3n_3 + gn_3l_3 + hl_3m_3 = 0,$$

so that the cone through the lines OP and OQ also passes through the line OR.

3. *Show that a cone of second degree can be found to pass through any five concurrent lines.*

Sol. Let origin be the point of concurrence of five lines which are

$$x/l_r = y/m_r = z/n_r, r = 1, 2, 3, 4, 5.$$

General second degree equation of the cone with vertex at origin is

$$ax^2 + by^2 + cz^2 + 2fyz + 2gzx + 2hxy = 0$$

i.e.,

$$x^2 + \frac{b}{a}y^2 + \frac{c}{a}z^2 + \frac{2f}{a}yz + \frac{2g}{a}zx + \frac{2h}{a}xy = 0$$

or

$$x^2 + b'y^2 + c'z^2 + 2f'yz + 2g'zx + 2h'xy = 0.$$

This contains five arbitrary constants and, therefore, can be determined by five independent conditions.

Since d.c.'s of generators satisfy the equation of a cone, so any five lines (passing through origin) are sufficient to determine the five arbitrary constants. Therefore a cone of second degree can be found to pass through five concurrent lines.

4. *The plane $x/a + y/b + z/c = 1$ meets the co-ordinate axes in A, B, C. Prove that the equation to the cone generated by lines drawn from O to meet the circle ABC is*

$$yz(b/c + c/b) + zx(c/a + a/c) + xy(a/b + b/a) = 0.$$

(*Bilaspur, 1997, 2001; Bhopal, 1998; Agra, 1998; Garhwal, 1995; Indore, 1994, 96;*
Kumaon. 2005. Jabalpur, 2000; Jiwaji, 1996, 2001; Lucknow, 1994, 96
Ravishankar, 1996; Rohilkhand, 1998)

Sol. Points A, B, C are $(a, 0, 0)$, $(0, b, 0)$ and $(0, 0, c)$ respectively. Equation of the sphere $OABC$ is

$$x^2 + y^2 + z^2 - ax - by - cz = 0 \qquad \qquad ...(i)$$

The circle ABC is obtained by intersection of given plane with (i).

Making (i) homogeneous with the help of given plane, the required cone is

$$(x^2 + y^2 + z^2) - (ax + by + cz)(x/a + y/b + z/c) = 0$$

$$\Rightarrow \qquad yz(b/c + c/b) + zx(c/a + a/c) + xy(a/b + b/a) = 0.$$

5. *Planes through OX and OY include an angle* α. *Show that their line of intersection lies on the cone* $z^2(x^2 + y^2 + z^2) = x^2 y^2 \tan^2 \alpha$.   (*Bhopal, 2002; Jabalpur, 1998; Vikram, 2002*)

Sol. Any plane through OX ($y = 0$, $z = 0$) is

$$y + \lambda z = 0 \qquad\qquad\qquad ...(i)$$

Also a plane through OY is

$$x + \mu z = 0 \qquad\qquad\qquad ...(ii)$$

The angle between two planes is α, *i.e.*,

$$\cos \alpha = \frac{0 \cdot 1 + 1 \cdot 0 + \lambda \mu}{\sqrt{1 + \lambda^2}\,\sqrt{1 + \mu^2}} = \frac{\mu \lambda}{\sqrt{1 + \lambda^2 + \mu^2 + \lambda^2 \mu^2}}$$

so that

$$\tan^2 \alpha = \frac{1 + \lambda^2 + \mu^2 + \lambda^2 \mu^2}{\lambda^2 \mu^2} - 1 = \frac{1 + \lambda^2 + \mu^2}{\lambda^2 \mu^2} \qquad ...(iii)$$

Eliminating λ and μ from (i), (ii) and (iii), the required cone is

$$\tan^2 \alpha = \frac{1 + \dfrac{y^2}{z^2} + \dfrac{x^2}{z^2}}{\left(\dfrac{y^2}{z^2}\right)\left(\dfrac{x^2}{z^2}\right)} = \frac{z^2(x^2 + y^2 + z^2)}{x^2 y^2}$$

$$\Rightarrow \qquad z^2(x^2 + y^2 + z^2) = x^2 y^2 \tan^2 \alpha.$$

EXERCISES

1. Find the equation to the cone which passes through the three co-ordinate axes as well as the two lines

$$\frac{x}{1} = \frac{y}{-2} = \frac{z}{3}, \frac{x}{3} = \frac{y}{-1} = \frac{z}{1}$$

(*Avadh, 1994; Bhopal, 1995; Garhwal, 2001; Sagar, 1995, 98; Vikram, 2001*)

[**Ans.** $3yz + 16zx + 15xy = 0$]

2. Find the equation of the cone which contains the three co-ordinate axes and the two lines through the origin with direction cosines (l_1, m_1, n_1) and (l_2, m_2, n_2).

[**Ans.** $\Sigma l_1 l_2 (m_1 n_2 - m_2 n_1)\, yz = 0$]

3. Find the equation of the quadric cone which passes through the three co-ordinate axes and the three mutually perpendicular lines

$$\frac{1}{2}x = y = -z,\ x = \frac{1}{3}y = \frac{1}{5}z,\ \frac{1}{8}x = -\frac{1}{11}y = \frac{1}{5}z.$$

[**Ans.** $16yz - 33zx - 25xy = 0$]

4. Show that the lines drawn through the point (α, β, γ) whose direction cosines satisfy $al^2 + bm^2 + cn^2 = 0$ generate the cone $a(x - \alpha)^2 + b(y - \beta)^2 + c(z - \gamma)^2 = 0$.

(*Kanpur, 2003*)

7.2. CONDITION THAT THE GENERAL EQUATION OF THE SECOND DEGREE SHOULD REPRESENT A CONE. CO-ORDINATES OF THE VERTEX

(Avadh, 2001; Bhopal, 1997; Kumaon, 2003; Rohilkhand, 1994)

We have seen that the equation of a cone with its vertex at the origin is necessarily homogenous and conversely. Thus, any given equation of the second degree will represent a cone if, and only if there exists a point such that on transferring the origin to the same the equation becomes homogeneous.

Let $\quad f(x, y, z) = ax^2 + by^2 + cz^2 + 2fyz + 2gzx + 2hxy + 2ux + 2vy + 2wz + d = 0$ ...(1)
represent a cone having its vertex at (x', y', z').

Shift the origin to the vertex (x', y', z') so that we change

$$x \text{ to } x + x', y \text{ to } y + y' \text{ and } z \text{ to } z + z'.$$

The transformed equation is

$$ax^2 + by^2 + cz^2 + 2fyz + 2gzx + 2hxy + 2[x(ax' + hy' + gz' + u)$$
$$+ y(hx' + by' + fz' + v) + z(gx' + fy' + cz' + w)] + f(x', y', z') = 0 \text{ ...(2)}$$

The equation (2) represents a cone with its vertex at the origin and must, therefore, be homogeneous. This gives

$$ax' + hy' + gz' + u = 0 \qquad \qquad \text{...(i)}$$
$$hx' + by' + fz' + v = 0 \qquad \qquad \text{...(ii)}$$
$$gx' + fy' + cz' + w = 0 \qquad \qquad \text{...(iii)}$$
$$f(x', y', z') = 0 \qquad \qquad \text{...(iv)}$$

Also, $\quad f(x', y', z') \equiv x'(ax' + hy' + gz' + u) + y'(hx' + by' + fz' + v)$
$$+ z'(gx' + fy' + cz' + w) + (ux' + vy' + wz' + d).$$

Thus, with the help of (i), (ii) and (iii), we see that (iv) is equivalent to

$$ux' + vy' + wz' + d = 0 \qquad \qquad \text{...(v)}$$

The system of equations (i), (ii), (iii), (iv) is equivalent to the system (i), (ii), (iii), (v).

Thus, if the given equation represent a cone, there exist (x', y', z') satisfying the equations (i), (ii), (iii), (v) implying that these four equations are consistent. The condition of consistency of the system (i), (ii), (iii) and (v) of four linear equation is

$$\begin{vmatrix} a & h & g & u \\ h & b & f & v \\ g & f & c & w \\ u & v & w & d \end{vmatrix} = 0.$$

This is the condition for the equation (1) of the second degree to represent a cone.

If the condition is satisfied, the co-ordinates (x', y', z') of the vertex are obtained by solving simultaneously the three linear equations (i), (ii) and (iii).

The point (x', y', z') is such that if we shift the origin to this point, the new equation will be homogeneous and as such will represent a cone.

Cor. *If* $F(x, y, z) \equiv ax^2 + by^2 + cz^2 + 2fyz + 2gzx + 2hxy + 2ux + 2vy + 2wz + d = 0$
represents a cone, the co-ordinates of its vertex satisfy the equations

$$F_x = 0, F_y = 0, F_z = 0, F_t = 0,$$

where 't' is used to make $F(x, y, z)$ homogeneous and is put equal to unity after differentiation.

Making $F(x, y, z)$ homogeneous, we write

$$F(x, y, z, t) = ax^2 + by^2 + cz^2 + 2fyz + 2gzx + 2hxy + 2uxt + 2vyt + 2wzt + dt^2$$

We have
$$F_x = 2\,(ax + hy + gz + ut),\ F_y = 2\,(hx + by + fz + vt),$$
$$F_z = 2\,(gx + fy + cz + wt),\ F_t = 2\,(ux + vy + wz + dt).$$

Putting $t = 1$, we see from (i), (ii), (iii) and (iv) that the vertex (x_1, y_1, z_1) satisfies the four linear equations
$$F_x = 0,\ F_y = 0,\ F_z = 0,\ F_t = 0.$$

Note. The student should note that the coefficients of second degree term in the transformed equation (2) are the same as those in the original equation (1).

Note. The equation $F\,(x, y, z) = 0$ represents a cone if, and only if, the four linear equations $F_x = 0,\ F_y = 0,\ F_z = 0,\ F_t = 0$ are consistent. In the case of consistency the vertex is given by any three of these.

In case we have
$$\begin{vmatrix} a & h & g & u \\ h & b & f & v \\ g & f & c & w \\ u & v & w & d \end{vmatrix} = 0 \text{ as well as } \begin{vmatrix} a & h & g \\ h & b & f \\ g & f & c \end{vmatrix} = 0$$

the equation will represent a pair of planes.

EXAMPLES

1. *Show that the equation*
$$4x^2 - y^2 + 2z^2 + 2xy - 3yz + 12x - 11y + 6z + 4 = 0,$$
represents a cone with vertex $(-1, -2, -3)$. *(Bhoj, 1999; Meerut, 2005)*

Sol. Making the equation homogeneous, we obtain
$$F\,(x, y, z, t) = 4x^2 - y^2 + 2z^2 + 2xy - 3yz + 12xt - 11yt + 6zt + 4t^2$$

Equating to zero the partial derivatives with respect to x, y, z and t, we obtain the four linear equations
$$8x + 2y + 12t = 0 \tag{i}$$
$$2x - 2y - 3z - 11t = 0 \tag{ii}$$
$$-3y + 4z + 6t = 0 \tag{iii}$$
$$12x - 11y + 6z + 8t = 0 \tag{iv}$$

Replacing t by unity and solving the three linear equations (i), (ii), (iii) for x, y, z, we obtain
$$x = -1,\ y = -2,\ z = -3.$$

The values satisfy (iv) also. The equations (i) to (iv) are thus consistent.

Thus, the given equation represents a cone with vertex $(-1, -2, -3)$.

2. *Prove that the equation*
$$ax^2 + by^2 + cz^2 + 2ux + 2vy + 2wz + d = 0,$$
represents a cone if
$$\frac{u^2}{a} + \frac{v^2}{b} + \frac{w^2}{c} = d.$$

(Avadh, 1995, 98; Kanpur, 1998; Bilaspur, 1997, 99, 2000; Indore, 1994, 98; Rewa, 1997; Rohilkhand, 2003)

Sol. Let
$$f(x, y, z, t) \equiv ax^2 + by^2 + cz^2 + 2uxt + 2vyt + 2vyt + 2wzt + dt^2 = 0$$

$\therefore$ $\qquad \dfrac{\partial F}{\partial x} = 0$ for $t = 1$ gives

$\qquad 2ax + 2u = 0$ or $x = -\dfrac{u}{a}$ $\qquad$ ...(1)

Similarly, $\qquad \dfrac{\partial F}{\partial y} = 0$ for $t = 1$ gives $y = -\dfrac{y}{b}$ $\qquad$ ...(2)

$\qquad \dfrac{\partial F}{\partial y} = 0$ for $t = 1$ gives $z = -\dfrac{w}{c}$ $\qquad$ ...(3)

and $\qquad \dfrac{\partial F}{\partial t} = 0$ for $t = 1$ gives $ux + vy + wz + d = 0$ $\qquad$ ...(4)

Substituting the values of x, y, z from (1), (2), (3) in (4), we get the required condition as

$$u\left(-\frac{u}{a}\right) + v\left(-\frac{v}{b}\right) + w\left(-\frac{w}{c}\right) + d = 0$$

$\Rightarrow$ $\qquad \dfrac{u^2}{a} + \dfrac{v^2}{b} + \dfrac{w^2}{c} = d.$

EXERCISES

1. Prove that
$$2x^2 + 2y^2 + 7z^2 - 10yz - 10zx + 2x + 2y + 26z - 17 = 0$$
represents a cone with vertex at (2, 2, 1).

(B.H.U., 1996; Garhwal, 1994; Sagar, 2002)

2. Show that the equation
$$x^2 - 2y^2 + 3z^2 - 4xy + 5yz - 6zx + 8x - 19y - 2z - 20 = 0$$
represents a cone with vertex (1, – 2, 3).

3. Show that the equation
$$2y^2 - 8yz - 4zx - 8xy + 6x - 4y - 2z + 5 = 0$$
represents a cone whose vertex is (– 7/6, 1/3, 5/6).

EXAMPLE

Find the equations to the lines in which the plane
$$2x + y - z = 0,$$

cuts the cone
$$4x^2 - y^2 + 3z^2 = 0.$$

Sol. Let $\qquad \dfrac{x}{l} = \dfrac{y}{m} = \dfrac{z}{n}$

be the equations of any one of the two lines in which the given plane meets the given cone so that we have
$$2l + m - n = 0, \quad 4l^2 - m^2 + 3n^2 = 0.$$

These two equations are now to be solved for l, m, n. Eliminating n, we have
$$4l^2 - m^2 + 3(2l + m)^2 = 0$$
$$8l^2 + 6lm + m^2 = 0$$

$\Rightarrow$ $\qquad \dfrac{l}{m} = \dfrac{-6 \pm \sqrt{36 - 32}}{16} = -\dfrac{1}{4}$ or $-\dfrac{1}{2}.$

We also have

$$2\frac{l}{m} + 1 - \frac{n}{m} = 0$$

$$\frac{l}{m} = -\frac{1}{4} \Rightarrow \frac{n}{m} = \frac{1}{2}$$

and

$$\frac{l}{m} = -\frac{1}{2} \Rightarrow \frac{n}{m} = 0$$

Now

$$\frac{l}{m} = -\frac{1}{4}, \frac{n}{m} = \frac{1}{2} \Rightarrow \frac{l}{-1} = \frac{m}{4} = \frac{n}{2}$$

and

$$\frac{l}{m} = -\frac{1}{2}, \frac{n}{m} = 0 \Rightarrow \frac{l}{-1} = \frac{m}{2}; n = 0.$$

Thus, the two required lines are

$$\frac{x}{-1} = \frac{y}{4} = \frac{z}{2}; \frac{x}{-1} = \frac{y}{2}; z = 0.$$

EXERCISES

1. Find the equations of the lines of intersection of the following planes and cones :
   (i) $x + 3y - 2z = 0$, $x^2 + 9y^2 - 4z^2 = 0$.
   (ii) $3x + 4y + z = 0$, $15x^2 - 32y^2 - 7z^2 = 0$.
   (iii) $x + 7y - 5z = 0$, $3yz + 14zx - 30xy = 0$.

   [**Ans.** (i) $x = 2z, y = 0; 3y = 2z, x = 0$, (ii) $\dfrac{x}{-3} = \dfrac{y}{2} = \dfrac{z}{1}, \dfrac{x}{2} = \dfrac{y}{-1} = \dfrac{z}{-2}$,

   (iii) $\dfrac{x}{1} = \dfrac{y}{2} = \dfrac{z}{3}, \dfrac{x}{3} = \dfrac{y}{1} = \dfrac{z}{2}$]

2. Show that the equation of the quadric cone which contains the three co-ordinate axes and the lines in which the plane $x - 5y - 3z = 0$, cuts the cone
   $7x^2 + 5y^2 - 3z^2 = 0$ is $yz + 10zx - 18xy = 0$.

3. Find the angle between the lines of intersection of
   (i) $x - 3y + z = 0$ and $x^2 - 5y^2 + z^2 = 0$.
   (ii) $10x + 7y - 6z = 0$ and $20x^2 + 7y^2 - 108z^2 = 0$.
   (iii) $4x - y - 5z = 0$ and $8yz + 3zx - 5xy = 0$.
   (iv) $x + y + z = 0$ and $6xy + 3yz - 2zx = 0$.
   (v) $x + y + z = 0$ and $x^2 - yz + xy - 3z^2 = 0$.

   [**Ans.** (i) $\cos^{-1}(5/6)$, (ii) $\cos^{-1}(16/21)$, (iii) $\pi/2$, (iv) $\pi/3$, (v) $\pi/6$]

7.3. CONE AND A PLANE THROUGH ITS VERTEX

To find the angle between the lines of intersection of the plane

$$ux + vy + wz = 0$$

and $f(x, y, z) \equiv ax^2 + by^2 + cz^2 + 2fyz + 2gzx + 2hxy = 0$ ...(1)

The plane

$$ux + vy + wz = 0$$ ...(2)

will cut the cone (1) in two lines passing through the origin.

Let one of these lines be

$$\frac{x}{l} = \frac{y}{m} = \frac{z}{n} \qquad \qquad ...(3)$$

Thus, line (3) lies in plane (2), therefore

$$ul + vm + wn = 0 \qquad \qquad ...(4)$$

Also, line (3) lies on (1), hence it is generator of the cone, *i.e.*, its d.c.'s satisfy the equation of the cone, hence

$$al^2 + bm^2 + cn^2 + 2fmn + 2gnl + 2hlm = 0 \qquad \qquad ...(5)$$

Putting $n = -\dfrac{ul + vm}{w}$ from (4) in (5), we have

$$al^2 + bm^2 + c\left(-\frac{ul + vm}{w}\right)^2 + (2fm + 2gl)\left(-\frac{ul + vm}{w}\right) + 2hlm = 0,$$

i.e., $l^2(aw^2 + cu^2 - 2gwu) + 2lm(cuv - fwu - gvw + hw^2) + m^2(bw^2 + cv^2 - 2fvw) = 0$

i.e., $\dfrac{l^2}{m^2}(aw^2 + cu^2 - 2gwu) + 2\dfrac{l}{m}(cuv - fwu - gvw + hw^2)$

$$+ (bw^2 + cv^2 + 2fvw) = 0 \qquad ...(6)$$

Now (6) is quadratic equation in l/m and shows that plane (2) cuts cone in two lines. If their direction ratios are l_1, m_1, n_1 and l_2, m_2, n_2 then we have

$$\frac{l_1}{m_1} \cdot \frac{l_2}{m_2} = \frac{bw^2 + cv^2 - 2fvw}{aw^2 + cu^2 - 2gwu}$$

i.e.,

$$\frac{l_1 l_2}{bw^2 + cv^2 - 2fvw} = \frac{m_1 m_2}{aw^2 + cu^2 - 2gwu} = \frac{n_1 n_2}{bu^2 + av^2 - 2huv} \quad \text{(similarly)}$$

$$= \frac{l_1 l_2 + m_1 m_2 + n_1 n_2}{(b + c)u^2 + (c + a)v^2 + (a + b)w^2 - 2fvw - 2gwu - 2huv}$$

$$= \frac{l_1 l_2 + m_1 m_2 + n_1 n_2}{(a + b + c)(u^2 + v^2 + w^2) - f(u, v, w)}$$

Also, sum of the roots of (6) gives

$$\frac{l_1}{m_1} + \frac{l_2}{m_2} = -\frac{2(cuv - fwu - gvw + hw^2)}{aw^2 + cu^2 - 2gwu}$$

i.e.,

$$\frac{l_1 m_2 + l_2 m_1}{-2(cuv - fwu - gvw + hw^2)} = \frac{m_1 m_2}{aw^2 + cu^2 - 2gwu}$$

$$= \frac{l_1 l_2}{bw^2 + cv^2 - 2fvw} = \frac{n_1 n_2}{av^2 + bu^2 - 2huv}$$

$$= \frac{[(l_1 m_2 + l_2 m_1)^2 - 4l_1 l_2 m_1 m_2]^{1/2}}{[4(cuv - fwu - gvw + hw^2)^2 - 4(bw^2 + cv^2 - 2fvw)(aw^2 + cu^2 - 2gwu)]^{1/2}}$$

$$= \frac{l_1 m_2 - l_2 m_1}{\pm 2wP} \quad \text{where } P^2 = \begin{vmatrix} a & h & g & u \\ h & b & f & v \\ g & f & c & w \\ u & v & w & 0 \end{vmatrix}$$

$$= \frac{m_1 n_2 - m_2 n_1}{\pm 2uP} = \frac{n_1 l_2 - n_2 l_1}{\pm 2vP} \qquad \text{(by symmetry)}$$

$$= \frac{[\Sigma (m_1 n_2 - m_2 n_1)^2]^{1/2}}{\pm 2P(u^2 + v^2 + w^2)^{1/2}}$$

If θ be the angle between the lines, then

$$\tan \theta = \frac{[\Sigma (m_1 n_2 - m_2 n_1)^2]^{1/2}}{l_1 l_2 + m_1 m_2 + n_1 n_2}$$

or $\qquad \tan \theta = \pm \dfrac{2P(u^2 + v^2 + w^2)^{1/2}}{(a+b+c)(u^2 + v^2 + w^2) - f(u, v, w)}$

Cor. Condition of Perpendicularity

To find the condition, so that lines in which plane $ux + vy + wz = 0$ cuts a cone
$$f(x, y, z) \equiv ax^2 + by^2 + cz^2 + 2fyz + 2gzx + 2hxy = 0$$
may be at right angles.

The angle θ between the two lines is given by

$$\tan \theta = \pm \frac{2P(u^2 + v^2 + w^2)^{1/2}}{(a+b+c)(u^2 + v^2 + w^2) - f(u, v, w)}$$

If $\theta = 90°$, $\tan \theta = \infty$

i.e., $\qquad\qquad\qquad (a + b + c)(u^2 + v^2 + w^2) - f(u, v, w) = 0$

This is the required condition.

7.3.1. Mutually Perpendicular Generators of a Cone

To show that the cone
$$ax^2 + by^2 + cz^2 + 2fyz + 2gzx + 2hxy = 0 \qquad ...(i)$$
admits of sets of three mutually perpendicular generators if and only if
$$a + b + c = 0. \qquad \text{(Kumaon, 1995; Vikram, 1994)}$$

Let $\qquad\qquad\qquad\qquad\qquad \dfrac{x}{\lambda} = \dfrac{y}{\mu} = \dfrac{z}{\nu} \qquad\qquad\qquad ...(ii)$

be a generator of the cone (*i*) implying that
$$a\lambda^2 + b\mu^2 + c\nu^2 + 2f\mu\nu + 2g\nu\lambda + 2h\lambda\mu = 0 \qquad ...(iii)$$

Equation of the plane through the origin perpendicular to the line (*ii*) is
$$\lambda x + \mu y + \nu z = 0 \qquad ...(iv)$$

If (l, m, n) be the direction cosines of any one of the two generators in which the plane cuts the given cone, we have
$$al^2 + bm^2 + cn^2 + 2fmn + 2gnl + 2hlm = 0 \qquad ...(v)$$
and $\qquad\qquad\qquad\qquad\qquad l\lambda + m\mu + n\nu = 0. \qquad\qquad\qquad ...(vi)$

Eliminating n between (*v*) and (*vi*), we obtain
$$l^2(a\nu^2 + c\lambda^2 - 2g\lambda\nu) + 2lm(c\lambda\mu + h\nu^2 - g\mu\nu + f\lambda\nu) + m^2(b\nu^2 + c\mu^2 - 2f\mu\nu) = 0$$
which, being a quadratic in $l : m$, we see that the plane (*iv*) cuts the given cone in two generators. Hence, if (l_1, m_1, n_1), (l_2, m_2, n_2) be the direction cosines of these two generators, we have
$$\frac{l_1 l_2}{m_1 m_2} = \frac{b\nu^2 + c\mu^2 - 2f\mu\nu}{a\nu^2 + c\lambda^2 - 2g\lambda\nu}$$

$\Rightarrow$ $$\frac{l_1 l_2}{bv^2 + c\mu^2 - 2f\mu v} = \frac{m_1 m_2}{av^2 + c\lambda^2 - 2g\lambda v}$$

From symmetry, each of these is further

$$= \frac{n_1 n_2}{a\mu^2 + b\lambda^2 - 2h\lambda\mu} = k, \text{ (say)}$$

Thus, we have

$$l_1 l_2 + m_1 m_2 + n_1 n_2 = k [a (\mu^2 + v^2) + b (v^2 + \lambda^2) + c (\lambda^2 + \mu^2) - 2f\mu v - 2gv\lambda - 2h\lambda\mu]$$
$$= k (a + b + c) + (\lambda^2 + \mu^2 + v^2) \qquad \qquad ...(viii)$$

with the help of (iii).

The two generators in which the plane (iv) intersects the curve (ii) will be at right angles if and only if

$$l_1 l_2 + m_1 m_2 + n_1 n_2 = 0$$

i.e., if and only if

$$a + b + c = 0.$$

We note that

$$x/\lambda = y/\mu = z/v$$

is an arbitrary generator of the cone and the condition that the planes through the vertex and perpendicular to the generators meet the cone in two perpendicular generators is independent of λ, μ, v.

Also we see that the two generators will themselves be perpendicular to the first generator so that the three generators will be perpendicular in pairs.

It follows that the cone (i) admits of *an infinite number of sets of three mutually perpendicular generators if and only if*

$$a + b + c = 0. \qquad \qquad (Kanpur, 1997)$$

In fact if this condition is satisfied, then the plane perpendicular to *any* generator *OP* of the cone cuts the same in two perpendicular generators *OQ*, *OR*, so that *OP*, *OQ*, *OR* is a set of three mutually perpendicular generators.

Note. If the general equation

$$ax^2 + by^2 + cz^2 + 2fyz + 2gzx + 2hxy + 2ux + 2vy + 2wz + d = 0$$

represents a cone having sets of three mutually perpendicular generators, then also

$$a + b + c = 0$$

for, on shifting the origin to its vertex, the coefficients of the second degree term remain unaffected.

EXAMPLES

1. *Prove that the plane ax + by + cz = 0 cuts the cone yz + zx + xy = 0 in perpendicular lines if 1/a + 1/b + 1/c = 0.* (Avadh, 2000; Ajmer, 1995, 96, 98; Bundelkhand, 1997, 2002; Bilaspur, 1996; Bhopal, 1997, 99; Rewa, 1996; Jiwaji, 1997; Indore, 1995, 97; Sagar, 1999; Vikram, 1999)

Sol. Let one of the lines of intersection be

$$x/l = y/m = z/n.$$

The line lies on given cone and plane, hence

$$mn + nl + lm = 0 \qquad \qquad ...(i)$$

and $$al + bm + cn = 0 \qquad \qquad ...(ii)$$

Putting the value of n from (ii) in (i), we get

$$(m + l)\left(-\frac{al + bm}{c}\right) + lm = 0$$

$$\Rightarrow \qquad al^2 + (a + b - c)\, lm + bm^2 = 0$$

$$\Rightarrow \qquad a\left(\frac{l}{m}\right)^2 + (a + b - c)\frac{l}{m} + b = 0$$

Let $\dfrac{l_1}{m_1}, \dfrac{l_2}{m_2}$ be the two roots, then

$$\frac{l_1}{m_1} \cdot \frac{l_2}{m_2} = \frac{b}{a}$$

$$\Rightarrow \qquad \frac{l_1 l_2}{1/a} = \frac{m_1 m_2}{1/b} = \frac{n_1 n_2}{1/c} \text{ (by symmetry)}$$

The angle between the lines will be a right angle if

$$l_1 l_2 + m_1 m_2 + n_1 n_2 = 0 \;\Rightarrow\; 1/a + 1/b + 1/c = 0.$$

2. *Prove that the angle between the lines given by $x + y + z = 0$, $ayz + bzx + cxy = 0$ is $\pi/2$ if $a + b + c = 0$ and $\pi/3$ if $1/a + 1/b + 1/c = 0$.*

(Bilaspur, 2000; Bhuj, 1999; Jiwaji, 1996; Meerut, 1995; Sagar, 1999)

Sol. Let the plane $x + y + z = 0$ cuts the cone $ayz + bzx + cxy = 0$ in a line

$$x/l = y/m = z/n.$$

Then $\qquad\qquad l + m + n = 0$ and $amn + bnl + clm = 0$.

Eliminating n between these relations, we get

$$(am + bl)\,(-l - m) + clm = 0 \;\Rightarrow\; bl^2 + (a + b - c)\, lm + am^2 = 0$$

$$\Rightarrow \qquad b\,(l/m)^2 + (a + b - c)\,(l/m) + a = 0. \qquad\qquad\qquad ...(i)$$

If the roots of this equation are l_1/m_1 and l_2/m_2, then

$$\frac{l_1}{m_1} \cdot \frac{l_2}{m_2} = \frac{a}{b} \;\Rightarrow\; \frac{l_1 l_2}{a} = \frac{m_1 m_2}{b} = \frac{n_1 n_2}{c} \text{ (by symmetry)} = k \text{ (say)} \qquad ...(ii)$$

If the angle between the lines is $\pi/2$, then

$$l_1 l_2 + m_1 m_2 + n_1 n_2 = 0 \;\Rightarrow\; a + b + c = 0.$$

Again, from (i), we get

$$\frac{l_1}{m_1} + \frac{l_2}{m_2} = \frac{c - b - a}{b}$$

$$\Rightarrow \qquad \frac{l_1 m_2 + l_2 m_1}{m_1 m_2} = \frac{c - b - a}{b} \;\Rightarrow\; \frac{l_1 m_2 + l_2 m_1}{c - b - a} = \frac{m_1 m_2}{b} = k.$$

Now, $\quad (l_1 m_2 - l_2 m_1)^2 = (l_1 m_2 + l_2 m_1)^2 - 4\, l_1 l_2 \cdot m_1 m_2$

$$= k^2\,(c - b - a)^2 - 4ak \cdot bk = k^2\,[(c - b - a)^2 - 4ab]$$

$$= k^2\,(a^2 + b^2 + c^2 - 2ab - 2bc - 2ca)$$

Now, $\qquad\qquad \tan\theta = \dfrac{\sqrt{\Sigma\,(l_1 m_2 - l_2 m_1)^2}}{l_1 l_2 + m_1 m_2 + n_1 n_2} = \dfrac{\sqrt{k^2\,[3\,(a^2 + b^2 + c^2 - 2bc - 2ca - 2ab)]}}{k\,(a + b + c)}$

If $\theta = \pi/3$, then

$$\tan^2 \frac{\pi}{3} = \frac{3(a^2 + b^2 + c^2 - 2bc - 2ca - 2ab)}{(a + b + c)^2}$$

$\Rightarrow \quad 3(a + b + c)^2 = 3(a^2 + b^2 + c^2 - 2bc - 2ca - 2ab)$ $\qquad [\because \ \tan(\pi/3) = \sqrt{3}]$

$\Rightarrow \quad 4(bc + ca + ab) = 0 \Rightarrow 1/a + 1/b + 1/c = 0.$

3. *Find the equation to the lines in which the planes* $2x + y - z = 0$ *cuts the cone* $4x^2 - y^2 + 3z^2 = 0.$ \hfill (*Bhopal, 2000; Jabalpur, 1994; Jiwaji, 1995, 2000; Vikram, 1997*)

Sol. The given cone is

$$4x^2 - y^2 + 3z^2 = 0 \qquad \qquad ...(i)$$

and the plane is $\qquad\qquad 2x + y - z = 0 \qquad\qquad ...(ii)$

Let one of the lines of intersection of (*i*) and (*ii*) be

$$\frac{x}{l} = \frac{y}{m} = \frac{z}{n}.$$

This line lies on (*i*) and (*ii*), then

$$4l^2 - m^2 + 3n^2 = 0 \qquad\qquad ...(iii)$$

and $\qquad\qquad\qquad 2l + m - n = 0 \qquad\qquad ...(iv)$

Eliminating n, we have

$$4l^2 - m^2 + 3(2l + m)^2 = 0$$

$\Rightarrow \qquad\qquad 8l^2 + 6lm + m^2 = 0, \text{ or } (2l + m)(4l + m) = 0$

When $2l + m = 0$, we have from (*iv*), $n = 0$,

i.e., $\qquad\qquad\qquad \dfrac{l}{1} = \dfrac{m}{-2} = \dfrac{n}{0}$

Hence one line is

$$\frac{x}{1} = \frac{y}{-2} = \frac{z}{0} \qquad\qquad ...(v)$$

Again, when $4l + m = 0$, $2l + n = 0$, $\qquad\qquad$ [from (*iv*)]

i.e., $\qquad\qquad\qquad \dfrac{l}{-1} = \dfrac{m}{4} = \dfrac{n}{2}$

Hence the other line is

$$\frac{x}{-1} = \frac{y}{4} = \frac{z}{2} \qquad\qquad ...(vi)$$

4. *If* $\dfrac{x}{1} = \dfrac{y}{2} = \dfrac{z}{3}$ *represents one of a set of three mutually perpendicular generators of the cone* $5yz - 8zx - 3xy = 0$, *find the equations of the other two.*

\hfill (*Bhopal, 1995, 2002; Indore, 2002; Jabalpur, 1998; Ravishankar, 1995; Vikram, 1998*)

Sol. The given line is

$$\frac{x}{1} = \frac{y}{2} = \frac{z}{3} \qquad\qquad ...(i)$$

and the cone is $\qquad\qquad 5yz - 8zx - 3xy = 0 \qquad\qquad ...(ii)$

Let a line perpendicular to (*i*) be

$$\frac{x}{l} = \frac{y}{m} = \frac{z}{n} \qquad \qquad ...(iii)$$

$$\therefore \qquad\qquad l + 2m + 3n = 0 \qquad\qquad ...(iv)$$

If (*iii*) is generator of (*ii*) then

$$5mn - 8nl - 3lm = 0 \qquad\qquad ...(v)$$

Eliminating *n* between (*iv*) and (*v*), we get

$$(5m - 8l)\left(-\frac{l + 2m}{3}\right) - 3lm = 0,$$

$$\Rightarrow \qquad\qquad 4l^2 + lm - 5m^2 = 0$$

$$\Rightarrow \qquad\qquad (l - m)(4l + 5m) = 0$$

When $l = m$, $n = -\dfrac{l + 2m}{3} = -l$

i.e.,

$$\frac{l}{1} = \frac{m}{1} = \frac{n}{-1} \qquad\qquad ...(vi)$$

Again, when $4l + 5m = 0$, $l = -\dfrac{5}{4}m$, $n = -\dfrac{1}{4}m$

i.e.,

$$\frac{l}{5} = \frac{m}{-4} = \frac{n}{1} \qquad\qquad ...(vii)$$

From (*vi*) and (*vii*), the other two mutually perpendicular generators are

$$\frac{x}{1} = \frac{y}{1} = \frac{z}{-1} \text{ and } \frac{x}{5} = \frac{y}{-4} = \frac{z}{1}.$$

5. *Show that the cone whose vertex is at the origin and which passes through the curve of intersection of the sphere $x^2 + y^2 + z^2 = 3a^2$, and any plane at a distance 'a' from the origin has mutually perpendicular generators.*

Sol. Any plane at a distance *a* from the origin is

$$lx + my + nz = a, \qquad\qquad ...(i)$$

where *l*, *m*, *n* are actual direction cosines of normal to the plane. Making equation of sphere homogeneous with its help, equation of the cone whose vertex is origin and base the given curve is

$$x^2 + y^2 + z^2 = 3a^2\left(\frac{lx + my + nz}{a}\right)^2$$

$$\Rightarrow \quad x^2(1 - 3l^2) + y^2(1 - 3m^2) + z^2(1 - 3n^2) - 6lmxy - 6mnyz - 6nlzx = 0$$

Now, coeff. of x^2 + coeff. of y^2 + coeff. of $z^2 = (1 - 3l^2) + (1 - 3m^2) + (1 - 3n^2)$

$$= 3 - 3(l^2 + m^2 + n^2) = 0$$

Hence, plane (*i*) cuts the cone in three mutually perpendicular generators.

EXERCISES

1. Prove that the plane $lx + my + nz = 0$ cuts the cone

$$(b - c)x^2 + (c - a)y^2 + (a - b)z^2 + 2fyz + 2gzx + 2hxy = 0$$

in perpendicular lines if

$$(b - c)l^2 + (c - a)m^2 + (a - b)n^2 + 2fmn + 2gnl + 2hlm = 0.$$

2. If
$$x = \frac{1}{2} y = z$$

represents one of a set of three mutually perpendicular generators of the cone
$$11yz + 6zx - 14xy = 0,$$

find the equations of the other two. $\left[\text{**Ans.** } \dfrac{x}{2} = \dfrac{y}{-3} = \dfrac{z}{4}; \dfrac{x}{-11} = \dfrac{y}{2} = \dfrac{z}{7}\right]$

3. Find the angle between the lines given by
$$x + y + z = 0, \quad \frac{yz}{b-c} + \frac{zx}{c-a} + \frac{xy}{a-b} = 0. \qquad \textit{(Avadh, 1996)} \text{ [**Ans.** } 60°]$$

4. If the plane $2x - y + cz = 0$ cuts the cone $yz + zx + xy = 0$ in perpendicular lines, find the value of c.   [**Ans.** $c = 2$]

5. Find the equations of the lines in which the plane $2x + y - z = 0$ cuts the cone
$$4x^2 - y^2 + 3z^2 = 0. \qquad \left[\text{**Ans.** } \dfrac{x}{-1} = \dfrac{y}{4} = \dfrac{z}{2}; \dfrac{x}{-1} = \dfrac{y}{2} = \dfrac{z}{0}\right]$$

6. If $\dfrac{x}{1} = \dfrac{y}{1} = \dfrac{z}{2}$ be one of a set of three mutually perpendicular generators of the cone $3yz - 2zx - 2xy = 0$, find the equations of other two generators.

[**Ans.** $x/2 = y/(-4) = z/1$; $x/3 = y/1 = z/(-2)$]

7. Show that the cone whose vertex is the origin and which passes through the curve of intersection of the surface $2x^2 - y^2 + 2z^2 = 3d^2$ and any plane at a distance d, from the origin has three mutually perpendicular generators.

8. Find the locus of a point from which three mutually perpendicular lines can be drawn to intersect the central conic
$$ax^2 + by^2 = 1, z = 0 \qquad \textit{(Bilaspur, 1997; Bhoj, 1999)}$$
[**Ans.** $a(x^2 + z^2) + b(y^2 + z^2) = 1$]

9. Show that the mutually perpendicular tangent lines can be drawn to the sphere
$$x^2 + y^2 + z^2 = r^2$$

from any point on the surface
$$2(x^2 + y^2 + z^2) = 3r^2.$$

10. Three points, P, Q, R, are taken on the ellipsoid
$$x^2/a^2 + y^2/b^2 + z^2/c^2 = 1$$
so that the lines joining P, Q, R to the origin the mutually perpendicular. Prove that the plane PQR touches a fixed sphere.

7.4. INTERSECTION OF A LINE WITH A CONE

To find the points of intersection of the line
$$\frac{x - \alpha}{l} = \frac{y - \beta}{m} = \frac{z - \gamma}{n} \qquad \qquad ...(i)$$

and the cone
$$f(x, y, z) \equiv ax^2 + by^2 + cz^2 + 2fyz + 2gzx + 2hxy = 0 \qquad ...(ii)$$

The point $(lr + \alpha, mr + \beta, nr + \gamma)$ which lies on the line (i) for all values of r will lie on the cone (ii) for values of r given by the equation

$$a(lr + \alpha)^2 + b(mr + \beta)^2 + c(nr + \gamma)^2 + 2f(mr + \beta)(nr + \gamma) + 2g(lr + \alpha)(nr + \gamma)$$
$$+ 2h(lr + \alpha)(mr + \beta) = 0,$$

$\Leftrightarrow \quad r^2 (al^2 + bm^2 + cn^2 + 2fmn + 2gnl + 2hlm) + 2r [l (a\alpha + h\beta + g\gamma) + m (h\alpha + b\beta + f\gamma)$
$$+ n (g\alpha + f\beta + c\gamma)] + f(\alpha, \beta, \gamma) = 0 \quad ...(A)$$

Let r_1, r_2 be the roots of this *quadratic* equation in r. The two points of intersection are

$$(lr_1 + \alpha, mr_1 + \beta, nr_1 + \gamma), (lr_2 + \alpha, mr_2 + \beta, nr_2 + \gamma).$$

Cor. A plane section of a quadratic cone is a conic, as every line in the plane meets the curve of intersection in two points.

Note. The equation (A) gives the distances of the points of intersection P and Q from the point (α, β, γ); if (l, m, n) are direction cosines.

EXERCISES

1. Show that the locus of mid-points of chords of the cone
$$ax^2 + by^2 + cz^2 + 2fyz + 2gx + 2hxy = 0$$
drawn parallel to the line
$$x/l = y/m = z/n$$
is the plane
$$x (al + hm + gn) + y (hl + bm + fn) + z (gl + fm + cn) = 0.$$

[**Hint.** If (α, β, γ) be the middle point of any such chord
$$\frac{x - \alpha}{l} = \frac{y - \beta}{m} = \frac{z - \gamma}{n},$$
the two roots of the equation (A) are equal and opposite and as such their sum is zero.]

2. Find the locus of the chords of a cone which are bisected at a fixed point.

7.4.1. The Tangent Lines and Tangent Plane at a Point

(Ajmer, 1995; Kumaon, 2001, 02, 04)

Let
$$\frac{x - \alpha}{l} = \frac{y - \beta}{m} = \frac{z - \gamma}{n} \quad ...(i)$$
be a line through a point (α, β, γ) of the cone
$$ax^2 + by^2 + cz^2 + 2fyz + 2gzx + 2hxy = 0 \quad ...(ii)$$
so that
$$a\alpha^2 + b\beta^2 + c\gamma^2 + 2f\beta\gamma + 2g\gamma\alpha + 2h\alpha\beta = 0.$$

Thus, one of the values of r given by the equation (A) of § 7.4 is zero and as such one of the two points of intersection coincides with (α, β, γ). The second point of intersection will also coincide with (α, β, γ) if the second root of the same equation is also zero. This requires
$$l (a\alpha + h\beta + g\gamma) + m (h\alpha + b\beta + f\gamma) + n (g\alpha + f\beta + c\gamma) = 0 \quad ...(iii)$$

The line (i) corresponding to the set of values of l, m, n satisfying the relation (iii) is a *tangent line* at (α, β, γ) to the cone (ii).

Eliminating l, m, n between (i) and (ii), we obtain the locus of all the tangent lines through (α, β, γ), *viz.*,
$$(x - \alpha) (a\alpha + h\beta + g\gamma) + (y - \beta) (h\alpha + b\beta + f\gamma) + (z - \gamma) (g\alpha + f\beta + c\gamma) = 0$$
$\Leftrightarrow \quad x (a\alpha + h\beta + g\gamma) + y (h\alpha + b\beta + f\gamma) + z (g\alpha + f\beta + c\gamma)$
$$= a\alpha^2 + b\beta^2 + c\gamma^2 + 2f\beta\gamma + 2g\gamma\alpha + 2h\alpha\beta = 0$$
which is a plane known as the **tangent plane.**

Clearly the tangent plane at any point of a cone passes through its vertex.

Cor. The tangent plane at *any* point $(k\alpha, k\beta, k\gamma)$ on the generator through the point (α, β, γ) is the same as the tangent plane at (α, β, γ).

Thus, we see that the *tangent plane at any point on a cone touches the cone at all points of the generator through that point and we say that the plane touches the cone along the generator.*

EXAMPLES

1. *Show that* $\qquad x/l = y/m = z/n$

is the line of intersection of the tangent planes to the cone
$$ax^2 + by^2 + cz^2 + 2fyz + 2gzx + 2hxy = 0$$

along the lines in which it is cut by the plane
$$x\,(al + hm + gn) + y\,(hl + bm + fn) + z\,(gl + fm + cn) = 0.$$

Sol. The tangent plane at any point (α, β, γ) of the given cone is
$$x\,(a\alpha + h\beta + g\gamma) + y\,(h\alpha + b\beta + f\gamma) + z\,(g\alpha + f\beta + c\gamma) = 0.$$

It will contain the line
$$x/l = y/m = z/n$$

if $\qquad l\,(a\alpha + h\beta + g\gamma) + m\,(h\alpha + b\beta + f\gamma) + n\,(g\alpha + f\beta + c\gamma) = 0$

$\Leftrightarrow \qquad \alpha\,(al + hm + gn) + \beta\,(hl + bm + fn) + \gamma\,(gl + fm + cn) = 0.$

Thus, the point (α, β, γ) lies on the plane
$$x\,(al + hm + gn) + y\,(hl + bm + fn) + z\,(gl + fm + cn) = 0.$$

Hence, the result.

2. *Show that the locus of the lines of intersection of tangent planes to the cone*
$$ax^2 + by^2 + cz^2 = 0$$

which touch along perpendicular generators is the cone
$$a^2\,(b + c)\,x^2 + b^2\,(c + a)\,y^2 + c^2\,(a + b)\,z^2 = 0. \qquad \text{(Kanpur, 1995)}$$

Sol. Let the tangent planes along two perpendicular generators of the cone meet in the line
$$\frac{x}{l} = \frac{y}{m} = \frac{z}{n} \qquad\qquad \text{...(i)}$$

Therefore, the equation of the plane containing the two generators is
$$alx + bmy + cnz = 0 \qquad\qquad \text{...(ii)}$$

Let λ, μ, ν be the direction ratios of any one of the two generators so that we have
$$al\lambda + bm\mu + cn\nu = 0 \qquad\qquad \text{...(iii)}$$
$$a\lambda^2 + b\mu^2 + c\nu^2 = 0 \qquad\qquad \text{...(iv)}$$

Eliminating ν from (iii) and (iv), we have
$$a\,(cn^2 + al^2)\,\lambda^2 + 2ablm\,\lambda\mu + b\,(cn^2 + bm^2)\,\mu^2 = 0.$$

If $(\lambda_1, \mu_1, \nu_1); (\lambda_2, \mu_2, \nu_2)$ be the direction cosines of the two generators, we have
$$\frac{\lambda_1\lambda_2}{\mu_1\mu_2} = \frac{b\,(cn^2 + bm^2)}{a\,(cn^2 + al^2)}$$

$\Rightarrow \qquad \dfrac{\lambda_1\lambda_2}{(cn^2 + bm^2)/a} = \dfrac{\mu_1\mu_2}{(cn^2 + al^2)/b}$

Hence, by symmetry, we get
$$\frac{\lambda_1\lambda_2}{(cn^2 + bm^2)/a} = \frac{\mu_1\mu_2}{(cn^2 + al^2)/b} = \frac{\nu_1\nu_2}{(al^2 + bm^2)/c}$$

The generators being at right angle, we have

$$\lambda_1\lambda_2 + \mu_1\mu_2 + \nu_1\nu_2 = 0$$

$$\Leftrightarrow \quad \frac{cn^2 + bm^2}{a} + \frac{cn^2 + al^2}{b} + \frac{al^2 + bm^2}{c} = 0$$

$$\Leftrightarrow \quad a^2(b+c)l^2 + b^2(c+a)m^2 + c^2(a+b)n^2 = 0 \qquad \ldots(v)$$

Eliminating l, m, n from (i) and (v), we obtain

$$a^2(b+c)x^2 + b^2(c+a)y^2 + c^2(a+b)z^2 = 0$$

as the required locus.

7.4.2. Condition for Tangency

To find the condition that the plane

$$lx + my + nz = 0, \qquad \ldots(1)$$

should touch the cone

$$ax^2 + by^2 + cz^2 + 2fyz + 2gzx + 2hxy = 0 \qquad \ldots(2)$$

$$(Garhwal, 2003)$$

If (α, β, γ) be the point of contact, the tangent plane

$$x(a\alpha + h\beta + g\gamma) + y(h\alpha + b\beta + f\gamma) + z(g\alpha + f\beta + c\gamma) = 0$$

thereat should be the same as the plane (1).

$$\therefore \quad \frac{a\alpha + h\beta + g\gamma}{l} = \frac{h\alpha + b\beta + f\gamma}{m} = \frac{g\alpha + f\beta + c\gamma}{n} = k, \text{ (say)}$$

Hence,

$$a\alpha + h\beta + g\gamma - lk = 0 \qquad \ldots(i)$$
$$h\alpha + b\beta + f\gamma - mk = 0 \qquad \ldots(ii)$$
$$g\alpha + f\beta + c\gamma - nk = 0 \qquad \ldots(iii)$$

Also, since (α, β, γ) lies on the plane (1), we have

$$l\alpha + m\beta + n\gamma = 0 \qquad \ldots(iv)$$

Eliminating α, β, γ, k between (i), (ii), (iii), (iv), we obtain

$$\begin{vmatrix} a & h & g & l \\ h & b & f & m \\ g & f & c & n \\ l & m & n & 0 \end{vmatrix} = 0$$

as the required condition.

The determinant on expansion, gives

$$Al^2 + Bm^2 + Cn^2 + 2Fmn + 2Gnl + 2Hlm = 0$$

where A, B, C, F, G, H are the co-factors of a, b, c, f, g, h respectively in the determinant

$$\begin{vmatrix} a & h & g \\ h & b & f \\ g & f & c \end{vmatrix}.$$

We may see that

$$A = bc - f^2, \ B = ca - g^2, \ C = ab - h^2,$$
$$F = gh - af, \ G = hf - bg, \ H = fg - ch.$$

7.4.3. Reciprocal Cones

To find the locus of lines through the vertex of the cone

$$ax^2 + by^2 + cz^2 + 2fyz + 2gzx + 2hxy = 0 \qquad \qquad ...(1)$$

perpendicular to its tangent planes.   (*Ajmer, 1998*)

Let $lx + my + nz = 0$ ...(2)

be a tangent plane to the cone (1) so that we have

$$Al^2 + Bm^2 + Cn^2 + 2Fmn + 2Gnl + 2Hlm = 0 \qquad \qquad ...(3)$$

The line through the vertex perpendicular to the tangent plane (2) is

$$\frac{x}{l} = \frac{y}{m} = \frac{z}{n} \qquad \qquad ...(4)$$

Eliminating l, m, n between (3) and (4), we get

$$Ax^2 + By^2 + Cz^2 + 2Fyz + 2Gzx + 2Hxy = 0 \qquad \qquad ...(5)$$

as the required locus which is again a quadric cone with its vertex at the origin.

If we now find the locus of lines through the origin perpendicular to the tangent planes to the cone (5), we have to substitute for A, B, C, F, G, H in its equation the corresponding co-factors in the determinant

$$\begin{vmatrix} A & H & G \\ H & B & F \\ G & F & C \end{vmatrix}$$

Since, we have, by actual manipulation,

$$BC - F^2 = aD, \quad CA - G^2 = bD, \quad AB - H^2 = cD;$$

$$GH - AF = fD, \quad HF - BG = gD, \quad FG - CH = hD;$$

where $D \equiv abc + 2fgh + af^2 - bg^2 - ch^2$

It follows that the required locus for the cone (5) is

$$ax^2 + by^2 + cz^2 + 2fyz + 2gzx + 2hxy = 0$$

which is the same as (1).

The two cones (1) and (5) are, therefore, such that each is the locus of the normals drawn through the origin to the tangent planes to the other and they are, on this account, called *Reciprocal cones.*

We have supposed that $D \neq 0$ implying that the equation (*i*) does not represent a pair of planes (Refer § 2.8).

Cor. *The condition for the cone*

$$ax^2 + by^2 + cz^2 + 2fyz + 2gzx + 2hxy = 0 \qquad \qquad ...(i)$$

to possess three mutually perpendicular tangent planes is

$$A + B + C = 0.$$

The cone (*i*) will clearly possess three mutually perpendicular tangent planes, if its reciprocal cone

$$Ax^2 + By^2 + Cz^2 + 2Fyz + 2Gzx + 2Hxy = 0$$

has three mutually perpendicular generators and this will be so if

$$A + B + C = 0 \iff bc + ca + ab = f^2 + g^2 + h^2.$$

EXAMPLES

1. *Show that the general equation of a cone which touches the three co-ordinate planes is*

$$\sqrt{fx} \pm \sqrt{gy} \pm \sqrt{hz} = 0;$$

f, g, h being parameters. (Agra, 1995, 96, 98; Ajmer, 1997; Avadh, 2000; Kanpur, 1994, 95, 97, 99; Garhwal, 1998, 99, 2002; Rohilkhand, 2002)

Sol. The reciprocal of a cone touching the three co-ordinate planes is a cone with three co-ordinate axes as three of its generators. Now, the general equation of a cone through the three axes is

$$fyz + gzx + hxy = 0.$$

Its reciprocal cone is

$$-f^2x^2 - g^2y^2 - h^2z^2 + 2ghyz + 2hfzx + 2fgxy = 0,$$

$\Leftrightarrow \qquad\qquad (fx + gy - hz)^2 = 4fgxy,$

$\Leftrightarrow \qquad\qquad fx + gy - hz = \pm\, 2\sqrt{fgxy},$

$\Leftrightarrow \qquad\qquad fx + gy \pm 2\sqrt{fgxy} = hz,$

$\Leftrightarrow \qquad\qquad (\sqrt{fx} \pm \sqrt{gh})^2 = hz,$

$\Leftrightarrow \qquad\qquad \sqrt{fx} \pm \sqrt{gy} \pm \sqrt{hz} = 0.$

2. *Show that the locus of the line of intersection of perpendicular tangent planes to the cone*
$$ax^2 + by^2 + cz^2 = 0,$$
is the cone $\qquad a\,(b+c)\,x^2 + b\,(c+a)\,y^2 + c\,(a+b)\,z^2 = 0.$ (Poorvanchal, 1996)

Sol. Generators of the reciprocal cone corresponding to the *perpendicular* tangent planes of the original cone are themselves perpendicular. Also, the line of intersection of the perpendicular tangent planes is perpendicular to the corresponding generators of the reciprocal cone. Combining these two facts, we see that the given question is equivalent to determining the locus of normals through the origin to the planes which cut the reciprocal cone along perpendicular generators.

Equation of the reciprocal cone is

$$\frac{x^2}{a} + \frac{y^2}{b} + \frac{z^2}{c} = 0 \;\Leftrightarrow\; bcx^2 + cay^2 + abz^2 = 0 \qquad\qquad ...(i)$$

Let the plane $\qquad\qquad\qquad lx + my + nz = 0 \qquad\qquad\qquad\qquad ...(ii)$

cut the cone (*i*) along perpendicular generators. The condition for this, as may be easily obtained, is

$$a\,(b+c)\,l^2 + b\,(c+a)\,m^2 + c\,(a+b)\,n^2 = 0 \qquad\qquad ...(iii)$$

The equations of the normal to the plane (*ii*) are

$$\frac{x}{l} = \frac{y}{m} = \frac{z}{n}. \qquad\qquad\qquad\qquad ...(iv)$$

Eliminating *l*, *m*, *n* from (*iii*) and (*iv*), we obtain
$$a\,(b+c)\,x^2 + b\,(c+a)\,y^2 + c\,(a+b)\,z^2 = 0$$

as the required locus.

3. *Prove that the tangent planes to the cone lyz + mzx + nxy = 0 are at right angles to the generator of the cone*

$$l^2x^2 + m^2y^2 + n^2z^2 - 2mnyz - 2nlzx - 2lmxy = 0.$$

Sol. The given cones are

$$lyz + mzx + nxy = 0 \qquad \qquad ...(i)$$

and
$$l^2x^2 + m^2y^2 + n^2z^2 - 2mnyz - 2nlzx - 2lmxy = 0 \qquad ...(ii)$$

To prove that tangent planes to (i) are at right angles to the generators of the cone (ii), prove that (i) and (ii) are reciprocal cones, etc.

4. *Prove that the cones* $ax^2 + by^2 + cz^2 = 0$ *and* $\dfrac{x^2}{a} + \dfrac{y^2}{b} + \dfrac{z^2}{c} = 0$ *are reciprocal.*

(*Bundelkhand, 1995, 99; Bilaspur, 2001; Garhwal, 2004; Jiwaji, 1996, 2000;*
Kanpur, 1998; Lucknow, 1996; Ravishankar, 1996, 99; Rohilkhand, 2004;
Sagar, 2001; Vikram, 2001; Poorvanchal 2004)

Sol. The reciprocal cone of

$$ax^2 + by^2 + cz^2 = 0$$

is
$$Ax^2 + By^2 + Cz^2 + 2Fyz + 2Gzx + 2Hxy = 0 \qquad ...(1)$$

where
$$\Delta = \begin{vmatrix} a & 0 & 0 \\ 0 & b & 0 \\ 0 & 0 & c \end{vmatrix} = abc$$

and
$$A = \frac{\partial \Delta}{\partial a} = bc, \; B = \frac{\partial \Delta}{\Delta b} = ac, \; C = \frac{\partial \Delta}{\partial c} = ab,$$

$$F = \frac{1}{2}\frac{\partial \Delta}{\partial f} = 0, \; G = \frac{1}{2}\frac{\partial \Delta}{\partial g} = 0, \; H = \frac{1}{2}\frac{\partial \Delta}{\partial h} = 0.$$

By putting these values, (1) becomes

$$bcx^2 + cay^2 + abz^2 = 0$$

or
$$\frac{x^2}{a} + \frac{y^2}{b} + \frac{z^2}{c} = 0.$$

5. *Prove that the equation* $\sqrt{fx} \pm \sqrt{gy} \pm \sqrt{hz} = 0$ *represents a cone that touches the co-ordinate planes; and that the equation to the reciprocal cone is* $fyz + gzx + hxy = 0$.

(*Kumaon, 2006; Avadh, 2000; Ajmer, 1997; Garhwal, 1996, 98, 99;*
Ravishankar, 1997; Rewa, 1996, 97, 2001; Kanpur, 1995; Rohilkhand 2006

Sol. The given equation can be written as

$$\sqrt{fx} \pm \sqrt{gy} = \mp \sqrt{hz}$$

$$\Rightarrow \qquad fx + gy \pm 2\sqrt{fgxy} = hz$$

$$\Rightarrow \qquad (fx + gy - hz)^2 = 4fgxy$$

$$\Rightarrow \qquad f^2x^2 + g^2y^2 + h^2z^2 - 2ghyz - 2hfzx - 2fgxy = 0 \qquad ...(i)$$

The equation is a homogeneous equation of second degree, hence it represents a quadratic cone.

The co-ordinate plane $x = 0$ meets (i) where

$$g^2y^2 + h^2z^2 - 2ghyz = 0 \; \Rightarrow \; (gy - hz)^2 = 0$$

which being a perfect square it follows that the plane $x = 0$ touches it. Similarly we can show that $y = 0$, $z = 0$ also touch the cone (i).

Again for the cone (i), we have

$$\text{`}a\text{'} = f^2, \text{ `}b\text{'} = g^2, \text{ `}c\text{'} = h^2, \text{ `}f\text{'} = -gh, \text{ `}g\text{'} = -hf, \text{ `}h\text{'} = -fg$$

$\therefore \quad A = bc - f^2 = g^2h^2 - (-gh)^2 = 0.$

Similarly, $B = C = 0,$

$$F = gh - af = (-hf)(-fg) - f^2(-gh) = 2f^2gh$$

Similarly, $G = 2g^2hf, H = 2h^2fg$

$\therefore$ The required equation of the cone reciprocal to (i) is

$$Ax^2 + By^2 + Cz^2 + 2Fyz + 2Gzx + 2Hxy = 0$$

$$\Rightarrow \qquad\qquad 2f^2ghyz + 2g^2hfzx + 2h^2fgxy = 0$$

$$\Rightarrow \qquad\qquad\qquad\quad fyz + gzx + hxy = 0.$$

6. *Find the condition that the lines of intersection of the plane $lx + my + nz = 0$ and cones $fyz + gzx + hxy = 0, ax^2 + by^2 + cz^2 = 0$ should be coincident.*

Sol. Any cone through the intersection of two cones is

$$ax^2 + by^2 + cz^2 + \lambda(fyz + gzx + hxy) = 0 \qquad\qquad ...(i)$$

Since the lines of section of the given cone with $lx + my + nz = 0$ are coincident, for some value of λ, (i) must represent a pair of planes of which one plane is $lx + my + nz = 0$. Let the other plane be $l'x + m'y + n'z = 0$. Then

$$ax^2 + by^2 + cz^2 + \lambda(fyz + gzx + hxy) = (lx + my + nz)(l'x + m'y + n'z)$$

$$\Rightarrow \qquad\qquad a = ll', b = mm', c = nn'$$

or $\qquad\qquad\qquad l' = \dfrac{a}{l}, m' = \dfrac{b}{m}, n' = \dfrac{c}{n}$

and $\qquad\qquad \lambda f = mn' + m'n = \dfrac{cm}{n} + \dfrac{bn}{m} = \dfrac{cm^2 + bn^2}{mn}$

and $\qquad\qquad \lambda g = \dfrac{an^2 + cl^2}{nl}, \lambda h = \dfrac{am^2 + bl^2}{lm}$

$$\Rightarrow \qquad \dfrac{cm^2 + bn^2}{fmn} = \dfrac{an^2 + cl^2}{gnl} = \dfrac{am^2 + bl^2}{hlm}$$

EXERCISES

1. Find the plane which touches the cone

$$x^2 + 2y^2 - 3z^2 + 2yz - 5zx + 3xy = 0,$$

along the generator whose direction ratios are 1, 1, 1.   **[Ans.** $y = z$**]**

2. Prove that the perpendiculars drawn from the origin to the tangent planes to the cone $ax^2 + by^2 + cz^2 = 0$ lie on the cone $x^2/a + y^2/b + z^2/c = 0.$

3. Prove that tangent planes to the cone

$$x^2 - y^2 + 2z^2 - 3yz + 4zx - 5xy = 0,$$

are perpendicular to the generators of the cone

$$17x^2 + 8y^2 + 29z^2 + 28yz - 46zx - 16xy = 0.$$

4. Prove that the cones

$$ayz + bzx + cxy = 0, (ax)^{1/2} + (by)^{1/2} + (cz)^{1/2} = 0$$

are reciprocal.

5. Prove that the cones $fyz + gzx + hxy = 0$; $\sqrt{fx} + \sqrt{gy} + \sqrt{hz} = 0$ are reciprocal.

                                                                        (Ravishankar, 1997, 2001)

6. Find the condition that the plane $ux + vy + wz = 0$ may touch the cone

$$ax^2 + by^2 + cz^2 = 0.\qquad \left[\textbf{Ans. } \frac{u^2}{a} + \frac{v^2}{b} + \frac{w^2}{c} = 0\right]$$

7. Show that a quadric cone can be found to touch any five planes which meet at a point provided no three of them intersect in a line.

   Find the equation of the cone which touches the three co-ordinate planes and the planes
   $$x + 2y + 3z = 0, \ 2x + 3y + 4z = 0.$$
   $$[\textbf{Ans. } (x)^{1/2} + (-6y)^{1/2} + (6z)^{1/2} = 0]$$

8. Show that a quadric cone can be found to touch any two sets of three mutually perpendicular planes which meet in a point.

9. Find the equation of the quadric cone which touches the three co-ordinate planes and the three mutually perpendicular planes
   $$x - y + z = 0, \ 2x + 3y + z = 0, \ 4x - y - 5z = 0.$$
   $$[\textbf{Ans. } 64x^2 + 9y^2 + 25z^2 - 30yz - 80zx + 48xy = 0]$$

7.5. INTERSECTION OF TWO CONES WITH A COMMON VERTEX

Sections of two cones, having a common vertex, by any plane are two coplanar conics which, in general, intersect in four points.

The four lines joining the common vertex to the four points of intersection of these two coplanar conics are the four common generators of the two cones.

Therefore, *two cones with a common vertex have, in general, four generators in common.* In case two cones with the same vertex have five common generators, they coincide.

If $S = 0, \ S' = 0$

be the equations of two cones with origin as the common vertex, then

$$S + kS' = 0$$

is clearly the general equation of a cone whose vertex is at the origin and which passes through the four common generators of the cones

$$S = 0, \ S' = 0.$$

If k be so chosen that $S + kS' = 0$ becomes the product of two linear factors, then the corresponding equations obtained by putting the linear factors equal to zero represent a pair of planes through the common generators.

Such values of k are the roots of the k-cubic equation

$$\begin{vmatrix} a + ka' & h + kh' & g + kg' \\ h + kh' & b + kb' & f + kf' \\ g + kg' & f + kf' & c + kc' \end{vmatrix} = 0.$$

The three values of k give the three pairs of planes through the four common generators.

EXERCISES

1. Find the equation of the cone which passes through the common generators of the cones
   $$-2x^2 + 4y^2 + z^2 = 0 \text{ and } 10xy - 2yz + 5zx = 0$$

   and the line with direction cosines proportional to 1, 2, 3.
   $$[\textbf{Ans. } 2x^2 - 4y^2 - z^2 + 10xy - yz + 5zx = 0]$$

2. Show that the equation of the cone through the intersection of the cones
$$x^2 - 2y^2 + 3z^2 - 4yz + 5zx - 6xy = 0 \text{ and } 2x^2 - 3y^2 + 4z^2 - 5yz + 6zx - 10xy = 0$$
and the line with direction cosines proportional to 1, 1, 1 is
$$y^2 - 2z^2 + 3yz - 4zx + 2xy = 0.$$

3. Show that the plane $3x + 2y - 4z = 0$ passes through a pair of common generators of the cones $27x^2 + 20y^2 - 32z^2 = 0$ and $2yz + zx - 4xy = 0$.

   Also show that the plane containing the other two generators is $9x + 10y + 8z = 0$.

4. Show that the plane $3x - 2y - z = 0$ cuts the cones
$$3yz - 2zx + 2xy = 0 \text{ and } 21x^2 - 4y^2 - 5z^2 = 0$$
in the same pair of perpendicular lines.

   Also show that the plane $7x + 2y + 5z = 0$ contains the remaining two common generators.

5. Two cones are described with guiding curves
$$xz = a^2, \; y = 0; \; yz = b^2, \; x = 0$$
and with any vertex. Show that if their four common generators meet the plane $z = 0$ in four concyclic points, the vertex lies on the surface $z\,(x^2 + y^2) = a^2 x + b^2 y$.

6. Find the conditions that the lines of section of the plane
$$lx + my + nz = 0$$
and the cones $fyz + gzx + hxy = 0$, $ax^2 + by^2 + cz^2 = 0$ should be coincident.

$$\left[\textbf{Ans.} \;\; \frac{bn^2 + cm^2}{fmn} = \frac{cl^2 + an^2}{gnl} = \frac{am^2 + bl^2}{hlm} \right]$$

7.6. THE RIGHT CIRCULAR CONE

7.6.1. Definition

A right circular cone is a surface generated by a line which passes through a fixed point, and makes a constant angle with a fixed line through the fixed point.

(Jiwaji, 1998; Kanpur, 1995)

The fixed point is called the *vertex*, the fixed line the *axis* and the fixed angle the *semi-vertical* angle of the cone.

The justification for the name right circular cone is contained in the result obtained below.

Every section of a right circular cone by a plane perpendicular to its axis is a circle.

Let a plane perpendicular to the axis ON of the right circular cone with semi-vertical angle, α, meet it at N.

Let P be any point of the section. Since ON is perpendicular to the plane which contains the line NP, we have

$$ON \perp NP$$

$$\Rightarrow \qquad \frac{PN}{ON} = \tan \angle NOP = \tan \alpha$$

$$\Rightarrow \qquad PN = ON \tan \alpha$$

so that NP is constant for every position of the point P of the section.

Hence, the section is a circle with N as its centre.

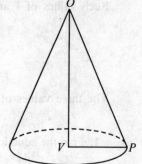

Fig. 39

7.6.2. Equation of a Right Circular Cone

To find the equation of the right circular cone whose vertex is the point $(\alpha, \quad$ $\neg d$ whose axis is the line

$$\frac{x-\alpha}{l} = \frac{y-\beta}{m} = \frac{z-\gamma}{n}$$

and semi-vertical angle θ.   (*Kanpur, 1995; Kumaon, 1996, 98; Patna, 2003*)

Let O be the vertex, and, OA, the axis of the cone.

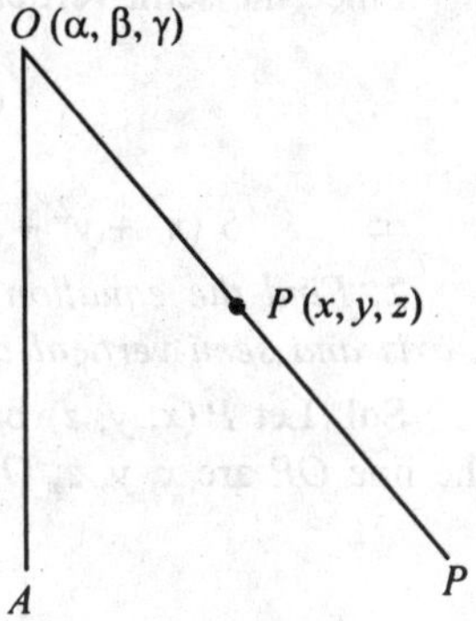

The required equation is to be obtained by using the condition that the line joining any point (x, y, z) on the curve to the vertex $O(\alpha, \beta, \gamma)$ makes an angle θ with the axis OA.

Direction cosines of the line OP, being proportional to

$$x - \alpha,\ y - \beta,\ z - \gamma,$$

we have

$$\cos\theta = \frac{l(x-\alpha) + m(y-\beta) + n(z-\gamma)}{\sqrt{l^2 + m^2 + n^2}\ \sqrt{(x-\alpha)^2 + (y-\beta)^2 + (z-\gamma)^2}}$$

The required equation of the cone, therefore, is

Fig. 40

$$[l(x-\alpha) + m(y-\beta) + n(z-\gamma)]^2 = (l^2 + m^2 + n^2)[(x-\alpha)^2 + (y-\beta)^2 + (z-\gamma)^2]\cos^2\theta.$$

Cor. 1. If the vertex be the origin, the equation of the cone becomes

$$(lx + my + nz)^2 = (l^2 + m^2 + n^2)(x^2 + y^2 + z^2)\cos^2\theta.$$

Cor. 2. If the vertex be the origin and axis of the cone be the Z-axis, then taking

$$l = 0,\ m = 0,\ n = 1$$

in the preceding Cor., we see that the equation of the cone becomes

$$z^2 = (x^2 + y^2 + z^2)\cos^2\theta \iff x^2 + y^2 = z^2\tan^2\theta. \qquad \ldots(1)$$

(*Kumaon, 2001, 03; Bhopal, 1994, 2001; Jabalpur, 2001;*
M.D.U. Rohtak, 1999; Sagar, 1999, 2001)

Cor. 3. *The semi-vertical angle of a right circular cone admitting sets of three mutually perpendicular generators is*

$$\tan^{-1}\sqrt{2},$$

for, the sum of the coefficients of x^2, y^2, z^2 in the equation of such a cone must be zero and this means that

$$1 + 1 - \tan^2\theta = 0,\ i.e.,\ \theta = \tan^{-1}\sqrt{2}. \qquad [\text{Refer (1), Cor. 2}]$$

Cor. 4. *The semi-vertical angle of a right circular cone having sets of three mutually perpendicular tangent planes is*

$$\tan^{-1}\sqrt{\frac{1}{2}},$$

for by Cor., to § 7.4.3, this will be so if   [Refer (1), Cor. 2]

$$1 - \tan^2\theta - \tan^2\theta = 0 \implies \theta = \tan^{-1}\sqrt{\frac{1}{2}}.$$

EXAMPLES

1. *Find the equation to the right circular cone whose vertex is $P(2, -3, 5)$, axis PQ which makes equal angles with the axes and semi-vertical angle is $30°$.*

Sol. Let $R (x, y, z)$ be any point on the surface of the cone, d.r.'s of PR are

$$x - 2, y + 3, z - 5.$$

Let the d.c.'s of the axis be l, m, n.

Given that $l = m = n \Rightarrow l = m = n = \dfrac{1}{\sqrt{3}}$.

Since the semi-vertical angle is 30°, we have

$$\cos 30° = \frac{1 \cdot (x - 2) + 1 \cdot (y - 3) + 1 \cdot (z - 5)}{\sqrt{3} \sqrt{(x - 2)^2 + (y - 3)^2 + (z - 5)^2}}$$

$$\Rightarrow \quad 5 (x^2 + y^2 + z^2) - 8 (yz + zx + xy) - 4x + 86y - 58z + 278 = 0.$$

2. *Find the equation to the right circular cone whose vertex is at origin, the axis along x-axis and semi-vertical angle* α. *(Bilaspur, 1994; Ajmer, 1995; Kumaon, 2000; Avadh, 2005)*

Sol. Let $P (x, y, z)$ be any point on the surface of the cone, so that the direction ratios of the line OP are x, y, z; O being the origin. The direction cosines of x-axis are 1, 0, 0.

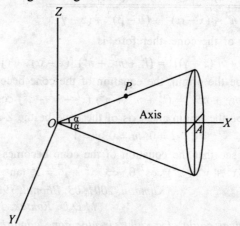

Fig. 41

$$\therefore \quad \cos \alpha = \frac{x \cdot 1 + y \cdot 0 + z \cdot 0}{\sqrt{x^2 + y^2 + z^2}}$$

$$\Rightarrow \quad (x^2 + y^2 + z^2) \cos^2 \alpha = x^2$$

$$\Rightarrow \quad y^2 + z^2 = x^2 \tan^2 \alpha.$$

3. *Lines are drawn through the origin with direction cosines proportional to* $(1, 2, 2)$, $(2, 3, 6)$, $(3, 4, 12)$. *Show that the axis of the right circular cone through them has direction cosines*

$$-\frac{1}{\sqrt{3}}, \frac{1}{\sqrt{3}}, \frac{1}{\sqrt{3}}$$

and that the semi-vertical angle of the cone is $\cos^{-1} (1 / \sqrt{3})$.

Obtain the equation of the cone also and show that it passes through the co-ordinate axes.

(Avadh, 2003)

Sol. Let (l, m, n) be the direction cosines of the axes of the right circular cone. Let O be the origin and P, Q, R be the points, so that d.r.'s of OP, OQ, OR are $(1, 2, 2), (2, 3, 6), (3, 4, 12)$ respectively.

Therefore, d.c.'s of OP are $\dfrac{1}{3}, \dfrac{2}{3}, \dfrac{2}{3}$, those of OQ are $\dfrac{2}{7}, \dfrac{3}{7}, \dfrac{6}{7}$ and those of OR are

$\dfrac{3}{13}, \dfrac{4}{13}, \dfrac{12}{13}$.

Let α be the semi-vertical angle of the cone, then

$$\cos\theta = \frac{1}{3}l + \frac{2}{3}m + \frac{2}{3}n = \frac{2}{7}l + \frac{3}{7}m + \frac{6}{7}n = \frac{3}{13}l + \frac{4}{13}m + \frac{12}{13}n$$

From first two relations

$$l + 5m - 4n = 0 \qquad \qquad \text{...(i)}$$

and from first and last, we get

$$2l + 7m - 5n = 0 \qquad \qquad \text{...(ii)}$$

Solving, we obtain

$$\frac{l}{-1} = \frac{m}{1} = \frac{n}{1} = \pm\frac{\sqrt{l^2 + m^2 + n^2}}{\sqrt{1+1+1}} = \pm\frac{1}{\sqrt{3}}$$

Therefore, direction cosines of the axis are

$$-\frac{1}{\sqrt{3}}, \frac{1}{\sqrt{3}}, \frac{1}{\sqrt{3}}.$$

Therefore, semi-vertical angle of the cone will be

$$\cos\alpha = \frac{1}{3}\left(-\frac{1}{\sqrt{3}}\right) + \frac{2}{3}\cdot\frac{1}{\sqrt{3}} + \frac{2}{3}\cdot\frac{1}{\sqrt{3}} = \frac{1}{\sqrt{3}} \Rightarrow \alpha = \cos^{-1}\left(\frac{1}{\sqrt{3}}\right)$$

If (x, y, z) be any point on the cone, then its equation will be

$$\cos\alpha = \frac{-1\cdot x + 1\cdot y + 1\cdot z}{\sqrt{3}\sqrt{x^2 + y^2 + z^2}} = \frac{1}{\sqrt{3}}$$

$\Rightarrow \qquad yz - zx - xy = 0.$

4. *Prove that $x^2 - y^2 + z^2 - 4x + 2y + 6z + 12 = 0$ represents a right circular cone whose vertex is the point $(2, 1, -3)$, whose axis is parallel to OY and whose semi-vertical angle is $45°$.*

Sol. The vertex of the cone is $V(2, 1, -3)$, its semi-vertical angle is $45°$ and its axis is parallel to OY, i.e., the direction cosines of its axis are $0, 1, 0$.

∴ The equation of the axis of the cone is

$$\frac{x-2}{0} = \frac{y-1}{1} = \frac{z+3}{0} \qquad \qquad \text{...(i)}$$

Let $P(x, y, z)$ be any point on the cone. Then the d.r.'s of the generator VP are $x - 2, y - 1, z + 3$.

Also, VP is making an angle of $45°$ with the axis whose d.c.'s are $0, 1, 0$ so the equation of the cone is

$$\cos 45° = \frac{(x-2)\cdot 0 + (y-1)\cdot 1 + (z+3)\cdot 0}{\sqrt{0^2 + 1^2 + 0^2}\sqrt{(x-2)^2 + (y-1)^2 + (z-3)^2}}$$

$\Rightarrow \qquad \dfrac{1}{\sqrt{2}} = \dfrac{(y-1)}{\sqrt{(x-2)^2 + (y-1)^2 + (z+3)^2}}$

$\Rightarrow \qquad (x-2)^2 - (y-1)^2 + (z+3)^2 = 0$

$\Rightarrow \qquad x^2 - y^2 + z^2 - 4x + 2y + 6z + 12 = 0.$

5. *Find the equation of the cone formed by rotating the line $2x + 3y = 6$, $z = 0$ about the y-axis.*   *(Bundelkhand, 1996)*

Sol. The axis of cone is y-axis, whose d.c.'s are 0, 1, 0 and the equation of any generator is given as $2x + 3y = 6$, $z = 0$, *i.e.*,

$$\frac{x}{3} = \frac{y-2}{-2} = \frac{z}{0} \qquad \qquad ...(i)$$

The point of intersection of y-axis and the line (i) is $(0, 2, 0)$, so the co-ordinates of the vertex of the cone is $V(0, 2, 0)$.

Let θ be the semi-vertical angle of the cone, then θ is the angle between y-axis and the line (i), so we have

$$\cos \theta = \frac{0 \cdot 3 + 1 \cdot (-2) + 0 \cdot 0}{\sqrt{0+1+0} \sqrt{(3)^2 + (-2)^2 + (0)^2}} = \frac{-2}{\sqrt{13}} \qquad ...(iii)$$

Also, let $P(x, y, z)$ be any point on the cone, then VP is a generator of the cone and its direction ratios are $x - 0$, $y - 2$, $z - 0$ or x, $y - 2$, z.

Also, θ is the angle between y-axis and VP, so we get

$$\cos \theta = \frac{0 \cdot x + 1 \cdot (y-2) + 0 \cdot z}{\sqrt{0+1+0} \sqrt{x^2 + (y-2)^2 + z^2}} \qquad ...(iii)$$

Equating the value of $\cos \theta$ from (ii) and (iii) we get the equation of the cone as

$$\frac{-2}{\sqrt{13}} = \frac{y-2}{\sqrt{x^2 + (y-2)^2 + z^2}}$$

$\Rightarrow \qquad 4[x^2 + (y-2)^2 + z^2] = 13(y-2)^2$

$\Rightarrow \qquad 4x^2 - 9(y-2)^2 + 4z^2 = 0.$

EXERCISES

1. Find the equation of the right circular cone with its vertex at the origin, axis along Z-axis and semi-vertical angle α.   *(Garhwal, 1999; Kumaon, 1997; Bhopal, 2001; Jabalpur, 2001; Sagar, 2001)*
                [**Ans.** $x^2 + y^2 = z^2 \tan^2 \alpha$]

2. Show that the equation of the right circular cone with vertex $(2, 3, 1)$, axis parallel to the line $-x = y/2 = z$ and one of its generators having direction cosines proportional to $(1, -1, 1)$ is $x^2 + 8y^2 + z^2 + 12xy - 12yz + 6zx + 46x + 36y + 22z - 19 = 0$.

3. Find the equation of the circular cone which passes through the point $(1, 1, 2)$ and has its vertex at the origin and axis the line $x/2 = -y/4 = z/3$.
          [**Ans.** $4x^2 + 40y^2 + 19z^2 - 48xy - 72yz + 36xz = 0$]

4. Find the equation of the right circular cone whose vertex is origin, axis of the line $x = t$, $y = 2t$, $z = 3t$, and whose semi-vertical angle is $60°$.   *(Jabalpur, 2000)*
          [**Ans.** $38x^2 + 26y^2 + 6z^2 - 16xy - 48yz - 24zx = 0$]

5. Find the equation of the right circular cone whose vertex is $(1, -2, -1)$, axis the line
   $$\frac{x-1}{3} = \frac{y+2}{4} = \frac{z+1}{5}$$
   and semi-vertical angle $60°$.   *(Indore, 2000; Ravishankar, 1995; Rohilkhand, 1996)*
         [**Ans.** $7x^2 - 7y^2 - 25z^2 + 48xy + 80yz - 60zx + 22x + 4y + 17z + 78 = 0$]

6. Find the equation of the right circular cone whose vertex is (3, 2, 1), axis the line

$$\frac{x-3}{4} = \frac{y-2}{1} = \frac{z-1}{3}$$

   and semi-vertical angle 30°.   (*Gorakhpur, 2001*)

7. Find the equation of right circular cone which passes through (1, 1, 1), whose vertex is (1, 0, 1) and axis of cone makes equal angle with co-ordinate axes.

   (*Sagar, 1995, 2002*) [**Ans.** $xy + yz + zx - x - 2y - z + 1 = 0$]

8. Find the equation of the cone generated by rotating the line

$$\frac{x}{l} = \frac{y}{m} = \frac{z}{n}$$

   about the line $\dfrac{x}{a} = \dfrac{y}{b} = \dfrac{z}{c}$ as axis.

   [**Ans.** $(al + bm + cn)^2 (x^2 + y^2 + z^2) = (ax + by + cz)^2 (l^2 + m^2 + n^2)$]

9. Find the equation of the right circular cone which passes through the point (1, 1, 2) and

   has its vertex at the origin, axis the line $\dfrac{x}{2} = \dfrac{y}{-4} = \dfrac{z}{3}$.   (*Rohilkhand, 1995*)

   [**Ans.** $12y^2 - 5z^2 - 16xy - 24yz - 12zx = 0$]

10. A right circular cone is passing through the point (1, 1, 1) and its vertex is at the point (1, 0, 1). The axis of the cone is equally inclined to the co-ordinate axes. Find the equation of the cone.   [**Ans.** $yz + zx - xy + x + 2y - 3z - 1 = 0$]

11. A cone has as base the circle $x^2 + y^2 + 2ax + 2by = 0$, $z = 0$ and passes through the fixed point (0, 0, c). If the section of the cone by zx-plane is a rectangular hyperbola, prove that the vertex lies on a fixed circle.

12. Find the equations of the circular cones which contain the three co-ordinate axes as generators.   [**Ans.** $yz \neq zx \neq xy = 0$]

13. Find the equation of the right circular cone generated by straight lines drawn from the origin to cut the circle through the three points (1, 2, 2), (2, 1, – 2) and (2, – 2, 1).

   [**Ans.** $8x^2 - 4y^2 - 4z^2 + 5xy + yz + 5zx = 0$]

14. If α is the semi-vertical angle of the right circular cone which passes through the lines Oy, Oz, $x = y = z$, show that $\cos \alpha = (9 - 4\sqrt{3})^{-1/2}$.

7.7. THE CYLINDER

Def. *A cylinder is a surface generated by a straight line which is always parallel to a fixed line and is subject to one more condition; for instance, it may intersect a given curve or touch a given surface.*

The given curve is called the *Guiding curve*.   (*Ajmer, 1998*)

7.7.1. Equation of a Cylinder

To find the equation of the cylinder whose generators intersect the conic

$$ax^2 + 2hxy + by^2 + 2gx + 2fy + c = 0, z = 0 \qquad \qquad ...(i)$$

and are parallel to the line

$$\frac{x}{l} = \frac{y}{m} = \frac{z}{n} \qquad \qquad ...(ii)$$

(*Bhopal, 1996; Kumaon, 1994, 98, 2000, 04; Patna, 2003; Rohilkhand, 1995; Vikram, 1999*)

Let (α, β, γ) be *any* point on the cylinder so that the equations of the generator through the point are

$$\frac{x - \alpha}{l} = \frac{y - \beta}{m} = \frac{z - \gamma}{n} \qquad \qquad \ldots(iii)$$

As in § 7.1.2, the line *(iii)* will intersect the conic *(i)*, if

$$\left(\alpha - \frac{l\gamma}{n}\right)^2 + 2h\left(\alpha - \frac{l\gamma}{n}\right)\left(\beta - \frac{m\gamma}{n}\right) + b\left(\beta - \frac{m\gamma}{n}\right)^2 + 2g\left(\alpha - \frac{l\gamma}{n}\right)$$
$$+ 2f\left(\beta - \frac{m\gamma}{n}\right) + c = 0$$

But this is the condition that the point (α, β, γ) should lie on the surface

$$a\left(x - \frac{lz}{n}\right)^2 + 2h\left(x - \frac{lz}{n}\right)\left(y - \frac{mz}{n}\right) + b\left(y - \frac{mz}{n}\right)^2 + 2g\left(x - \frac{lz}{n}\right)$$
$$+ 2f\left(y - \frac{mz}{n}\right) + c = 0$$

$$\Rightarrow \quad a(nx - lz)^2 + 2h(nx - lz)(ny - mz) + b(ny - nz)^2 + 2gn(nx - lz)$$
$$+ 2fn(ny - mz) + cn^2 = 0$$

which is, therefore, the required equation of the cylinder.

Cor. If the generators be parallel to Z-axis so that

$$l = 0 = m \text{ and } n = 1$$

the equation of the cylinder becomes

$$ax^2 + 2hxy + by^2 + 2gx + 2fy + c = 0$$

as is already known to the reader.

EXAMPLES

1. *Find the equation of a cylinder whose generating lines have the direction cosines* (l, m, n) *and which passes through the circle*

$$x^2 + z^2 = a^2, \ y = 0.$$

Sol. Let (α, β, γ) be any point on the cylinder. Then equations of generators are

$$\frac{x - \alpha}{l} = \frac{y - \beta}{m} = \frac{z - \gamma}{n}.$$

This meets the plane $y = 0$ at the point

$$\left(\alpha - \frac{l\beta}{m}, \ 0, \ \gamma - \frac{n\beta}{m}\right).$$

This point will lie on the curve $x^2 + z^2 = a^2$, if

$$\left(\alpha - \frac{l\beta}{m}\right)^2 + \left(\gamma - \frac{n\beta}{m}\right)^2 = a^2$$

Hence, locus of (α, β, γ) is

$$\left(x - \frac{ly}{m}\right)^2 + \left(z - \frac{ny}{m}\right)^2 = a^2$$

or $(mx - ly)^2 + (mz - ny)^2 = a^2m^2.$

2. *Find the equation of the cylinder whose generators are parallel to the line*

$$\frac{x}{1} = \frac{y}{-2} = \frac{z}{3}$$

and whose guiding curve is the ellipse $x^2 + 2y^2 = 1, z = 0.$

(Agra, 1998; Bhopal, 1997; Bundelkhand, 1999; Gorakhpur, 1999;
Indore, 2001; Jabalpur, 1996, 2000; Poorvanchal, 1998;
Rohilkhand, 1994, 2000; Meerut 2005; Poorvanchal, 2004)

Sol. Let (α, β, γ) be any point on the cylinder, then equations of a generator through (α, β, γ) are

$$\frac{x - \alpha}{1} = \frac{y - \beta}{-2} = \frac{z - \gamma}{3}.$$

This meets the plane $z = 0$ at the point given by

$$\frac{x - \alpha}{1} = \frac{y - \beta}{-2} = -\frac{\gamma}{3}$$

i.e., at

$$\left(\alpha - \frac{\gamma}{3}, \beta + \frac{2\gamma}{3}, 0\right)$$

Therefore, the generator intersects the given curve if

$$\left(\alpha - \frac{\gamma}{3}\right)^2 + 2\left(\beta + \frac{2\gamma}{3}\right)^2 = 1$$

Hence locus of (α, β, γ) is

$$\left(x - \frac{z}{3}\right)^2 + 2\left(y + \frac{2z}{3}\right)^2 = 1$$

or

$$3x^2 + 6y^2 + 3z^2 - 2zx + 8yz - 3 = 0$$

3. *Find the equation of the cylinder whose generators are parallel to*

$$\frac{x}{1} = \frac{y}{-2} = \frac{z}{3}$$

and whose guiding curve is the ellipse $x^2 + 2y^2 = 1, z = 3.$

(Agra, 1998; Bhopal, 2000; Sagar, 1999, 2002; Jiwaji, 1995, 99; Gorakhpur, 1999,
Poorvanchal, 1998; Kanpur, 1998; Lucknow, 1996;
Garhwal, 1999, 2004, 2006; Indore, 1994)

Sol. Let (α, β, γ) be any point on the surface of the cylinder so that the equations of its generators through this point are

$$\frac{x - \alpha}{1} = \frac{y - \beta}{-2} = \frac{z - \gamma}{3}$$

This line meets the plane $z = 3$ at the point given by

$$\frac{x - \alpha}{1} = \frac{y - \beta}{-2} = \frac{3 - \gamma}{3},$$

i.e.,

$$\left(\alpha + \frac{3 - \gamma}{3}, \beta + \frac{2\gamma - 6}{3}, 3\right)$$

This point will lie on the surface

$$x^2 + 2y^2 = 1,$$

if

$$\left(\alpha + \frac{3-\gamma}{3}\right)^2 + 2\left(\beta + \frac{2\gamma - 6}{3}\right)^2 = 1$$

or

$$(3\alpha - \gamma + 3)^2 + 2(3\beta + 2\gamma - 6)^2 = 9$$

Hence locus of the point (α, β, γ) will be

$$(3x - z + 3)^2 + 2(3y + 2z - 6)^2 = 9$$

or

$$3x^2 + 6y^2 + 3z^2 + 8yz - 2zx + 6x - 24y - 18z + 24 = 0.$$

This is the required equation of the cylinder.

4. *Find the equation of the quadric cylinder with generators parallel to x-axis and passing through the curve $ax^2 + by^2 + cz^2 = 1$, $lx + my + nz = p$.*

(*Bhopal, 1994; Bhoj, 1999; Jabalpur, 1995; Kanpur, 1996;
Kumaon, 2004; Rewa, 1997; Vikram, 2000*)

Sol. The equation of the required cylinder is obtained by eliminating x between the equations

$$ax^2 + by^2 + cz^2 = 1 \text{ and } lx + my + nz = p.$$

For this, substituting the value of $x = \dfrac{p - my - nz}{l}$ in the other equation, we get

$$a\left(\frac{p - my - nz}{l}\right)^2 + by^2 + cz^2 = 1$$

or

$$a(p - my - nz)^2 + bl^2y^2 + cl^2z^2 = l^2$$

or

$$(bl^2 + am^2)y^2 + (cl^2 - am^2)z^2 + 2amnyz - 2apmy - 2apnz + ap^2 - l^2 = 0.$$

This is the equation of required cylinder.

EXERCISES

1. Find the equation of the cylinder whose generators intersect the curve $ax^2 + by^2 = 2z$, $lx + my + nz = p$ and are parallel to the Z-axis.

[**Hint.** Eliminate z from the equations.]   (*Bundelkhand, 1995, 96; Avadh, 2000;*
Garhwal, 1995; Gorakhpur, 1997, 2003; Utkal, 2003)
[**Ans.** $n(ax^2 + by^2) + 2lx + 2my - 2p = 0$]

2. Find the equation to the cylinder whose generators are parallel to

$$\frac{x}{1} = \frac{y}{2} = \frac{z}{3}$$

and guiding curve is $x^2 + y^2 = 16$, $z = 0$.

(*Kanpur, 1999, 2002; Indore, 2000; Jabalpur, 1995*)
[**Ans.** $9x^2 + 9y^2 + 5z^2 - 12yz - 6zx - 144 = 0$]

3. Find the equation of the cylinder whose generators are parallel to z-axis and guiding curve is given by $ax^2 + by^2 + cz^2 = 1$, $lx + my + nz = p$.

(*Avadh, 1998; Jabalpur, 1995; Jiwaji, 1998; Rohilkhand, 1998; Ujjain, 2002*)
[**Ans.** $(an^2 + cl^2)x^2 + (bn^2 + cm^2)y^2 + 2lcmxy - 2cplx - 2cpmy + (cp^2 - n^2) = 0$]

4. Find the equation of cylinder whose generator is parallel to $y = mx$, $z = nx$ and which intersect the conic $\dfrac{x^2}{a^2} + \dfrac{y^2}{b^2} = 1$, $z = 0$.   (*Bilaspur, 1995; Rewa, 2000*)

[**Ans.** $b^2(nx - z)^2 + a^2(ny - mz)^2 = n^2a^2b^2$]

5. Find the equation of the circular cylinder, whose generating lines have the direction cosines l, m, n and which passes through the fixed circle $x^2 + y^2 = a^2$ in the ZOX-plane.

[**Ans.** $(mx - ly)^2 + (mz - ny)^2 = m^2$]

6. Show that the equation of the tangent plane at any point (α, β, γ) of the cylinder

$$ax^2 + 2hxy + by^2 + 2gx + 2fy + c = 0$$

is $\quad x(a\alpha + h\beta + g) + y(h\alpha + b\beta + f) + (g\alpha + f\beta + c) = 0$

and that it touches the cylinder at all points of the generator through the point.

7.7.2. Enveloping Cylinder

To find the equation to the cylinder whose generators touch the sphere

$$x^2 + y^2 + z^2 = a^2, \qquad \qquad ...(i)$$

and are parallel to the line

$$\frac{x}{l} = \frac{y}{m} = \frac{z}{n} \qquad \qquad ...(ii)$$

(Agra, 1996; Kanpur, 1999; Kumaon, 1996, 99; Ajmer, 1998)

Let (α, β, γ) be any point on the cylinder so that the equations of the generator through it are

$$\frac{x - \alpha}{l} = \frac{y - \beta}{m} = \frac{z - \gamma}{n} \qquad \qquad ...(iii)$$

The line *(iii)* will touch the sphere *(i)*, if

$$(l\alpha + m\beta + n\gamma)^2 = (l^2 + m^2 + n^2)(\alpha^2 + \beta^2 + \gamma^2 - a^2).$$

But this is the condition that the point (α, β, γ) should lie on the surface

$$(lx + my + nz)^2 = (l^2 + m^2 + n^2)(x^2 + y^2 + z^2 - a^2)$$

which is, therefore, the required equation of the cylinder and is known as *Enveloping cylinder of the sphere (i)*.

EXAMPLES

1. *Find the equation of the enveloping cylinder of the sphere* $x^2 + y^2 + z^2 = 25$, *whose generators are parallel to the line* $\dfrac{x}{1} = \dfrac{y}{2} = \dfrac{z}{3}$. *(M.D.U. Rohtak, 1996, 98)*

Sol. Let (α, β, γ) be any point on the cylinder.

∴ Equation of generator is

$$\frac{x - \alpha}{1} = \frac{y - \beta}{2} = \frac{z - \gamma}{3} = r \text{ (say)}$$

Any point on generator is $(r + \alpha, 2r + \beta, 3r + \gamma)$. It will lie on a sphere, hence

$$(r + \alpha)^2 + (2r + \beta)^2 + (3r + \gamma)^2 = 25$$

$$\Rightarrow \quad 14r^2 + 2r(\alpha + 2\beta + 3\gamma) - (\alpha^2 + \beta^2 + \gamma^2 - 25) = 0$$

It will touch the sphere if

$$4(\alpha + 2\beta + 3\gamma)^2 = 4 \cdot 14(\alpha^2 + \beta^2 + \gamma^2 - 25)$$

$$\Rightarrow \quad 13\alpha^2 + 10\beta^2 + 5\gamma^2 - 4\alpha\beta - 6\gamma\alpha - 12\beta\gamma - 350 = 0$$

∴ Locus of (α, β, γ) is

$$13x^2 + 10y^2 + 5z^2 - 4xy - 6zx - 12yz - 350 = 0.$$

2. *Find the enveloping cylinder of the sphere*

$$x^2 + y^2 + z^2 - 2x + 4y = 1,$$

having its generators parallel to $x = y = z$. *Also find its guiding curve.*

(Bhopal, 2002; Garhwal, 1996; Gorakhpur, 1998, 2002; Jabalpur, 1998; Jiwaji, 1998; Kumaon, 1994, 97, 2002; M.D.U. Rohtak, 1997, 99; Ravishankar, 2001)

Sol. Let (α, β, γ) be any point on the surface of the cylinder so that the equations of its generator through this point are

$$\frac{x - \alpha}{1} = \frac{y - \beta}{1} = \frac{z - \gamma}{1} = r \text{ (say)} \qquad \text{...(1)}$$

Any point on this line is

$$(\alpha + r, \beta + r, \gamma + r).$$

This point will lie on the sphere

$$x^2 + y^2 + z^2 - 2x + 4y = 1 \qquad \text{...(2)}$$

if

$$(\alpha + r)^2 + (\beta + r)^2 + (\gamma + r)^2 - 2(\alpha + r) + 4(\beta + r) = 1$$

or

$$3r^2 + 2r(\alpha + \beta + \gamma + 1) + (\alpha^2 + \beta^2 + \gamma^2 - 2\alpha + 4\beta - 1) = 0$$

Since the generator (1) touches (2), the roots of this quadratic equation in r must be identical, for which

$$4(\alpha + \beta + \gamma + 1)^2 = 12(\alpha^2 + \beta^2 + \gamma^2 - 2\alpha + 4\beta - 1)$$

or

$$\alpha^2 + \beta^2 + \gamma^2 - \beta\gamma - \gamma\alpha - \alpha\beta - 4\alpha + 5\beta - \gamma - 2 = 0$$

Therefore the locus of (α, β, γ) is

$$x^2 + y^2 + z^2 - yz - zx - xy - 4x + 5y - z - 2 = 0.$$

This is the required equations of the enveloping cylinder.

Now, equation to the plane passing through the centre $(1, -2, 0)$ of the sphere (2) and perpendicular to the generators of the cylinder whose direction cosines are proportional to $(1, 1, 1)$ is

$$1 \cdot (x - 1) + 1 \cdot (y + 2) + 1 \cdot (z - 0) = 0$$

or

$$x + y + z + 1 = 0 \qquad \text{...(3)}$$

Clearly the guiding curve is the curve of intersection of the sphere (2) and the plane (3), *i.e.*, the equations of the guiding curve are

$$x^2 + y^2 + z^2 - 2\bar{x} + 4y - 1 = 0,$$

$$x + y + z + 1 = 0.$$

EXERCISES

1. Find the equation of the enveloping cylinder of the conicoid

$$\frac{x^2}{a^2} + \frac{y^2}{b^2} + \frac{z^2}{c^2} = 1$$

whose generators are parallel to the line (*i*) $\dfrac{x}{l} = \dfrac{y}{m} = \dfrac{z}{n}$; (*ii*) $x = y = z$.

(Avadh, 2005)

$$\left[\textbf{Ans. } (i) \left(\frac{lx}{a^2} + \frac{my}{b^2} + \frac{nz}{c^2}\right)^2 = \left(\frac{l^2}{a^2} + \frac{m^2}{b^2} + \frac{n^2}{c^2}\right)\left(\frac{x^2}{a^2} + \frac{y^2}{b^2} + \frac{z^2}{c^2} - 1\right)\right.$$

$$\left. (ii) \left(\frac{x}{a^2} + \frac{y}{b^2} + \frac{z}{c^2}\right)^2 = \left(\frac{1}{a^2} + \frac{1}{b^2} + \frac{1}{c^2}\right)\left(\frac{x^2}{a^2} + \frac{y^2}{b^2} + \frac{z^2}{c^2} - 1\right)\right]$$

2. Obtain the equation of a cylinder whose generators touch the sphere

$$x^2 + y^2 + z^2 + 2ux + 2vy + 2wz + d = 0$$

whose generators are parallel to the line $\dfrac{x}{l} = \dfrac{y}{m} = \dfrac{z}{n}$. *(Kanpur, 1997; Kumaon, 2000)*

$$[\textbf{Ans. } \{l(x + u) + m(y + v) + n(z + w)\}^2$$
$$= (l^2 + m^2 + n^2)(x^2 + y^2 + z^2 + 2ux + 2vy + 2wz + d)]$$

3. Find the equation of a right circular cylinder which envelopes a sphere with centre (a, b, c) and radius r and has the generators parallel to the direction cosines (l, m, n).

[**Ans.** $\{l\,(a - x) + m\,(b - y) + n\,(c - z)\}^2$
$$= (l^2 + m^2 + n^2)\,\{(a - x)^2 + (b - y)^2 + (c - z)^2 - r^2\}]$$

4. Prove that the enveloping cylinders of ellipsoid $\dfrac{x^2}{a^2} + \dfrac{y^2}{b^2} + \dfrac{z^2}{c^2} = 1$, whose generators

are parallel to the line $\dfrac{x}{0} = \dfrac{y}{\pm\sqrt{a^2 - b^2}} = \dfrac{z}{c}$ meet the plane $z = 0$ in circles.

(*Kumaon, 2006; Gorakhpur, 1997; Indore, 1996; Garhwal; 2006*)

5. Show that the enveloping cylinder of the conicoid $ax^2 + by^2 + cz^2 = 1$ with generators perpendicular to x-axis meets the plane $z = 0$ in parabolas.

6. Find the equation of the enveloping cylinder of the conicoid $ax^2 + by^2 + cz^2 = 1$ whose generators are parallel to the line $x = y = z$.

[**Ans.** $(b + c)\,x^2 + (c + a)\,y^2 + (a + b)\,z^2 - 2abxy - 2bcyz - 2cazx - (a + b + c) = 0$]

7.8. THE RIGHT CIRCULAR CYLINDER

7.8.1. Definition

A right circular cylinder is a surface generated by a line which intersects a fixed circle, called the guiding circle, and is perpendicular to its plane. (*Jiwaji, 1997; Kumaon, 2001*)

The normal to the plane of the guiding circle through its centre is called the *Axis* of the cylinder.

Section of a right circular cylinder by any plane perpendicular to its axis is called a *Normal section*.

Clearly all the normal sections of a right circular cylinder are circles having the same radius which is also called the radius of the cylinder.

The length of the perpendicular from any point on a right circular cylinder to its axis is equal to its radius.

7.8.2. Equation of a Right Circular Cylinder

To find the equation of the right circular cylinder whose axis is the line
$$\frac{x - \alpha}{l} = \frac{y - \beta}{m} = \frac{z - \gamma}{n}$$

and whose radius is r. (*Ajmer, 1995; Jabalpur, 1997; Kumaon, 1995, 97, 2001; Banglore, 2001*)

Let (x, y, z) be a point on the cylinder. Equating the perpendicular distance of the point from the axis to the radius r, we get

$$(x - \alpha)^2 + (y - \beta)^2 + (z - \gamma)^2 - \frac{[l\,(x - \alpha) + m\,(y - \beta) + n\,(z - \gamma)]^2}{l^2 + m^2 + n^2} = r^2$$

which is the required equation of the cylinder.

EXAMPLES

1. *Find the equation of the right circular cylinder of radius 2 whose axis passes through the point $(1, 2, 3)$ and has direction cosines proportional to $(2, -3, 6)$.*

(*Avadh, 1997; Kanpur, 1997; Bhopal, 1999;*
Kumaon, 1999; Ravishankar, 1997; Rohilkhand, 2001)

Sol. The axis of the right circular cylinder is

$$\frac{x-1}{2} = \frac{y-2}{-3} = \frac{z-3}{6} \quad \Leftrightarrow \quad \frac{x-1}{2/7} = \frac{y-2}{-3/7} = \frac{z-3}{6/7}$$

Let (f, g, h) be *any* point of the cylinder. The square of the perpendicular distance of the point (f, g, h) from the axis is

$$(f-1)^2 + (g-2)^2 + (h-3)^2 - \left[\frac{2}{7}(f-1) - \frac{3}{7}(g-2) + \frac{6}{7}(h-3)\right]^2$$

Equating this perpendicular distance to the square of the radius 2, we see that the point (f, g, h) satisfies the equation

$$45f^2 + 40g^2 + 13h^2 + 36gh - 24hf + 12fg - 42f - 280g - 126h + 294 = 0$$

so that the required equation is

$$45x^2 + 40y^2 + 13z^2 + 36yz - 24zx + 12xy - 42x - 280y - 126z + 294 = 0.$$

2. *Find the equation of a circular cylinder whose guiding curve is* $x^2 + y^2 + z^2 = 9$, $x - y + z = 3.$
(*Agra, 1995, 96, 98; Avadh, 2003, 2006; Ajmer, 1996, 97;*
Bilaspur, 1994, 95, 96, 99; Bhopal, 2001; Bundelkhand, 1998;
Garhwal, 1994; Gorakhpur, 1997, 2001; Indore, 2002; Jabalpur, 2002;
Kanpur, 1997; M.D.U. Rohtak, 2001; Ravishankar, 1997; Rohilkhand, 1999, 2003, 04;
Sagar, 1997, 99; Vikram, 2000)

Sol. We know that the radius of a right circular cylinder is equal to the radius of the guiding curve and the axis of the cylinder is a line passing through the centre of the circle and hence of the sphere and perpendicular to the plane of the circle.

Here, radius of the sphere = 3.

Length of the perpendicular from the centre $O\,(0, 0, 0)$ to the given plane

$$= \frac{-3}{\sqrt{1+1+1}} = -\sqrt{3}$$

∴ Radius of the circle $= \sqrt{3^2 - 3} = \sqrt{6}.$

The axis of the cylinder passes through $(0, 0, 0)$ and is perpendicular to the plane $x - y + z = 3.$

Hence its equations are

$$\frac{x}{1} = \frac{y}{-1} = \frac{z}{1}.$$

Therefore, the equation of the circular cylinder is

$$\left(\frac{1}{\sqrt{3}}\right)^2 \left\{ \begin{vmatrix} y & z \\ -1 & 1 \end{vmatrix}^2 + \begin{vmatrix} z & x \\ 1 & 1 \end{vmatrix}^2 + \begin{vmatrix} x & y \\ 1 & -1 \end{vmatrix}^2 \right\} = (\sqrt{6})^2$$

or $$(y+z)^2 + (z-x)^2 + (-x-y)^2 = 18$$

or $$2x^2 + 2y^2 + 2z^2 + 2yz - 2zx + 2xy = 18$$

or $$x^2 + y^2 + z^2 + xy + yz - zx - 9 = 0.$$

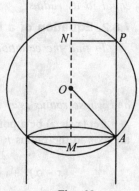

Fig. 42

3. *Find the right circular cylinder whose radius is 2 and axis is the line*

$$\frac{x-1}{2} = \frac{y-2}{1} = \frac{z-3}{2}.$$

(*Avadh, 2000, 01; Bhopal, 1998; Bilaspur, 2000; Bundelkhand, 1994, 97; Garhwal, 2001;*
Indore, 1995, 97; Jabalpur, 2001; Jiwaji, 1996, 2001; Kumaon, 2005; Lucknow, 1996;
Poorvanchal, 1994, 96, 99; Ravishankar, 1995, 2000; Vikram, 2001; Rohilkhand, 2005)

Sol. Let $P(x_1, y_1, z_1)$ be any point on the cylinder. The length of the perpendicular from $P(x_1, y_1, z_1)$ to the given line must be equal to the radius.

$$\therefore \quad 2^2(2^2 + 1^2 + 2^2) = \{2(y_1 - 2) - 1(z_1 - 3)\}^2 + \{2(z_1 - 3) - 2(x_1 - 1)\}^2$$
$$+ \{1(x_1 - 1) - 2(y_1 - 2)\}^2$$
$$\Rightarrow 36 = (2y_1 - z_1 - 1)^2 + (2z_1 - 2x_1 - 4)^2 + (x_1 - 2y_1 + 3)^2$$

$\therefore$ The required equation of the locus of $P(x_1, y_1, z_1)$ is

$$(2y - z - 1)^2 + (2z - 2x - 6)^2 + (x - 2y + 3)^2 = 36$$
$$\Rightarrow 5x^2 + 8y^2 + 5z^2 - 4xy - 4yz - 8zx + 22x - 16y - 14z - 10 = 0.$$

4. *Obtain the equation of the right circular cylinder whose guiding curve is the circle through the points* $(1, 0, 0)$, $(0, 1, 0)$, $(0, 0, 1)$.

(Avadh, 1999; Garhwal, 2002; Kumaon, 1998, 2003; Rohilkhand, 1997)

Sol. The circle ABC can be taken as the intersection of sphere $OABC$ and plane ABC, O being the origin. Therefore, the equations of the circle ABC are

$$x^2 + y^2 + z^2 - x - y - z = 0 \qquad\qquad ...(i)$$

and
$$x + y + z = 1 \qquad\qquad ...(ii)$$

The axis of the cylinder will be perpendicular to the plane (ii). Hence, the generators of the cylinder will have the direction ratios $1, 1, 1$.

Let (α, β, γ) be any point on the cylinder. Then the generator through (α, β, γ) is

$$\frac{x - \alpha}{1} = \frac{y - \beta}{1} = \frac{z - \gamma}{1} = r \text{ (say)} \qquad\qquad ...(iii)$$

Suppose this generator meets the circle at the point $(r + \alpha, r + \beta, r + \gamma)$. Substituting this point in (i) and (ii), we get

$$(r + \alpha)^2 + (r + \beta)^2 + (r + \gamma)^2 - (r + \alpha) - (r + \beta) - (r + \gamma) = 0 \qquad\qquad ...(iv)$$

and
$$r = \frac{(1 - \alpha - \beta - \gamma)}{3} \qquad\qquad ...(v)$$

Eliminating r between (iv) and (v), we get

$$(\alpha^2 + \beta^2 + \gamma^2) - (\alpha\beta + \beta\gamma + \gamma\alpha) - 1 = 0$$

Generalising it, we get the equation of cone as

$$x^2 + y^2 + z^2 - xy - yz - zx - 1 = 0.$$

EXERCISES

1. Find the equation of the right circular cylinder of radius 2 whose axis is the line

$$(x - 1)/2 = (y - 2)/2 = (z - 2)/2.$$

[**Ans.** $5x^2 + 8y^2 + 5z^2 - 4xy - 4yz - 8zx + 22x - 16y - 14z - 10 = 0$]

2. The axis of a right circular cylinder of radius 2 is

$$\frac{x - 1}{2} = \frac{y}{3} = \frac{z - 3}{1};$$

show that its equation is $10x^2 + 5y^2 + 13z^2 - 12xy - 6yz - 4zx - 8x + 30y - 74z + 59 = 0$.

(Bilaspur, 1997, 2001; M.D.U. Rohtak, 1998; Sagar, 1998, 2001; Vikram, 1995)

3. Find the equation of the right circular cylinder of radius 3 and having for its axis the line

$$\frac{x - 1}{2} = \frac{y - 3}{2} = \frac{5 - z}{7}.$$

(Kumaon, 2006; Garhwal, 2003; Kanpur, 1998; Rohilkhand, 2002)

[**Ans.** $5x^2 + 5y^2 + 8z^2 - 8xy + 4yz + 4zx - 6x - 42y - 96z + 225 = 0$]

4. Find the equation of the right circular cylinder whose axis is

$$\frac{x-2}{2} = \frac{y-1}{1} = \frac{z}{3},$$

and pass through $(0, 0, 3)$.   (*Vikram, 1994*)

[**Ans.** $10x^2 + 13y^2 + 5z^2 - 4xy - 6yz - 12zx - 36x - 18y + 24z + 18 = 0$]

5. Find the equation of the right circular cylinder of radius 5 and having for its axis the line

$$\frac{1}{2}x = \frac{1}{3}y = \frac{1}{6}z.$$

(*Jabalpur, 1997; Jiwaji, 2000; Ravishankar, 1999*)

[**Ans.** $45x^2 + 40y^2 + 13z^2 - 12xy - 36yz - 24zx - 1225 = 0$]

6. Find the equation of the right circular cylinder whose axis is $x - 2 = z, y = 0$ and passes through the point $(3, 0, 0)$.   [**Ans.** $x^2 + 2y^2 + z^2 - 2zx - 4x + 2z + 3 = 0$]

7. Prove that the right circular cylinder whose one section is the circle

$$x^2 + y^2 + z^2 - x - y - z = 0, \; x + y + z = 1,$$

is $x^2 + y^2 + z^2 - yz - zx - xy = 1.$ (*Jiwaji, 1995*)

8. Find the right circular cylinder whose guiding curve is the circle through the three points $(a, 0, 0)$, $(0, b, 0)$ and $(0, 0, c)$. Find also the axis of the cylinder.

$$\left[\textbf{Ans. } (x^2 + y^2 + z^2 - ax - by - cz)(a^{-2} + b^{-2} + c^2)\right.$$

$$\left. = \left(\frac{x}{a} + \frac{y}{b} + \frac{z}{c} - 1\right)\left(\frac{x}{a} + \frac{y}{b} + \frac{z}{c} - 2\right); \; a\left(x - \frac{a}{2}\right) = b\left(y - \frac{b}{2}\right) = c\left(z - \frac{c}{2}\right)\right]$$

9. Find the right circular cylinder of radius 4 and axis the line $x = 2y = -z$. Also prove that the area of cross-section of the cylinder by the plane $z = 0$ is 24π.

[**Ans.** $5x^2 + 8y^2 + 5z^2 + 4yz + 8zx - 4xy - 144 = 0$]

OBJECTIVE QUESTIONS

I. Multiple Choice Questions

Note : *For each of the following questions, four alternatives are given for the answer. Only one of them is correct. Choose the correct alternative.*

1. Number of arbitrary constants in the equation of a cone is :

(*a*) 3   (*b*) 4   (*c*) 5   (*d*) 7.

2. General equation to the cone which passes through the axes is :

(*a*) $ax^2 + by^2 + cz^2 = 1$ (*b*) $ax^2 + by^2 + cz^2 = 0$

(*c*) $fyz + gzx + hxy = 1$ (*d*) $fyz + gzx + hxy = 0$.

(*Rohilkhand, 2003*)

3. A cone of second degree can be found to pass through ..... concurrent lines :

(*a*) 5   (*b*) 6   (*c*) 4   (*d*) 3.

(*Avadh, 2005*)

4. Equation of the cone whose vertex is the origin and base curve $z = k, f(x, y) = 0$ is :

(*a*) $f\left(\frac{xz}{k}, \frac{yz}{k}\right) = 0$ (*b*) $f\left(\frac{xk}{z}, \frac{yk}{z}\right) = 0$

(*c*) $f\left(\frac{3k}{x}, \frac{3k}{y}\right) = 0$ (*d*) None of these.

5. Equation $ax^2 + by^2 + cz^2 + 2ux + 2vy + 2wz + d = 0$ represents a cone if :

(a) $au^2 + bv^2 + cw^2 + d = 0$

(b) $\dfrac{u^2}{a} + \dfrac{v^2}{b} + \dfrac{w^2}{c} = d$

(c) $\dfrac{u^2}{a} + \dfrac{v^2}{b} + \dfrac{w^2}{c} = 0$

(d) None of these.

6. The equation $yz + zx + xy = 0$ represents :

(a) a pair of planes   (b) a sphere   (c) a cone   (d) a cylinder.

(Avadh, 2001)

7. Which one of the following cones does not have three mutually perpendicular generators ?

(a) $yz + zx + xy = 0$

(b) $x^2 + 2y^2 - 3z^2 = 0$

(c) $x^2 - 2y + 3z^2 = 0$

(d) $2x^2 + 3y^2 - 5z^2 + xy + yz + zx = 0.$

(Avadh, 2004)

8. A surface generated by a variable line passing through a fixed point and intersecting a given curve or touching a given surface. Such type of surface is called :

(a) cone   (b) cylinder   (c) sphere   (d) plane.

(Kanpur, 2002)

9. The condition that a cone $ax^2 + by^2 + cz^2 + 2fyz + 2gzx + 2hxy = 0$ may have three mutually perpendicular generators is :

(a) $ab + bc + ac = 0$ (b) $a + b + c = 1$ (c) $a + b + c = 0$ (d) $\dfrac{1}{a} + \dfrac{1}{b} + \dfrac{1}{c} = 0.$

(Avadh, 2001)

10. If a right circular cone has three mutually perpendicular generators then semi-vertical angle is :

(a) $\tan^{-1} \sqrt{2}$ (b) $\tan^{-1} 2$ (c) $\pi/4$ (d) $\pi/2.$

(Garhwal, 2002)

11. The locus of the lines through the vertex of a cone normal to the tangent planes is called :

(a) Right circular cone

(b) Enveloping cone

(c) Reciprocal cone

(d) None of these.

12. The condition that the cone $ax^2 + by^2 + cz^2 + 2fyz + 2gzx + 2hxy = 0$ will have three mutually perpendicular tangent planes is :

(a) $bc + ca + ab = 0$

(b) $f^2 + g^2 + h^2 = 0$

(c) $a + b + c = 0$

(d) $bc + ca + ab = f^2 + g^2 + h^2.$

13. If the vertex of the cone be at origin and the axis be z-axis, then equation to the cone, with semi-vertical angle, θ is :

(a) $x^2 + y^2 = z^2 \tan^2 \theta$

(b) $y^2 + z^2 = x^2 \tan^2 \theta$

(c) $(y^2 + z^2) \tan^2 \theta = x^2$

(d) $(x^2 + y^2) \tan^2 \theta = z^2.$

14. The equation of the enveloping cone can be written as :

(a) $S = T^2$ (b) $SS_1 = T^2$ (c) $T = S_1$ (d) None of these.

(Avadh, 2003; Rohilkhand, 2003)

15. Equation to the right circular cone whose vertex is at origin, the axis along x-axis and semi-vertical angle α, is :

(a) $x^2 + y^2 = z^2 \tan^2 \alpha$

(b) $y^2 + z^2 = x^2 \tan^2 \alpha$

(c) $y^2 \tan^2 \alpha$

(d) None of these.   *(Rohilkhand, 2003)*

16. If a right circular cone has three mutually perpendicular generators, then the semi-vertical angle will be :

(a) $\cot^{-1}(\sqrt{2})$ (b) $\tan^{-1}(\sqrt{2})$ (c) $\cos^{-1}(\sqrt{2})$ (d) $\sin^{-1}(\sqrt{2})$.

(*U.P.P.C.S., 2004; Garhwal, 2002*)

17. The line which generates the surface of the cylinder is called :

(a) generator   (b) axis   (c) guiding line   (d) None of these.

18. If the generators of the cylinder are parallel to z-axis, then equation of the cylinder is :

(a) $ax^2 + 2gzx + cz^2 + 2gx + 2hz + c = 0$ (b) $ax^2 + 2hxy + by^2 + 2gx + 2fy + c = 0$

(c) $y^2 + 2hyz + cz^2 + 2fy + 2gz + c = 0$ (d) None of these.

19. The locus of the lines drawn in a given direction or parallel to a given line so as to touch a given surface is called :

(a) General cylinder   (b) Right circular cylinder

(c) Enveloping cylinder   (d) None of these.

20. Guiding curve of a right circular cylinder is :

(a) ellipse   (b) circle

(c) pair of straight lines   (d) any closed curve.   (*Avadh, 2003*)

21. Equation of the right circular cylinder whose radius is 4 and axis the line $x = 2y = -z$ is :

(a) $5x^2 + 8y^2 + 5z^2 + 4yz + 8zx - 4xy - 144 = 0$

(b) $8x^2 + 5y^2 + 5z^2 + 4yz + 8zx - 4xy - 144 = 0$

(c) $5x^2 + 8y^2 - 5z^2 - 4yz - 8zx - 4xy - 144 = 0$

(d) $5x^2 + 8y^2 - 5z^2 + 8zx - 4xy = 0$.

ANSWERS

1. (c)	**2.** (d)	**3.** (a)	**4.** (b)	**5.** (b)	**6.** (c)	**7.** (c)
8. (a)	**9.** (c)	**10.** (a)	**11.** (c)	**12.** (d)	**13.** (a)	**14.** (b)
15. (b)	**16.** (b)	**17.** (a)	**18.** (b)	**19.** (c)	**20.** (b)	**21.** (a)

II. Fill in the Blanks

Note : *Fill in the blanks "......." so that the following statements are complete and correct.*

1. The equation of the cone with vertex at the origin is a ..... second degree equation in x, y and z.

2. The general equation of a cone of second degree which passes through the co-ordinate axis is ..... = 0.

3. Any straight line lying on the surface of cone is called its ....

4. All the generators of a cone pass through a fixed point called the ..... of the cone.

5. The equation of the cone with vertex at $(0, 0, 0)$ and whose base is the circle through the points $(a, 0, 0)$, $(0, b, 0)$ and $(0, 0, c)$ is ..... = 0.

6. The equation $ax^2 + by^2 + cz^2 + 2ux + 2vy + 2wz + d = 0$ represents a cone if ..... = d.

7. If the plane $ux + vy + wz = 0$ cuts the cone

$$f(x, y, z) \equiv ax^2 + by^2 + cz^2 + 2fyz + 2gzx + 2hxy = 0$$

in two perpendicular generators, then $f(u, v, w) = (a + b + c)$ (.....).

8. The equation of the cone with vertex at the origin and the direction cosines of its generators satisfying the relation $2l^2 + m^2 - 5n^2 = 0$ is ....

9. The tangent plane at any point of a cone passes through its ..... .

10. The reciprocal cone of a given cone is the locus of the ..... through the vertex to the tangent planes of the given cone.

11. The cone $ax^2 + by^2 + cz^2 + 2fyz + 2gzx + 2hxy = 0$ has three mutually perpendicular generators if $a + b + c = ...$.   (*Meerut, 2001*)

12. The cones $ax^2 + by^2 + cz^2 = 0$ and $(x^2/a) + (y^2/b) + (z^2/c) = 0$ are ..... to each other.

13. The equation of the right circular cone with vertex at $(0, 0, 0)$ and z-axis as its axis is ..... $= z^2 \tan^2 \theta$, where θ is the semi-vertical angle of the cone.

14. The equation $f(x, y) = 0$ represents a cylinder, whose generators are parallel to the axis of ..... .

15. The equation of a cone whose vertex is origin and which passes through the curve given by $ax^2 + by^2 = 2z$, $lx + my + nz = p$ is $ax^2 + by^2 = ...$.   (*Meerut, 2001*)

16. The equation of the enveloping cylinder of the sphere $x^2 + y^2 + z^2 = a^2$ and whose generators are parallel to the line $x/l = y/m = z/n$ is
$$(lx + my + nz)^2 = (l^2 + m^2 + n^2)\ (.....).$$ (*Meerut, 2001*)

17. Two cones which are such that each is the locus of the normals through the vertex to the tangent planes to the other are called ..... .

18. A cone may have three mutually perpendicular tangent planes if its reciprocal cone has three mutually perpendicular ..... .

19. The section of a right circular cone by a plane perpendicular to its axis is a ..... .

20. The equation of a right circular cone with vertex at the origin, axis the x-axis and semi-vertical angle θ is $y^2 + z^2 = ...$.

21. Any line on the surface of a cylinder is called its ..... .

22. The equation of the right circular cylinder of radius 4 whose axis is the y-axis is ..... .

23. The equation of the cylinder whose axis is z-axis and whose generators intersect the circle $x^2 + y^2 = a^2$, $z = 0$ is ..... .

24. The surface generated by the tangent lines to the sphere $x^2 + y^2 + z^2 = 25$ which are parallel to the given line $x/1 = y/2 = z/3$ is an enveloping ..... of the given sphere.

ANSWERS

1. homogeneous;   2. $fyz + gzx + hxy = 0$;   3. generator;   4. vertex;

5. $\Sigma\, a\, (b^2 + c^2)\, yz$;   6. $u^2/a + v^2/b + w^2/a$;   7. $u^2 + v^2 + w^2$;

8. $2x^2 + y^2 - 5z^2 = 0$;   9. vertex;   10. normals;   11. 0;

12. reciprocal;   13. $x^2 + y^2$;   14. z;

15. $2z\,(lx + my + nz)/p$;   16. $x^2 + y^2 + z^2 - a^2$;   17. reciprocal cones;   18. generators;

19. circle;   20. $x^2 \tan^2 \theta$;   21. generator;   22. $x^2 + z^2 = 16$;

23. $x^2 + y^2 = a^2$;   24. cylinder.

III. True / False Statements

Note : *Write 'T' for true and 'F' for false statements.*

1. Every homogeneous equation of second degree in x, y and z either represents a cone with its vertex at the origin or pair of planes passing through the origin.

2. The general equation of a cone of second degree which passes through its co-ordinate axes is $ax^2 + by^2 + cz^2 = 0$.

3. The equation to the cone which has vertex at the origin and passes through the curve given by $ax^2 + by^2 = 2z$, $lx + my + nz = p$ is $p (ax^2 + by^2) = 2z (lx + my + nz)$.

4. The equation $ax^2 + by^2 + cz^2 + 2fyz + 2gzx + 2hxy = 0$ always represents a cone with its vertex at the origin.

5. The straight line $\dfrac{x}{1} = \dfrac{y}{-2} = \dfrac{z}{3}$ is a generator of the cone $x^2 + 2y^2 - z^2 = 0$.

6. The equation $3yz - 4zx + 5xy = 0$ represents a cone passing through each of the three co-ordinate axes.

7. The cone $x^2 - y^2 + 2z^2 = 0$ has three mutually perpendicular generators.

8. The cone $5yz - 8zx - 3xy = 0$ has three mutually perpendicular generators.

9. The semi-vertical angle of a right circular cone which has three mutually perpendicular generators is constant.

10. The plane $ux + vy + wz = 0$ cuts the cone
$$f(x, y, z) \equiv ax^2 + by^2 + cz^2 + 2fyz + 2gzx + 2hxy = 0$$
in two perpendicular generators, then
$$f(u, v, w) = (a + b + c) (u^2 + v^2 + w^2).$$

11. The angle between the lines in which the plane $x + y + z = 0$ cuts the cone
$$ayz + bzx + cxy = 0$$
will be $\pi/2$ if $a + b + c = 0$.

12. The general equation to a cone which touches the co-ordinate planes is
$$a^2x^2 + b^2y^2 + c^2z^2 = 2bcyz + 2cazx + 2abxy.$$

13. The enveloping cylinder of the conicoid $ax^2 + by^2 + cz^2 = 1$ with generators perpendicular to x-axis meets the plane $z = 0$ in ellipses.

14. All the generators of a cylinder are parallel straight lines.

15. All the generators of a cylinder meet at a point.

16. If all the generators of a cylinder intersect a curve then curve is called the guiding curve of the cylinder.

ANSWERS

1. T	**2.** F	**3.** T	**4.** F	**5.** T	**6.** T	**7.** F	**8.** T
9. T	**10.** F	**11.** T	**12.** T	**13.** T	**14.** T	**15.** F	**16.** T

8

The Conicoid

8.1. THE GENERAL EQUATION OF THE SECOND DEGREE

The locus of the general equation

$$ax^2 + by^2 + cz^2 + 2fyz + 2gzx + 2hxy + 2ux + 2vy + 2wz + d = 0,$$

of the second degree in x, y, z is called a Conicoid or Quadric.

It is easy to show that every straight line meets a surface whose equation is of the second degree in two points and consequently every plane section of such a surface is a conic. This property justifies the name "Conicoid" as applied to such a surface.

The general equation of second degree contains *nine* effective constants and, therefore, a conicoid can be determined to satisfy nine conditions each of which gives rise to one relation between the constants, *e.g.*, a conicoid can be determined so as to pass through *nine* given points no four of which are coplanar.

The general equation of the second degree can, by transformation of co-ordinate axes, be reduced to any one of the following forms; the actual reduction being given in Chapter 11. (The name of the particular surface which is the locus of the equation is written along with it).

1. $x^2/a^2 + y^2/b^2 + z^2/c^2 = 1$, Ellipsoid.
2. $x^2/a^2 + y^2/b^2 + z^2/c^2 = -1$, Imaginary ellipsoid.
3. $x^2/a^2 + y^2/b^2 - z^2/c^2 = 1$, Hyperboloid of one sheet.
4. $x^2/a^2 - y^2/b^2 - z^2/c^2 = 1$, Hyperboloid of two sheets.
5. $x^2/a^2 + y^2/b^2 + z^2/c^2 = 0$, Imaginary cone.
6. $x^2/a^2 + y^2/b^2 - z^2/c^2 = 0$, Cone.
7. $x^2/a^2 + y^2/b^2 = 2z/c$, Elliptic paraboloid.
8. $x^2/a^2 - y^2/b^2 = 2z/c$, Hyperbolic paraboloid.
9. $x^2/a^2 + y^2/b^2 = 1$, Elliptic cylinder.
10. $x^2/a^2 - y^2/b^2 = 1$, Hyperbolic cylinder.
11. $x^2/a^2 + y^2/b^2 = -1$, Imaginary cylinder.
12. $x^2/a^2 - y^2/b^2 = 0$, Pair of intersecting planes.
13. $x^2/a^2 + y^2/b^2 = 0$, Pair of imaginary planes.
14. $y^2 = 4ax$, Parabolic cylinder.
15. $y^2 = a^2$, Two real parallel planes.
16. $y^2 = -a^2$, Two imaginary planes.
17. $y^2 = 0$, Two coincident planes.

The equations representing cones and cylinders have already been considered and the reader is familiar with the nature of the surfaces represented by them.

In this chapter we propose to discuss the nature and some of the important geometrical properties of the surfaces represented by the equation, 1, 2, 3, 4, 7, 8.

8.2. SHAPES OF SOME SURFACES

8.2.1. The Ellipsoid $\dfrac{x^2}{a^2}+\dfrac{y^2}{b^2}+\dfrac{z^2}{c^2}=1$

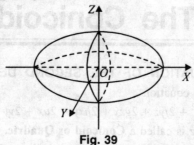

Fig. 39

The *following facts* enable us to have an idea of the shape of the surface represented by this equation

$$\frac{x^2}{a^2}+\frac{y^2}{b^2}+\frac{z^2}{c^2}=1.$$

(*i*) We have

(x, y, z) satisfies the equation $\Leftrightarrow$ $(-x, -y, -z)$ satisfies the equation.

The points (x, y, z), $(-x, -y, -z)$ lying on a straight line through the origin and equidistant from the origin, it follows that the origin bisects every chord which passes through it and is, on this account, called the *Centre* of the surface.

(*ii*) We have

(x, y, z) satisfies the equation $\Leftrightarrow$ $(x, y, -z)$ satisfies the equation.

The line joining the points (x, y, z), $(x, y, -z)$ is bisected at right angle by the *XOY* plane. It follows that the *XOY* plane bisects every chord perpendicular to it and the surface is symmetrical with respect to this plane.

Similarly the surface is symmetrical with respect to the *YOZ* and the *ZOX* planes.

These three planes are called **principal planes** in as much as they bisect all chords perpendicular to them. The three lines of intersection of the three principal planes taken in pairs are called **principal axes.** Co-ordinate axes are the principal axes in the present case.

(*iii*) x cannot take a value which is numerically greater than a, for otherwise y^2 or z^2 would be negative. Thus, we have $-a \le x \le a$ for every point (x, y, z) on the surface. Similarly y and z cannot be numerically greater than b and c respectively so that we have for every point (x, y, z) on the surface

$$-a \le x \le a, -b \le y \le b, -c \le z \le c$$

Hence, the surface lies between the planes

$$x = a, x = -a; y = b, y = -b; z = c, z = -c$$

and so is a *closed* surface.

(*iv*) The *X*-axis meets the surface in the two points $(a, 0, 0)$ and $(-a, 0, 0)$, so that the surface intercepts a length $2a$ on *X*-axis. Similarly the lengths intercepted on the *Y*-axis and *Z*-axis are $2b$ and $2c$ respectively.

The lengths $2a, 2b, 2c$ intercepted on the principal axes are called the lengths of the axes of the ellipsoid.

(v) The sections of the surface by the planes $z = k$ which are parallel to the XOY plane are similar ellipses having equations

$$\frac{x^2}{a^2} + \frac{y^2}{b^2} = 1 - \frac{k^2}{c^2}, \ z = k; \ -c \leq k \leq c. \qquad \ldots(1)$$

These ellipses have their centres on the Z-axis and diminish in size as k varies from 0 to c. The ellipsoid may, therefore, be generated by the variable ellipse (1) as k varies from $-c$ to c.

It may similarly be shown that the sections by planes parallel to the other co-ordinate planes are also ellipses and the ellipsoid may be supposed to be generated by them.

8.2.2. The Hyperboloid of One Sheet $\dfrac{x^2}{a^2} + \dfrac{y^2}{b^2} - \dfrac{z^2}{c^2} = 1$. (Kumaon, 1999)

(i) The origin bisects all chords through it and is, therefore, the centre of the surface.

(ii) The co-ordinate planes bisect all chords perpendicular to them and are, therefore, the planes of symmetry or the **principal planes** of the surface. The co-ordinate axes are its **principal axes.**

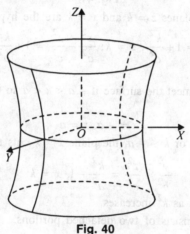

Fig. 40

(iii) The X-axis meets the surface in the points $(a, 0, 0)$, $(-a, 0, 0)$ so that the surface intercepts length $2a$ on X-axis. Similarly the length intercepted on Y-axis is $2b$. The Z-axis does not meet the surface.

The sections by the planes $z = k$ which are parallel to the XOY plane are the similar ellipses

$$\frac{x^2}{a^2} + \frac{y^2}{b^2} = 1 + \frac{k^2}{c^2}, \ z = k \qquad \ldots(1)$$

whose centres lie on Z-axis and which increase in size as k increases. There is no limit to the increase of k. The surface may, therefore, be generated by the variable ellipse (1) where k varies from $-\infty$ to $+\infty$.

Again, the sections by the planes $x = k$ and $y = k$ are hyperbolas

$$\frac{y^2}{b^2} - \frac{z^2}{c^2} = 1 - \frac{k^2}{a^2}, \ x = k; \quad \frac{x^2}{a^2} - \frac{z^2}{c^2} = 1 - \frac{k^2}{b^2}, \ y = k$$

respectively.

Ex. Trace the surfaces

(i) $\dfrac{x^2}{a^2} + \dfrac{y^2}{b^2} + \dfrac{z^2}{c^2} = 1.$ \qquad (ii) $-\dfrac{x^2}{a^2} + \dfrac{y^2}{b^2} + \dfrac{z^2}{c^2} = 1.$

8.2.3. The Hyperboloid of Two Sheets $\dfrac{x^2}{a^2} - \dfrac{y^2}{b^2} - \dfrac{z^2}{c^2} = 1.$

(*i*) Origin is the **centre**; co-ordinate planes are the **principal planes**; and co-ordinate axes the **principal axes** of the surface.

(*ii*) X-axis meets the surface in the points $(a, 0, 0)$ and $(- a, 0, 0)$ whereas the Y and Z-axis do not meet the surface.

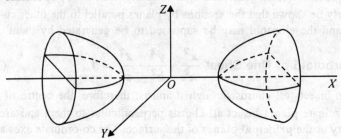

Fig. 41

(*iii*) The sections by the planes $z = k$ and $y = k$ are the hyperbolas

$$\frac{x^2}{a^2} - \frac{y^2}{b^2} = 1 + \frac{k^2}{c^2}, \; z = k; \quad \frac{x^2}{a^2} - \frac{z^2}{c^2} = 1 + \frac{k^2}{b^2}, \; y = k$$

respectively.

The plane $x = k$ does not meet the surface if $- a < k < a$ so that there is no portion of the surface between the planes

$$x = - a, \; x = a$$

when $k^2 > a^2$ i.e., when $k \geq a$ or $k \leq - a$, the plane $x = k$ cuts the surface in the ellipse

$$\frac{y^2}{b^2} + \frac{z^2}{c^2} = \frac{k^2}{a^2} - 1, \; x = k.$$

These ellipses increase in size as k^2 increases.

The surface, therefore, consists of two detached portions.

Ex. Trace the surfaces

$$(i) \; - \frac{x^2}{a^2} + \frac{y^2}{b^2} - \frac{z^2}{c^2} = 1. \qquad\qquad (ii) \; - \frac{x^2}{a^2} - \frac{y^2}{b^2} + \frac{z^2}{c^2} = 1.$$

8.2.4. Central Conicoids   (*Kumaon, 1997, 98, 2003; Rohilkhand, 2001*)

The equations considered above are of the form

$$ax^2 + by^2 + cz^2 = 1. \qquad\qquad ...(1)$$

If a, b, c are all positive, the surface is an ellipsoid; if two are positive and one negative, hyperboloid of one sheet, and finally if two are negative and one positive, hyperboloid of two sheets.

No point (x, y, z) satisfies the equation

$$ax^2 + by^2 + cz^2 = 1$$

if a, b, c are all negative.

All *these surfaces have a centre and three principal planes* and are as such known as *central conicoids*.

On the basis of the preceding discussion, the reader would do well to give precise definitions of

(*i*) *Centre* (*ii*) *Principal planes* (*iii*) *Principal axes* of a central conicoid.

In what follows, we shall consider the equation (1) and the geometrical results deducible from it will, therefore, hold in the case of all central conicoids.

Ex. Show that the surface represented by the equation

$$ax^2 + by^2 + cz^2 + 2fyz + 2gzx + 2hxy = d$$

is a central conicoid; origin being the centre.

Note. Cone is also a central conicoid, vertex being its centre; this fact is clear from the general equation of a cone with its vertex at the origin.

8.3. INTERSECTION OF A LINE WITH A CONICOID

To find the points of intersection of the line

$$\frac{x - \alpha}{l} = \frac{y - \beta}{m} = \frac{z - \gamma}{n} \qquad \qquad ...(i)$$

with the central conicoid

$$ax^2 + by^2 + cz^2 = l \qquad \qquad ...(ii)$$

A point

$$(lr + \alpha, \ mr + \beta, \ nr + \gamma)$$

on the line (*i*) shall also lie on the surface (*ii*), if and only if,

$$a \ (lz + \alpha)^2 + b \ (mr + \beta)^2 + c \ (nr + \gamma)^2 = 1$$

$$\Leftrightarrow \quad r^2 \ (a^2 + bm^2 + cn^2) + 2r \ (al\alpha + bm\beta + cn\gamma) + (a\alpha^2 + b\beta^2 + c\gamma^2 - 1) = 0 \qquad ...(A)$$

Let r_1, r_2 be the two roots of (A), which we suppose to be real. Then

$$(lr_1 + \alpha, \ mr_1 + \beta, \ nr_1 + \gamma), \ (lr_2 + \alpha, \ mr_2 + \beta, \ nr_2 + \gamma)$$

are the two points of intersection.

Hence, *every line meets a central conicoid in two points.*

We also see that *a plane section of a central conicoid is a conic for every line in the plane meets the curve of intersection in two points only.*

The two values r_1 and r_2 of r obtained from equation (A) are the measures of the distances of the points of intersection P and Q from the point (α, β, γ) if (l, m, n) are the direction cosines of the line.

Note. The equation (A) of this article will frequently be used in what follows.

Ex. 1. Find the points of intersection of the line

$$-\frac{1}{3}(x + 5) = (y - 4) = \frac{1}{7}(z - 11)$$

with the conicoid

$$12x^2 - 17y^2 + 7z^2 = 7. \qquad \qquad \textbf{[Ans. (1, 2, -3), (-2, 3, 4)]}$$

Ex. 2. Prove that the sum of the squares of the reciprocals of any three mutually perpendicular semi-diameters of a central conicoid is constant.

Ex. 3. Any three mutually orthogonal lines drawn through a fixed point C meets the quadric

$$ax^2 + by^2 + cz^2 = 1$$

in points P_1, P_2; Q_1, Q_2; R_1, R_2 respectively; prove that

$$\frac{P_1P_2{}^2}{CP_1{}^2 \cdot CP_2{}^2} + \frac{Q_1Q_2{}^2}{CQ_1{}^2 \cdot CQ_2{}^2} + \frac{R_1R_2{}^2}{CR_1{}^2 \cdot CR_2{}^2} \quad \text{and} \quad \frac{1}{CP_1 \cdot CP_2} + \frac{1}{CQ_1 \cdot CQ_2} + \frac{1}{CR_1 \cdot CR_2}$$

are constants.

8.3.1. Tangent Lines and Tangent Plane at a Point

(*Garhwal, 2002; Kumaon, 1996, 97, 2000, 02, 03, 06; Rohilkhand, 1997*)

Let

$$\frac{x-\alpha}{l} = \frac{y-\beta}{m} = \frac{z-\gamma}{n} \qquad \qquad ...(i)$$

be a line through the point (α, β, γ) of the surface

$$ax^2 + by^2 + cz^2 = 1 \qquad \qquad ...(ii)$$

Thus, we have

$$a\alpha^2 + b\beta^2 + c\gamma^2 = 1 \qquad \qquad ...(iii)$$

One root of the equation (A) in § 8.3 is, therefore, zero.

The line (*i*) will touch the conicoid (*ii*) at the point (α, β, γ) if both the values of r given by the equation (A) in § 8.3 are zero.

The second value will also be zero, if

$$al\alpha + bm\beta + cn\gamma = 0 \qquad \qquad ...(iv)$$

which is thus the condition for the line (*i*) to be a tangent line to the surface (*ii*) at (α, β, γ).

The locus of the tangent line to the surface, at (α, β, γ) obtained by eliminating l, m, n between (*i*) and (*ii*), is

$$a\alpha(x-\alpha) + b\beta(y-\beta) + c\gamma(z-\gamma) = 0$$

$$\Rightarrow \qquad a\alpha x + b\beta y + c\gamma z = a\alpha^2 + b\beta^2 + c\gamma^2 = 1$$

which is a plane.

Hence, the tangent lines to the surface (*ii*) at the point (α, β, γ) lie in the plane

$$a\alpha x + b\beta y + c\gamma z = 1$$

which is, therefore, the *tangent plane* at (α, β, γ) to the conicoid

$$ax^2 + by^2 + cz^2 = 1.$$

Note. A tangent line at any point is a line which meets the surface in two coincident points and the tangent plane at a point is the locus of tangent lines at the point.

8.3.2. Condition of Tangency

(*Ajmer, 1994, 98; Agra, 1996, 98; Garhwal, 2004; Kumaon, 1995, 99, 2001, 04; Rohilkhand, 1996, 2000, 01; Poorvanchal, 2004*)

To find the condition that the plane

$$lx + my + nz = p, \qquad \qquad ...(i)$$

should touch the central conicoid

$$ax^2 + by^2 + cz^2 = 1 \qquad \qquad ...(ii)$$

If (α, β, γ) be the point of contact, the tangent plane

$$a\alpha x + b\beta y + c\gamma z = 1 \qquad \qquad ...(iii)$$

thereat should be the same as the plane (*i*).

Comparing the two equations (*i*) and (*iii*), we get

$$\alpha = \frac{l}{ap}, \beta = \frac{m}{bp}, \gamma = \frac{n}{cp}.$$

and since

$$a\alpha^2 + b\beta^2 + c\gamma^2 = 1$$

we obtain the required condition

$$\frac{l^2}{a} + \frac{m^2}{b} + \frac{n^2}{c} = p^2.$$

Also the point of contact then, is,

$$\left(\frac{l}{ap}, \frac{m}{bp}, \frac{n}{cp} \right)$$

Thus, we deduce that the planes

$$lx + my + nz = \pm \sqrt{l^2/a + m^2/b + n^2/c}$$

touch the conicoid (ii) for all values of l, m, n.

Cor. There are two tangent planes to a central conicoid parallel to a given plane.

8.3.3. Director Sphere

To show that the locus of the point of intersection of three mutually perpendicular tangent planes to a central conicoid is a sphere concentric with the conicoid.

(Avadh, 1995, 97; Garhwal, 1996, 98, 2003; Gorakhpur, 1996; Kumaon, 2001; Poorvanchal, 1995, 98; Rohilkhand, 2000, 01, 03)

Let

$$l_1 x + m_1 y + n_1 z = \left(\frac{l_1^2}{a} + \frac{m_1^2}{b} + \frac{n_1^2}{c} \right)^{1/2} \qquad \ldots (i)$$

$$l_2 x + m_2 y + n_2 z = \left(\frac{l_2^2}{a} + \frac{m_2^2}{b} + \frac{n_2^2}{c} \right)^{1/2} \qquad \ldots (ii)$$

$$l_3 x + m_3 y + n_3 z = \left(\frac{l_3^2}{a} + \frac{m_3^2}{b} + \frac{n_3^2}{c} \right)^{1/2} \qquad \ldots (iii)$$

be three mutually perpendicular tangent planes so that

$$\Sigma l_1 m_1 = \Sigma m_1 n_1 = \Sigma n_1 l_1 = 0$$
$$\Sigma l_1^2 = \Sigma m_1^2 = \Sigma n_1^2 = 1 \qquad \ldots (iv)$$

The co-ordinates of the point of intersection satisfy the three equations and its locus is, therefore, obtained by the elimination of $l_1, m_1, n_1; l_2, m_2, n_2; l_3, m_3, n_3$.

This is easily done by squaring and adding the three equations and using the relations (iv), so that we obtain

$$x^2 + y^2 + z^2 = 1/a + 1/b + 1/c$$

as the required locus which is a concentric sphere called the *Director sphere* of the given quadric. Its centre is the same as that of the central conicoid.

EXAMPLES

1. *Find the equations to the tangent planes to*
$$7x^2 - 3y^2 - z^2 + 21 = 0,$$
which pass through the line
$$7x - 6y + 9 = 0, z = 3.$$

Sol. Any plane
$$7x - 6y + 9 + k(z - 3) = 0 \iff 7x - 6y + kz = 3k - 9,$$
through the given line will touch the given surface.

$$7x^2 - 3y^2 - z^2 + 21 = 0 \iff -\frac{1}{3}x^2 + \frac{1}{7}y^2 + \frac{1}{21}z^2 = 1$$

if and only if $\quad \dfrac{7^2}{-1/3} + \dfrac{(-6)^2}{-1/7} + \dfrac{k^2}{-1/21} = (3k-9)^2 \iff 2k^2 + 9k + 4 = 0.$

This gives

$$k = -4, -\frac{1}{2}.$$

Therefore, the required planes are

$$7x - 6y - 4z + 21 = 0, \ 7x - 6y - \frac{1}{2}z + \frac{21}{2} = 0.$$

2. *Obtain the tangent planes to the ellipsoid*
$$x^2/a^2 + y^2/b^2 + z^2/c^2 = 1,$$
which are parallel to the plane
$$lx + my + nz = 0. \qquad\qquad (Garhwal, 1998; Agra, 1996)$$
If 2r is the distance between two parallel tangent planes to the ellipsoid, prove that the line through the origin and perpendicular to the planes lies on the cone
$$x^2 (a^2 - r^2) + y^2 (b^2 - r^2) + z^2 (c^2 - r^2) = 0.$$

Sol. The two tangent planes parallel to the plane $\Sigma \, lx = 0$, are

$$\Sigma \, lx = \pm \sqrt{\Sigma a^2 l^2} \qquad\qquad\qquad ...(1)$$

The distance between these parallel planes which is twice the distance of either from the origin is

$$2\sqrt{\Sigma a^2 l^2} / \sqrt{\Sigma l^2}$$

Thus, we have

$$\frac{2\sqrt{\Sigma a^2 l^2}}{\sqrt{\Sigma l^2}} = 2r \ \Rightarrow \ \Sigma(a^2 - r^2) \, l^2 = 0$$

Hence, the locus of the line

$$x/l = y/m = z/n$$

which is perpendicular to the plane (1), is

$$\Sigma \, (a^2 - r^2) \, x^2 = 0.$$

3. *Tangent planes are drawn to the conicoid* $ax^2 + by^2 + cz^2 = 1$ *through* (α, β, γ)*. Show that the perpendiculars from the centre of the conicoid to these planes generate the cone*
$$(\alpha x + \beta y + \gamma z)^2 = x^2/a + y^2/b + z^2/c.$$
$$(Garhwal, 1996; Poorvanchal, 1995, 98; Gorakhpur, 2000)$$

Sol. Any plane through (α, β, γ) is

$$l \, (x - \alpha) + m \, (y - \beta) + n \, (z - \gamma) = 0$$

or $\qquad\qquad\qquad lx + my + nz = l\alpha + m\beta + n\gamma \qquad\qquad ...(i)$

If it is a tangent plane to the given conicoid, then

$$l^2/a + m^2/b + n^2/c = (l\alpha + m\beta + n\gamma)^2 \qquad\qquad ...(ii)$$

Also, the equation of the line through the centre of the conicoid perpendicular to (i) is

$$x/l = y/m = z/n$$

Its locus will be [by eqn. (ii)]

$$\frac{x^2}{a} + \frac{y^2}{b} + \frac{z^2}{c} = (\alpha x + \beta y + \gamma z)^2.$$

4. *A tangent plane to the conicoid* $ax^2 + by^2 + cz^2 = 1$, *meets the co-ordinate axes in P, Q and R. Find the locus of the centroid of the triangle PQR.* (Avadh, 1998, 2003; Ajmer, 1996; Garhwal, 1998; Gorakhpur, 1997; Poorvanchal, 1999)

Sol. Any tangent plane to the given conicoid is

$$lx + my + nz = \sqrt{l^2/a + m^2/b + n^2/c} \qquad \qquad ...(i)$$

Hence,

$$P \equiv \left[\frac{1}{l} \sqrt{l^2/a + m^2/b + n^2/c}, \ 0, \ 0 \right]$$

$$Q \equiv \left[0, \ \frac{1}{m} \sqrt{l^2/a + m^2/b + n^2/c}, \ 0 \right]$$

$$R \equiv \left[0, \ 0, \ \frac{1}{n} \sqrt{l^2/a + m^2/b + n^2/c} \right]$$

If (x_1, y_1, z_1) be the centroid of $\triangle PQR$, then

$$x_1 = \frac{1}{3l} \sqrt{l^2/a + m^2/b + n^2/c}, \quad y_1 = \frac{1}{3m} \sqrt{l^2/a + m^2/b + n^2/c}$$

and

$$z_1 = \frac{1}{3n} \sqrt{l^2/a + m^2/b + n^2/c}$$

$$(3lx_1)^2 = \frac{l^2}{a} + \frac{m^2}{b} + \frac{n^2}{c} = (3my_1)^2 = (3nz_1)^2$$

or

$$\frac{9l^2}{a} + \frac{9m^2}{b} + \frac{9n^2}{c} = \left(\frac{l^2}{a} + \frac{m^2}{b} + \frac{n^2}{c} \right) \left(\frac{1}{ax_1^2} + \frac{1}{by_1^2} + \frac{1}{cz_1^2} \right)$$

$$\Rightarrow \quad \frac{1}{ax_1^2} + \frac{1}{by_1^2} + \frac{1}{cz_1^2} = 9$$

Hence, required locus is

$$\frac{1}{ax^2} + \frac{1}{by^2} + \frac{1}{cz^2} = 9.$$

5. *If P be the point of contact of a tangent plane ABC to the ellipsoid* $x^2/a^2 + y^2/b^2 + z^2/c^2 = 1$ *and PD, PE, PF are perpendiculars from P on the axes. Prove that* $OD \cdot OA = a^2$, $OE \cdot OB = b^2$, $OF \cdot OC = c^2$; *A, B, C being the points where the tangent plane at P meets the co-ordinate axes.*

Sol. Let P be (α, β, γ). The tangent plane ABC will be

$$\frac{\alpha x}{a^2} + \frac{\beta y}{b^2} + \frac{\gamma z}{c^2} = 1 \qquad \qquad ...(i)$$

$$\Rightarrow \qquad OA = \frac{a^2}{\alpha}, \quad OB = \frac{b^2}{\beta} \quad \text{and} \quad OC = \frac{c^2}{\gamma}.$$

Also PD, PE, PF are perpendiculars from P on the axes

$$\therefore \qquad OD = \alpha, \quad OE = \beta, \quad \text{and} \quad OF = \gamma.$$

Hence,

$$OD \cdot OA = \alpha \cdot \frac{a^2}{\alpha} = a^2, \text{ etc.}$$

6. *If the line of intersection of two perpendicular tangent planes to the ellipsoid whose equation, referred to rectangular axes, is*

$$x^2/a^2 + y^2/b^2 + z^2/c^2 = 1,$$

passes through the fixed point $(0, 0, k)$, *show that it lies on the cone*

$$x^2 (b^2 + c^2 - k^2) + y^2 (c^2 + a^2 - k^2) + (z - k)^2 (a^2 + b^2) = 0.$$

(Gorakhpur, 2001)

Sol. Equation of any plane through $(0, 0, k)$ is

$$lx + my + nz = nk \qquad \qquad ...(i)$$

If it touches the given ellipsoid, then

$$a^2l^2 + b^2m^2 + c^2n^2 = n^2k^2 \qquad \qquad ...(ii)$$

Any line through $(0, 0, k)$ is

$$x/\lambda = y/\mu = (z - k)/\nu \qquad \qquad ...(iii)$$

The plane (i) will contain (iii), if

$$l\lambda + m\mu + n\nu = 0 \qquad \qquad ...(iv)$$

Eliminating l between (ii) and (iv), we get

$$a^2 \left(-\frac{m\mu + n\nu}{\lambda}\right)^2 + b^2m^2 + c^2n^2 - n^2k^2 = 0$$

or $\qquad (a^2\mu^2 + b^2\lambda^2)\left(\dfrac{m}{n}\right)^2 + 2a^2\mu\nu\left(\dfrac{m}{n}\right) + (a^2\nu^2 + c^2\lambda^2 - k^2\lambda^2) = 0$

Let its two roots be $\dfrac{m_1}{n_1}, \dfrac{m_2}{n_2}$.

$$\therefore \qquad \frac{m_1}{n_1} \cdot \frac{m_2}{n_2} = \frac{a^2\nu^2 + c^2\lambda^2 - k^2\lambda^2}{a^2\mu^2 + b^2\lambda^2}$$

or $\qquad \dfrac{m_1 m_2}{a^2\nu^2 + c^2\lambda^2 - k^2\lambda^2} = \dfrac{n_1 n_2}{a^2\mu^2 + b^2\lambda^2}$

Similarly eliminating m, we get

$$\frac{l_1 l_2}{b^2\nu^2 + c^2\mu^2 - k^2\mu^2} = \frac{n_1 n_2}{a^2\mu^2 + b^2\lambda^2}$$

$$\therefore \qquad \frac{l_1 l_2}{b^2\nu^2 + c^2\mu^2 - k^2\mu^2} = \frac{m_1 m_2}{a^2\nu^2 + c^2\lambda^2 - k^2\lambda^2}$$

$$= \frac{n_1 n_2}{a^2\mu^2 + b^2\lambda^2} = \frac{l_1 l_2 + m_1 m_2 + n_1 n_2}{(b^2 + c^2 - k^2)\lambda^2}$$

$$+ (c^2 + a^2 - k^2)\mu^2 + (a^2 + b^2)\nu$$

Since the planes are perpendicular to each other, hence

$$(b^2 + c^2 - k^2)\lambda^2 + (c^2 + a^2 - k^2)\mu^2 + (a^2 + b^2)\nu^2 = 0$$

Hence, the locus of (iii) is

$$(b^2 + c^2 - k^2)x^2 + (c^2 + a^2 - k^2)y^2 + (a^2 + b^2)(z - k)^2 = 0.$$

7. *Prove that the equation of two tangent planes to the conicoid $ax^2 + by^2 + cz^2 = 1$ which pass through the line*

$$u \equiv lx + my + nz - p = 0, \ u' \equiv l'x + m'y + n'z - p' = 0$$

is

$$u^2 \left(l'^2/a + m'^2/b + n'^2/c - p'^2 \right) - 2uu' \left(ll'/a + mm'/b + nn'/c - pp' \right)$$
$$+ u'^2 \left(l^2/a + m^2/b + n^2/c - p^2 \right) = 0. \qquad \text{(Rohilkhand, 1998)}$$

Sol. Equation of any plane through the given line is

$$u + \lambda u' = 0$$

or

$$(l + \lambda l') x + (m + \lambda m') y + (n + \lambda n') z - (p + \lambda p') = 0.$$

It touches the given conicoid, hence

$$\frac{(l + \lambda l')^2}{a} + \frac{(m + \lambda m')^2}{b} + \frac{(n + \lambda n')^2}{c} = (p + \lambda p')^2$$

or

$$\lambda^2 \left(l'^2/a + m'^2/b + n'^2/c - p'^2 \right) + 2\lambda \left(ll'/a + mm'/b + nn'/c - pp' \right)$$
$$+ \left(l^2/a + m^2/b + n^2/c - p^2 \right) = 0$$

If λ_1 and λ_2 be two values of λ; then

$$\lambda_1 + \lambda_2 = -\frac{2 \left(ll'/a + mm'/b + nn'/c - pp' \right)}{\left(l'^2/a + m'^2/b + n'^2/c - p'^2 \right)}$$

and

$$\lambda_1 \lambda_2 = -\frac{\left(l^2/a + m^2/b + n^2/c - p^2 \right)}{\left(l'^2/a + m'^2/b + n'^2/c - p'^2 \right)}$$

Combined equation of two planes will be

$$(u + \lambda_1 u') (u + \lambda_2 u') = 0$$

or

$$u^2 + (\lambda_1 + \lambda_2) uu' + \lambda_1 \lambda_2 u'^2 = 0, \text{ etc.}$$

8. *The tangent planes to an ellipsoid at the points P_1, P_2, P_3, P_4 form a tetrahedron A_1, A_2, A_3, A_4 where A_1 is the vertex which is not on the tangent plane at P_1. Prove that the planes*

$$A_1 A_2 P_2, \ A_1 A_3 P_3, \ A_3 A_4 P_4$$

have a line in common.

Sol. The tangent planes at points

$$P_1 (x_1, y_1, z_1), \ P_2 (x_2, y_2, z_2), \ P_3 (x_3, y_3, z_3), \ P_4 (x_4, y_4, z_4)$$

to the ellipsoid

$$\frac{x^2}{a^2} + \frac{y^2}{b^2} + \frac{z^2}{c^2} = 1$$

are

(i) $\dfrac{xx_1}{a^2} + \dfrac{yy_1}{b^2} + \dfrac{zz_1}{c^2} = 1,$ (ii) $\dfrac{xx_2}{a^2} + \dfrac{yy_2}{b^2} + \dfrac{zz_2}{c^2} = 1,$

(iii) $\dfrac{xx_3}{a^2} + \dfrac{yy_3}{b^2} + \dfrac{zz_3}{c^2} = 1,$ (iv) $\dfrac{xx_4}{a^2} + \dfrac{yy_4}{b^2} + \dfrac{zz_4}{c^2} = 1,$

respectively. Then point A_1 is the intersection of the planes *(ii)*, *(iii)*, *(iv)* and A_2 is the intersection of the planes *(i)*, *(iii)* and *(iv)*.

Thus, the line $A_1 A_2$ is the line of intersection of the planes *(iii)* and *(iv)*. Also P_2 is (x_2, y_2, z_2). We may now easily show that the equation of the plane $A_1 A_2 P_2$ is

$$\left(\sum \frac{xx_3}{a^2} - 1 \right) \left(\sum \frac{x_2 x_4}{a^2} - 1 \right) = \left(\sum \frac{xx_4}{a^2} - 1 \right) \left(\sum \frac{x_2 x_3}{a^2} - 1 \right)$$

Similarly the two planes $A_1A_3P_3$ and $A_1A_4P_4$ are

$$\left(\sum \frac{xx_2}{a^2} - 1 \right)\left(\sum \frac{x_3x_4}{a^2} - 1 \right) = \left(\sum \frac{xx_4}{a^2} - 1 \right)\left(\sum \frac{x_3x_2}{a^2} - 1 \right)$$

$$\left(\sum \frac{xx_2}{a^2} - 1 \right)\left(\sum \frac{x_4x_3}{a^2} - 1 \right) = \left(\sum \frac{xx_3}{a^2} - 1 \right)\left(\sum \frac{x_4x_2}{a^2} - 1 \right)$$

From these it follows that these three planes all pass through the line

$$\left(\sum \frac{xx_3}{a^2} - 1 \right)\left(\sum \frac{x_2x_4}{a^2} - 1 \right) = \left(\sum \frac{xx_4}{a^2} - 1 \right)\left(\sum \frac{x_2x_3}{a^2} - 1 \right)$$

$$= \left(\sum \frac{xx_2}{a^2} - 1 \right)\left(\sum \frac{x_3x_4}{a^2} - 1 \right).$$

Hence, the result.

EXERCISES

1. Show that the tangent planes at the extremities of any diameter of a central conicoid are parallel.

2. Show that the plane $3x + 12y - 6z - 17 = 0$ touches the conicoid $3x^2 - 6y^2 + 9z^2 + 17 = 0$, and find the point of contact.   **[Ans. $(-1, 2, 2/3)$]**

3. Find the equation of the tangent planes to the curve $x^2 - 2y^2 + 3z^2 = 2$ and parallel to the plane $x - 2y + 3z = 0$.   (*M.D.U. Rohtak, 2000*) **[Ans. $x - 2y + 3z = \pm 2$]**

4. Find the equations to the tangent planes to the surface $4x^2 - 5y^2 + 7z^2 + 13 = 0$, parallel to the plane $4x + 20y - 21z = 0$. Find their points of contact also.
                        [Ans. $4x + 20y - 21z \neq 13 = 0$; $(\pm 1, \neq 4, \neq 3)$]

5. Find the equations to the two planes which contain the line given by $7x + 10y - 30 = 0$, and touch the ellipsoid $7x^2 + 5y^2 + 3z^2 = 60$.   (*M.D.U. Rohtak, 2001*)
                  [Ans. $7x + 5y + 3z - 30 = 0$, $14x + 5y + 9z - 60 = 0$]

6. Find the equation to the tangent planes to $2x^2 - 6y^2 + 3z^2 = 5$ which pass through the line $x + 9y - 3z = 0 = 3x - 3y + 6z - 5$.   (*Ajmer, 1997; Garhwal, 1995, 99, 2004;*
                          Poorvanchal, 1995; Rohilkhand, 1998, 2002)
                      [Ans. $2x - 12y + 9z = 5$, $4x + 6y + 3z = 5$]

7. P, Q are any two points on a central conicoid. Show that the plane through the centre and the line of intersection of the tangent planes at P, Q will bisect PQ. Also show that if the planes through the centre parallel to the tangent planes at P, Q cut the chord in P', Q', then $PP' = QQ'$.

8. Prove that the locus of the foot of the central perpendicular on varying tangent planes of the ellipsoid, $x^2/a^2 + y^2/b^2 + z^2/c^2 = 1$, is the surface
$$(x^2 + y^2 + z^2)^2 = a^2x^2 + b^2y^2 + c^2z^2. \quad (Ajmer, 1995, 98; Garhwal, 1998;$$
                      Gorakhpur, 1998; Poorvanchal, 1997; Rohilkhand, 1999)

9. Find the locus of the perpendiculars from the origin to the tangent planes to the surface $x^2/a^2 + y^2/b^2 + z^2/c^2 = 1$ which cut off from its axes intercepts the sum of whose reciprocals is equal to the constant $1/k$.   **[Ans. $a^2x^2 + b^2y^2 + c^2z^2 = k^2(x + y + z)^2$]**

10. Show that the lines through (α, β, γ) drawn perpendicular to the tangent planes to
$$x^2/a^2 + y^2/b^2 + z^2/c^2 = 1$$
which pass through it generate the cone
$$[\alpha(x - \alpha) + \beta(y - \beta) + \gamma(z - \gamma)]^2 = a^2(x - \alpha)^2 + b^2(y - \beta)^2 + c^2(z - \gamma)^2.$$

11. If P is the point on the ellipsoid, $x^2 + 2y^2 + \frac{1}{3}z^2 = 1$, such that the perpendicular from the origin on the tangent plane at P is of unit length, show that P lies on one or other of the planes $3y = \pm z$.

8.3.4. Normal

Def. *The normal at any point of a quadric is the line through the point perpendicular to the tangent plane thereat.* (*Ajmer, 1998; Kumaon, 2006; Rohilkhand, 2001, U.P.P.C.S., 1999*)

The equation of the tangent plane at (α, β, γ) to the surface

$$ax^2 + by^2 + cz^2 = 1 \qquad \qquad ...(i)$$

is
$$a\alpha x + b\beta y + c\gamma z = 1 \qquad \qquad ...(ii)$$

The equations to the normal at (α, β, γ), therefore, are

$$\frac{x - \alpha}{a\alpha} = \frac{y - \beta}{b\beta} = \frac{z - \gamma}{c\gamma} \qquad \qquad ...(iii)$$

so that $a\alpha$, $b\beta$, $c\gamma$ are the direction ratios of the normal.

If p, is the length of the perpendicular from the origin to the tangent plane (ii), we have

$$\frac{1}{a^2\alpha^2 + b^2\beta^2 + c^2\gamma^2} = p^2 \iff (a\alpha p)^2 + (b\beta p)^2 + (c\gamma p)^2 = 1.$$

It follows that $a\alpha p$, $b\beta p$, $c\gamma p$ are the actual direction cosines of the normal at (α, β, γ).

8.3.5. Number of Normals From a Given Point

We shall now show that *through any given point six normals can be drawn to a central conicoid.* (*Ajmer, 1997, 98; Gorakhpur, 2003; Avadh, 1997, 2000; Kumaon, 1998; Poorvanchal, 1997, 98; Rohilkhand, 2001*)

If the normal (iii) at a point (α, β, γ) passes through a *given* point (f, g, h), we have

$$\frac{f - \alpha}{a\alpha} = \frac{g - \beta}{b\beta} = \frac{h - \gamma}{c\gamma} = r, \text{ (say)}$$

$$\iff \qquad \alpha = \frac{f}{1 + ar}, \ \beta = \frac{g}{1 + br}, \ \gamma = \frac{h}{1 + cr} \qquad \qquad ...(iv)$$

Since (α, β, γ) lies on the conicoid (i), we have the relation

$$\frac{af^2}{(1 + ar)^2} + \frac{bg^2}{(1 + br)^2} + \frac{ch^2}{(1 + cr)^2} = 1, \qquad \qquad ...(v)$$

which, being an equation of the *sixth* degree, gives six values of r, to each of which there corresponds a point (α, β, γ), as obtained from (iv).

Therefore, there are *six* points on a central quadric the normals at which pass through a given point, *i.e., through a given point, six normals, in general, can be drawn to a central quadric.*

8.3.6. Cubic Curve Through the Feet of Normals

The feet of the six normals from a given point to a central quadric are the intersections of the quadric with a certain cubic curve.

Consider the curve whose parametric equations are

$$x = \frac{f}{1 + ar}, \ y = \frac{g}{1 + br}, \ z = \frac{h}{1 + cr} \qquad \qquad ...(vi)$$

r being the *parameter*.

The points (x, y, z) on this curve, arising from those of the values of r which are the roots of the equation (v), are the six feet of the normals from the point (f, g, h).

Again, the points of intersection of this curve with any plane

$$Ax + By + Cz + D = 0$$

are given by

$$\frac{Af}{1 + ar} + \frac{Bg}{1 + br} + \frac{Ch}{1 + cr} + D = 0$$

which determines three values of r. Hence, the curve (vi) cuts *any* plane in three points and is, as such, a *cubic* curve.

Therefore, the six feet of the normals from (f, g, h) are the intersections of the conicoid and the cubic curve (vi).

8.3.7. Quadric Cone Through Six Concurrent Normals

The six normals drawn from any point to a central quadric are the generators of a quadric cone.   *(Poorvanchal, 1998; Gorakhpur, 2003)*

We first prove that the lines drawn from (f, g, h) to intersect the cubic curve (vi) generate a quadric cone.

If *any* line

$$\frac{x - f}{l} = \frac{y - g}{m} = \frac{z - h}{n} \qquad \qquad ...(vii)$$

through (f, g, h) intersects the cubic curve, we have

$$\frac{\dfrac{f}{1 + ar} - f}{l} = \frac{\dfrac{g}{1 + br} - g}{m} = \frac{\dfrac{h}{1 + cr} - h}{n}$$

$$\Rightarrow \qquad \frac{af / l}{1 + ar} = \frac{bg / m}{1 + br} = \frac{ch / m}{1 + cr}$$

whence eliminating r, we get

$$\frac{af}{l}(b - c) + \frac{bg}{m}(c - a) + \frac{ch}{n}(a - b) = 0$$

which is the condition for the line (vii) to intersect the cubic curve (vi).

Eliminating l, m, n between the equations of the line and this condition, we get

$$\frac{af\,(b - c)}{x - f} + \frac{bg\,(c - a)}{y - g} + \frac{ch\,(a - b)}{z - h} = 0$$

which represents a cone of the second degree generated by lines drawn from (f, g, h) to intersect the cubic curve.

As the six feet of the normals drawn from a point (f, g, h) to the quadric lie on the cubic curve, the normals are, in particular, the generators of this cone of the second degree.

Note. The importance of this result lies in the fact that while five given concurrent lines determine a unique quadric cone, the six normals through a point lie on a quadric cone, *i.e.*, *the quadric cone through any of the five normals through a point also contains the six normals through the point.*

8.3.8. The General Equation of the Conicoid Through the Six Feet of the Normals

The co-ordinates (α, β, γ) of the foot of any of the six normals from (f, g, h) satisfy the relations

$$\frac{\alpha - f}{a\alpha} = \frac{\beta - g}{b\beta} = \frac{\gamma - h}{c\gamma}$$

so that we see that the feet of the normals lie on three cylinders

$$ax\,(y-g) = by\,(x-f) \iff (a-b)\,xy - agx + bfy = 0$$
$$by\,(z-h) = cz\,(y-g) \iff (b-c)\,yz - bhy + cgz = 0$$
$$cz\,(x-f) = ax\,(z-h) \iff (c-a)\,zx - cfz + ahx = 0$$

The six feet of the normals are the common points of the three cylinders and the conicoid

$$ax^2 + by^2 + cz^2 = 1.$$

The equation

$$ax^2 + by^2 + cz^2 - 1 + k_1\,[xy\,(a-b) - agx + bfy] + k_2\,[yz\,(b-c) - bhy + cgz]$$
$$+ k_3\,[zx\,(c-a) - cfz + ahx] = 0$$

is satisfied by the *six* feet of the normals and contains *three* arbitrary parameters k_1, k_2, k_3. Therefore, it represents the general equation of the conicoid through them.

EXAMPLES

1. *The normal at any point P of a central conicoid meets the three principal planes at G_1, G_2, G_3, show that PG_1, PG_2, PG_3 are in a constant ratio.*

(*Avadh, 1998; Ajmer, 1996; Agra, 1998; Gorakhpur, 1998, 2000; Poorvanchal, 1997. U.P.P.C.S., 1998*

Sol. The equations of the normal at (α, β, γ) are

$$\frac{x-\alpha}{a\alpha p} = \frac{y-\beta}{b\beta p} = \frac{z-\gamma}{c\gamma p}.$$

Now since $a\alpha p$, $b\beta p$, $c\gamma p$ are the direction cosines, each of these fractions represents the distance between the points (α, β, γ) and (x, y, z).

Thus, the distance PG_1, of the point $P\,(\alpha, \beta, \gamma)$ from the point G_1 where the normal meets the co-ordinate plane $x = 0$ is $-1/cp$.

Similarly $PG_2 = -1/bp,\ PG_3 = -1/cp.$

Thus, we have

$$PG_1 : PG_2 : PG_3 :: a^{-1} : b^{-1} : c^{-1}.$$

2. *Show that the lines drawn from the origin parallel to the normals to the central conicoid*

$$ax^2 + by^2 + cz^2 = 1,$$

at its points of intersection with the planes

$$lx + my + nz = p,$$

generate the cone

$$p^2\left(\frac{x^2}{a} + \frac{y^2}{b} + \frac{z^2}{c}\right) = \left(\frac{lx}{a} + \frac{my}{b} + \frac{nz}{c}\right)^2.$$

Sol. Let (f, g, h) be any point, on the curve of intersection of

$$ax^2 + by^2 + cz^2 = 1 \text{ and } lx + my + nz = p \qquad \qquad ...(1)$$

The normal to the quadric at (f, g, h) is

$$\frac{x-f}{af} = \frac{y-g}{bg} = \frac{z-h}{ch} \qquad \qquad ...(2)$$

The line through the origin parallel to this normal is

$$\frac{x}{af} = \frac{y}{bg} = \frac{z}{ch}.$$

Also (f, g, h) satisfies the two equations (1), so that we have

$$af^2 + bg^2 + ch^2 = 1, \quad lf + mg + nh = p \qquad \qquad ...(3)$$

The required locus is obtained by eliminating f, g, h between (2) and (3).

The equations (3) give

$$af^2 + bg^2 + ch^2 = \left(\frac{lf + mg + nh}{p} \right)^2 \qquad \qquad ...(4)$$

which is a second degree homogeneous expression in f, g, h. From (2) and (4), we can easily obtain the required locus.

3. *Prove that two normals to the ellipsoid*

$$\frac{x^2}{a^2} + \frac{y^2}{b^2} + \frac{z^2}{c^2} = 1,$$

lie in the plane

$$lx + my + nz = 0,$$

and the line joining their feet has direction cosines proportional to

$$a^2 (b^2 - c^2) \, mn, \; b^2 (c^2 - a^2) \, nl, \; c^2 (a^2 - b^2) \, lm.$$

Also obtain the co-ordinates of these points.

Sol. Let (f, g, h) be any point on the ellipsoid. The normal at this point, *viz.*,

$$\frac{x - f}{f/a^2} = \frac{y - g}{g/b^2} = \frac{z - h}{h/c^2}$$

lies in the given plane, if

$$\left. \begin{array}{l} lf + mg + nh = 0 \\ lf/a^2 + mg/b^2 + nh/c^2 = 0 \end{array} \right\}$$

These give

$$\frac{f/a}{amn (b^2 - c^2)} = \frac{g/b}{bnl (c^2 - a^2)} = \frac{h/c}{clm (a^2 - b^2)}$$

$$= \pm \frac{\sqrt{\Sigma f^2 / a^2}}{\sqrt{\Sigma a^2 m^2 n^2 (b^2 - c^2)^2}} = \pm \frac{1}{\sqrt{\Sigma a^2 m^2 n^2 (b^2 - c^2)^2}}$$

Therefore, the required two points are

$$\left[\pm \frac{a^2 mn (b^2 - c^2)}{d}, \; \pm \frac{b^2 nl (c^2 - a^2)}{d}, \; \pm \frac{c^2 lm (a^2 - b^2)}{d} \right]$$

where

$$d = \sqrt{\Sigma a^2 m^2 n^2 (b^2 - c^2)}$$

The direction cosines of the line joining these points are proportional to

$$a^2 mn (b^2 - c^2), \text{ etc.}$$

4. *Prove that for all values of* λ, *the normals to the conicoid*

$$\frac{x^2}{a^2 + \lambda} + \frac{y^2}{b^2 + \lambda} + \frac{z^2}{c^2 + \lambda} = 1,$$

which pass through a given point (α, β, γ) *meet the plane* $z = 0$ *in points on the conic*

$$(b^2 - c^2) \, \beta x + (c^2 - a^2) \, \alpha y + (a^2 - b^2) \, xy = 0, \; z = 0.$$

Sol. It can be shown that the equation of the quadric cone containing the normals to

$$\frac{x^2}{a^2 + \lambda} + \frac{y^2}{b^2 + \lambda} + \frac{z^2}{c^2 + \lambda} = 1$$

drawn from the point (α, β, γ) is

$$\sum \frac{1}{a^2 + \lambda} \alpha \left(\frac{1}{b^2 + \lambda} - \frac{1}{c^2 + \lambda} \right) \frac{1}{x - \alpha} = 0 \qquad \text{(§ 8.3.7)}$$

$$\Rightarrow \qquad \sum \frac{\alpha(c^2 - b^2)}{x - \alpha} = 0$$

Thus, it meets the plane $z = 0$, where

$$\frac{\alpha(c^2 - b^2)}{x - \alpha} + \frac{\beta(a^2 - c^2)}{y - \beta} - (b^2 - a^2) = 0$$

$$\Leftrightarrow \quad \alpha(y - \beta)(c^2 - b^2) + \beta(x - \alpha)(a^2 - c^2) - (x - \alpha)(y - \beta)(b^2 - a^2) = 0,$$

$$\Leftrightarrow \qquad (b^2 - c^2)\beta x + (c^2 - a^2)\alpha y + (a^2 - b^2)xy = 0.$$

5. *The normals at P and P', two points of the ellipsoid*

$$x^2/a^2 + y^2/b^2 + z^2/c^2 = 1,$$

meet the plane XOY and make angles θ, θ' *with PP'. Prove that*

$$PA \cos \theta + P'A' \cos \theta' = 0.$$

Sol. If P and P' be (α, β, γ) and $(\alpha', \beta', \gamma')$, then normals are

$$\frac{x - \alpha}{p\alpha/a^2} = \frac{y - \beta}{p\beta/b^2} = \frac{z - \gamma}{p\gamma/c^2} = r \qquad \qquad \dots(i)$$

and

$$\frac{x - \alpha'}{p'\alpha'/a^2} = \frac{y - \beta'}{p'\beta'/b^2} = \frac{z - \gamma'}{p'\gamma'/c^2} = r' \qquad \dots(ii)$$

where

$$p = 1/\sqrt{\alpha^2/a^4 + \beta^2/b^4 + \gamma^2/c^4}$$

and

$$p' = 1/\sqrt{\alpha'^2/a^4 + \beta'^2/b^4 + \gamma'^2/c^4}$$

From (i) and (ii), we get

$$A \equiv \left(\alpha - \frac{\alpha c^2}{a^2},\ \beta - \frac{\beta c^2}{b^2},\ 0 \right)$$

$$A' \equiv \left(\alpha' - \frac{\alpha' c^2}{a^2},\ \beta' - \frac{\beta' c^2}{b^2},\ 0 \right)$$

direction cosines of the line PP' are $\dfrac{\alpha' - \alpha}{PP'},\ \dfrac{\beta' - \beta}{PP'},\ \dfrac{\gamma' - \gamma}{PP'}.$

$$\therefore \qquad \cos \theta = \frac{p\alpha}{a^2} \left(\frac{\alpha' - \alpha}{PP'} \right) + \frac{p\beta}{b^2} \left(\frac{\beta' - \beta}{PP'} \right) + \frac{p\gamma}{c^2} \left(\frac{\gamma' - \gamma}{PP'} \right)$$

$$= \frac{p}{PP'} \left[\frac{\alpha(\alpha' - \alpha)}{a^2} + \frac{\beta(\beta' - \beta)}{b^2} + \frac{\gamma(\gamma' - \gamma)}{c^2} \right] \qquad \dots(iii)$$

Similarly,

$$\cos \theta' = \frac{p'}{PP'} \left[\frac{\alpha'(\alpha' - \alpha)}{a^2} + \frac{\beta'(\beta' - \beta)}{b^2} + \frac{\gamma'(\gamma' - \gamma)}{c^2} \right] \qquad \dots(iv)$$

Putting $z = 0$ in (i),

$$r = -\frac{1}{p/c^2} = PA \Rightarrow PA = \frac{c^2}{p}$$

Similarly $P'A' = c^2/p'$

$$\therefore \quad PA \cos\theta + P'A' \cos\theta' = \frac{c^2}{PP'}\left[\frac{\alpha(\alpha'-\alpha)}{a^2} + \frac{\beta(\beta'-\beta)}{b^2} + \frac{\gamma(\gamma'-\gamma)}{c^2}\right]$$

$$+ \frac{c^2}{PP'}\left[\frac{\alpha'(\alpha'-\alpha)}{a^2} + \frac{\beta'(\beta'-\beta)}{b^2} + \frac{\gamma'(\gamma'-\gamma)}{c^2}\right] = 0.$$

6. *If* P, Q, R *and* P', Q', R' *are the feet of the six normals from a point to the ellipsoid* $x^2/a^2 + y^2/b^2 + z^2/c^2 = 1$, *and the plane* PQR *is given by* $lx + my + nz = p$, *then the plane* $P'Q'R'$ *is given by*

$$x/a^2l + y/b^2m + z/c^2n + l/p = 0.$$

Sol. Let plane $P'Q'R'$ be

$$l'x + m'y + n'z = p'.$$

Then the feet of the six normals from any given point (x', y', z') lie on the locus given by the equation

$$(lx + my + nz - p)(l'x + m'y + n'z - p') = 0 \qquad \qquad ...(i)$$

Let (α, β, γ) be a foot of the normal from (x', y', z').

$$\therefore \qquad (l\alpha + m\beta + n\gamma - p)(l'\alpha + m'\beta + n'\gamma - p') = 0 \qquad ...(ii)$$

Also, the normal at (α, β, γ) passes through (x', y', z').

$$\therefore \qquad \frac{x'-\alpha}{\alpha/a^2} = \frac{y'-\beta}{\beta/b^2} = \frac{z'-\gamma}{\gamma/c^2} = \lambda,$$

$$\therefore \qquad \alpha = \frac{a^2x'}{a^2+\lambda}, \quad \beta = \frac{b^2y'}{b^2+\lambda}, \quad \gamma = \frac{c^2z'}{c^2+\lambda}$$

But (α, β, γ) lies on the given ellipsoid

$$\therefore \qquad \frac{a^2x'^2}{(a^2+\lambda)^2} + \frac{b^2y'^2}{(b^2+\lambda)^2} + \frac{c^2z'^2}{(c^2+\lambda)^2} = 1 \qquad \qquad ...(iii)$$

This equation being a sixth degree equation in λ, gives six values of λ corresponding to the six feet of the normals.

Also putting the values of α, β, γ in (ii), we get

$$\left(\frac{a^2x'l}{a^2+\lambda} + \frac{b^2y'm}{b^2+\lambda} + \frac{c^2z'n}{c^2+\lambda} - p\right)\left(\frac{a^2x'l'}{a^2+\lambda} + \frac{b^2y'm'}{b^2+\lambda} + \frac{c^2z'n'}{c^2+\lambda} - p'\right) = 0 \qquad ...(iv)$$

This is also sixth degree equation in λ, gives six values of λ corresponding to the six feet of the normals. Hence, equation (iii) and (iv) are identical.

Comparing coefficients of like terms in (iii) and (iv), we get

$$\frac{a^4ll'}{a^2} = \frac{b^4mm'}{b^2} = \frac{c^4nn'}{c^2} = \frac{-pp'}{1}$$

or

$$l' = \frac{-pp'}{a^2l}, \quad m' = \frac{-pp'}{b^2m}, \quad n' = \frac{-pp'}{c^2n}$$

Substituting these values, the equation of plane $P'Q'R'$ may be found.

EXERCISES

1. If a point G be taken on the normal at any point P of the ellipsoid
$$x^2/a^2 + y^2/b^2 + z^2/c^2 = 1,$$
such that $$3PG = PG_1 + PG_2 + PG_3,$$
show that the locus of G is
$$\frac{a^2x^2}{(2a^2 - b^2 - c^2)^2} + \frac{b^2y^2}{(2b^2 - c^2 - a^2)^2} + \frac{c^2z^2}{(2c^2 - a^2 - b^2)^2} = \frac{1}{9}.$$

2. If a length PQ be taken on the normal at any point P of the ellipsoid
$$x^2/a^2 + y^2/b^2 + z^2/c^2 = 1$$
such that $PQ = k^2/p$, where k is a constant and p is the length of the perpendicular from the origin to the tangent planes at p, the locus of Q is
$$\frac{a^2x^2}{(a^2 + k^2)^2} + \frac{b^2y^2}{(b^2 + k^2)^2} + \frac{c^2z^2}{(c^2 + k^2)^2} = 1.$$

3. Show that, in general, the normals to the ellipsoid $x^2/a^2 + y^2/b^2 + z^2/c^2 = 1$ lie in a given plane. Determine the co-ordinates of the two points on the ellipsoid the normals at which lie in the plane
$$by - cz = \frac{1}{2}(b^2 - c^2). \qquad \left[\textbf{Ans. } \left(\pm\sqrt{\frac{1}{2}}\,a, \frac{1}{2}\,b, \frac{1}{2}\,c\right)\right]$$

4. If the feet of the three normals from P to the ellipsoid $x^2/a^2 + y^2/b^2 + z^2/c^2 = 1$ lie on the plane
$$\frac{x}{a} + \frac{y}{b} + \frac{z}{c} = 1,$$
prove that the feet of the other three lie on the plane
$$\frac{x}{a} + \frac{y}{b} + \frac{z}{c} + 1 = 0$$
and P lies on the line
$$a(b^2 - c^2)x = b(c^2 - a^2)y = c(a^2 - b^2)z. \qquad (Garhwal, 1997)$$

5. Prove that through any point (α, β, γ) six normals can be drawn to the ellipsoid $x^2/a^2 + y^2/b^2 + z^2/c^2 = 1$ and that the feet of the normals lie on the curve of intersection of the ellipsoid and the cone
$$\frac{a^2(b^2 - c^2)\alpha}{x} + \frac{b^2(c^2 - a^2)\beta}{y} + \frac{c^2(a^2 - b^2)\gamma}{z} = 0.$$
$$(Ajmer, 1998; Garhwal, 2003; Lucknow, 1994; Poorvanchal, 1998)$$

6. Show that the locus of points on a central quadric, the normals at which intersect a given diameter is the curve of intersection with a cone having the principal axes of the quadric as generators.

7. Show that the normals at the point (x_1, y_1, z_1) and (x_2, y_2, z_2) to $x^2/a^2 + y^2/b^2 + z^2/c^2 = 1$ intersect, if
$$\frac{(b^2 - c^2)x_1}{x_1 - x_2} + \frac{(c^2 - a^2)y_1}{y_1 - y_2} + \frac{(a^2 - b^2)z_1}{z_1 - z_2} = 0,$$

and that if (f, g, h) be their point of intersection,

$$a^2 f \left(\frac{1}{x_1} - \frac{1}{x_2} \right) = b^2 g \left(\frac{1}{y_1} - \frac{1}{y_2} \right) = c^2 h \left(\frac{1}{z_1} - \frac{1}{z_2} \right).$$

Deduce that the points on the surface normals at which intersect the normal at a given point, lie on a quadric cone having its vertex at the given point.

8. Prove that six normals drawn from any point to a central conicoid meet a principal plane in six points which lie on a rectangular hyperbola.

9. The normals at six point in $x^2/a^2 + y^2/b^2 + z^2/c^2 = 1$ meet in the point (f, g, h); show that the mean position of the six points is

$$\left[\frac{-f(b^2 + c^2 - 2a^2) a^2}{3(a^2 - b^2)(a^2 - c^2)}, \frac{-g(c^2 + a^2 - 2b^2) b^2}{3(b^2 - c^2)(b^2 - a^2)}, \frac{-h(a^2 + b^2 + 2c^2) c^2}{3(c^2 - a^2)(c^2 - b^2)} \right].$$

10. Show that the greatest value of the shortest distance between the axis of x and a normal

to the ellipsoid $\dfrac{x^2}{a^2} + \dfrac{y^2}{b^2} + \dfrac{z^2}{c^2} = 1$ is $b - c$.   *(U.P.P.C.S. 2003)*

8.4. PLANE OF CONTACT

The tangent plane

$$axx' + byy' + czz' = 1,$$

at the point (x', y', z') to the quadric $ax^2 + by^2 + cz^2 = 1$, passes through the point (α, β, γ), if

$$a\alpha x' + b\beta y' + c\gamma z' = 1.$$

This shows that the points on the quadric the tangent planes at which pass through the point (α, β, γ) lie on the plane

$$a\alpha x + b\beta y + c\gamma z = 1$$

which is called the *Plane of contact* for the point (α, β, γ).

8.5. THE POLAR PLANE OF A POINT

If a secant APQ through a given point A meets a conicoid in points P and Q and a point R be taken on this line such that points A and R divide the segment PQ internally and externally in the same ratio, then the locus of the point R is a plane called the polar plane of A.

It may be easily seen that if the points A and R divide the segment PQ internally and externally in the same ratio, then the points P, Q divide the segment AR also internally and externally in the same ratio.

Let A, be a point (α, β, γ) and let (x, y, z) be the co-ordinates of R.

The co-ordinates of the point which divides AR in the ratio $\lambda : 1$ are

$$\left(\frac{\lambda x + \alpha}{\lambda + 1}, \frac{\lambda y + \beta}{\lambda + 1}, \frac{\lambda z + \gamma}{\lambda + 1} \right)$$

This point will lie on the conicoid

$$ax^2 + by^2 + cz^2 = 1$$

for those of the values of λ which are the roots of the equation

$$a \left(\frac{\lambda x + \alpha}{\lambda + 1} \right)^2 + b \left(\frac{\lambda x + \beta}{\lambda + 1} \right)^2 + c \left(\frac{\lambda x + \gamma}{\lambda + 1} \right)^2 = 1$$

$$\lambda^2 (ax^2 + by^2 + cz^2 - 1) + 2\lambda (a\alpha x + b\beta y + c\gamma z - 1) + (a\alpha^2 + b\beta^2 + c\gamma^2 - 1) = 0 \quad ...(1)$$

The two roots λ_1, λ_2 of this equation are the ratios in which the points P, Q divide the segment AR. Since P, Q divide the segment AR internally and externally in the same ratio, we have

$$\lambda_1 + \lambda_2 = 0$$

so that, from (1) $a\alpha x + b\beta y + c\gamma z - 1 = 0$ ...(2)

Now the equation (2) of the first degree being a relation between the co-ordinates (x, y, z) of the point gives a plane as the locus of the point R.

Thus, *the polar plane of the point* (α, β, γ) *with respect to the conicoid*

$$ax^2 + by^2 + cz^2 = 1$$

is the plane

$$a\alpha x + b\beta y + c\gamma z = 0.$$

Any point is called the pole of its polar plane.

Note. The reader acquainted with cross-ratios and, in particular, harmonic cross-ratios, would know that the fact that the points P, Q divide AR internally and externally in the same ratio is also expressed by the statement

$$(AR, PQ) = -1$$

This is further equivalent to the relation

$$\frac{2}{AR} = \frac{1}{AP} + \frac{1}{AQ}.$$

Cor. The polar plane of a point on a conicoid coincides with the tangent plane thereat and that of a point outside it coincides with the plane of contact for that point.

Ex. 1. Show that the point of intersection of the tangent planes at three points on a quadric is the pole of the plane formed by their points of contact.

Ex. 2. Find the pole of the plane $lx + my + nz = p$ with respect to the quadric

$$ax^2 + by^2 + cz^2 = 1. \qquad \textbf{[Ans.} \, l/ap, \, m/bp, \, n/cp]$$

8.5.1. Conjugate Points and Conjugate Planes

It is easy to show that if the polar plane of a point P passes through point Q, then the polar plane of Q passes through P.

Two such points are called *Conjugate Points*.

Also it can be shown that if the pole of a plane α lies on plane β, then the pole of the plane β lies on the plane α. *(Ajmer, 1998)*

Two such planes are called *Conjugate Planes*.

8.5.2. Polar Lines

Consider a line

$$\frac{x - \alpha}{l} = \frac{y - \beta}{m} = \frac{z - \gamma}{n}. \qquad \textit{(Ajmer, 1998; Gorakhpur, 1999)}$$

The polar plane of any point $(lr + \alpha, \, mr + \beta, \, nr + \gamma)$ on this line is

$$a(lr + \alpha)x + b(mr + \beta)y + c(nr + \gamma)z = 1$$

$$\Rightarrow \qquad a\alpha x + b\beta y + c\gamma z - 1 + r(alx + bmy + cnz) = 0$$

which clearly passes through the line of intersection of the planes

$$a\alpha x + b\beta y + c\gamma z - 1 = 0, \quad alx + bmy + cnz = 0$$

for all values of r.

Thus, *the polar planes of all the points on a line l pass through another line l'*.

Now, since the polar planes of an arbitrary point P on a line l pass through every point of l', therefore, the polar planes of any point of l' will pass through the point P on l and as P is arbitrary, it passes through every point on l, *i.e.*, passes through l.

It follows that *if the polar plane of any point on a line l passes through the line l', then the polar plane of any point on l' passes through l.*

Two such lines are said to be *Polar Lines* with respect to the conicoid.

To find the polar line of any given line, we have only to find the line of intersection of the polar planes of any two points on it.

8.5.3. Conjugate Lines

Let l, m be any two lines and l', m' their polar lines. We suppose that the line m *intersects* the line l.

We shall now show that the line l' also intersects the line m.

Let P be the point where the lines m' and l intersect.

As P lies on m' and also on l, its polar plane contains the polar lines m and l' of m' and l respectively, *i.e.*, the lines m and l' are coplanar and hence they intersect.

It follows that *if a line l intersects the polar of a line m, then the line m intersects the polar of the line l.*

Two such lines l and m are called *Conjugate Lines*.

EXAMPLES

1. *Find the locus of straight lines drawn through a fixed point* (α, β, γ) *at right angles to their polars with respect to the central conicoid* $ax^2 + by^2 + cz^2 = 1$.

(Garhwal, 1995, 2001; Gorakhpur, 2001; Rohilkhand, 1998)

Sol. Let

$$\frac{x - \alpha}{l} = \frac{y - \beta}{m} = \frac{z - \gamma}{n} \qquad \qquad ...(1)$$

be a line perpendicular to its polar line. Now the polar line of (1) is the intersection of the planes

$$a\alpha x + b\beta y + c\gamma z = 1, \quad alx + bmy + cnz = 0$$

If λ, μ, ν be the direction ratios of this line, we have

$$a\alpha\lambda + b\beta\mu + c\gamma\nu = 0, \quad al\lambda + bm\mu + cn\nu = 0$$

$$\Rightarrow \qquad \frac{a\lambda}{n\beta - m\gamma} = \frac{b\mu}{l\gamma - n\alpha} = \frac{c\nu}{m\alpha - \beta l}$$

The perpendicularity of the line (1) to its polar lines implies

$$l\lambda + m\mu + n\nu = 0$$

$$\therefore \qquad \frac{l(n\beta - m\gamma)}{a} + \frac{m(l\gamma - n\alpha)}{b} + \frac{n(m\alpha - l\beta)}{c} = 0$$

$$\Rightarrow \qquad \alpha mn\left(\frac{1}{b} - \frac{1}{c}\right) + \beta nl\left(\frac{1}{c} - \frac{1}{a}\right) + \gamma lm\left(\frac{1}{a} - \frac{1}{b}\right) = 0$$

$$\Rightarrow \qquad \frac{\alpha}{l}\left(\frac{1}{b} - \frac{1}{c}\right) + \frac{\beta}{m}\left(\frac{1}{c} - \frac{1}{a}\right) + \frac{\gamma}{n}\left(\frac{1}{a} - \frac{1}{b}\right) = 0 \qquad ...(2)$$

Eliminating l, m, n between (1) and (2), we see that the required locus is

$$\frac{\alpha}{x - \alpha}\left(\frac{1}{b} - \frac{1}{c}\right) + \frac{\beta}{y - \beta}\left(\frac{1}{c} - \frac{1}{a}\right) + \frac{\gamma}{z - \gamma}\left(\frac{1}{a} - \frac{1}{b}\right) = 0.$$

2. *Show that any normal to the conicoid*

$$\frac{x^2}{pa + q} + \frac{y^2}{pb + q} + \frac{z^2}{pc + q} = 1$$

is perpendicular to its polar line with respect to the conicoid

$$x^2/a + y^2/b + z^2/c = 1.$$

Sol. Let

$$\frac{x - \alpha}{l} = \frac{y - \beta}{m} = \frac{z - \gamma}{n} \qquad \qquad ...(i)$$

be the equations of the normal at any point (α, β, γ) of the conicoid

$$\frac{x^2}{pa + q} + \frac{y^2}{pb + q} + \frac{z^2}{pc + q} = 1 \qquad \qquad ...(ii)$$

so that $l = \dfrac{\alpha}{pa + q}, \ m = \dfrac{\beta}{pb + q}, \ n = \dfrac{\gamma}{pc + q}$

Now, equations of polar line of (i) with respect to conicoid

$$\frac{x^2}{a} + \frac{y^2}{b} + \frac{z^2}{c} = 1 \qquad \qquad ...(iii)$$

are

$$\left. \begin{array}{l} \dfrac{\alpha x}{a} + \dfrac{\beta y}{b} + \dfrac{\gamma z}{c} = 1 \\[2mm] \dfrac{lx}{a} + \dfrac{my}{b} + \dfrac{nz}{c} = 0 \end{array} \right\} \qquad ...(iv)$$

If the direction cosines of this line be proportional to λ, μ, ν, then

$$\frac{\lambda}{\dfrac{1}{bc}(\beta n - \gamma m)} = \frac{\mu}{\dfrac{1}{ca}(\gamma l - \alpha n)} = \frac{\nu}{\dfrac{1}{ab}(\alpha m - \beta l)}$$

Lines (i) and (iv) will be perpendicular if

$$\lambda l + \mu m + \nu n = 0$$

$$\Rightarrow \qquad \frac{1}{bc}(\beta n - \gamma m) + \frac{m}{ca}(\gamma l - \alpha n) + \frac{n}{ab}(\alpha m - \beta l) = 0$$

$$\Rightarrow \qquad a\left(\frac{\beta}{m} - \frac{\gamma}{n}\right) + b\left(\frac{\gamma}{n} - \frac{\alpha}{l}\right) + c\left(\frac{\alpha}{l} - \frac{\beta}{m}\right) = 0$$

$$\Rightarrow \qquad \frac{\alpha}{l}(b - c) + \frac{\beta}{m}(c - a) + \frac{\gamma}{n}(a - b) = 0$$

$$\Rightarrow \qquad (pa + q)(b - c) + (pb + q)(c - a) + (pc + q)(a - b) = 0$$

$$\Rightarrow \qquad p\,[a\,(b - c) + b\,(c - a) + c\,(a - b)] + q\,[(b - c) + (c - a) + (a - b)] = 0$$

which is true. Hence, the normal to (ii) is perpendicular to its polar line with respect to the conicoid (iii).

EXERCISES

1. Prove that the locus of the poles of the tangent planes of the conicoid $ax^2 + by^2 + cz^2 = 1$ with respect to the conicoid $\alpha x^2 + \beta y^2 + \gamma z^2 = 1$ is the conicoid

$$\frac{\alpha^2 x^2}{a} + \frac{\beta^2 y^2}{b} + \frac{\gamma^2 z^2}{c} = 1. \qquad \qquad (Avadh,\ 1999)$$

2. Show that the locus of the poles of the plane

$$lx + my + nz = p,$$

with respect to the system of conicoids

$$\frac{x^2}{a^2 + \lambda} + \frac{y^2}{b^2 + \lambda} + \frac{z^2}{c^2 + \lambda} = 1,$$

where λ is the parameter, is a straight line perpendicular to the given plane.

$$(Garhwal,\ 1996)$$

3. Show that the polar line of the line
$$(x - 1)/2 = (y - 2)/3 = (z - 3)/4$$
with respect to the quadric
$$x^2 - 2y^2 + 3z^2 - 4 = 0$$
is the line
$$(x + 6)/3 = (y - 2)/3 = (z - 2)/1.$$

4. Find the locus of straight line drawn through a fixed point (f, g, h) such that its polar lines with respect to the quadrics
$$ax^2 + by^2 + cz^2 = 1 \text{ and } \alpha x^2 + \beta y^2 + \gamma z^2 = 1$$
are coplanar.

$$\left[\text{Ans. } \sum \frac{(\alpha - a)(b\gamma - c\beta)f}{x - f} = 0 \right]$$

5. Find the conditions that the lines
$$\frac{x - \alpha}{l} = \frac{y - \beta}{m} = \frac{z - \gamma}{n}, \frac{x - \alpha'}{l'} = \frac{y - \beta'}{m'} = \frac{z - \gamma'}{n'}$$
should be (i) polar, (ii) conjugate with respect to the conicoid
$$ax^2 + by^2 + cz^2 = 1.$$

(*Gorakhpur, 1995, 99; Poorvanchal, 1996, 99, Kumaon 2005*)

[**Ans.**   (i) $\Sigma a\alpha\alpha' = 1, \Sigma a\alpha'l = 0, \Sigma a\alpha l' = 0, \Sigma all' = 0$

(ii) $(\Sigma a\alpha l')(\Sigma a\alpha'l) = (\Sigma all')(\Sigma a\alpha\alpha' - 1)]$

8.6.1. The Enveloping Cone

Def. *The locus of tangent lines to a quadric through any point is called an enveloping cone.*

To find the enveloping cone of the conicoid
$$ax^2 + by^2 + cz^2 = 1,$$
with its vertex at (α, β, γ).

Any line
$$\frac{x - \alpha}{l} = \frac{y - \beta}{m} = \frac{z - \gamma}{n} \qquad \qquad ...(i)$$
through the point (α, β, γ) will meet the surface in two coincident points if the equation (A) of § 8.3 has equal roots, *i.e.,* if
$$(al\alpha + bm\beta + cn\gamma)^2 \doteq (al^2 + bm^2 + cn^2)(a\alpha^2 + b\beta^2 + c\gamma^2 - 1) \qquad ...(ii)$$
Eliminating l, m, n between (i) and (ii), we obtain
$$[a\alpha(x - \alpha) + b\beta(y - \beta) + c\gamma(z - \gamma)]^2$$
$$= [a(x - \alpha)^2 + b(y - \beta)^2 + c(z - \gamma)^2](a\alpha^2 + b\beta^2 + c\gamma^2 - 1)$$
which is the required equation of the **enveloping cone.**

If we write
$$S \equiv ax^2 + by^2 + cz^2 - 1, S_1 \equiv a\alpha^2 + b\beta^2 + c\gamma^2 - 1, T_1 \equiv a\alpha x + b\beta y + c\gamma z - 1$$
we see that the equation of the enveloping cone can briefly be written as
$$(T_1 - S_1)^2 = (S - 2T_1 + S_1)S_1 \iff SS_1 = T_1^2$$
$$\iff (ax^2 + by^2 + cz^2 - 1)(a\alpha^2 + b\beta^2 + c\gamma^2 - 1) = (a\alpha x + b\beta y + c\gamma z - 1)^2.$$

Note. Obviously the enveloping cone passes through the points common to the conicoid and the polar plane $a\alpha x + b\beta y + c\gamma z = 1$ of the vertex (α, β, γ).

Thus, the enveloping cone may be regarded as a cone whose vertex is the given point and guiding curve the section of the conicoid by its polar plane.

EXERCISES

1. A point P moves so that the section of the enveloping cone of the ellipsoid

$$x^2/a^2 + y^2/b^2 + z^2/c^2 = 1$$

with P as vertex by the plane $z = 0$ is a circle; show that P lies on one of the conics

$$\frac{y^2}{b^2 - a^2} + \frac{z^2}{c^2} = 1, \ x = 0; \quad \frac{x^2}{a^2 - b^2} + \frac{z^2}{c^2} = 1, \ y = 0.$$

2. If the section of the enveloping cone of the ellipsoid

$$x^2/a^2 + y^2/b^2 + z^2/c^2 = 1,$$

whose vertex is P by the plane $z = 0$ is a rectangular hyperbola, show that the locus of P is

$$\frac{x^2 + y^2}{a^2 + b^2} + \frac{z^2}{c^2} = 1.$$

3. Find the locus of the points from which three mutually perpendicular tangent lines can be drawn to the conicoid $ax^2 + by^2 + cz^2 = 1$.

[**Ans.** $a(b + c) x^2 + b(c + a) y^2 + c(a + b) z^2 = a + b + c$]

4. A pair of perpendicular tangent planes to the ellipsoid

$$x^2/a^2 + y^2/b^2 + z^2/c^2 = 1$$

passes through the fixed point $(0, 0, k)$. Show that their line of intersection lies on the cone

$$x^2 (b^2 + c^2 - k^2) + y^2 (c^2 + a^2 - k^2) + (z - k)^2 (a^2 + b^2) = 0.$$

[**Hint.** The required locus is the locus of the line of intersection of perpendicular tangent planes to the enveloping cone of the given ellipsoid with vertex at $(0, 0, k)$.]

8.6.2. Enveloping Cylinder

Def. *The locus of tangent lines to a quadric parallel to any given line is called an Enveloping cylinder of the quadric.*

To find the enveloping cylinder of the conicoid

$$ax^2 + by^2 + cz^2 = 1$$

with its generators parallel to the line

$$\frac{x}{l} = \frac{y}{m} = \frac{z}{n}.$$

Let (α, β, γ) be a point on the *enveloping* cylinder, so that the equations of the generator through it are

$$\frac{x - \alpha}{l} = \frac{y - \beta}{m} = \frac{z - \gamma}{n} \qquad \qquad ...(i)$$

As in § 8.6.1, the line (i) will touch the conicoid, if,

$$(al\alpha + bm\beta + cn\gamma)^2 = (al^2 + bm^2 + cn^2)(a\alpha^2 + b\beta^2 + c\gamma^2 - 1)$$

Thus, the locus of (α, β, γ) is the surface

$$(ax^2 + by^2 + cz^2 - 1)(al^2 + bm^2 + cn^2) = (alx + bmy + cnz)^2$$

which is the required equation of the **Enveloping cylinder.**

Note. Equation of enveloping cylinder deduced from that of enveloping cone. Use of elements at infinity. Since each of the lines parallel to the line

$$x/l = y/m = z/n$$

passes through the point $(l, m, n, 0)$ which is, in fact, the point at infinity on each member of this system of parallel lines, we see that the enveloping cylinder is the enveloping cone with vertex $(l, m, n, 0)$.

The homogeneous equation of the surface being

$$ax^2 + by^2 + cz^2 - t^2 = 0$$

the equation of the enveloping cylinder is

$$(ax^2 + by^2 + cz^2 - t^2)(al^2 + bm^2 + cn^2 - 0) = (alx + bmy + cnz - t \cdot 0)^2; \ (SS_1 = T^2)$$

so that in terms of ordinary cartesian co-ordinates, this equation is

$$(ax^2 + by^2 + cz^2 - 1)(al^2 + bm^2 + cn^2) = (alx + bmy + cnz)^2.$$

Note. Clearly the generators of the enveloping cylinder touch the quadric at points where it is met by the plane $alx + bmy + cnz = 0$ which is known as the plane of contact.

EXERCISES

1. Show that the enveloping cylinders of the ellipsoid

   $$ax^2 + by^2 + cz^2 = 1,$$

   with generators perpendicular to Z-axis meet the plane $z = 0$ in parabolas.

2. Enveloping cylinders of the quadric $ax^2 + by^2 + cz^2 = 1$ meet the plane $z = 0$ in rectangular hyperbola; show that the central perpendiculars to their planes of contact generate the cone $b^2cx^2 + a^2cy^2 + ab(a + b)z^2 = 0$.

3. Prove that the enveloping cylinders of the ellipsoid

   $$\frac{x^2}{a^2} + \frac{y^2}{b^2} + \frac{z^2}{c^2} = 1$$

   whose generators are parallel to the lines

   $$x = 0, \ \pm \frac{y}{\sqrt{a^2 - b^2}} = \frac{z}{c}$$

   meet the plane $z = 0$ in circles.

8.7.1. Locus of Chords Bisected at a Given Point. Section With a Given Centre

(*Ajmer, 1998*)

Let the given point be (α, β, γ).

If a chord

$$\frac{x - \alpha}{l} = \frac{y - \beta}{m} = \frac{z - \gamma}{n} \qquad \text{...(1)}$$

of the quadric $ax^2 + by^2 + cz^2 = 1$ is bisected at (α, β, γ), the two roots r_1 and r_2 of the equation (A) of § 8.3 are equal and opposite so that $r_1 + r_2 = 0$, implying

$$al\alpha + bm\beta + cn\gamma = 0 \qquad \text{...(2)}$$

Therefore, the required locus, obtained by eliminating l, m, n between (1) and (2), is

$$a\alpha(x - \alpha) + b\beta(y - \beta) + c\gamma(z - \gamma) = 0$$

which is a plane and can briefly be written as

$$T_1 = S_1.$$

The section of the quadric by this plane is a conic whose centre is (α, β, γ); for this point bisects all chords of the conic through it.

Cor. *The plane which cuts the quadric* $ax^2 + by^2 + cz^2 = 1$, *in a conic whose centre is* (α, β, γ) *is*

$$\Sigma \, a\alpha x = \Sigma \, a\alpha^2$$

EXAMPLES

1. *Show that the locus of the centres of sections of a central conicoid which pass through a given line is a conic.*

Sol. Let the central conicoid be

$$ax^2 + by^2 + cz^2 = 1 \qquad \qquad ...(i)$$

The section of this conicoid whose centre is the point (α, β, γ) is given by

$$a\alpha \, (x - \alpha) + b\beta \, (y - \beta) + c\gamma \, (z - \gamma) = 0$$

This passes through the given line

$$\frac{x - x'}{l} = \frac{y - y'}{m} = \frac{z - z'}{n}$$

if

$$a\alpha \, (x' - \alpha) + b\beta \, (y' - \beta) + c\gamma \, (z' - \gamma) = 0$$

and

$$a\alpha l + b\beta m + c\gamma n = 0$$

Hence, the locus of centres is given by the equations

$$ax \, (x' - x) + by \, (y' - y) + cz \, (z' - z) = 0$$

and

$$alx + bmy + cnz = 0$$

or

$$ax^2 + by^2 + cz^2 = axx' + byy' + czz' \qquad \qquad ...(ii)$$

and

$$alx + bmy + cnz = 0 \qquad \qquad ...(iii)$$

These two equations determine a conic.

2. *Triads of tangent planes at right angles are drawn to the ellipsoid* $x^2/a^2 + y^2/b^2 + z^2/c^2 = 1$. *Show that the locus of the centre of section of the surface by the plane through their points of contact is*

$$x^2 + y^2 + z^2 = \left(\frac{x^2}{a^2} + \frac{y^2}{b^2} + \frac{z^2}{c^2} \right)(a^2 + b^2 + c^2).$$

Sol. Suppose that (α, β, γ) is the centre of section of the surface by a plane through the points of contact of a triad of mutually perpendicular tangent planes. The pole of this section must thus be a point of the director sphere

$$x^2 + y^2 + z^2 = a^2 + b^2 + c^2$$

The equation of the section is $T_1 = S_1$, *i.e.*,

$$\frac{\alpha x}{a^2} + \frac{\beta y}{b^2} + \frac{\gamma z}{c^2} = \frac{\alpha^2}{a^2} + \frac{\beta^2}{b^2} + \frac{\gamma^2}{c^2} \qquad \qquad ...(i)$$

If (f, g, h) be its pole, the equation (i) must be the same as

$$\frac{fx}{a^2} + \frac{gy}{b^2} + \frac{hz}{c^2} = 1 \qquad \qquad ...(ii)$$

Comparing (i) and (ii), we have

$$f = \frac{\alpha}{\Sigma \, (\alpha^2 / a^2)}, \; g = \frac{\beta}{\Sigma \, (\alpha^2 / a^2)}, \; h = \frac{\gamma}{\Sigma \, (\alpha^2 / a^2)}$$

Since $f^2 + g^2 + h^2 = a^2 + b^2 + c^2$

we have $\alpha^2 + \beta^2 + \gamma^2 = [(\Sigma\, \alpha^2/a^2)]^2\, (a^2 + b^2 + c^2).$

Replacing α, β, γ by x, y, z respectively, we have the required result.

3. *Prove that the middle points of chords of*
$$ax^2 + by^2 + cz^2 = 1$$
which are parallel to $x = 0$ and touch $x^2 + y^2 + z^2 = r^2$ lie on the surface
$$by^2\, (bx^2 + by^2 + cz^2 - br^2) + cz^2\, (cx^2 + by^2 + cz^2 - cr^2) = 0.$$

Sol. Equations of any chord parallel to $x = 0$ are

$$\frac{x - \alpha}{0} = \frac{y - \beta}{m} = \frac{z - \gamma}{n} \qquad\qquad ...(1)$$

where (α, β, γ) are the co-ordinates of the middle point of this chord.

Since (α, β, γ) lies on the diametral plane $bxm + czn = 0$

$$b\beta m + c\gamma n = 0 \qquad\qquad ...(2)$$

Also (1) touches the sphere $x^2 + y^2 + z^2 = r^2$. Therefore the length of the perpendicular from its centre $(0, 0, 0)$ on (1) should be $\pm\, r$, *i.e.,*

$$\pm\, r = \left[(0 - \alpha)^2 + (0 - \beta)^2 + (0 - \gamma)^2 \right.$$

$$\left. - \left\{ (0 - \alpha)\, 0 + (0 - \beta)\, \frac{m}{\sqrt{m^2 + n^2}} + (0 - \gamma)\, \frac{n}{\sqrt{m^2 + n^2}} \right\}^2 \right]^{1/2}$$

Squaring, we have

$$r^2 = \alpha^2 + \beta^2 + \gamma^2 - \frac{(\beta m + \gamma n)^2}{m^2 + n^2}$$

or $(\alpha^2 + \beta^2 + \gamma^2 - r^2)\, (m^2 + n^2) = (\beta m + \gamma n)^2$

or $(\alpha^2 + \beta^2 + \gamma^2 - r^2)\left(1 + \dfrac{n^2}{m^2}\right) = \left(\beta + \gamma \cdot \dfrac{n}{m}\right)^2$

Substituting the value of $\dfrac{n}{m}$ from (2), we have

$$(\alpha^2 + \beta^2 + \gamma^2 - r^2)\left(1 + \frac{b^2\beta^2}{c^2\gamma^2}\right) = \left(\beta - \gamma \cdot \frac{b\beta}{c\gamma}\right)^2$$

or $(\alpha^2 + \beta^2 + \gamma^2 - r^2)\, (b^2\beta^2 + c^2\gamma^2) = (\beta c\gamma - \beta b\gamma)^2$

or $(\alpha^2 + \beta^2 + \gamma^2 - r^2)\, (b^2\beta^2 + c^2\gamma^2) = \beta^2\gamma^2\, (c - b)^2.$

Therefore locus of (α, β, γ) is

$$(x^2 + y^2 + z^2 - r^2)\, (b^2y^2 + c^2z^2) - y^2z^2\, (c - b)^2 = 0$$

or $by^2\, (bx^2 + by^2 + cz^2 - br^2) + cz^2\, (cx^2 + by^2 + cz^2 - cr^2) = 0.$

4. *Prove that the locus of the centres of all sections of the conicoid $ax^2 + by^2 + cz^2 = 1$ by planes which pass through a fixed point (x', y', z') is the quadric*
$$ax\, (x - x') + by\, (y - y') + az\, (z - z') = 0.$$ *(Rohilkhand, 1994, 95)*

Sol. Let (α, β, γ) be the centre of the section. Then the equation of the section is

$$a\alpha\, (x - \alpha) + b\beta\, (y - \beta) + c\gamma\, (z - \gamma) = 0 \qquad\qquad ...(i)$$

If (*i*) passes through a fixed point (x', y', z'),
$$a\alpha (x' - \alpha) + b\beta (y' - \beta) + c\gamma (z' - \gamma) = 0 \qquad ...(ii)$$
Hence the locus of the centre (α, β, γ) subject to the condition (*ii*) is
$$ax (x - x') + by (y - y') + cz (z - z') = 0.$$

5. *Show that the line joining a point P to the centre of a conicoid passes through the centre of the section of the conicoid by the polar plane of P.*

Sol. Let *P* be the point (α, β, γ) and the conicoid be
$$ax^2 + by^2 + cz^2 = 1 \qquad ...(i)$$
Then the polar plane of *P* w.r.t. (*i*) is
$$a\alpha x + b\beta y + c\gamma z = 1 \qquad ...(ii)$$
Let $(\alpha', \beta', \gamma')$ be the centre of the conic in which this plane cuts (*i*).
This section with $(\alpha', \beta', \gamma')$ as its centre is given by
$$a\alpha' (x - \alpha') + b\beta' (y - \beta') + c\gamma' (z - \gamma') = 0 \qquad ...(iii)$$
The plane (*iii*) should be identical with the plane (*ii*).
Comparing coefficients in (*ii*) and (*iii*), we get
$$\frac{\alpha'}{\alpha} = \frac{\beta'}{\beta} = \frac{\gamma'}{\gamma}$$
This shows that $(\alpha', \beta', \gamma')$ lies on the line
$$\frac{x}{\alpha} = \frac{y}{\beta} = \frac{z}{\gamma}$$
which is the line *OP* joining $P (\alpha, \beta, \gamma)$ to the centre $O (0, 0, 0)$.

EXERCISES

1. Find the equation of the plane which cuts the surface
$$x^2 - 2y^2 + 3z^2 = 4$$
in a conic whose centre is at the point (5, 7, 6).   [**Ans.** $5x - 14y + 18z = 35$]

2. Find the centres of the conics
   (*i*) $4x + 9y + 4z = - 15, 2x^2 - 3y^2 + 4z^2 = 1$;
   (*ii*) $2x - 2y - 5z + 5 = 0, 3x^2 + 2y^2 - 15z^2 = 4$.   [**Ans.** (*i*) (2, − 3, 1), (*ii*) (− 2, 3, − 1)]

3. Prove that the plane through the three extremities of the different axes of a central conicoid cuts it in a conic whose centre coincides with the centroid of the triangle formed by those extremities.

4. Show that the centre of the conic
$$lx + my + nz = p, ax^2 + by^2 + cz^2 = 1$$
is the point
$$\left(\frac{lp}{ap_0^2}, \frac{mp}{bp_0^2}, \frac{np}{cp_0^2} \right)$$
where $l^2 + m^2 + n^2 = 1$ and $p_0 = \sqrt{\Sigma t^2 / a}$.

5. A variable plane makes intercepts on the axes of a central conicoid whose sum is zero. Show that the locus of the centre of the section determined by it is a cone which has the axes of the conicoid as its generators.

6. Find the locus of the centres of sections which pass through a given point.

7. Show that the centres of sections of $ax^2 + by^2 + cz^2 = 1$ by planes which are at a constant distance, p, from the origin lie on the surface

$$(ax^2 + by^2 + cz^2) = p^2 (a^2x^2 + b^2y^2 + c^2z^2).$$

8. Find the locus of centres of sections of $ax^2 + by^2 + cz^2 = 1$, which touch

$$\alpha x^2 + \beta y^2 + \gamma z^2 = 1.$$

[**Ans.** $a^2\alpha^{-1}x^2 + b^2\beta^{-1}y^2 + c^2\gamma^{-1}z^2 = (ax^2 + by^2 + cz^2)^2$]

(Ajmer, 1997; Avadh, 1996; Rohilkhand, 1995)

8.7.2. Locus of Mid-Points of a System of Parallel Chords

Let l, m, n be proportional to the direction cosines of a given system of parallel chords and let (α, β, γ) be the mid-point of one of them.

As the chord

$$\frac{x - \alpha}{l} = \frac{y - \beta}{m} = \frac{z - \gamma}{n}$$

of the quadric is bisected at (α, β, γ), we have, as in § 8.7.1,

$$a l\alpha + b m\beta + c n\gamma = 0.$$

Now l, m, n being fixed, the locus of the mid-points (α, β, γ) of the parallel chords is the plane

$$alx + bmy + cnz = 0,$$

which clearly passes through the centre of the quadric and is known as the *Diametral plane conjugate to the direction l, m, n.*

Conversely, a plane $Ax + By + Cz = 0$ through the centre is the *diametral plane* conjugate to the direction l, m, n given by

$$\frac{al}{A} = \frac{bm}{B} = \frac{cn}{C}.$$

Thus, *every central plane is a diametral plane conjugate to some direction.*

Note. If P be a point on the conicoid, then the plane bisecting chords parallel to the line OP is called the *diametral plane of OP*.

Note. Another method. Use of elements at infinity. We know that the mid-point of a line AB is the harmonic conjugate of the point at infinity on the line w.r.t. A and B. Thus, the *locus of the mid-points of a system of parallel chords is the polar plane of the point at infinity common to the chords of the system.*

We know that $(l, m, n, 0)$ is the point at infinity lying on a line with direction ratios l, m, n. Its polar plane w.r.t. the conicoid

$$ax^2 + by^2 + cz^2 - w^2 = 0$$

expressed in cartesian homogeneous co-ordinates, is

$$alx + bmy + cnz - w \cdot 0 = 0$$

$\Leftrightarrow \qquad\qquad alx + bmy + cnz = 0.$

EXERCISES

1. $P(1, 3, 2)$ is a point on the conicoid

$$x^2 - 2y^2 + 3z^2 + 5 = 0.$$

Find the locus of the mid-points of chords drawn parallel to OP.

[**Ans.** $x - 6y + 6z = 0$]

2. Find the equation of the chord of the quadric $4x^2 - 5y^2 + 6z^2 = 7$ which passes through the point (2, 3, 4) and is bisected by the plane $2x - 5y + 3z = 0$.

$$\left[\text{Ans. } (x - 2) = \frac{1}{2}(y - 3) = (z - 4)\right]$$

8.8. CONJUGATE DIAMETERS AND DIAMETRAL PLANES

In what follows, we shall confine our attention to the ellipsoid only.

Let $P(x_1, y_1, z_1)$ be a point on the ellipsoid

$$\frac{x^2}{a^2} + \frac{y^2}{b^2} + \frac{z^2}{c^2} = 1$$

The equation of the diametral plane bisecting chords parallel to the line OP is

$$\frac{xx_1}{a^2} + \frac{yy_1}{b^2} + \frac{zz_1}{c^2} = 1$$

Let $Q(x_2, y_2, z_2)$ be a point on the section of the ellipsoid by this plane so that we have

$$\frac{x_1 x_2}{a^2} + \frac{y_1 y_2}{b^2} + \frac{z_1 z_2}{c^2} = 0$$

which is the condition that the diametral plane of OP should pass through Q and, by symmetry, it is also the condition that the diametral plane of OQ should pass through P.

Thus, *if the diametral plane of OP passes through Q, then the diametral plane of OQ also passes through P.*

Let $R(x_3, y_3, z_3)$ be one of the two points where the line of intersection of diametral planes of OP and OQ meets the conicoid.

Since the point R is on the diametral planes of OP and OQ, the diametral plane

$$\frac{xx_3}{a^2} + \frac{yy_3}{b^2} + \frac{zz_3}{c^2} = 0$$

of OR passes through the points P and Q.

Thus, we obtain the following two sets of relations :

$$\left.\begin{aligned}\frac{x_1^2}{a^2} + \frac{y_1^2}{b^2} + \frac{z_1^2}{c^2} &= 1, \\ \frac{x_2^2}{a^2} + \frac{y_2^2}{b^2} + \frac{z_2^2}{c^2} &= 1, \\ \frac{x_3^2}{a^2} + \frac{y_3^2}{b^2} + \frac{z_3^2}{c^2} &= 1. \end{aligned}\right\}\ \text{...(A)} \qquad \left.\begin{aligned}\frac{x_2 x_3}{a^2} + \frac{y_2 y_3}{b^2} + \frac{z_2 z_3}{c^2} &= 0, \\ \frac{x_3 x_1}{a^2} + \frac{y_3 y_1}{b^2} + \frac{z_3 z_1}{c^2} &= 0, \\ \frac{x_1 x_2}{a^2} + \frac{y_1 y_2}{b^2} + \frac{z_1 z_2}{c^2} &= 0. \end{aligned}\right\}\ \text{...(B)}$$

The three semi-diameters OP, OQ, OR are called **conjugate semi-diameters** *if the plane containing any two of them is the diametral plane of the third.*

The co-ordinates of the extremities of the conjugate semi-diameters are connected by the relations (A) and (B) above.

Conjugate Planes. *The three diametral planes POQ, QOR, ROP are called* **conjugate planes** *if each is the diametral plane of the line of intersection of the other two.*

We shall now obtain two more sets of relations (C), (D), equivalent to the relations (A), (B).

By virtue of the relations (A), we see that

$$\frac{x_1}{a}, \frac{y_1}{b}, \frac{z_1}{c}; \frac{x_2}{a}, \frac{y_2}{b}, \frac{z_2}{c}; \frac{x_3}{a}, \frac{y_3}{b}, \frac{z_3}{c}$$

can be considered as the direction cosines of some three straight lines and the relations (B) show that these three straight lines are also mutually perpendicular.

Hence, as in § 5.2, we have

$$\frac{x_1}{a}, \frac{x_2}{a}, \frac{x_3}{a}; \frac{y_1}{b}, \frac{y_2}{b}, \frac{y_3}{b}; \frac{z_1}{c}, \frac{z_2}{c}, \frac{z_3}{c}$$

are also the direction cosines of three mutually perpendicular straight lines. Therefore, we have

$$\left.\begin{array}{l} x_1^2 + x_2^2 + x_3^2 = a^2, \\ y_1^2 + y_2^2 + y_3^2 = b^2, \\ z_1^2 + z_2^2 + z_3^2 = c^2. \end{array}\right\} \;...\text{(C)} \qquad \left.\begin{array}{l} y_1 z_1 + y_2 z_2 + y_3 z_3 = 0, \\ z_1 x_1 + z_2 x_2 + z_3 x_3 = 0, \\ x_1 y_1 + x_2 y_2 + x_3 y_3 = 0. \end{array}\right\} \;...\text{(D)}$$

Properties of Conjugate Semi-Diameters

8.8.1. *The sum of the squares of three conjugate semi-diameters is constant.*

(Ajmer, 1998; Kumaon, 1996; Poorvanchal, 1998, 99)

Adding the relations (C), we get

$$OP^2 + OQ^2 + OR^2 = a^2 + b^2 + c^2$$

which is constant.

8.8.2. *The volume of the parallelopiped formed by three conjugate semi-diameters as coterminous edges is constant.*

The results (B) give

$$\frac{x_1/a}{\dfrac{y_2 z_3 - y_3 z_2}{bc}} = \frac{y_1/b}{\dfrac{z_2 x_3 - z_3 x_2}{ca}} = \frac{z_1/c}{\dfrac{x_2 y_3 - x_3 y_2}{ab}} = \frac{\sqrt{\sum x_1^2 / a^2}}{\sqrt{\sum \left(\dfrac{y_2 z_3 - y_3 z_2}{bc}\right)^2}} = \pm 1$$

since $\sum \left(\dfrac{y_2 z_3 - y_3 z_2}{bc}\right)^2$ is the sine of the angle between two perpendicular lines with direction cosines

$$\frac{x_2}{a}, \frac{y_2}{b}, \frac{z_2}{c} \text{ and } \frac{x_3}{a}, \frac{y_3}{b}, \frac{z_3}{c}$$

We have

$$\frac{x_1}{a} = \pm \frac{y_2 z_3 - y_3 z_2}{bc}, \frac{y_1}{b} = \pm \frac{z_2 x_3 - z_3 x_2}{ca}, \frac{z_1}{c} = \pm \frac{x_2 y_3 - x_3 y_2}{ab}$$

Now the volume of the parallelopiped whose coterminous edges are OP, OQ, OR

$$= 6 \times \text{volume of the tetrahedron } OPQR$$

$$= \begin{vmatrix} 0 & 0 & 0 & 1 \\ x_1 & y_1 & z_1 & 1 \\ x_2 & y_2 & z_2 & 1 \\ x_3 & y_3 & z_3 & 1 \end{vmatrix} = \begin{vmatrix} x_1 & y_1 & z_1 \\ x_2 & y_2 & z_2 \\ x_3 & y_3 & z_3 \end{vmatrix}$$

$$= x_1 (y_2 z_3 - y_3 z_2) + y_1 (z_2 x_3 - z_3 x_2) + z_1 (x_2 y_3 - x_3 y_2)$$

$$= \pm \frac{bcx_1^2}{a} \pm \frac{cay_1^2}{b} \pm \frac{abz_1^2}{c}$$

$$= \pm abc \, \Sigma \frac{x_1^2}{a^2} = \pm abc, \text{ which is a constant.}$$

The same result can also be proved in the following manner :

$$\begin{vmatrix} x_1 & y_1 & z_1 \\ x_2 & y_2 & z_2 \\ x_3 & y_3 & z_3 \end{vmatrix} \times \begin{vmatrix} x_1 & y_1 & z_1 \\ x_2 & y_2 & z_2 \\ x_3 & y_3 & z_3 \end{vmatrix} = \begin{vmatrix} \Sigma x_1^2 & \Sigma x_1 y_1 & \Sigma x_1 z_1 \\ \Sigma x_1 y_1 & \Sigma y_1^2 & \Sigma y_1 z_1 \\ \Sigma x_1 z_1 & \Sigma y_1 z_1 & \Sigma z_1^2 \end{vmatrix}$$

(By the rule of multiplication of determinants)
$$= a^2 b^2 c^2, \text{ from (C) and (D).}$$

8.8.3. *The sum of the squares of the areas of the faces of the parallelopiped formed with any three conjugate semi-diameters as coterminous edges is constant.*

Let A_1, A_2, A_3 be the areas of the triangles OQR, ORP, OPQ, and let l_i, m_i, n_i $(i = 1, 2, 3)$ be the direction cosines of the normals to the planes respectively.

Now, the projection of the triangle OQR on the YZ plane is the triangle with vertices $(0, 0, 0)$, $(0, y_2, z_2), (0, y_3, z_3)$ whose area is $\frac{1}{2}(y_2 z_3 - y_3 z_2)$. Also this is $A_1 l_1$. Thus, we have

$$A_1 l_1 = \frac{1}{2}(y_2 z_3 - y_3 z_2) = \pm \frac{bcx_1}{2a}$$

Similarly
$$A_1 m_1 = \pm \frac{cay_1}{2b}, \quad A_1 n_1 = \pm \frac{abz_1}{2c}$$

Squaring and adding, we obtain

$$A_1^2 = \frac{b^2 c^2 x_1^2}{4a^2} + \frac{c^2 a^2 y_1^2}{4b^2} + \frac{a^2 b^2 z_1^2}{4c^2}$$

Similarly projecting the areas ORP and OPQ on the co-ordinate planes, we get

$$A_2^2 = \frac{b^2 c^2 x_2^2}{4a^2} + \frac{c^2 a^2 y_2^2}{4b^2} + \frac{a^2 b^2 z_2^2}{4c^2}$$

$$A_3^2 = \frac{b^2 c^2 x_3^2}{4a^2} + \frac{c^2 a^2 y_3^2}{4b^2} + \frac{a^2 b^2 z_3^2}{4c^2}$$

Adding, we get

$$A_1^2 + A_2^2 + A_3^2 = \frac{1}{4}(b^2 c^2 + c^2 a^2 + a^2 b^2)$$

which is a constant.

8.8.4. *The sum of the squares of the projections of three semi-conjugate diameters on any line or plane is constant.*

Let l, m, n be the direction cosines of any given line so that the sum of the squares of the projections of three semi-conjugate diameters OP, OQ, OR on the line is

$$= (lx_1 + my_1 + nz_1)^2 + (lx_2 + my_2 + nz_2)^2 + (lx_3 + my_3 + nz_3)^2$$
$$= l^2 \Sigma x_1^2 + m^2 \Sigma y_1^2 + n^2 \Sigma z_1^2 + 2lm \Sigma x_1 y_1 + 2mn \Sigma y_1 z_1 + 2nl \Sigma z_1 x_1$$
$$= a^2 l^2 + b^2 m^2 + c^2 n^2$$

which is a constant.

Again, let l, m, n be the direction cosines of normal of any given plane so that the sum of the squares of the projections of OP, OQ, OR on this plane is

$$= OP^2 - (lx_1 + my_1 + nz_1)^2 + OQ^2 - (lx_2 + my_2 + nz_2)^2 + OR^2 - (lx_3 + my_3 + nz_3)^2$$
$$= a^2 + b^2 + c^2 - a^2l^2 - b^2m^2 - c^2n^2$$
$$= a^2(m^2 + n^2) + b^2(n^2 + l^2) + c^2(l^2 + m^2)$$

which is a constant.

EXAMPLES

1. *Show that the equation of the plane through the extremities*
$$(x_k, y_k, z_k), k = 1, 2, 3,$$
of the conjugate semi-diameters of the ellipsoid
$$x^2/a^2 + y^2/b^2 + z^2/c^2 = 1,$$

is
$$\frac{x(x_1 + x_2 + x_3)}{a^2} + \frac{y(y_1 + y_2 + y_3)}{b^2} + \frac{z(z_1 + z_2 + z_3)}{c^2} = 1.$$

(Agra, 1995; Aimer, 1997; Garhwal, 2000; Purvanchal, 2004, 96; Rohilkhand, 2003

Sol. Let
$$lx + my + nz = p$$
be the plane through the three extremities of the given conjugate semi-diameter, so that we have
$$lx_1 + my_1 + nz_1 = p$$
$$lx_2 + my_2 + nz_2 = p$$
$$lx_3 + my_3 + nz_3 = p$$

Multiplying these by x_1, x_2, x_3 respectively and adding we obtain
$$la^2 = p \, \Sigma x_1$$
Similarly $\qquad mb^2 = p \, \Sigma y_1$ and $nc^2 = p \, \Sigma z_1$
Hence, the required equation.

2. *Find the locus of the equal conjugate diameters of the ellipsoid*
$$\frac{x^2}{a^2} + \frac{y^2}{b^2} + \frac{z^2}{c^2} = 1.$$

(Agra, 1996; Gorakhpur, 2002; Ajmer, 1994; Garhwal, 2002;
Avadh 2006, Poorvanchal, 1995, 98; Rohilkhand, 1999)

Sol. Let OP, OQ, OR be three equal conjugate semi-diameters. We have
$$\begin{cases} OP^2 + OQ^2 + OR^2 = a^2 + b^2 + c^2; \\ \qquad OP^2 = OQ^2 = OR^2 \end{cases}$$

$\Rightarrow \qquad\qquad OP^2 = \dfrac{1}{3}(a^2 + b^2 + c^2)$

Let P be the point (x_1, y_1, z_1). We require the locus of the line
$$\frac{x}{x_1} = \frac{y}{y_1} = \frac{z}{z_1} \qquad\qquad \text{...(1)}$$

where
$$x_1^2 + y_1^2 + z_1^2 = \frac{1}{3}(a^2 + b^2 + c^2) \qquad\qquad \text{...(2)}$$

and
$$\frac{x_1^2}{a^2} + \frac{y_1^2}{b^2} + \frac{z_1^2}{c^2} = 1 \qquad\qquad \text{..(3)}$$

From (2) and (3), we obtain the homogeneous relation

$$\frac{x_1^2}{a^2} + \frac{y_1^2}{b^2} + \frac{z_1^2}{c^2} = \frac{3(x_1^2 + y_1^2 + z_1^2)}{(a^2 + b^2 + c^2)} \qquad \ldots(4)$$

Eliminating x_1, y_1, z_1 from (1) and (4), we obtain the required locus, viz.,

$$\frac{x^2}{a^2} + \frac{y^2}{b^2} + \frac{z^2}{c^2} = \frac{3(x^2 + y^2 + z^2)}{(a^2 + b^2 + c^2)}.$$

3. *Show that if a cone*
$$Ax^2 + By^2 + Cz^2 + 2Fyz + 2Gzx + 2Hxy = 0,$$
has three of its generators along conjugate diameters of the ellipsoid

$$\frac{x^2}{a^2} + \frac{y^2}{b^2} + \frac{z^2}{c^2} = 1$$

then $\qquad\qquad Aa^2 + Bb^2 + Cc^2 = 0.$

Sol. Let OP, OQ, OR, where P, Q, R are the extremities of conjugate semi-diameters, be generators of the given cone.

Let $\qquad\qquad (x_1, y_1, z_1), (x_2, y_2, z_2), (x_3, y_3, z_3)$

be the co-ordinates of the points P, Q, R respectively. Since these points lie on the given cone, we have

$$Ax_1^2 + By_1^2 + Cz_1^2 + 2Fy_1z_1 + 2Gz_1x_1 + 2Hx_1y_1 = 0,$$

and two similar results.

Adding these three results and making use of the relations (C) and (D) of § 8.8, we obtain the given relation.

4. *With any point on the surface of an ellipsoid as centre, a sphere is described such that the tangent planes can be drawn to it from the centre of the ellipsoid which are conjugate diametral planes of the ellipsoid. Show that its radius is the same for all positions of its centre.*

Sol. Consider a point (f, g, h) on the ellipsoid

$$\frac{x^2}{a^2} + \frac{y^2}{b^2} + \frac{z^2}{c^2} = 1.$$

Let the three conjugate diametral planes

$$\frac{xx_1}{a^2} + \frac{yy_1}{b^2} + \frac{zz_1}{c^2} = 0, \quad \frac{xx_2}{a^2} + \frac{yy_2}{b^2} + \frac{zz_2}{c^2} = 0, \quad \frac{xx_3}{a^2} + \frac{yy_3}{b^2} + \frac{zz_3}{c^2} = 0,$$

be tangent planes to the sphere with centre (f, g, h) and radius r. The distance of the point (f, g, h) from each of the three planes being equal to r, we have

$$r = \frac{\Sigma(fx_1/a^2)}{\sqrt{(\Sigma x_1^2/a^4)}} \quad \Leftrightarrow \quad r^2 \Sigma \frac{x_1^2}{a^4} = \left(\Sigma \frac{fx_1}{a^2}\right)^2$$

$$r = \frac{\Sigma(fx_2/a^2)}{\sqrt{(\Sigma x_2^2/a^4)}} \quad \Leftrightarrow \quad r^2 \Sigma \frac{x_2^2}{a^4} = \left(\Sigma \frac{fx_2}{a^2}\right)^2$$

$$r = -\frac{\Sigma(fx_3/a^2)}{\sqrt{(\Sigma x_3^2/a^4)}} \quad \Leftrightarrow \quad r^2 \Sigma \frac{x_3^2}{a^4} = \left(\Sigma \frac{fx_3}{a^2}\right)^2$$

Adding and making use of the relations (C) and (D) of § 8.8, we have

$$r^2 \left[\sum \frac{1}{a^2} \right] = \sum \frac{f^2}{a^2} = 1$$

$$\Leftrightarrow \qquad\qquad r^2 = (\Sigma\, a^{-2})^{-1}.$$

Hence, the result.

5. *Show that the locus of the foot of the perpendicular from the centre to the plane through the extremities of three conjugate semi-diameters of the ellipsoid*

$$\frac{x^2}{a^2} + \frac{y^2}{b^2} + \frac{z^2}{c^2} = 1$$

is

$$a^2x^2 + b^2y^2 + c^2z^2 = 3\,(x^2 + y^2 + z^2)^2. \qquad\qquad \textit{(Garhwal, 1999)}$$

Sol. Let $P(x_1, y_1, z_1)$, $Q(x_2, y_2, z_2)$, $R(x_3, y_3, z_3)$ be the extremities of the three conjugate semi-diameters of the given ellipsoid with centre O.

Let (α, β, γ) be the foot of the perpendicular from the centre O of the ellipsoid on the plane PQR.

Equations of the perpendicular are

$$\frac{x}{\alpha} = \frac{y}{\beta} = \frac{z}{\gamma}.$$

Therefore equation of the plane PQR is

$$\alpha\,(x - \alpha) + \beta\,(y - \beta) + \gamma\,(z - \gamma) = 0$$

or

$$\alpha x + \beta y + \gamma z = \alpha^2 + \beta^2 + \gamma^2$$

P, Q, R lie on this plane. Therefore

$$\alpha x_1 + \beta y_1 + \gamma z_1 = \alpha^2 + \beta^2 + \gamma^2, \qquad\qquad ...(i)$$

$$\alpha x_2 + \beta y_2 + \gamma z_2 = \alpha^2 + \beta^2 + \gamma^2, \qquad\qquad ...(ii)$$

and

$$\alpha x_3 + \beta y_3 + \gamma z_3 = \alpha^2 + \beta^2 + \gamma^2 \qquad\qquad ...(iii)$$

Multiplying (*i*) by x_1, (*ii*) by x_2 and (*iii*) by x_3, and adding, we get

$$\alpha\,(x_1^2 + x_2^2 + x_3^2) + \beta\,(x_1y_1 + x_2y_2 + x_3y_3) + \gamma\,(z_1x_1 + z_2x_2 + z_3x_3)$$
$$= (x_1 + x_2 + x_3)\,(\alpha^2 + \beta^2 + \gamma^2)$$

Using relations (C) and (D) of § 8.8, we have

$$\alpha a^2 = (x_1 + x_2 + x_3)\,(\alpha^2 + \beta^2 + \gamma^2)$$

or

$$\alpha a = \left(\frac{x_1 + x_2 + x_3}{a} \right)(\alpha^2 + \beta^2 + \gamma^2) \qquad\qquad :...(iv)$$

Similarly

$$\beta b = \left(\frac{y_1 + y_2 + y_3}{b} \right)(\alpha^2 + \beta^2 + \gamma^2) \qquad\qquad ...(v)$$

and

$$\gamma c = \left(\frac{z_1 + z_2 + z_3}{c} \right)(\alpha^2 + \beta^2 + \gamma^2) \qquad\qquad ...(vi)$$

Now squaring and adding these equations, we get

$$\alpha^2 a^2 + \beta^2 b^2 + \gamma^2 c^2 = (\alpha^2 + \beta^2 + \gamma^2)^2 \left[\left(\frac{x_1 + x_2 + x_3}{a} \right)^2 + \left(\frac{y_1 + y_2 + y_3}{b} \right)^2 \right.$$
$$\left. + \left(\frac{z_1 + z_2 + z_3}{c} \right)^2 \right]$$

$$= (\alpha^2 + \beta^2 + \gamma^2)^2 \left[\frac{x_1^2 + x_2^2 + x_3^2}{a^2} + \frac{y_1^2 + y_2^2 + y_3^2}{b^2} + \frac{z_1^2 + z_2^2 + z_3^2}{c^2} \right.$$

$$\left. + 2\left(\frac{x_1 x_2}{a^2} + \frac{y_1 y_2}{b^2} + \frac{z_1 z_2}{c^2} \right) + 2\left(\frac{x_3 x_1}{a^2} + \frac{y_3 y_1}{b^2} + \frac{z_3 z_1}{c^2} \right) + 2\left(\frac{x_2 x_3}{a^2} + \frac{y_2 y_3}{b^2} + \frac{z_2 z_3}{c^2} \right) \right]$$

Using relations (B) and (C) of § 8.8, we obtain

$$\alpha^2 a^2 + \beta^2 b^2 + \gamma^2 c^2 = (\alpha^2 + \beta^2 + \gamma^2)^2 (1 + 1 + 1)$$

or

$$a^2 \alpha^2 + b^2 \beta^2 + c^2 \gamma^2 = 3 (\alpha^2 + \beta^2 + \gamma^2)^2$$

Hence the locus of the foot of perpendicular is

$$a^2 x^2 + b^2 y^2 + c^2 z^2 = 3 (x^2 + y^2 + z^2)^2.$$

6. *Find the locus of the point of intersection of three tangent planes to*

$$\frac{x^2}{a^2} + \frac{y^2}{b^2} + \frac{z^2}{c^2} = 1$$

which are parallel to conjugate diametral planes of

$$\frac{x^2}{\alpha^2} + \frac{y^2}{\beta^2} + \frac{z^2}{\gamma^2} = 1.$$

Sol. Let $P(x_1, y_1, z_1)$, $Q(x_2, y_2, z_2)$ and $R(x_3, y_3, z_3)$ be the extremities of the conjugate diameters of the ellipsoid

$$\frac{x^2}{\alpha^2} + \frac{y^2}{\beta^2} + \frac{z^2}{\gamma^2} = 1. \qquad \qquad \ldots(i)$$

Equations of the diametral planes are

$$\frac{xx_1}{\alpha^2} + \frac{yy_1}{\beta^2} + \frac{zz_1}{\gamma^2} = 0, \qquad \qquad \ldots(ii)$$

$$\frac{xx_2}{\alpha^2} + \frac{yy_2}{\beta^2} + \frac{zz_2}{\gamma^2} = 0, \qquad \qquad \ldots(iii)$$

and

$$\frac{xx_3}{\alpha^2} + \frac{yy_3}{\beta^2} + \frac{zz_3}{\gamma^2} = 0. \qquad \qquad \ldots(iv)$$

Planes which are parallel to these planes and touch the ellipsoid

$$\frac{x^2}{a^2} + \frac{y^2}{b^2} + \frac{z^2}{c^2} = 1$$

are given by the equations

$$\frac{xx_1}{\alpha^2} + \frac{yy_1}{\beta^2} + \frac{zz_1}{\gamma^2} = \pm \sqrt{ \frac{x_1^2 a^2}{\alpha^4} + \frac{y_1^2 b^2}{\beta^4} + \frac{z_1^2 c^2}{\gamma^4} },$$

$$\frac{xx_2}{\alpha^2} + \frac{yy_2}{\beta^2} + \frac{zz_2}{\gamma^2} = \pm \sqrt{ \frac{x_2^2 a^2}{\alpha^4} + \frac{y_2^2 b^2}{\beta^4} + \frac{z_2^2 c^2}{\gamma^4} },$$

and

$$\frac{xx_3}{\alpha^2} + \frac{yy_3}{\beta^2} + \frac{zz_3}{\gamma^2} = \pm \sqrt{ \frac{x_3^2 a^2}{\alpha^4} + \frac{y_3^2 b^2}{\beta^4} + \frac{z_3^2 c^2}{\gamma^4} }.$$

Squaring and adding these equations, we get

$$\frac{x^2}{\alpha^4}(x_1^2 + x_2^2 + x_3^2) + \frac{y^2}{\beta^4}(y_1^2 + y_2^2 + y_3^2) + \frac{z^2}{\gamma^4}(z_1^2 + z_2^2 + z_3^2)$$

$$+ \frac{2yz}{\beta^2\gamma^2}(y_1z_1 + y_2z_2 + y_3z_3) + \frac{2zx}{\gamma^2\alpha^2}(z_1x_1 + z_2x_2 + z_3x_3)$$

$$+ \frac{2xy}{\alpha^2\beta^2}(x_1y_1 + x_2y_2 + x_3y_3)$$

$$= \frac{a^2}{\alpha^4}(x_1^2 + x_2^2 + x_3^2) + \frac{b^2}{\beta^4}(y_1^2 + y_2^2 + y_3^2) + \frac{c^2}{\gamma^2}(z_1^2 + z_2^2 + z_3^2).$$

Using the relations (C) and (D) of § 8.8, we obtain

$$\frac{x^2}{\alpha^2} + \frac{y^2}{\beta^2} + \frac{z^2}{\gamma^2} = \frac{a^2}{\alpha^2} + \frac{b^2}{\beta^2} + \frac{c^2}{\gamma^2}$$

which is the required locus of the point of intersection of the tangent planes.

7. *Prove that the pole of the plane PQR lies on the ellipsoid*

$$\frac{x^2}{a^2} + \frac{y^2}{b^2} + \frac{z^2}{c^2} = 3,$$

where OP, OQ, OR are the conjugate semi-diameters of the ellipsoid

$$\frac{x^2}{a^2} + \frac{y^2}{b^2} + \frac{z^2}{c^2} = 1. \qquad (Avadh, 2003; Gorakhpur, 2003)$$

Sol. Equation of the plane PQR through the extremities $P(x_1, y_1, z_1)$, $Q(x_2, y_2, z_2)$, $R(x_3, y_3, z_3)$ is

$$\frac{x}{a^2}(x_1 + x_2 + x_3) + \frac{y}{b^2}(y_1 + y_2 + y_3) + \frac{z}{c^2}(z_1 + z_2 + z_3) = 1. \qquad ...(i)$$

If (α, β, γ) be the pole of the plane PQR, then its equation is

$$\frac{\alpha x}{a^2} + \frac{\beta y}{b^2} + \frac{\gamma z}{c^2} = 1 \qquad ...(ii)$$

(*i*) and (*ii*) represent the same plane, therefore,

$$\alpha = x_1 + x_2 + x_3,$$
$$\beta = y_1 + y_2 + y_3,$$
$$\gamma = z_1 + z_2 + z_3.$$

Now multiplying these relations by $1/a$, $1/b$, $1/c$ respectively; squaring and adding, we get

$$\frac{\alpha^2}{a^2} + \frac{\beta^2}{b^2} + \frac{\gamma^2}{c^2} = \left(\frac{x_1 + x_2 + x_3}{a}\right)^2 + \left(\frac{y_1 + y_2 + y_3}{b}\right)^2 + \left(\frac{z_1 + z_2 + z_3}{c}\right)^2$$

On using relations (B) and (C) of § 8.8, this simplifies to

$$\frac{\alpha^2}{a^2} + \frac{\beta^2}{b^2} + \frac{\gamma^2}{c^2} = 3$$

Hence the locus of (α, β, γ) is the ellipsoid

$$\frac{x^2}{a^2} + \frac{y^2}{b^2} + \frac{z^2}{c^2} = 3.$$

EXERCISES

1. Show that the lines
$$\frac{x}{1} = \frac{y}{4} = \frac{z}{3}, \frac{x}{4} = \frac{y}{1} = \frac{z}{-9}, \frac{x}{26} = \frac{y}{-28} = \frac{z}{45},$$
are three mutually conjugate diameters of the ellipsoid
$$\frac{x^2}{2} + \frac{y^2}{4} + \frac{z^2}{9} = 1.$$

2. Find the equations of the diameters in the plane $x + y + z = 0$, conjugate to
$$x = -\frac{1}{2}y = \frac{1}{3}z$$
with respect to the conicoid $3x^2 + y^2 - 2z^2 = 1$. What are the equations of the third conjugate diameter ?

$$\left[\textbf{Ans.} \ \frac{x}{4} = \frac{y}{-9} = \frac{z}{5}, \frac{x}{34} = \frac{y}{42} = \frac{z}{3}\right]$$

3. Show that for the ellipsoid $x^2 + 4y^2 + 5z^2 = 1$ the two diameters $\frac{1}{3}x = -\frac{1}{2}y = \frac{1}{3}z$ and $x = 0$, $2y = 5z$ are conjugate. Obtain the equations of the third conjugate diameter.
[**Ans.** $x/16 = y = -z/2$]

4. If p_1, p_2, p_3; π_1, π_2, π_3 be the projections of the three conjugate diameters on any two given lines, then $p_1\pi_1 + p_2\pi_2 + p_3\pi_3$ is constant.

5. If three conjugate diameters vary so that OP, OQ lie respectively in the fixed planes
$$\frac{\alpha_1 x}{a^2} + \frac{\beta_1 y}{b^2} + \frac{\gamma_1 z}{c^2} = 0, \frac{\alpha_2 x}{a^2} + \frac{\beta_2 y}{b^2} + \frac{\gamma_2 z}{c^2} = 0$$
show that the locus of OR is the cone
$$\Sigma \alpha^2 (\beta_1 z - \gamma_1 y)(\beta_2 z - \gamma_2 y) = 0.$$
[**Hint.** The required locus of OR is obtained from the fact that the lines of intersection of the diametral plane of OR with the given planes are conjugate lines.]

6. From a fixed point H perpendiculars HA, HB, HC are drawn to the conjugate diameters OP, OQ, OR respectively; show that
$$OP^2 \cdot HA^2 + OQ^2 \cdot HB^2 + OR^2 \cdot HC^2$$
is constant.

7. OP, OQ, OR are conjugate diameters of an ellipsoid
$$x^2/a^2 + y^2/b^2 + z^2/c^2 = 1.$$
At Q and R tangent lines are drawn parallel to OP and p_1, p_2 are their distances from O. The perpendicular from O to the tangent planes at right angles to OP is p. Prove that
$$p^2 + p_1^2 + p_2^2 = a^2 + b^2 + c^2.$$

8. Show that the plane $lx + my + nz = p$ will pass through the extremities of conjugate semi-diameters if $a^2l^2 + b^2m^2 + c^2n^2 = 3p^2$.

(*Avadh, 2000; Agra, 1996; Gorakhpur, 1997; Lucknow, 1995*)

9. Show that the locus of the centre of the section of the ellipsoid
$$x^2/a^2 + y^2/b^2 + z^2/c^2 = 1,$$
by the plane PQR is the ellipsoid
$$x^2/a^2 + y^2/b^2 + z^2/c^2 = 1/3$$
Prove that this locus coincides with the locus of the centroid of the triangle PQR.

10. Prove that the plane PQR touches the ellipsoid
$$x^2/a^2 + y^2/b^2 + z^2/c^2 = 1/3$$
at the centroid of the triangle PQR.   (*Gorakhpur, 2001*)

11. If one of the three extremities $P(x_1, y_1, z_1)$ of conjugate diameters be kept fixed, show that the locus of the line joining the centre of the centroid of the triangle PQR is the cone
$$\left(\frac{x^2}{a^2} + \frac{y^2}{b^2} + \frac{z^2}{c^2}\right) = 3\left(\frac{xx_1}{a^2} + \frac{yy_1}{b^2} + \frac{zz_1}{c^2}\right)^2.$$

12. If $(x_1, y_1, z_1), (x_2, y_2, z_2), (x_3, y_3, z_3)$ be the extremities of three conjugate diameters of the ellipsoid $x^2/a^2 + y^2/b^2 + z^2/c^2 = 1$, show that the equation of the plane through the three points
$$(x_1, x_2, x_3), (y_1, y_2, y_3), (z_1, z_2, z_3)$$
is
$$\left(\frac{x_1}{a^2} + \frac{y_1}{b^2} + \frac{z_1}{c^2}\right)x + \left(\frac{x_2}{a^2} + \frac{y_2}{b^2} + \frac{z_2}{c^2}\right)y + \left(\frac{x_3}{a^2} + \frac{y_3}{b^2} + \frac{z_3}{c^2}\right)z = 1$$
and that it touches the sphere
$$(x^2 + y^2 + z^2)(a^{-2} + b^{-2} + c^{-2}) = 1.$$

13. The enveloping cone from a point P to the ellipsoid $\Sigma \, x^2/a^2 = 1$ has three generating lines parallel to conjugate diameters of the ellipsoid; show that the locus of P is the ellipsoid
$$\frac{x^2}{a^2} + \frac{y^2}{b^2} + \frac{z^2}{c^2} = \frac{3}{2}x.$$

14. Show that any two sets of conjugate diameters of the ellipsoid lie on a quadric cone [**Hint.** Deduce from Example 3, page 249)]

15. Prove that the plane through a pair of equal conjugate diameters touch the cone
$$\frac{x^2}{a^2(2a^2 - b^2 - c^2)} + \frac{y^2}{b^2(2b^2 - c^2 - a^2)} + \frac{z^2}{c^2(2c^2 - a^2 - b^2)} = 0.$$
                                                              (*Poorvanchal, 1994, 99*)

PARABOLOIDS

8.9. Having discussed the nature and geometrical properties of central conicoids, we now proceed to the consideration of *paraboloids*.

8.9.1. The Elliptic Paraboloids $x^2/a^2 + y^2/b^2 = 2z/c$

We have the following particulars about this surface :

(*i*) The co-ordinate planes $x = 0$ and $y = 0$ bisect chords perpendicular to them and are, therefore, its two planes of symmetry or **Principal Planes.**

(*ii*) z cannot be negative, and hence there is no part of the surface on the negative side of the plane $z = 0$. We have taken c positive.

(*iii*) The sections by the planes $z = k$, $(k > 0)$, parallel to the XY plane, are similar ellipses
$$\frac{x^2}{a^2} + \frac{y^2}{b^2} = \frac{2k}{c}, \, z = k \qquad \qquad \dots(i)$$
whose centres lie on Z-axis and which increase in size as k increases; there being no limit to the increase of k. The surface may thus be supposed to be generated by the variable ellipse (*i*).

Hence, the surface is entirely on the positive side of the plane $z = 0$, and extends to infinity.

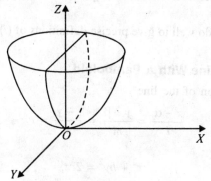

Fig. 46

(*iv*) The section of the surface by planes parallel to the YZ and ZX planes are clearly parabolas.

Figure 46 shows the nature of the surface.

Ex. Trace the surface $x^2/a^2 + y^2/b^2 = -2z/c$, $(c > 0)$.

8.9.2. The Hyperbolic Paraboloid $x^2/a^2 - y^2/b^2 = 2z/c$

(*i*) The co-ordinate planes $x = 0$ and $y = 0$ are the two **Principal Planes.**

(*ii*) The sections by the planes $z = k$ are the similar hyperbolas

$$\frac{x^2}{a^2} - \frac{y^2}{b^2} = \frac{2k}{c}, \ z = k,$$

with their centres on Z-axis.

If k be positive, the real axis of the hyperbola is parallel to X-axis, and if k be negative, the real axis is parallel to Y-axis.

The section by the plane $z = 0$ is the pair of lines

$$\frac{x}{a} = \frac{y}{b}, \ z = 0 \text{ and } \frac{x}{a} = -\frac{y}{b}, \ z = 0.$$

(*iii*) The section by the planes parallel to YZ and YX planes are parabolas.

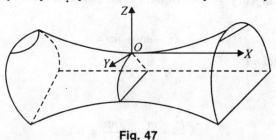

Fig. 47

Figure 47 shows the nature of the surface.

Note. The two equations considered in the last two articles are clearly both included in the form

$$ax^2 + by^2 = 2cz$$

This equation represents an elliptic paraboloid if a and b are both positive or both negative, and a hyperbolic paraboloid if one is positive and the other negative.

Hence, for an elliptic paraboloid, ab is positive but, for hyperbolic paraboloid, ab is negative.

The geometrical results deducible from the equation $ax^2 + by^2 = 2cz$ will hold for both the types of paraboloids.

Note. The reader would do well to give precise definitions of (i) vertex, (ii) principal planes, (iii) axis of a paraboloid.

8.9.3. Intersection of a Line With a Paraboloid

The points of intersection of the line

$$\frac{x - \alpha}{l} = \frac{y - \beta}{m} = \frac{z - \gamma}{n} = r$$

with the paraboloid

$$ax^2 + by^2 = 2cz,$$

are

$$(lr + \alpha, \ mr + \beta, \ nr + \gamma)$$

for the *two* values of r which are the roots of the quadric equation

$$r^2 (al^2 + bm^2) + 2r (al\alpha + bm\beta - cn)(a\alpha^2 + b\beta^2 - 2c\gamma) = 0 \qquad \text{...(A)}$$

We thus see that every line meets a paraboloid in two points.

It follows from this that the *plane sections of paraboloids are conics.*

Also, if $l = m = 0$, one value of r is infinite and hence any line parallel to Z-axis meets the paraboloid in one point at an infinite distance from (α, β, γ) and so meets it in one finite point only. Such lines are called **Diameters of the paraboloid.**

In particular, Z-axis meets the surface at the origin only.

8.9.4. From the equation (A), § 8.9.3 above, we deduce certain results similar to those obtained for central conicoids. The proofs of some of them are left as an exercise to the student.

1. The *tangent plane to* $ax^2 + by^2 = 2cz$ at any point (α, β, γ) on the surface is

$$a\alpha x + b\beta y = c (z + \gamma).$$

In particular, $z = 0$ is the tangent plane at the origin and Z-axis is the normal thereat.

The origin O is called the **vertex** of the paraboloid and Z-axis, the **axis** of the paraboloid.

2. Condition of Tangency   *(Ajmer, 1998; Gorakhpur, 1998, 2000; Rohilkhand, 1997)*

The plane

$$lx + my + nz = p$$

will touch the paraboloid

$$ax^2 + by^2 = 2cz \qquad \text{...(1)}$$

if

$$\frac{l^2}{a} + \frac{m^2}{b} + \frac{2np}{c} = 0$$

and assuming the condition to be satisfied, the point of contact is

$$\left(\frac{-lc}{an}, \ \frac{-mc}{bn}, \ \frac{-p}{n} \right)$$

Thus, *the plane*

$$2n (lx + my + nz) + c (l^2/a + m^2/b) = 0,$$

touches the surface (1) for all values of l, m, n.

3. Locus of the point of intersection of the three mutually perpendicular tangent planes

(Ajmer, 1994; Gorakhpur, 1999)

$$2n_r\,(l_r x + m_r y + n_r z) + c\left(\frac{lr_2^{\,2}}{a} + \frac{mr_2^{\,2}}{b}\right) = 0,\ (r = 1, 2, 3)$$

be three mutually perpendicular tangent planes, the locus of their point of intersection is obtained by eliminating l_r, m_r, n_r, which is done by adding the three equations and is, therefore,

$$2z + c\left(\frac{1}{a} + \frac{1}{b}\right) = 0,$$

and is a plane at right angles to the Z-axis; the axis of the paraboloid.

4. Equations of the *normal* at (α, β, γ) are

$$\frac{x - \alpha}{a\alpha} = \frac{y - \beta}{b\beta} = \frac{z - \gamma}{-c}.$$

(Ajmer, 1998; Kumaon 2005)

5. The *polar plane* of the point (α, β, γ) is

$$a\alpha x + b\beta y = c\,(\gamma + z).$$

6. The equation of the *enveloping cone* with (α, β, γ) as its vertex is

$$SS_1 = T_1^{\,2}$$

$$\Leftrightarrow \quad (ax^2 + by^2 - 2cz)\,(a\alpha^2 + b\beta^2 - 2c\gamma) = (a\alpha x + b\beta y - cz - cy)^2$$

Its *plane of contact* with the paraboloid is the polar plane

$$a\alpha x + b\beta y - cz - c\gamma = 0$$

of the vertex (α, β, γ).

7. The equation of the *enveloping cylinder* having its generators parallel to the line

$$\frac{x}{l} = \frac{y}{m} = \frac{z}{n}$$

is

$$(ax^2 + by^2 - 2cz)\,(al^2 + bm^2) = (alx + bmy - cn)^2$$

Its *plane of contact* is the plane

$$alx + bmy - cn = 0.$$

8. *The locus of chords bisected at a point (α, β, γ) is the plane*

$$T_1 = S_1$$

$$\Leftrightarrow \quad a\alpha\,(x - \alpha) + b\beta\,(y - \beta) - c\gamma\,(z - \gamma) = 0$$

This plane will meet the paraboloid in a conic whose centre is at (α, β, γ).

9. The *locus of mid-point of a system of parallel chords*, with direction ratios, l, m, n is the plane

$$alx + bmy - cn = 0$$

which is parallel to Z-axis, the axis of the paraboloid. The plane is called the *Diametral plane* conjugate to the given direction.

A plane $Ax + By + D = 0$ parallel to the axis of the paraboloid is easily seen, by comparison, to be the diametral plane for the system of parallel chords with direction ratios

$$A/a,\ B/b,\ -D/c$$

A plane parallel to the axis of a paraboloid is, thus, a diametral plane.

EXAMPLES

1. *Show that the plane $2x - 4y - z + 3 = 0$ touches the paraboloid $x^2 - 2y^2 = 3z$.*

Find also the co-ordinates of the point of contact. (*Rohilkhand, 1996, 2002, Avadh 2006*

Sol. We know that the equation of tangent plane at any point (α, β, γ) of the paraboloid $ax^2 + by^2 = 2cz$ is

$$a\alpha x + b\beta y = c(z + \gamma)$$

Here $a = 1, b = -2,$ and $2c = 3$.

Therefore tangent plane at (α, β, γ) to the given plane is

$$\alpha x - 2\beta y = \frac{3}{2}(z + \gamma)$$

or $2\alpha x - 4\beta y - 3z - 3\gamma = 0$,

This plane and the given plane should be the same.

Therefore comparing the coefficients, we have

$$\frac{2\alpha}{2} = \frac{-4\beta}{-4} = \frac{-3}{-1} = \frac{-3\gamma}{3}$$

or $\alpha = \beta = -\gamma = 3$.

Clearly the point $(3, 3, -3)$ satisfies the equation of the given paraboloid.

Hence the given plane touches the paraboloid, and its point of contact is $(3, 3, -3)$.

2. *Two perpendicular tangent planes to the paraboloid $x^2/a + y^2/b = 2z$ intersects in a straight line lying in the plane $x = 0$. Show that the line touches the parabola*

$$x = 0, y^2 = (a + b)(2z + a).$$ (*Rohilkhand, 2001*)

Sol. Equations of any line in the plane $x = 0$ is

$$x = 0, my + nz = p \qquad\qquad ...(i)$$

Any plane through this line is

$$\lambda x + my + nz - p = 0 \qquad\qquad ...(ii)$$

If this is a tangent plane to the paraboloid, then

$$a\lambda^2 + bm^2 + 2np = 0 \qquad\qquad ...(iii)$$

This is quadratic in λ and, therefore, gives the values λ_1, λ_2 and thus two tangent planes through the line (i) which are

$$\lambda_1 x + my + nz - p = 0$$

and $\lambda_2 x + my + nz - p = 0$

These planes are perpendicular if

$$\lambda_1 \lambda_2 + m^2 + n^2 = 0$$

$$\Rightarrow \qquad \frac{bm^2 + 2np}{a} + m^2 + n^2 = 0$$

$$\Rightarrow \qquad (a + b)m^2 + 2np + an^2 = 0 \qquad\qquad ...(iv)$$

Required parabola is the envelope of line (i) subject to the condition (iv). Eliminating p between (i) and (iv), we get

$$(a + b)m^2 + 2n(my + nz) + an^2 = 0, x = 0$$

or $(a + b)\left(\frac{m}{n}\right)^2 + 2y\left(\frac{m}{n}\right) + (a + 2z) = 0, x = 0$

Therefore, the envelope of the line is given by
$$(2y)^2 - 4(a + b)(a + 2z) = 0, x = 0$$
$$\Rightarrow \qquad y^2 = (a + b)(a + 2z), x = 0.$$

3. *Show that the feet of the normals from the point* (α, β, γ) *to the paraboloid* $x^2 + y^2 = 2az$ *lie on the sphere*

$$x^2 + y^2 + z^2 - y\left(\frac{\alpha^2 + \beta^2}{2\beta}\right) - z(a + \gamma) = 0. \qquad\qquad (Ajmer, 1995)$$

Sol. Normal at any point (x', y', z') to the given paraboloid is

$$\frac{x - x'}{x'} = \frac{y - y'}{y'} = \frac{z - z'}{-a} = \lambda \text{ (say)}.$$

If it passes through (α, β, γ), then

$$\frac{\alpha - x'}{x'} = \frac{\beta - y'}{y'} = \frac{\gamma - z'}{-a} = \lambda$$

$$\therefore \qquad x' = \frac{\alpha}{1 + \lambda}, \; y' = \frac{\beta}{1 + \lambda}, \; z' = \gamma + a\lambda$$

i.e., the feet of normals are

$$\left(\frac{\alpha}{1 + \lambda}, \frac{\beta}{1 + \lambda}, \gamma + a\lambda\right)$$

It lies on the paraboloid, therefore,

$$\left(\frac{\alpha}{1 + \lambda}\right)^2 + \left(\frac{\beta}{1 + \lambda}\right)^2 = 2a(\gamma + a\lambda)$$

$$\Rightarrow \qquad (\alpha^2 + \beta^2) = 2a(\gamma + a\lambda)(1 + \lambda)^2 \qquad\qquad ...(i)$$

If it lies on the sphere, then

$$\left(\frac{\alpha}{1 + \lambda}\right)^2 + \left(\frac{\beta}{1 + \lambda}\right)^2 + (\gamma + a\lambda)^2 - \frac{\beta}{1 + \lambda}\left(\frac{\alpha^2 + \beta^2}{2\beta}\right) - (\gamma + a\lambda)(a + \lambda) = 0$$

or $\quad \dfrac{1 - \lambda}{2(1 + \lambda)^2}[(\alpha^2 + \beta^2) - 2a(\gamma + a\lambda)(1 + \lambda)^2] = 0$

Since $\lambda \neq 1$, hence, eqn. (i) holds.

4. *Find the locus of the point of intersection of three mutually perpendicular tangent planes to the paraboloid* $ax^2 + by^2 = 2cz$.

(*Gorakhpur, 1995, 97, 99, 2002; Purvanchal, 1995, 97, 98, 99; Rohilkhand, 1995*)

Sol. The plane $lx + my + nz = p$ touches the paraboloid $ax^2 + by^2 = 2cz$, when

$$\frac{l^2}{a} + \frac{m^2}{b} + \frac{2np}{c} = 0 \text{ or } p = -\frac{c}{2n}\left(\frac{l^2}{a} + \frac{m^2}{b}\right).$$

By putting the value of p, we have

$$lx + my + nz + \frac{c}{2n}(l^2/a + m^2/b) = 0$$

or $\quad 2n(lx + my + nz) + c(l^2/a + m^2/b) = 0$

This plane always touches the given paraboloid.

Let three mutually perpendicular tangent planes be

$$2n_r (l_r x + m_r y + n_r z) + c (l_r^2/a + m_r^2/b) = 0, r = 1, 2, 3 \qquad ...(i)$$

Since the three planes and hence their normals are mutually perpendicular, hence

$$l_1^2 + m_1^2 + n_1^2 = 1, \; l_1^2 + l_2^2 + l_3^2 = 1, \text{ etc.}$$

$$l_1 l_2 + m_1 m_2 + n_1 n_2 = 0, \; l_1 m_1 + l_2 m_2 + l_3 m_3 = 0, \text{ etc.}$$

The locus of the point of intersection is obtained by eliminating l_r, m_r, n_r from the eqns. (i).

For, we add these planes obtained by putting $r = 1, 2, 3$ and use the above relations. Thus, we get

$$2 (n_1^2 + n_2^2 + n_3^2) z + c \left(\frac{l_1^2 + l_2^2 + l_3^2}{a} + \frac{m_1^2 + m_2^2 + m_3^2}{b} \right) = 0$$

$$\Rightarrow \qquad\qquad 2z + c \left(\frac{1}{a} + \frac{1}{b} \right) = 0.$$

This is the required plane.

EXERCISES

1. Show that the plane $8x - 6y - z = 5$ touches the paraboloid $x^2/2 - y^2/3 = z$; and find the co-ordinates of the points of contact.   (*Ajmer, 1996; Gorakhpur, 2001;*
   M.D.U. Rohtak, 1999; Rohilkhand, 1999, 2001) [**Ans.** (8, 9, 5)]

2. Show that the equation to the two tangent planes to the surface

$$ax^2 + by^2 = 2z,$$

   which passes through the line

$$u \equiv lx + my + nz - p = 0, \; u' \equiv l'x + m'y + n'z - p' = 0$$

   is

$$u^2 \left(\frac{l'^2}{a} + \frac{m'^2}{b} - 2n' p' \right) - 2uu' (ll' + mm' - n'p - n'p) + u'^2 \left(\frac{l^2}{a} + \frac{m^2}{b} - 2np \right) = 0.$$

   (Garhwal, 1995)

3. Tangent planes at two points P and Q of a paraboloid meet in the line RS; show that the plane through RS and the middle point of PQ is parallel to the axis of the paraboloid.

4. Find the equation of the plane which cuts the paraboloid

$$x^2 - \frac{1}{2} y^2 = z$$

   in a conic with its centre at the point (2, 3, 4).   [**Ans.** $4x - 3y - z + 5 = 0$]

5. Show that the locus of the centres of a system of parallel plane sections of a paraboloid is a diameter.

6. Show that the centre of the conic

$$ax^2 + by^2 = 2z, \; lx + my + nz = p$$

   is the point

$$\left(\frac{l}{an}, -\frac{m}{bn}, \frac{k^2}{n^2} \right)$$

   where

$$k^2 = \frac{l^2}{a} + \frac{m^2}{b} + np.$$

7. Find the chord through the point $(2, 3, 4)$ which is bisected by the diametral plane $10x - 24y = 21$ of the paraboloid $5x^2 - 6y^2 = 7z$.

$$\left[\textbf{Ans.}\ (x - 2) = \frac{1}{2}(y - 3) = \frac{1}{3}(z - 4)\right]$$

8. Show that the centre of the conic
$$ax^2 + by^2 = 2z, \quad lx + my + nz = p,$$

is the point
$$\left(\frac{-l}{an}, \frac{-m}{bn}, \frac{k^2}{n^2}\right)$$

where
$$k^2 = \frac{l^2}{a} + \frac{m^2}{b} + np.$$

9. Find the locus of a point from which three mutually perpendicular lines can be drawn to touch the paraboloid $ax^2 + by^2 + 2z = 0$. (*Gorakhpur, 2000*)

[**Ans.** $ab(x^2 + y^2) - z^2 = 2c(a + b)z$]

8.9.5. Number of Normals From a Given Point

(*Ajmer, 1998; Gorakhpur, 2000; Poorvanchal, 1996, 99*)

If the normal at (α, β, γ) passes through a given point (f, g, h), then

$$\frac{f - \alpha}{a\alpha} = \frac{g - \beta}{b\beta} = \frac{h - \gamma}{-c} = r, \text{ (say)}$$

$$\Leftrightarrow \qquad \alpha = \frac{f}{1 + ar}, \ \beta = \frac{g}{1 + br}, \ \gamma = h + cr \qquad \ldots(i)$$

Since (α, β, γ) lies on the paraboloid, we have the relation

$$a\frac{f^2}{(1 + ar)^2} + b\frac{g^2}{(1 + br)^2} = 2c(h + cr) \qquad \ldots(ii)$$

which, being an equation of the fifth degree in r, gives five values of r, to each of which there corresponds a point (α, β, γ), from (i).

Therefore, there are *five* points, on a paraboloid the normals at which pass through a given point, *i.e.*, *through a given point five normals, in general, can be drawn to a paraboloid.*

Cor. I. Cubic curve through the feet of the normals (*Ajmer, 1998*)

If the normal at (α, β, γ) to the paraboloid
$$ax^2 + by^2 = 2cz$$

passes through a given point (x', y', z'), we have as above

$$\alpha = \frac{x'}{1 + a\lambda}, \ \beta = \frac{y'}{1 + b\lambda}, \ \gamma = z' + c\lambda.$$

Thus, the feet of the normals lie on the curve, defined by the parametric equations. is given by

$$x = \frac{x'}{1 + a\lambda}, \ y = \frac{y'}{1 + b\lambda}, \ z = z' + c\lambda, \qquad \ldots(1)$$

where λ is the parameter.

The points where this curve meets any given plane, say,

$$ux + vy + wz + d = 0 \qquad \ldots(2)$$

are given by

$$\frac{ux'}{1+a\lambda} + \frac{vy'}{1+b\lambda} + w(z'+c\lambda) + d = 0.$$

This is a cubic in λ, giving three values of λ.

Therefore the plane (2) meets the curve (1) in three points, and hence it follows that the curve is a cubic curve.

Cor. II. Cone through the five normals   *(Gorakhpur, 2001)*

If the normal at (α, β, γ) to the paraboloid $ax^2 + by^2 = 2cz$ passes through (x', y', z'), then

$$\alpha = \frac{x'}{1+a\lambda}, \quad \beta = \frac{y'}{1+b\lambda}, \quad \gamma = z' + c\lambda$$

Also the direction cosines of the normal at (α, β, γ) are proportional to $a\alpha, b\beta, -c$.

If the line

$$\frac{x-x'}{l} = \frac{y-y'}{m} = \frac{z-z'}{n} \qquad \qquad ...(1)$$

is a normal at (α, β, γ), then

$$\frac{l}{a\alpha} = \frac{m}{b\beta} = \frac{n}{-c}$$

$$\Rightarrow \qquad \frac{l(1+a\lambda)}{ax'} = \frac{m(1+b\lambda)}{by'} = \frac{n}{-c}$$

$$\Rightarrow \qquad \frac{l\left(\dfrac{1}{a}+\lambda\right)}{x'} = \frac{m\left(\dfrac{1}{b}+\lambda\right)}{y'} = \frac{n}{-c}$$

$$\Rightarrow \qquad \frac{\dfrac{1}{a}+\lambda}{x'/l} = \frac{\dfrac{1}{b}+\lambda}{y'/m} = \frac{n}{-c} = \frac{\dfrac{1}{a}-\dfrac{1}{b}}{\dfrac{x'}{l}-\dfrac{y'}{m}}$$

Hence

$$n\left(\frac{x'}{l}-\frac{y'}{m}\right) = -c\left(\frac{1}{a}-\frac{1}{b}\right)$$

or

$$\frac{x'}{l}-\frac{y'}{m}+\frac{c}{n}\left(\frac{1}{a}-\frac{1}{b}\right) = 0$$

Therefore the locus of the normal (1) is

$$\frac{x'}{x-x'}-\frac{y'}{y-y'}+\frac{c}{z-z'}\left(\frac{b-a}{ab}\right) = 0$$

which is the equation of a cone.

Hence the five normals from (x', y', z') to the paraboloid are generators of this cone.

8.9.6. Conjugate diametral planes

Consider any two *diametral planes*

$$lx + my + p = 0 \qquad \qquad ...(i)$$

and $$l'x + m'y + p' = 0 \qquad \qquad ...(ii)$$

The plane (*i*) bisects chords parallel to the line

$$\frac{x}{l/a} = \frac{y}{m/b} = \frac{z}{-p/c} \qquad \ldots(iii)$$

which will be parallel to the plane (*ii*), if

$$\frac{ll'}{a} + \frac{mm'}{b} = 0. \qquad \ldots(iv)$$

The symmetry of the result shows that the plane (*i*) is also parallel to the chords bisected by the plane (*ii*).

Thus, if α and β be two diametral planes, such that *the plane* α *is parallel to the chords bisected by the plane* β, *then the plane* β *is parallel to the chords bisected by the plane* α.

Two such planes are called *conjugate diametral planes*.

Equation (*iv*) is the condition for the diametral planes (*i*) and (*ii*) to be conjugate.

EXAMPLES

1. *Show that the planes*

$$x + 3y = 3 \text{ and } 2x - y = 1$$

are conjugate diametral planes of the paraboloid

$$2x^2 + 3y^2 = 4z.$$

Sol. Equation of any diametral plane with respect to the paraboloid $ax^2 + by^2 = 2cz$ is

$$alx + bmy - cn = 0$$

In this case $a = 2, b = 3, c = 2.$

Therefore the equation of the diametral plane is

$$2lx + 3my - 2n = 0 \qquad \ldots(1)$$

If this plane and $x + 3y = 3$ are the same, then comparing the coefficients, we have

$$\frac{2l}{1} = \frac{3m}{3} = \frac{-2n}{-3}$$

or

$$\frac{l}{1/2} = \frac{m}{1} = \frac{n}{3/2}, \text{ i.e., } \frac{l}{1} = \frac{m}{2} = \frac{n}{3},$$

i.e., the direction cosines of the chords which are bisected by the plane $x + 3y = 3$ are proportional to 1, 2, 3.

This shows that these chords are parallel to the plane $2x - y = 1$.

Hence the given planes are conjugate diametral planes.

2. *Prove that any diametral plane of a paraboloid cuts it in a parabola, and that parallel diametral planes cut it in equal parabolas.*

Sol. Let the equation of the parabola be

$$ax^2 + by^2 = 2cz \qquad \ldots(1)$$

Therefore the diametral plane which bisects chords parallel to the line

$$\frac{x}{l} = \frac{y}{m} = \frac{z}{n}$$

is

$$alx + bmy - cn = 0 \qquad \ldots(2)$$

Now to prove that the section of the paraboloid (1) by the plane (2) is a parabola, it is sufficient to prove that the projection of the section on a co-ordinate plane is a parabola, for the projection of a conic is a conic of the same species. So taking the projection of the section of (1) by the diametral plane (2) on *YOZ* plane, we have

$$a \left(\frac{cn - bmy}{al} \right)^2 + by^2 = 2cz, \ x = 0$$

$\Rightarrow \qquad (cn - bmy)^2 + al^2 (by^2 - 2cz) = 0, \ x = 0$

$\Rightarrow \qquad b (al^2 + bm^2) y^2 - 2bcmny + n^2 - 2cal^2z = 0, \ x = 0$

$\Rightarrow \qquad b (al^2 + bm^2) y^2 - 2bcmny + n^2 = 2cal^2z, \ x = 0$

This is obviously a parabola whose latus rectum is

$$\frac{2cal^2}{b (al^2 + bm^2)},$$

which is independent of *n*.

Hence it also follows that sections by parallel diametral planes are equal parabolas.

EXERCISES

1. Prove that the diametral planes $2x + 3y = 4$ and $3x - 4y = 7$ are conjugate diametral planes for the paraboloid $x^2 + 2y^2 = 4z$.

2. The plane $3x + 4y = 1$ is a diametral plane of the paraboloid $5x^2 + 6y^2 = 2z$. Find the equation to the chord through (3, 4, 5) which it bisects.

$$\left[\textbf{Ans.} \ \frac{x-3}{9} = \frac{y-4}{10} = \frac{z-5}{15} \right]$$

3. Show that in general three normals can be drawn from a given point to the paraboloid of revolution $x^2 + y^2 = 2az$ but if the point lies on the surface $27a (x^2 + y^2) + 8 (a - z)^2 = 0$ two of them coincide.

4. Show that the centre of the circle through the feet of the three normals from the point (α, β, γ) to the paraboloid $x^2 + y^2 = 2az$ is

$$\left(\frac{\alpha}{4}, \frac{\beta}{4}, \frac{\gamma + \alpha}{2} \right).$$

OBJECTIVE QUESTIONS

I. Multiple Choice Questions

Note : *For each of the following questions, four alternatives are given for the answer. Only one of them is correct. Choose the correct alternative.*

1. The equation $\dfrac{x^2}{a^2} + \dfrac{y^2}{b^2} = \dfrac{2z}{c}$ represents :

   (*a*) an ellipsoid   (*b*) a hyperboloid

   (*c*) an elliptic paraboloid   (*d*) a hyperbolic paraboloid.

                                                    (*Avadh, 2003; Rohilkhand, 2002*)

2. The surface represented by the equation $\dfrac{x^2}{a^2} - \dfrac{y^2}{b^2} - \dfrac{z^2}{c^2} = 1$ is :

   (*a*) ellipsoid   (*b*) hyperboloid of two sheets

   (*c*) hyperboloid of one sheet   (*d*) paraboloid   (*Avadh, 2001*)

3. The equation $\dfrac{x^2}{2} - \dfrac{y^2}{3} = z$ represents :

(a) cylinder   (b) hyperboloid   (c) ellipsoid   (d) paraboloid.

(Garhwal, 2002)

4. The equation of tangent plane at (α, β, γ) to be the conicoid $ax^2 + by^2 + cz^2 = 1$:

(a) $a\alpha x + b\beta y + c\gamma z = 1$ (b) $a\alpha x + b\beta y + c\gamma z$

(c) $ax + by + cz = \sqrt{\alpha^2 + \beta^2 + \gamma^2}$ (d) $\alpha x + \beta y + \gamma z = \sqrt{a^2 + b^2 + c^2}$.

5. The condition that the plane $lx + my + nz = p$ may touch the conicoid $ax^2 + by^2 + cz^2 = 1$ is :

(a) $\dfrac{l}{a} + \dfrac{m}{b} + \dfrac{n}{c} = p$ (b) $\dfrac{l^2}{a} + \dfrac{m^2}{b} + \dfrac{n^2}{c} = p^2$

(c) $\dfrac{l}{a^2} + \dfrac{m}{b^2} + \dfrac{n}{c^2} = p^2$ (d) $\dfrac{l^2}{a} + \dfrac{m^2}{b} + \dfrac{n^2}{c} = p$.

(Avadh, 2001; Garhwal, 2003. Kumaon, 2006)

6. The equation of the director sphere of the conicoid $ax^2 + by^2 + cz^2 = 1$ is :

(a) $x^2 + y^2 + z^2 = a + b + c$ (b) $x^2 + y^2 + z^2 = abc$

(c) $x^2 + y^2 + z^2 = a^{-1} + b^{-1} + c^{-1}$ (d) $x^2 + y^2 + z^2 = a^2 + b^2 + c^2$.

7. How many normals can be drawn from any point to a conicoid ?

(a) 8   (b) 6   (c) 4   (d) 2.

(Garhwal, 2002; Rohilkhand, 2002)

8. The central conicoid $ax^2 + by^2 + cz^2 = 1$ will represent an ellipsoid if :

(a) a, b, c are all negative   (b) a, b are positive and c is negative

(c) a, b are negative and c is positive   (d) a, b, c are all positive.

(Rohilkhand, 2002)

9. A straight line which intersects a central conicoid in two coincident points is called a :

(a) polar line   (b) tangent line

(c) chord of contact   (d) diameter.

10. Condition that the plane $lx + my + nz = p$ should touch the ellipsoid $\dfrac{x^2}{a^2} + \dfrac{y^2}{b^2} + \dfrac{z^2}{c^2} = 1$

is :

(a) $\dfrac{l^2}{a} + \dfrac{m^2}{b} + \dfrac{n^2}{c} + p^2$ (b) $\dfrac{l^2}{a} + \dfrac{m^2}{b} + \dfrac{n^2}{c} = 0$ *(Garhwal, 2006)*

(c) $a^2 l^2 + b^2 m^2 + c^2 n^2 = p^2$ (d) None of the above.

11. Equation of the tangent plane to the surface $3x^2 + y^2 + z^2 = 21$ at the point $(2, 3, 0)$ is :

(a) $3x + 2y = 21$ (b) $6x + 3y = 21$ (c) $2x + y = 7$ (d) $x + 2y = 7$.

12. Co-ordinates of the pole of the plane $lx + my + nz = p$ with respect to conicoid

$$ax^2 + by^2 + cz^2 = 1$$

are :

(a) $\left(\dfrac{ap}{l}, \dfrac{bp}{m}, \dfrac{cp}{n} \right)$ (b) $\left(\dfrac{l}{ap}, \dfrac{m}{bp}, \dfrac{c}{np} \right)$ (c) $\left(\dfrac{p}{al}, \dfrac{p}{bm}, \dfrac{p}{cn} \right)$ (d) (apl, bpm, cpn).

(Rohilkhand, 2002)

13. A plane which bisects a system of parallel chords of a central conicoid is called :

(a) Tangent plane   (b) Plane of contact (c) Diametral plane (d) Polar plane.

14. Equation of normal to the ellipsoid $\dfrac{x^2}{a^2} + \dfrac{y^2}{b^2} + \dfrac{z^2}{c^2} = 1$ at point (α, β, γ) is :

(a) $\dfrac{x-\alpha}{a\alpha} = \dfrac{y-\beta}{b\beta} = \dfrac{z-\gamma}{c\gamma}$

(b) $\dfrac{x}{\alpha/a} = \dfrac{y}{\beta/b} = \dfrac{z}{\gamma/c}$

(c) $\dfrac{x-\alpha}{1} = \dfrac{y-\beta}{1} = \dfrac{z-\gamma}{1}$

(d) $\dfrac{x-\alpha}{\alpha/a^2} = \dfrac{y-\beta}{\beta/b^2} = \dfrac{z-\gamma}{\gamma/c^2}$.

(Garhwal, 2004)

15. The plane $2x + 3y + 4z = 3$ touches the conicoid $2x^2 + 3y^2 + 4z^2 = 1$ at :

(a) $\left(\dfrac{2}{3}, 1, \dfrac{4}{3}\right)$ (b) $(1, 1, 1)$ (c) $\left(\dfrac{1}{3}, \dfrac{1}{3}, \dfrac{1}{3}\right)$ (d) $(2, 3, 4)$.

(Avadh, 2004)

16. The locus of the centres of sections of a central conicoid which pass through a given line is a :

(a) conic

(b) circle

(c) pair of straight lines

(d) paraboloid.

17. Equation to the plane which cuts the surface $2x^2 - 3y^2 + 5z^2 = 1$ in a conic whose centre is the point $(2, 1, 3)$ is :

(a) $2x - 3y + 5z = 1$

(b) $4x - 3y + 15z = 1$

(c) $4x - 3y + 15z = 50$

(d) None of the above.

18. The sum of the squares of any three conjugate semi-diameters of an ellipsoid is :

(a) positive   (b) negative   (c) zero   (d) constant.

19. The sum of the squares of the lengths of three conjugate semi-diameters of the conicoid $x^2 + 2y^2 + 3z^2 = 6$ is :

(a) 6   (b) 11   (c) 14   (d) None of these.

(Avadh, 2004)

20. The volume of the parallelopiped formed by the three conjugate semi-diameters as coterminous edges :

(a) depends on lengths of semi-diameters

(b) is constant

(c) is sum of reciprocals of axes

(d) None of these.

21. Locus of the point of intersection of the three mutually perpendicular tangent planes of a paraboloid $ax^2 + by^2 = 2cz$ is :

(a) $2z + c\left(\dfrac{1}{a} + \dfrac{1}{b}\right) = 0$

(b) $2z = c\left(\dfrac{1}{a} + \dfrac{1}{b}\right)$

(c) $z = 2c\,(a + b)$

(d) $2z = c\,(a + b)$. *(Rohilkhand, 2006)*

22. Number of normals that can be drawn through a given point to a paraboloid is :

(a) 3   (b) 5   (c) 6   (d) 9.

(Avadh, 2003)

23. The co-ordinates of the point of contact of the plane $2x - 4y - z + 3 = 0$ to the paraboloid $x^2 - 2y^2 = 3z$ are :

(a) $(-3, 3, 3)$ (b) $(3, -3, 3)$ (c) $(3, 3 - 3)$ (d) $(3, 3, 3)$.

24. Equation of tangent plane to the paraboloid $\dfrac{x^2}{a^2} + \dfrac{y^2}{b} = \dfrac{2z}{c}$ at the point (α, β, γ) is :

(a) $\dfrac{\alpha x}{a^2} + \dfrac{\beta y}{b^2} + \dfrac{\gamma z}{c}$

(b) $\dfrac{\alpha x}{a^2} + \dfrac{\beta y}{b^2} = \dfrac{(z + \gamma)}{c}$

(c) $\dfrac{a^2}{\alpha x} + \dfrac{b^2}{\beta y} = \dfrac{c}{\gamma z}$

(d) None of these.

25. If the plane $8x - 6y - z = 5$ touches the paraboloid $\dfrac{x^2}{2} - \dfrac{y^2}{3} = z$, then the co-ordinates

of the point of contact are :

(a) $(8, 9, 5)$ (b) $(8, -9, 5)$ (c) $(8, 9, -5)$ (d) $(-8, 9, 5)$.

(Rohilkhand, 2002)

26. If the plane $x + 2y - 2z = 4$ touches the paraboloid $3x^2 + 4y^2 = 24z$, then the point of

contact is :

(a) $(2, 3, 2)$ (b) $(3, 2, 1)$ (c) $(1, 2, 3)$ (d) None of these.

(Rohilkhand, 2004)

ANSWERS

1. (c)   2. (b)   3. (d)   4. (a)   5. (b)   6. (c)   7. (b)   8. (d)
9. (b)   10. (c)   11. (c)   12. (b)   13. (c)   14. (d)   15. (c)   16. (a)
17. (c)   18. (d)   19. (b)   20. (b)   21. (a)   22. (b)   23. (c)   24. (b)
25. (a)   26. (a)

II. Fill in the Blanks

Note : *Fill in the blanks "........" so that the following statements are complete and correct.*

1. The equation $\dfrac{x^2}{a^2} - \dfrac{y^2}{b^2} - \dfrac{z^2}{c^2} = 1$ represents a hyperboloid of ....

2. $ax^2 + by^2 + cz^2 = 1$ is the ..... equation of the conicoid.

3. The central conicoid $ax^2 + by^2 + cz^2 = 1$ is an ellipsoid if the constant a, b, c are all ....

4. The centre of the central conicoid $ax^2 + by^2 + cz^2 = 1$ is at the ....

5. The equation of the tangent plane to the central conicoid $ax^2 + by^2 + cz^2 = 1$ at the point (x_1, y_1, z_1) on it is ....

6. The equation of the tangent plane at $(1, 1, -1)$ to the conicoid $2x^2 + 3y^2 - z^2 = 4$ is ....

7. The plane $lx + my + nz = p$ will touch the conicoid $ax^2 + by^2 + cz^2 = 1$, provided ..... $= p^2$.

8. The equation of tangent plane to the ellipsoid $3x^2 + 5y^2 + 7z^2 = 15$ at the point $(1, -1, 1)$ on it is ....

9. The plane $lx + my + nz = p$ touches the ellipsoid $x^2/a^2 + y^2/b^2 + z^2/c^2 = 1$ if ..... $= p^2$.

10. The director sphere of a central conicoid is the locus of the point of intersection of three mutually perpendicular ..... to that conicoid.

11. The equation of the director sphere of the central conicoid $ax^2 + by^2 + cz^2 = 1$ is $x^2 + y^2 + z^2 = $ ..... .

12. The radius of the director sphere of the ellipsoid $\dfrac{1}{6}x^2 + \dfrac{1}{4}y^2 + \dfrac{1}{15}z^2 = 1$ is ....

13. The centre of the director sphere of the central conicoid $3x^2 + 4y^2 - 5z^2 = 1$ is the point ....

14. The locus of the foot of the central perpendicular on varying tangent planes to the ellipsoid $\dfrac{x^2}{a^2} + \dfrac{y^2}{b^2} + \dfrac{z^2}{c^2} = 1$ is $(x^2 + y^2 + z^2)^2 = $...... .

15. The pole of the plane $lx + my + nz = p$ with respect to the conicoid $ax^2 + by^2 + cz^2 = 1$ is ....

16. The equations of the normal to the central conicoid $ax^2 + by^2 + cz^2 = 1$ at the point (x_1, y_1, z_1) on it are ....

17. The direction cosines of the normal to the central conicoid $ax^2 + by^2 + cz^2 = 1$ at the point (x_1, y_1, z_1) on it are $ax_1 p,\ by_1 p,\ cz_1 p$, where $p^2 = $...... .

18. ...... normals can be drawn to an ellipsoid from a given point.

19. The locus of the asymptotic line drawn from the origin to the conicoid $ax^2 + by^2 + cz^2 = 1$ is ...... $= 0$.

20. The equations of the normal to the ellipsoid $3x^2 + 4y^2 + 5y^2 = 64$ at the point $(1, 2, 3)$ on it are $\dfrac{x-1}{3} = \dfrac{y-2}{.....} = \dfrac{z-3}{15}$.

21. If $P(x_1, y_1, z_1)$, $Q(x_2, y_2, z_2)$ and $R(x_3, y_3, z_3)$ be the extremities of three conjugate semi-diameters of the ellipsoid $\dfrac{x^2}{a^2} + \dfrac{y^2}{b^2} + \dfrac{z^2}{c^2} = 1$, then

    (i) $z_1 x_1 + z_2 x_2 + z_3 x_3 = $......   (ii) $y_1^2 + y_2^2 + y_3^2 = $......

22. The general equation of a hyperbolic paraboloid is $\dfrac{x^2}{a^2} - \dfrac{y^2}{b^2} = $...... .

23. The equation $ax^2 + by^2 = 2cz$ represents an elliptic paraboloid if a and b are ....

24. The equation $ax^2 + by^2 = 2cz$ represents a hyperbolic paraboloid if a and b are of ....

25. The equation of the tangent plane at the point (α, β, γ) on the paraboloid $ax^2 + by^2 = 2cz$ is ....

26. The condition that the plane $lx + my + nz = p$ touches the paraboloid $ax^2 + by^2 = 2cz$ is $\dfrac{l^2}{a} + \dfrac{m^2}{b} + $...... $= 0$.

27. The locus of point of intersection of three mutually perpendicular tangent planes to the paraboloid $ax^2 + by^2 = 2cz$ is $2z + c\,[.....] = 0$.

28. The equation of the locus of chords of the paraboloid $ax^2 + by^2 = 2cz$ at the point (α, β, γ) are $\dfrac{x-\alpha}{a\alpha} = \dfrac{y-\beta}{b\beta} = \dfrac{z-\gamma}{.....}$.

29. In general ...... normals can be drawn from a given point (α, β, γ) to the paraboloid $ax^2 + by^2 = 2cz$.

30. Two diametral planes of the paraboloid $ax^2 + by^2 = 2cz$ are called ...... if each bisects the chords parallel to the other.

ANSWERS

1. two sheets;   2. standard;   3. positive;   4. origin;

5. $axx_1 + byy_1 + czz_1 = 1$;   6. $2x + 3y + z = 4$;

7. $\dfrac{l^2}{a} + \dfrac{m^2}{b} + \dfrac{n^2}{c}$;   8. $3x - 5y + 7z = 15$;   9. $a^2l^2 + b^2m^2 + c^2n^2$;

10. tangent planes;   11. $\dfrac{1}{a} + \dfrac{1}{b} + \dfrac{1}{c}$;   12. 5;   13. $(0, 0, 0)$;

14. $a^2x^2 + b^2y^2 + c^2z^2$;   15. $(l/ap, m/bp, n/cp)$;   16. $\dfrac{x - x_1}{ax_1} = \dfrac{y - y_1}{by_1} = \dfrac{z - z_1}{cz_1}$;

17. $\dfrac{1}{a^2x_1^2 + b^2y_1^2 + c^2z_1^2}$;   18. six;   19. $ax^2 + by^2 + cz^2$;

20. 8;   21. (*i*) 0, (*ii*) b^2;   22. $\dfrac{2z}{c}$;   23. of the same sign;

24. opposite signs;   25. $a\alpha x + b\beta y = c\,(\gamma + z)$;   26. $\dfrac{2np}{c}$;

27. $\dfrac{1}{a} + \dfrac{1}{b}$;   28. $z + \gamma$;   29. five;   30. conjugate.

III. True/False Statements

Note : *Write 'T' for true and 'F' for false statements.*

1. The equation $\dfrac{x^2}{a^2} - \dfrac{y^2}{b^2} = \dfrac{2z}{c}$ represents a hyperboloid of one sheet.

2. The equation $2x^2 + 3y^2 + 5z^2 = 1$ represents an ellipsoid.

3. The equation $x^2 - 2y^2 - 3z^2 = 1$ represents a hyperboloid of one sheet.

4. $-4x^2 + 6y^2 + 7z^2 = 4$ represents a hyperboloid of two sheets.

5. The planes $lx + my + nz = \pm \sqrt{a^2l^2 + b^2m^2 + c^2n^2}$ always touch the ellipsoid
$$x^2/a^2 + y^2/b^2 + z^2/c^2 = 1.$$

6. $x^2 + y^2 + z^2 = a^2 + b^2 + c^2$ is the equation of the director sphere of the ellipsoid
$$x^2/a^2 + y^2/b^2 + z^2/c^2 = 1.$$

7. The tangent planes at the extremities of any diameter of an ellipsoid are perpendicular.

8. The radius of the director sphere of the conicoid $\dfrac{x^2}{4} + \dfrac{y^2}{15} - \dfrac{z^2}{10} = 1$ is 3.

9. The equation of the tangent plane to the conicoid $2x^2 - 3y^2 + 5z^2 = 35$ at the point $(1, 2, 3)$ is $2x - 6y + 10z = 35$.

10. The condition that the plane $lx + my + nz = p$ may touch the ellipsoid $\dfrac{x^2}{a^2} + \dfrac{y^2}{b^2} + \dfrac{z^2}{c^2} = 1$

is $\dfrac{l^2}{a} + \dfrac{m^2}{b} + \dfrac{n^2}{c} = p^2$.

11. The equation of the normal to $ax^2 + by^2 + cz^2 = 1$ at (α, β, γ) is $\dfrac{x - \alpha}{a} = \dfrac{y - \beta}{b} = \dfrac{z - \gamma}{c}$.

12. The equation of the normal to the ellipsoid $2x^2 + 3y^2 + 4z^2 = 18$ at the point $(-1, 2, -1)$

on it are $\dfrac{x + 1}{-2} = \dfrac{y - 2}{6} = \dfrac{z + 1}{4}$.

13. Sum of the squares of the projections of three conjugate semi-diameters of the ellipsoid $\frac{x^2}{a^2} + \frac{y^2}{b^2} + \frac{z^2}{c^2} = 1$ on any line is not constant.

14. If $P(x_1, y_1, z_1)$, $Q(x_2, y_2, z_2)$ and $R(x_3, y_3, z_3)$ be the extremities of three conjugate semi-diameters of the ellipsoid $\frac{x^2}{a^2} + \frac{y^2}{b^2} + \frac{z^2}{c^2} = 1$, then $x_1y_1 + x_2y_2 + x_3y_3 = a^2 + b^2$.

15. Locus of the chords with (x_1, y_1, z_1) as mid-point of the conicoid $ax^2 + by^2 + cz^2 = 1$ is $ax_1^2 + by_1^2 + cz_1^2 = axx_1 + byy_1 + czz_1$.

16. The direction cosines of the normal to the ellipsoid $x^2 + 2y^2 + 3z^2 = 4$ at the point $(1, 0, 1)$ on it are $\frac{1}{\sqrt{10}}, 0, \frac{-3}{\sqrt{10}}$.

17. The plane $x + 2y - 3z = 6$ touches the conicoid $x^2 + 2y^2 + 3z^2 = 6$.

18. The equation of the locus of the mid-point of a system of parallel chords with direction cosines l, m, n of the conicoid $ax^2 + by^2 + cz^2 = 1$ is $alx + bmy + cnz = 0$.

19. The length of the perpendicular drawn from the centre of the conicoid $x^2 - y^2 + z^2 = 1$ to the tangent plane to it at the point $(1, 1, 1)$ is $1/\sqrt{3}$.

20. The general equation of a paraboloid is $ax^2 + by^2 = 2cz$.

21. The plane $2(lx + my + nz)n + c[l^2/a + m^2/b] = 0$ always touches the paraboloid $ax^2 + by^2 = 2cz$.

22. The five feet of the normals that can be drawn to a paraboloid from a given point are the intersection of a certain cubic curve with the paraboloid.

23. The locus of the middle points of a system of parallel chords of the paraboloid $ax^2 + by^2 = 2cz$ is called a diametral plane.

24. The locus of the point of intersection of three mutually perpendicular tangent planes to the paraboloid $ax^2 + by^2 = 2cz$ is a sphere.

25. The plane $lx + my + nz = p$ touches the paraboloid $ax^2 + by^2 = 2cz$ provided $\frac{a^2}{l} + \frac{b^2}{m} + \frac{2cp}{n} = 0$.

26. The equation of the normal to the paraboloid $ax^2 + by^2 = 2cz$ at the point (α, β, γ) are $\frac{x - \alpha}{a\alpha} = \frac{y - \beta}{b\beta} = \frac{z - \gamma}{c\gamma}$.

27. Enveloping cylinder of the paraboloid $ax^2 + by^2 = 2cz$ with its generators parallel to the line $x/l = y/m = z/n$ is $(alx + bmy - cn)^2 = (al^2 + bm^2)(ax^2 + by^2 - 2cz)$

28. $a\alpha x + b\beta y = c(z + \gamma)$ is the equation of the polar plane of the point (α, β, γ) with respect to the paraboloid $ax^2 + by^2 = 2cz$.

ANSWERS

1. F	2. T	3. F	4. F	5. T
6. T	7. F	8. T	9. F	10. F
11. F	12. F	13. F	14. F	15. T
16. F	17. T	18. T	19. T	20. T
21. T	22. T	23. T	24. F	25. F
26. F	27. T	28. T		

9

Plane Sections of Conicoids

9.1. INTRODUCTION

Having seen that all plane sections of a conicoid are conics, we shall now proceed to determine the nature, the lengths, and the direction ratios of the axes of a plane section of a given conicoid.

We shall first consider the section of central conicoids, and then the paraboloids.

While determining the nature of plane sections of conicoids, we shall *assume* that the orthogonal projection of a parabola is another parabola, of a hyperbola is another hyperbola and of an ellipse is another ellipse or in some cases a circle.

9.2. NATURE OF THE PLANE SECTION OF A CENTRAL CONICOID

To determine the nature of the section of the central conicoid

$$ax^2 + by^2 + cz^2 = 1 \qquad \qquad ...(1)$$

by the plane

$$lx + my + nz = p \qquad \qquad ...(2)$$

The equation to the cylinder passing through the section and having its generators parallel to Z-axis, obtained by eliminating z from (1) and (2), is

$$x^2 (an^2 + cl^2) + 2clmxy + y^2 (bn^2 + cm^2) - 2clpx - 2cpmy + (cp^2 - n^2) = 0$$

The plane $z = 0$ which is perpendicular to the generating lines of the cylinder cuts it in the conic with equations

$$z = 0$$
$$x^2 (an^2 + cl^2) + 2clmxy + y^2 (bn^2 + cm^2) - 2cplx - 2cpmy + (cp^2 - n^2) = 0$$

This conic is the projection of the given section on the plane

$$z = 0$$

The projection and, therefore, also the given section is a parabola, hyperbola or ellipse according as

$$c^2 l^2 m^2 \; \begin{cases} = \\ > \\ < \end{cases} \; (an^2 + cl^2)(bn^2 + cm^2) \quad \Leftrightarrow \quad bcl^2 + cam^2 + abn^2 \; \begin{cases} = \\ < \\ > \end{cases}$$

Thus, we find that the section is

$$\left. \begin{array}{l} \text{a parabola} \\ \text{a hyperbola} \\ \text{an ellipse} \end{array} \right\} \text{according as } bcl^2 + cam^2 + abn^2 \; \begin{cases} = \\ < \\ > \end{cases} 0$$

271

9.2.1. Axes of a Central Plane Section   (*Gorakhpur, 1996*)

To determine the lengths and direction cosines of the section of the central conicoid

$$ax^2 + by^2 + cz^2 = 1 \qquad \qquad ...(1)$$

by the central plane

$$lx + my + nz = 0 \qquad \qquad ...(2)$$

Take a concentric sphere

$$x^2 + y^2 + z^2 = r^2 \qquad \qquad ...(3)$$

The extremities of all the semi-diameters of length r of the conicoid lie on the curve of intersection of the conicoid and the sphere.

The lines joining the origin to the points on this curve form a cone whose equation, obtained by making (1) and (3) homogeneous, is

$$(ar^2 - 1) x^2 + (br^2 - 1) y^2 + (cr^2 - 1) z^2 = 0. \qquad \qquad ...(4)$$

The plane (2) cuts this cone in two generators which determine the directions of two equal diameters of length $2r$ of the section and which are, therefore, equally inclined to the axes of the section.

In case $2r$ is the length of either axis of the section, the generators coincide and as such the plane touches the cone, the generator of contact being one of the axes.

Now, the condition for the plane (2) to touch the cone (4) is

$$\frac{l^2}{ar^2 - 1} + \frac{m^2}{br^2 - 1} + \frac{n^2}{cr^2 - 1} = 0$$

$$\Leftrightarrow \ (bcl^2 + cam^2 + abn^2) \, r^4 - [(b + c) \, l^2 + (c + a) \, m^2 + (a + b) \, n^2] \, r^2$$
$$+ (l^2 + m^2 + n^2) = 0 \qquad \qquad ...(5)$$

which is a quadratic equation in r^2 and has two roots $r_1{}^2$, $r_2{}^2$ which are the squares of the semi-axes of the section.

If λ, μ, ν be the direction ratios of the axis of length $2r$, the plane (2) touches the cone (4) along the line

$$\frac{x}{\lambda} = \frac{y}{\mu} = \frac{z}{\nu},$$

and is, therefore, identical with the plane

$$(ar^2 - 1) \, \lambda x + (br^2 - 1) \, \mu y + (cr^2 - 1) \, \nu z = 0 \qquad \qquad ...(6)$$

The equations (2) and (6) representing the same plane, we have

$$\frac{\lambda \, (ar^2 - 1)}{l} = \frac{\mu \, (br^2 - 1)}{m} = \frac{\nu \, (cr^2 - 1)}{n} \qquad \qquad ...(7)$$

The equations (7) determine the direction ratios of the axis of length $2r$; r being given by the equation (5).

9.2.2. Area of Plane Sections

Assuming that the section is an ellipse, its area

$$= \pi r_1 r_2 = \pi \cdot \frac{\sqrt{l^2 + m^2 + n^2}}{\sqrt{bcl^2 + cam^2 + abn^2}}$$

If p, be the length of the perpendicular from the origin to the tangent plane

$$lx + my + nz = \left(\frac{l^2}{a} + \frac{m^2}{b} + \frac{n^2}{c} \right)^{1/2}$$

parallel to the given plane $lx + my + nz = 0$, we have

$$p = \frac{\left(\dfrac{l^2}{a} + \dfrac{m^2}{b} + \dfrac{n^2}{c}\right)^{1/2}}{\sqrt{l^2 + m^2 + n^2}} = \frac{\sqrt{bcl^2 + cam^2 + abn^2}}{\sqrt{l^2 + m^2 + n^2}} \sqrt{\frac{1}{abc}}$$

$$\Rightarrow \qquad \text{area} = \frac{\pi}{p\sqrt{abc}}$$

9.2.3. Axes and Area of Any Central Plane Section of an Ellipsoid $\dfrac{x^2}{a^2} + \dfrac{y^2}{b^2} + \dfrac{z^2}{c^2} = 1$ by the plane $lx + my + nz = 0$

From eqn. (5) of § 9.2.1, we have the equation quadratic in r^2 as

$$r^4 (a^2l^2 + b^2m^2 + c^2n^2) - r^2 [a^2 (b^2 + c^2) l^2 + b^2 (c^2 + a^2) m^2 + c^2 (a^2 + b^2) n^2]$$
$$+ a^2b^2c^2 (l^2 + m^2 + n^2) = 0 \qquad \text{...}(i)$$

The direction ratios λ, μ, ν of the axis of length $2r$ are given by

$$\frac{\lambda (r^2 - a^2)}{a^2l} = \frac{\mu (r^2 - b^2)}{b^2m} = \frac{\nu (r^2 - c^2)}{c^2n} \qquad \text{...}(ii)$$

And the area of the section

$$= \pi \left[\frac{a^2b^2c^2 (l^2 + m^2 + n^2)}{a^2l^2 + b^2m^2 + c^2n^2} \right]^{1/2} \qquad \text{...}(iii)$$

$$= \frac{\pi abc}{p} \qquad \text{...}(iv)$$

where p is the length of the perpendicular distance from the centre to the parallel tangent plane

$$lx + my + nz = \sqrt{a^2l^2 + b^2m^2 + c^2n^2}.$$

All the above results can also be deduced from § 9.2.1 and § 9.2.2 putting $\dfrac{1}{a^2}$ for a, $\dfrac{1}{b^2}$ for b

and $\dfrac{1}{c^2}$ for c in the corresponding results.

9.2.4. Axes and Area of a Central Plane Section of the Surface $f(x, y, z) \equiv ax^2 + by^2 + cz^2 + 2fyz + 2gzx + 2hxy = 1$ By the Plane $lx + my + nz = 0$ and to Show that the Axes are the Lines in Which the Plane Cuts a Certain Cone

Let any concentric sphere be

$$x^2 + y^2 + z^2 = r^2 \qquad \text{...}(i)$$

The semi-diameters of length r are generating lines of the cone given by

$$x^2 \left(a - \frac{1}{r^2} \right) + y^2 \left(b - \frac{1}{r^2} \right) + z^2 \left(c - \frac{1}{r^2} \right) + 2fyz + 2gzx + 2hxy = 0 = F(x, y, z) \text{ (say)}$$

$$\text{...}(ii)$$

Equation (ii) is obtained by making the equation of the surface homogeneous with the help of (i).

The given plane will be a tangent plane to (ii) at the extremities of the semi-axis of length r, if r equals either semi-axes of the section.

By the condition of tangency, we get

$$\begin{vmatrix} a-(1/r^2) & h & g & l \\ h & b-(1/r^2) & f & m \\ g & f & c-(1/r^2) & n \\ l & m & n & 0 \end{vmatrix} = 0 \qquad ...(iii)$$

where r is the length of either semi-axes of the section.

$$\Rightarrow \sum \left[\left(b - \frac{1}{r^2} \right) \left(c - \frac{1}{r^2} \right) - f^2 \right] l^2 + 2 \sum \left[gh - \left(a - \frac{1}{r^2} \right) f \right] mn = 0$$

$$\Rightarrow r^4 \left[\sum (bc - f^2) \, l^2 + 2\sum (gh - af) \, mn \right] - r^2 \left[\sum (b+c) \, l^2 - \sum 2fmn \right]$$
$$+ l^2 + m^2 + n^2 = 0 \qquad ...(iv)$$

Again, tangent plane to the cone (ii) containing the axes along

$$\frac{x}{\lambda} = \frac{y}{\mu} = \frac{z}{\nu}$$

is

$$x \frac{\partial F}{\partial \lambda} + y \frac{\partial F}{\partial \mu} + z \frac{\partial F}{\partial \nu} = 0 \qquad ...(v)$$

If this is the same plane

$$lx + my + nz = 0 \qquad ...(vi)$$

then comparing (v) and (vi), we get

$$\frac{\partial F / \partial \lambda}{l} = \frac{\partial F / \partial \mu}{m} = \frac{\partial F / \partial \nu}{n} = t \text{ (say)} \qquad ...(vii)$$

which gives d.c.'s λ, μ, ν of the axes.

$$\therefore \qquad \frac{\partial F}{\partial \lambda} = lt \text{ or } \frac{\partial F}{\partial \lambda} - lt = 0 \text{ etc.}$$

$$\therefore \qquad \left(a - \frac{1}{r^2} \right) \lambda + g\nu + h\nu - lt = 0 \text{ etc.}$$

$$\therefore \qquad \left. \begin{array}{l} \dfrac{\partial f}{\partial \lambda} - \dfrac{1}{r^2} \lambda - lt = 0 \\[2mm] \dfrac{\partial f}{\partial \mu} - \dfrac{1}{r^2} \mu - mt = 0 \\[2mm] \dfrac{\partial f}{\partial \nu} - \dfrac{1}{r^2} \nu - nt = 0 \end{array} \right\} \qquad ...(viii)$$

and

Hence, we get

$$\begin{vmatrix} \partial f / \partial \lambda & \lambda & l \\ \partial f / \partial \mu & \mu & m \\ \partial f / \partial \nu & \nu & n \end{vmatrix} = 0 \qquad ...(ix)$$

i.e., the axes lie on the cone

$$\sum (mz - ny) \frac{\partial f}{\partial x} = 0$$

which is obtained by eliminating λ, μ, ν between (ix) and

$$\frac{x}{\lambda} = \frac{y}{\mu} = \frac{z}{\nu}$$

Also the area of the section

$$= \pi r_1 r_2 = \pi \left[\frac{(l^2 + m^2 + n^2)}{\Sigma(bc - f^2)l^2 + 2\Sigma(gh - af)mn} \right] \qquad \text{[from } (iv)]$$

9.2.5. Condition for the Section to be a Rectangular Hyperbola

For a rectangular hyperbola, we have

$$r_1^2 + r_2^2 = 0,$$

$$\Leftrightarrow \qquad (b + c)\, l^2 + (c + a)\, m^2 + (a + b)\, n^2 = 0.$$

Ex. Obtain the condition for the section of the conicoid

$$ax^2 + by^2 + cz^2 = 1$$

by the plane $lx + my + nz = p$ to be a parabola, an ellipse, a hyperbola or a circle from the eqn. (5) of § 9.2.1. $\qquad$ (For a circle, $r_1^2 = r_2^2$)

[**Ans.** The conditions for a circle are

$$l = 0,\ m^2(c - a) = n^2(a - b);\ \text{or } m = 0,\ n^2(a - b) = l^2(b - a)$$

or $\qquad n = 0,\ l^2(b - c) = m^2(c - a)]$

9.2.6. To Find the Condition for the Two Lines

$$\frac{x}{l_1} = \frac{y}{m_1} = \frac{z}{n_1}, \frac{x}{l_2} = \frac{y}{m_2} = \frac{z}{n_2} \qquad \qquad ...(i)$$

to be the Axes of the Section by the Plane Through Them

The quadric is

$$ax^2 + by^2 + cz^2 = 1$$

As each of the two lines in (i) will bisect chords of the section parallel to the other, we see that each of them must belong to the diametral plane conjugate to the other.

Now the diametral plane

$$al_1 x + am_1 y + cn_1 z = 0$$

conjugate to the line

$$\frac{x}{l_1} = \frac{y}{m_1} = \frac{z}{n_1}$$

will contain the second line if

$$al_1 l_2 + bm_1 m_2 + cn_1 n_2 = 0 \qquad \qquad ...(ii)$$

The condition (ii) is the one sought.

In addition to (ii), we also have the condition

$$l_1 l_2 + m_1 m_2 + n_1 n_2 = 0$$

for the axes are necessarily perpendicular.

EXAMPLES

1. *Planes are drawn through the origin so as to cut the quadric*

$$ax^2 + by^2 + cz^2 = 1,$$

in rectangular hyperbolas. Prove that the normals to the planes through the origin lie on a quadric cone.

Sol. Consider a plane

$$lx + my + nz = 0 \qquad \qquad ...(1)$$

through the origin. The condition for this plane to cut the given quadric in a rectangular hyperbola is

$$(b + c)\, l^2 + (c + a)\, m^2 + (a + b)\, n^2 = 0 \qquad \qquad ...(2)$$

The normal to the plane (1) through the origin is

$$\frac{x}{l} = \frac{y}{m} = \frac{z}{n} \qquad \qquad ...(3)$$

Eliminating l, m, n between (2) and (3), we see that the normals, in question, lie on the surface

$$(b + c)\, x^2 + (c + a)\, y^2 + (a + b)\, z^2 = 0$$

which is a quadric cone.

2. *Prove that the axes of the section of the conicoid $ax^2 + by^2 + cz^2 = 1$ by the plane $lx + my + nz = 0$ lie on the cone*

$$(b - c)\, \frac{l}{x} + (c - a)\, \frac{m}{y} + (a - b)\, \frac{n}{v} = 0. \quad \text{(Gorakhpur, 2002; Avadh, 2006;}$$

Also prove that this can pass through the normal to the plane of the section and the diameter to which the plane of section is diametral plane.

Sol. Let λ, μ, ν be the direction ratios of the axis of the section.

Then we have

$$\frac{\lambda\,(ar^2 - 1)}{l} = \frac{\mu\,(br^2 - 1)}{m} = \frac{\nu\,(cr^2 - 1)}{n} = k \ \text{(say)} \qquad \qquad ...(1)$$

$$\therefore \qquad \frac{lk}{\lambda} = ar^2 - 1, \ \frac{mk}{\mu} = br^2 - 1 \ \text{and} \ \frac{nk}{\nu} = cr^2 - 1 \qquad \qquad ...(2)$$

Multiplying the relations in (2) by $(b - c)$, $(c - a)$ and $(a - b)$ respectively and adding, we get

$$\frac{l\,(b - c)}{\lambda} + \frac{m\,(c - a)}{\mu} + \frac{n\,(a - b)}{\nu} = \frac{1}{k}\,[(ar^2 - 1)\,(b - c) + (br^2 - 1)\,(c - a)$$

$$+ (a - b)\,(cr^2 - 1)] = 0 \quad ...(3)$$

Hence the axis

$$\frac{x}{\lambda} = \frac{y}{\mu} = \frac{z}{\nu}$$

lies on the cone

$$\frac{l\,(b - c)}{x} + \frac{m\,(c - a)}{y} + \frac{n\,(a - b)}{z} = 0 \qquad \qquad ...(4)$$

Now, equations of the normal to the plane

$$lx + my + nz = 0 \qquad \qquad ...(5)$$

are

$$\frac{x}{l} = \frac{y}{m} = \frac{z}{n} \qquad \qquad ...(6)$$

Also, the cone whose generators are the axes of the section of conicoid

$$ax^2 + by^2 + cz^2 = 1$$

is given by equation (4).

This cone will contain the line (6) if
$$(b - c) + (c - a) + (a - b) = 0$$
which is obviously true.

Again, equations to the diameter to which (5) is the diametral plane are
$$\frac{x}{l/a} = \frac{y}{m/b} = \frac{z}{n/c} \qquad \qquad ...(7)$$

∴   The cone (4) will pass through the above line if
$$(b - c)\frac{l}{l/a} + (c - a)\frac{m}{m/a} + (a - b)\frac{n}{n/c} = 0$$
or
$$a(b - c) + b(c - a) + c(a - b) = 0$$
which holds identically.

Hence the cone (4) also passes through the diameter (7).

3. *Show that the section of the surface yz + zx + xy = a² by the plane lx + my + nz = p will be a parabola if*
$$\sqrt{l} + \sqrt{m} + \sqrt{n} = 0.$$

Sol. The equation of the cylinder which passes through the section and has its generators parallel to z-axis, may be found by eliminating z between the equations of surface and the plane, i.e.,
$$xy + (x + y)\left(\frac{p - lx - my}{n}\right) = a^2 \qquad \qquad ...(1)$$

The projection of the given section on the plane z = 0 is given by
$$lx^2 + my^2 + xy(l + m - n) - px - py + na^2 = 0, \; z = 0 \qquad ...(2)$$
This projection and hence the given section will be a parabola if
$$\left(\frac{l + m - n}{2}\right)^2 = lm \qquad \qquad [\because \; H^2 = AB]$$

or $\quad\quad (l + m - n) = \pm\, 2\sqrt{lm}$

or $\quad\quad l + m - n = -2\sqrt{lm} \qquad\qquad$ [taking − ve sign]

or $\quad\quad (\sqrt{l} + \sqrt{m})^2 = (\sqrt{n})^2$

or $\quad\quad (\sqrt{l} + \sqrt{m} + \sqrt{n})(\sqrt{l} + \sqrt{m} - \sqrt{n}) = 0$

or $\quad\quad \sqrt{l} + \sqrt{m} + \sqrt{n} = 0.$

4. *Prove that the section of the conicoid ax² + by² + cz² = 1 by a tangent plane to the cone*
$$x^2/(b + c) + y^2/(c + a) + z^2/(a + b) = 0$$
is a rectangular hyperbola. $\qquad\qquad$ (Avadh, 2006; Gorakhpur, 1997)

Sol. The lengths of the semi-axes of the section of ax² + by² + cz² = 1 by the plane
$$lx + my + nz = 0$$
are given by
$$r^4(bcl^2 + cam^2 + abn^2) - r^2[(b + c)l^2 + (c + a)m^2 + (a + b)n^2] + (l^2 + m^2 + n^2) = 0$$

The section will be a rectangular hyperbola if the sum of the squares of its semi-axes is zero, i.e.,
$$r_1^2 + r_2^2 = 0$$

i.e., if $\qquad\qquad (b + c)l^2 + (c + a)m^2 + (a + b)n^2 = 0$

which shows that the given plane envelopes the cone

$$\frac{x^2}{(b+c)} + \frac{y^2}{(c+a)} + \frac{z^2}{(a+b)} = 0$$

Since the given plane touches the above cone, we have

$$(b+c)\,l^2 + (c+a)\,m^2 + (a+b)\,n^2 = 0$$

Hence the proposition.

5. *Lines are drawn from the centre of the quadric*

$$ax^2 + by^2 + cz^2 = 1,$$

having lengths proportional to the area of the perpendicular central section; show that the locus of their extremities is a quadric, i.e.,

$$\frac{x^2}{a} + \frac{y^2}{b} + \frac{z^2}{c} = constant.$$

Sol. Consider a central plane section

$$'lx + my + nz = 0 \qquad\qquad ...(1)$$

The area of the conic in which this plane cuts the given quadric is

$$= \pi / p \sqrt{abc} = A$$

where p, the length of the perpendicular from the origin to the tangent plane parallel to the plane (1) is given by

$$p = \frac{\left(\sum \dfrac{l^2}{a}\right)^{1/2}}{\sqrt{\sum l^2}} = \left(\sum \frac{l^2}{a}\right)^{1/2}$$

where, we have supposed that (l, m, n) are actual direction cosines.

We require the locus of the point (x, y, z), where

$$x = lAk, \; y = mAk, \; z = nAk$$

k being the constant of proportionality.

$$\therefore \qquad x = \frac{l\pi}{\left(\sum \dfrac{l^2}{a} \sqrt{abc}\right)^{1/2}} k = \frac{1}{\left(\sum \dfrac{l^2}{a}\right)^{1/2}} k', \text{ etc.}$$

where $k' = \pi k \sqrt{abc}$.

Thus, we have

$$\frac{x^2}{a} + \frac{y^2}{b} + \frac{z^2}{c} = k^2.$$

Hence, the result.

6. *Show that the axes of the sections of the surface*

$$ax^2 + by^2 + cz^2 = 1,$$

by planes through the line

$$\frac{x}{l} = \frac{y}{m} = \frac{z}{n},$$

lie on the cone ·

$$\frac{(b-c)\,(mz-ny)}{x} + \frac{(c-a)\,(nx-lz)}{y} + \frac{(a-b)\,(ly-mx)}{z} = 0.$$

Sol. Let

$$\frac{x}{l_1} = \frac{y}{m_1} = \frac{z}{n_1} \qquad \qquad ...(i)$$

$$\frac{x}{l_2} = \frac{y}{m_2} = \frac{z}{n_2} \qquad \qquad ...(ii)$$

be the principal axes of any section through the given line

$$\frac{x}{l} = \frac{y}{m} = \frac{z}{n} \qquad \qquad ...(iii)$$

The axes being perpendicular to each other, we have

$$l_1 l_2 + m_1 m_2 + n_1 n_2 = 0 \qquad \qquad ...(iv)$$

Also as in § 9.2.6, page 275, we have

$$al_1 l_2 + bm_1 m_2 + cn_1 n_2 = 0. \qquad \qquad ...(v)$$

Also the lines (i), (ii), (iii) are coplanar, so that we have

$$\begin{vmatrix} l_1 & m_1 & n_1 \\ l_2 & m_2 & n_2 \\ l & m & n \end{vmatrix} = 0, \qquad \qquad ...(vi)$$

$$\Leftrightarrow \qquad l_1(m_2 n - mn_2) + m_1(n_2 l - nl_2) + n_1(l_2 m - lm_2) = 0$$

Eliminating l_1, m_1, n_1 from (iv), (v) and (vi), we have

$$\begin{vmatrix} l_2 & m_2 & n_2 \\ al_2 & bm_2 & cn_2 \\ m_2 n - mn_2 & n_2 l - nl_2 & l_2 m - lm_2 \end{vmatrix} = 0 \qquad \qquad ...(vii)$$

Now, eliminating l_2, m_2, n_2 from (ii) and (iii), we obtain the locus as required.

7. *One axis of a central section of the conicoid*

$$ax^2 + by^2 + cz^2 = 1$$

lies in the plane

$$ux + vy + wz = 0.$$

Show that the other lies on the cone

$$(b - c) uyz + (c - a) vzx + (a - b) wxy = 0.$$

Sol. Let

$$\frac{x}{l_1} = \frac{y}{m_1} = \frac{z}{n_1}, \quad \frac{x}{l_2} = \frac{y}{m_2} = \frac{z}{n_2}$$

be the two axes of a central section such that the second lies in the given plane for which we have the condition

$$ul_2 + vm_2 + wn_2 = 0 \qquad \qquad ...(i)$$

Also, as in § 9.2.6,

$$l_1 l_2 + m_1 m_2 + n_1 n_2 = 0 \qquad \qquad ...(ii)$$

$$al_1 l_2 + bm_1 m_2 + cn_1 n_2 = 0 \qquad \qquad ...(iii)$$

Eliminating l_2, m_2, n_2 from (i), (ii) and (iii), we have

$$\begin{vmatrix} u & v & w \\ l_1 & m_1 & n_1 \\ al_1 & bm_1 & cn_1 \end{vmatrix} = 0$$

$\Rightarrow$ $\qquad um_1n_1 (b - c) + vn_1l_1 (c - a) + wl_1m_1 (a - b) = 0$

With the help of this condition we see that the locus of the axis

$$x/l_1 = y/m_1 = z/n_1$$

is the cone

$$(b - c) uyz + (c - a) vzx + (a - b) wxy = 0.$$

EXERCISES

1. Show that the section of the ellipsoid $9x^2 + 6y^2 + 14z^2 = 3$, by the plane $x + y + z = 0$, is an ellipse with semi-axes $1/2$ and $\sqrt{9/22}$. Also obtain their equations.

   Gorakhpur, 1999, Rohilkhand 2006) [**Ans.** $x/2 = y = -(1/3) z; x/4 = -y/5 = z$]

2. Show that the curve

   $$x^2 + 7y^2 - 10z^2 + 9 = 0, x + 2y + 3z = 0$$

   is a hyperbola whose transverse axis is 6 and the direction cosines of whose axes are proportional to $(6, 3 - 4)$ and $(17, - 22, 9)$.

3. A_1, A_2, A_3 are the areas of three mutually perpendicular central sections of an ellipsoid; show that $A_1^{-2} + A_2^{-2} + A_3^{-2}$ is constant.

4. Show that all plane sections of $ax^2 + by^2 + cz^2 = 1$ which are rectangular hyperbolas and which pass through the point (α, β, γ) touch the cone

   $$\frac{(x - \alpha)^2}{b + c} + \frac{(y - \beta)^2}{c + a} + \frac{(z - \gamma)^2}{a + b} = 0.$$

5. Show that any plane whose normal lies on the cone $bcx^2 + cay^2 + abz^2 = 0$, cuts the surface $ax^2 + by^2 + cz^2 = 1$, in a parabola. *(Garhwal, 1997)*

6. The director circle of a plane central section of the ellipsoid

   $$x^2/a^2 + y^2/b^2 + z^2/c^2 = 1$$

   has a radius of constant length r. Show that the plane section touches the cone

   $$\frac{x^2}{a^2 (b^2 + c^2 - r^2)} + \frac{y^2}{b^2 (c^2 + a^2 - r^2)} + \frac{z^2}{c^2 (a^2 + b^2 - r^2)} = 0.$$

7. If a length PQ be taken on the normal at a point P of the ellipsoid

   $$x^2/a^2 + y^2/b^2 + z^2/c^2 = 1,$$

   equal in length to $l^2A/\pi abc$, where l is a constant and A is the area of the section of the ellipsoid by the diametral plane of OP, show that the locus of Q is

   $$\frac{a^2x^2}{(a^2 + l^2)^2} + \frac{b^2y^2}{(b^2 + l^2)^2} + \frac{c^2z^2}{(c^2 + l^2)^2} = 1.$$

8. Prove that if $l_1, m_1, n_1; l_2, m_2, n_2$ are the direction ratios of the principal axes of any plane section of the quadric $ax^2 + by^2 + cz^2 = 1$, then

   $$\frac{l_1l_2}{b - c} = \frac{m_1m_2}{c - a} = \frac{n_1n_2}{a - b}.$$

9. Find the equation of the central plane section of the quadric $ax^2 + by^2 + cz^2 = 1$ which has one of its axes along the line $x/l = y/m = z/n$.

   [**Ans.** $\Sigma \{m^2 (a - b) + n^2 (a - c)\} (lx = 0)$]

10. Show that central plane sections of an ellipsoid of constant area touch a quadric cone.

    (Avadh, 1995)

9.3. AXES OF NON-CENTRAL PLANE SECTIONS

To determine the lengths and direction ratios of the section of the central conicoid

$$ax^2 + by^2 + cz^2 = 1 \qquad \text{...(1)}$$

by the plane

$$lx + my + nz = p \qquad \text{...(2)}$$

Centre of the plane section, *now*, is *not* the origin. If (α, β, γ) is the centre of the section, the plane (2) is also represented by the equation

$$a\alpha x + b\beta y + c\gamma z = a\alpha^2 + b\beta^2 + c\gamma^2$$

so that

$$\frac{a\alpha}{l} = \frac{b\beta}{m} = \frac{c\gamma}{n} = \frac{a\alpha^2 + b\beta^2 + c\gamma^2}{p} = k, \text{ (say)}$$

$\Leftrightarrow \qquad \alpha = \dfrac{lk}{a}, \ \beta = \dfrac{mk}{b}, \ \gamma = \dfrac{nk}{c}$

$\Leftrightarrow \qquad k = \dfrac{a\alpha^2 + b\beta^2 + c\gamma^2}{p} = \dfrac{k^2}{p}\left(\dfrac{l^2}{a} + \dfrac{m^2}{b} + \dfrac{n^2}{c}\right)$

$\Leftrightarrow \qquad k = \dfrac{p}{l^2/a + m^2/b + n^2/c}$

If we write

$$p_0^2 = \frac{l^2}{a} + \frac{m^2}{b} + \frac{n^2}{c}$$

we get

$$\left(\frac{lp}{ap_0^2}, \frac{mp}{bp_0^2}, \frac{np}{cp_0^2}\right)$$

as the co-ordinates of the centre of the section. The equation of the conicoid referred to this point as origin is

$$a\left(x + \frac{lp}{ap_0^2}\right)^2 + b\left(y + \frac{mp}{bp_0^2}\right)^2 + c\left(z + \frac{np}{cp_0^2}\right)^2 = 1$$

$\Leftrightarrow \qquad ax^2 + by^2 + cz^2 + \dfrac{2p}{p_0^2}(lx + my + nz) + \dfrac{p^2}{p_0^2} = 1 \qquad \text{...(3)}$

Also, the equation of the plane (2) becomes

$$lx + my + nz = 0 \qquad \text{...(4)}$$

Now the conic

$$ax^2 + by^2 + cz^2 + (2p/p_0^2)(lx + my + nz) = 1 - (p^2/p_0^2), \ lx + my + nz = 0 \quad \text{...(5)}$$

is the same as the conic

$$ax^2 + by^2 + cz^2 = 1 - (p^2/p_0^2), \ lx + my + nz = 0 \qquad \text{...(6)}$$

for, points whose co-ordinates satisfy the equations (5) also satisfy the equations (6) and *vice-versa*.

Putting $\qquad\qquad 1 - (p^2/p_0{}^2) = d^2$

and replacing a, b, c by a/d^2, b/d^2, c/d^2 respectively in the equations (5) and (6) of the previous article 9.2.1, we get

$$\frac{l^2}{ar^2d^{-2} - 1} + \frac{m^2}{br^2d^{-2} - 1} + \frac{n^2}{cr^2d^{-2} - 1} = 0 \qquad \text{...(7)}$$

$$\frac{\lambda\,(ar^2d^{-2} - 1)}{l} = \frac{\mu\,(br^2d^{-2} - 1)}{m} = \frac{\nu\,(cr^2d^{-2} - 1)}{n} \qquad \text{...(8)}$$

which give the *lengths* r_1, r_2 and the *direction ratios* l, m, n respectively at the corresponding semi-axes of the section.

9.3.1. Area of the Plane Section

Assuming that the section is an ellipse, its area

$$= \pi r_1 r_2 = \pi d^2 \left(\frac{l^2 + m^2 + n^2}{bcl^2 + cam^2 + abn^2} \right)^{1/2}$$

$$= \pi \left(1 - \frac{p^2}{l^2/a + m^2/b + n^2/c} \right) \left(\frac{l^2 + m^2 + n^2}{bcl^2 + cam^2 + abn^2} \right)^{1/2}$$

9.3.2. Parallel Plane Sections

Comparing the equations (7) and (8) with the equations (5) and (6) of the previous article, we see that if α, β be the lengths of the semi-axis of the section by the central plane

$$lx + my + nz = 0 \qquad \text{...(9)}$$

then the semi-axes of the section by the parallel plane

$$lx + my + nz = p \qquad \text{...(10)}$$

are $\qquad\qquad\qquad d\alpha$ and $d\beta$

$$\Leftrightarrow \qquad\qquad \alpha \left(1 - \frac{p^2}{p_0{}^2} \right)^{1/2} \text{ and } \beta \left(1 - \frac{p^2}{p_0{}^2} \right)^{1/2}$$

and the corresponding axes are parallel.

Thus, we see that *parallel plane sections of a central conicoid are similar and similarly situated conics.*

Again, if A_0 and A are the areas of the sections by the planes (9) and (10), we have

$$A_0 = \pi\alpha\beta, \; A = \pi d^2 \alpha\beta = A_0 \left(1 - \frac{p^2}{p_0{}^2} \right)$$

It follows that $\qquad\qquad \dfrac{A}{A_0} = \left(1 - \dfrac{p^2}{\Sigma\, l^2/a} \right).$

Note. p/p_0 can easily be seen to be the ratio of the lengths of the perpendiculars from the centre to the given plane and to the parallel tangent plane.

9.3.3. Comparison of Lengths of the Axes of Any Section and Those of Parallel Central Section of the Conicoid, $ax^2 + by^2 + cz^2 = 1$

We have already shown that the lengths of the axes of the conic $ax^2 + by^2 + cz^2 = 1$, $lx + my + nz = 1$ are given by

$$\frac{l^2}{ar^2-1}+\frac{m^2}{br^2-1}+\frac{n^2}{cr^2-1}=0 \qquad \ldots(1)$$

[By § 9.2.1]

And those of the conic $ax^2 + by^2 + cz^2 = 1$, $lx + my + nz = p$ are given by

$$\frac{l^2}{a\dfrac{r^2}{k^2}-1}+\frac{m^2}{b\dfrac{r^2}{k^2}-1}+\frac{n^2}{c\dfrac{r^2}{k^2}-1}=0 \qquad \ldots(2)$$

[By § 9.3]

Hence if r_1^2 and r_2^2 are the roots of (1) and R_1^2 and R_2^2 those of (2), we have by comparing (1) and (2),

$$\frac{R_1^2}{k^2}=r_1^2 \text{ and } \frac{R_2^2}{k^2}=r_2^2$$

i.e.,
$$R_1=kr_1 \text{ and } R_2=kr_2.$$

∴ The area A_0 of the section by the parallel central plane $lx + my + nz = 0$ is given by $A = \pi r_1 r_2$.

And the area A of the section by the non-central plane $lx + my + nz = p$ is given by
$$A = \pi R_1 R_2 = \pi k^2 r_1 r_2 = k^2 A_0 (1 - p^2/p_0^2).$$

EXAMPLES

1. *Show that the area of the section of an ellipsoid by a plane which passes through the extremities of three conjugate semi-diameters is in a constant ratio to the area of the parallel central section.*

Sol. Consider the ellipsoid

$$\frac{x^2}{a^2}+\frac{y^2}{b^2}+\frac{z^2}{c^2}=1$$

Let $P(x_1, y_1, z_1)$, $Q(x_2, y_2, z_2)$, $R(x_3, y_3, z_3)$, be the co-ordinates of the extremities of the three conjugate semi-diameters of the ellipsoid. The equation of the plane PQR is

$$\frac{x_1+x_2+x_3}{a^2}x+\frac{y_1+y_2+y_3}{b^2}y+\frac{z_1+z_2+z_3}{c^2}z=1 \qquad \ldots(1)$$

The central plane parallel to the plane (1) is

$$\frac{x_1+x_2+x_3}{a^2}x+\frac{y_1+y_2+y_3}{b^2}y+\frac{z_1+z_2+z_3}{c^2}z=0 \qquad \ldots(2)$$

Rewriting these equations as
$$lx + my + nz = 1, \ lx + my + nz = 0$$
we see that the ratio of the areas of the two sections

$$= \left(1 - \frac{i}{\Sigma a^2 l^2}\right) \qquad (\S\ 9.3.2)$$

Again
$$\Sigma a^2 l^2 = \sum \frac{(x_1+x_2+x_3)^2}{a^2} = 3$$

making use of relations (C), (D), of § 8.8.

Hence, the result.

2. *Prove that the tangent planes to*

$$\frac{x^2}{a^2} + \frac{y^2}{b^2} + \frac{z^2}{c^2} + 1 = 0$$

which cut

$$\frac{x^2}{a^2} + \frac{y^2}{b^2} + \frac{z^2}{c^2} - 1 = 0$$

in ellipse of constant area πk^2 *have their points of contact on the surface*

$$\frac{x^2}{a^4} + \frac{y^2}{b^4} + \frac{z^2}{c^4} = \frac{k^4}{4a^2b^2c^2}.$$ *(Garhwal, 1996; Gorakhpur, 2001)*

Sol. Equation of tangent plane to

$$\frac{x^2}{a^2} + \frac{y^2}{b^2} - \frac{z^2}{c^2} + 1 = 0$$

at any point (x_1, y_1, z_1) is

$$\frac{xx_1}{a^2} + \frac{yy_1}{b^2} - \frac{zz_1}{c^2} = -1 \qquad \ldots(1)$$

where

$$\frac{x_1^2}{a^2} + \frac{y_1^2}{b^2} - \frac{z_1^2}{c^2} = -1 \qquad \ldots(2)$$

Now, if A_0 be the area of the corresponding central section $\frac{xx_1}{a^2} + \frac{yy_1}{b^2} - \frac{zz_1}{c^2} = 0$ of the second conicoid

$$\frac{x^2}{a^2} + \frac{y^2}{b^2} - \frac{z^2}{c^2} = 1$$

then

$$A = \left(1 - \frac{p^2}{p_0^2}\right) A_0 \qquad \ldots(3)$$

Now, $A = \pi k^2$ given and $p^2 = (-1)^2 = 1$,

and

$$p_0^2 = a^2 \frac{x_1^2}{a^4} + b^2 \frac{y_1^2}{b^4} - c^2 \frac{z_1^2}{c^4} = -1, \qquad \text{[from (2)]}$$

and

$$A_0 = \frac{\pi ab \sqrt{-c^2} \sqrt{l^2 + m^2 + n^2}}{\sqrt{a^2l^2 + b^2m^2 - c^2n^2}}$$

In the usual formula c^2 is put equal to $-c^2$,

$$= \frac{\pi ab \sqrt{-c^2} \sqrt{\dfrac{x_1^2}{a^4} + \dfrac{y_1^2}{b^4} + \dfrac{z_1^2}{c^4}}}{\sqrt{-1}} \qquad \text{[from (2)]}$$

Squaring relation (3) and putting the values, we get

$$\pi^2 k^4 = \left(1 - \frac{1}{-1}\right)^2 \frac{\pi^2 a^2 b^2 (-c)^2}{-1} \left(\frac{x_1^2}{a^4} + \frac{y_1^2}{b^4} + \frac{z_1^2}{c^4}\right)$$

or
$$\frac{k^4}{4a^2b^2c^2} = \frac{x_1^2}{a^4} + \frac{y_1^2}{b^4} + \frac{z_1^2}{c^4}$$

Hence the locus of (x_1, y_1, z_1) we have

$$\frac{x^2}{a^4} + \frac{y^2}{b^4} + \frac{z^2}{c^4} = \frac{k^4}{4a^2b^2c^2}.$$

3. *Prove that the axes of the section of the cone* $ax^2 + by^2 + cz^2 = 0$ *by the plane*

$$lx + my + nz = p$$

are given by

$$\frac{l^2}{ap_0^2 r^2 + p^2} + \frac{m^2}{bp_0^2 r^2 + p^2} + \frac{n^2}{cp_0^2 r^2 + p^2} = 0$$

where
$$p_0^2 = \frac{l^2}{a} + \frac{m^2}{b} + \frac{n^2}{c}.$$

Sol. Let (α, β, γ) be the centre of the section of the cone

$$ax^2 + by^2 + cz^2 = 0 \qquad \ldots(i)$$

by the plane
$$lx + my + nz = p \qquad \ldots(ii)$$

The above plane may be represented as

$$(x - \alpha)\, a\alpha - (y - \beta)\, b\beta + (z - \gamma)\, c\gamma = 0 \qquad \ldots(iii)$$

Comparing coefficients of (ii) and (iii), get

$$\frac{a\alpha}{l} = \frac{b\beta}{m} = \frac{c\gamma}{n} = \frac{a\alpha^2 + b\beta^2 + c\gamma^2}{p} = \sqrt{\frac{a\alpha^2 + b\beta^2 + c\gamma^2}{l^2/a + m^2/b + n^2/c}}$$

$\therefore$
$$a\alpha^2 + b\beta^2 + c\gamma^2 = \frac{p^2}{p_0^2} \qquad \ldots(iv)$$

where
$$p_0^2 = \frac{l^2}{a} + \frac{m^2}{b} + \frac{n^2}{c}.$$

Hence
$$\alpha = \frac{lp}{ap_0^2}, \ \beta = \frac{mp}{bp_0^2}, \ \gamma = \frac{np}{cp_0^2}.$$

The equation to the cone (i) referred to parallel axes through (α, β, γ) is

$$a\left(x + \frac{lp}{ap_0^2}\right)^2 + b\left(y + \frac{mp}{bp_0^2}\right)^2 + c\left(z + \frac{np}{cp_0^2}\right)^2 = 0$$

or
$$ax^2 + by^2 + cz^2 + \frac{2p}{p_0^2}(lx + my + nz) + \frac{p^2}{p_0^4}\left(\frac{l^2}{a} + \frac{m^2}{b} + \frac{n^2}{c}\right) = 0$$

or
$$ax^2 + by^2 + cz^2 + \frac{2p}{p_0^2}(lx + my + nz) + \frac{p^2}{p_0^4} = 0 \qquad \ldots(v)$$

$\therefore$ The section of (v) by (vi) is the same as the conic which is the section of

$$ax^2 + by^2 + cz^2 + \frac{p^2}{p_0^2} = 0 \qquad \ldots(vi)$$

and
$$lx + my + nz = 0 \qquad \ldots(vii)$$

As the extremities of semi-diameters of length r of (vi) lie upon the sphere

$$x^2 + y^2 + z^2 = r^2 \qquad \qquad ...(viii)$$

the equation to the cone through them is obtained by making (vi) homogeneous with the help of ($viii$).

Hence the cone is

$$p^2 (x^2 + y^2 + z^2) + p_0^2 r^2 (ax^2 + by^2 + cz^2) = 0$$

or $\qquad \qquad \qquad \qquad \Sigma \, x^2 (ar^2 p_0^2 + p^2) = 0 \qquad \qquad ...(ix)$

If r is the length of either semi-axis of the section of (vi) by (v), then the plane (v) will touch (ix).

This is so, if

$$\frac{l^2}{(ap_0^2 r^2 + p^2)} + \frac{m^2}{(bp_0^2 r^2 + p^2)} + \frac{n^2}{(cp_0^2 r^2 + p^2)} = 0.$$

4. *Through a given point* (α, β, γ) *planes are drawn parallel to three conjugate diametral planes of the ellipsoid*

$$\frac{x^2}{a^2} + \frac{y^2}{b^2} + \frac{z^2}{c^2} = 1.$$

Show that the sum of the ratios of the areas of the section by these planes to the areas of the parallel diametral planes is

$$3 - \frac{\alpha^2}{a^2} - \frac{\beta^2}{b^2} - \frac{\gamma^2}{c^2}.$$

Sol. Equations of the conjugate diametral planes are

$$\frac{xx_1}{a^2} + \frac{yy_1}{b^2} + \frac{zz_1}{c^2} = 0 \text{ etc.} \qquad \qquad ...(1)$$

and that of a parallel plane through (α, β, γ) is

$$(x - a)\frac{x_1}{a^2} + (y - \beta)\frac{y_1}{b^2} + (z - \gamma)\frac{z_1}{c^2} = 0$$

or $\qquad \dfrac{xx_1}{a^2} + \dfrac{yy_1}{b^2} + \dfrac{zz_1}{c^2} = \dfrac{\alpha x_1}{a^2} + \dfrac{\beta y_1}{b^2} + \dfrac{\gamma z_1}{c^2} = p_1 \text{ (say)} \qquad \qquad ...(2)$

Let A_1 be the area of the section of the ellipsoid

$$\frac{x^2}{a^2} + \frac{y^2}{b^2} + \frac{z^2}{c^2} = 1$$

by (1) and A_1' be the corresponding area of the section by (2), then we know that

$$A_1' = \left(1 - \frac{p_1^2}{p_0^2}\right) A_1$$

$$\therefore \qquad \qquad \frac{A_1'}{A_1} = 1 - \frac{p_1^2}{p_0^2}$$

where $\qquad \qquad \qquad p_0^2 = \dfrac{l^2}{a} + \dfrac{m^2}{b} + \dfrac{n^2}{c}$

when the conicoid is $ax^2 + by^2 + cz^2 = 1$ and the plane is $lx + my + nz = p$. Hence p_0^2 in this case will be

$$a^2 \cdot \frac{x_1^2}{a^4} + b^2 \cdot \frac{y_1^2}{b^4} + c^2 \cdot \frac{z_1^2}{c^4} = \frac{x_1^2}{a^2} + \frac{y_1^2}{b^2} + \frac{z_1^2}{c^2} = 1.$$

$$\therefore \qquad \frac{A_1'}{A_1} = 1 - p_1^2 = 1 - \left(\frac{\alpha x_1}{a^2} + \frac{\beta y_1}{b^2} + \frac{\gamma z_1}{c^2} \right)^2 \qquad \text{[from (2)]}$$

$$\therefore \qquad \sum \frac{A_1'}{A_1} = \left[1 - \left(\frac{\alpha x_1}{a^2} + \frac{\beta y_1}{b^2} + \frac{\gamma z_1}{c^2} \right)^2 \right] + \left[1 - \left(\frac{\alpha x_2}{a^2} + \frac{\beta y_2}{b^2} + \frac{\gamma z_2}{c^2} \right)^2 \right]$$

$$+ \left[1 - \left(\frac{\alpha x_3}{a^2} + \frac{\beta y_3}{b^2} + \frac{\gamma z_3}{c^2} \right)^2 \right]$$

$$= 3 - \left[\frac{\alpha^2}{a^4} \sum x_1^2 + \frac{\beta^2}{b^4} \sum y_1^2 + \frac{\gamma^2}{c^4} \sum z_1^2 \right] \qquad \text{[other terms vanish]}$$

$$= 3 - \frac{\alpha^2}{a^2} - \frac{\beta^2}{b^2} - \frac{\gamma^2}{c^2}.$$

5. *Prove that if l_1, m_1, n_1; l_2, m_2, n_2 are the direction cosines of the axes of any plane section of the ellipsoid*

$$\frac{x^2}{a^2} + \frac{y^2}{b^2} + \frac{z^2}{c^2} = l,$$

then

$$\frac{l_1 l_2}{a^2 (b^2 - c^2)} = \frac{m_1 m_2}{b^2 (c^2 - a^2)} = \frac{n_1 n_2}{c^2 (a^2 - b^2)}.$$

Sol. Let l, m, n be the d.c.'s of either axis of the section of

$$\frac{x^2}{a^2} + \frac{y^2}{b^2} + \frac{z^2}{c^2} = 1 \qquad \qquad \qquad ...(1)$$

by the plane $\qquad \qquad Lx + My + Nz = p \qquad \qquad \qquad ...(2)$

then $\qquad \dfrac{r^2 - a^2 k^2}{L a^2 k^2 / l} = \dfrac{r^2 - b^2 k^2}{M b^2 k^2 / m} = \dfrac{r^2 - c^2 k^2}{N c^2 k^2 / n} = \lambda \text{ (say)}$

$$\therefore \qquad \frac{L a^2 k^2}{l} (b^2 - c^2) + \frac{M b^2 k^2}{m} (c^2 - a^2) + \frac{N c^2 k^2}{n} (a^2 - b^2)$$

$$= \left(\frac{1}{\lambda} \right) [(r^2 - a^2 k^2)(b^2 - c^2) + (r^2 - b^2 k^2)(c^2 - a^2)$$

$$+ (r^2 - c^2 k^2)(a^2 - b^2)] = 0$$

or $\qquad \sum \dfrac{L a^2}{l} (b^2 - c^2) = 0 \qquad \qquad \qquad ...(3)$

Again, since the axes lie in the plane (2), hence

$$lL + mM + nN = 0 \qquad \qquad \qquad ...(4)$$

Eliminating n between (3) and (4), we get

$$\frac{L a^2 (b^2 - c^2)}{l} + \frac{M b^2 (c^2 - a^2)}{m} - \frac{N c^2 (a^2 - b^2) N}{(Ll + Mm)} = 0$$

or $\quad LMb^2l^2 (c^2 - a^2) + lm [L^2a^2 (b^2 - c^2) + M^2b^2 (c^2 - a^2) - N^2c^2 (a^2 - b^2)]$
$$+ LMa^2m^2 (b^2 - c^2) = 0 \quad ...(5)$$

Now, the d.c.'s of axes satisfy (3) and (4), and hence satisfy (5).

Thus if l_1, m_1, n_1 and l_2, m_2, n_2 are the d.c.'s of the axes, we have

$$\frac{l_1 l_2}{LMa^2 (b^2 - c^2)} = \frac{m_1 m_2}{LMb^2 (c^2 - a^2)}$$

or

$$\frac{l_1 l_2}{a^2 (b^2 - c^2)} = \frac{m_1 m_2}{b^2 (c^2 - a^2)} = \frac{n_1 n_2}{c^2 (a^2 - b^2)}.$$

6. *The normal section of an enveloping cylinder of the ellipsoid*

$$\frac{x^2}{a^2} + \frac{y^2}{b^2} + \frac{z^2}{c^2} = 1$$

has a given area πk^2. Prove that the plane of contact of the cylinder and ellipsoid touches the cone

$$\frac{x^2}{a^4 (b^2c^2 - k^4)} + \frac{y^2}{b^4 (c^2a^2 - k^4)} + \frac{z^2}{c^4 (a^2b^2 - k^4)} = 0. \qquad \text{(Garhwal, 1997)}$$

Sol. The enveloping cylinder is given by

$$\left(\frac{x^2}{a^2} + \frac{y^2}{b^2} + \frac{z^2}{c^2} - 1\right)\left(\frac{l^2}{a^2} + \frac{m^2}{b^2} + \frac{n^2}{c^2}\right) = \left(\frac{lx}{a^2} + \frac{my}{b^2} + \frac{nz}{c^2}\right)^2 \qquad ...(1)$$

its generators being parallel to

$$\frac{x}{l} = \frac{y}{m} = \frac{z}{n}. \qquad ...(2)$$

The plane of contact being the diametral plane of (2) is given by

$$\frac{lx}{a^2} + \frac{my}{b^2} + \frac{nz}{c^2} = 0 \equiv Lx + My + Nz = 0 \text{ (say)} \qquad ...(3)$$

The area A of the section of $\dfrac{x^2}{a^2} + \dfrac{y^2}{b^2} + \dfrac{z^2}{c^2} = 1$ by the plane (3) is given by

$$A = \pi abc \sqrt{\frac{L^2 + M^2 + N^2}{a^2 L^2 + b^2 M^2 + c^2 N^2}} = \pi abc \left[\frac{l^2/a^4 + m^2/b^4 + n^2/c^4}{l^2/a^2 + m^2/b^2 + n^2/c^2}\right]^{1/2}$$

Now, all the normal sections of the cylinder are equal and the central normal section being perpendicular to the generators (2) is

$$lx + my + nz = 0 \qquad ...(4)$$

Let θ be the angle between two sections (3) and (4), so that

$$\cos \theta = \frac{l^2/a^2 + m^2/b^2 + n^2/c^2}{\sqrt{l^2 + m^2 + n^2} \sqrt{l^2/a^4 + m^2/b^4 + n^2/c^4}}$$

$\therefore$ The area of normal section $= A \cos \theta$

$$= \frac{\pi abc}{\sqrt{l^2 + m^2 + n^2}}\left(\frac{l^2}{a^2} + \frac{m^2}{b^2} + \frac{n^2}{c^2}\right)^{1/2}$$

$$= \pi k^2 \text{ (given)}$$

or $\qquad a^2b^2c^2\left(\dfrac{l^2}{a^2}+\dfrac{m^2}{b^2}+\dfrac{n^2}{c^2}\right)=k^4(l^2+m^2+n^2)$

or $\qquad (b^2c^2-k^4)l^2+(c^2a^2-k^4)m^2+(a^2b^2-k^4)n^2=0$

Hence the normal to the plane of contact

$$\frac{x}{l/a^2}=\frac{y}{m/b^2}=\frac{z}{n/c^2}$$

generates the cone

$$a^4(b^2c^2-k^4)x^2+b^4(c^2a^2-k^4)y^2+c^4(a^2b^2-k^4)z^2=0$$

and the plane of contact touches the reciprocal cone

$$\frac{x^2}{a^4(b^2c^2-k^4)}+\frac{y^2}{b^4(c^2a^2-k^4)}+\frac{z^2}{c^4(a^2b^2-k^4)}=0.$$

7. *Find the angle between the asymptotes of the conic*
$$ax^2+by^2+cz^2=1,\ lx+my+nz=p.$$

Sol. Let θ be the required angle. If $r_1{}^2$, $r_2{}^2$ be the squares of the semi-axes of conic, we have

$$\tan\frac{\theta}{2}=\sqrt{\frac{-r_2{}^2}{r_1{}^2}}$$

$\Rightarrow\qquad \tan^2\theta=\dfrac{-4r_1{}^2r_2{}^2}{(r_1{}^2+r_2{}^2)^2}=\dfrac{-4(l^2+m^2+n^2)(bcl^2+cam^2+abn^2)}{[(b+c)l^2+(c+a)m^2+(a+b)n^2]^2}.$

EXERCISES

1. Find the lengths and directions of the axes of the section of the ellipsoid
$$9x^2+6y^2+14z^2=3$$
by the plane $x+y+z=1$.   **[Ans.** $3/22$, $44\sqrt{22}$, $(4,-5,1)$, $(2,1,-3)$,**]**

2. Show that the plane $x+y+z=1$ cuts the quadric $11x^2-13y^2-4z^2=5$ in a hyperbola and find the direction ratios of its axes.   **[Ans.** $-3,1,2;1,-5,4$**]**

3. Show that the plane $x+2y+3z=4$ cuts the conicoid $2x^2+y^2-2z^2=1$ in a parabola, the direction cosines of whose axis are proportional to $1,4,-3$.

4. The ellipsoid $x^2+2y^2+3z^2=1$ is cut by parallel planes
$$2x+3y+4z=2,\ 2x+3y+4z=3;$$
show that the areas of the sections made by the planes are in the ratio $59:29$.

5. Find the locus of the centres of the section of the ellipsoid
$$x^2/a^2+y^2/b^2+z^2/c^2=1$$
which are of constant area πk^2.

$$\left[\textbf{Ans. } a^2b^2c^2\left(\frac{x^2}{a^4}+\frac{y^2}{b^4}+\frac{z^2}{c^4}\right)\left(1-\frac{x^2}{a^2}-\frac{y^2}{b^2}-\frac{z^2}{c^2}\right)^2=k^2\left(\frac{x^2}{a^2}+\frac{y^2}{b^2}+\frac{z^2}{c^2}\right)\right]$$

6. Prove that the area of the section of the ellipsoid
$$\frac{x^2}{a^2}+\frac{y^2}{b^2}+\frac{z^2}{c^2}=1$$

by the plane $lx + my + nz = p$, is given by

$$\frac{\pi abc\,(l^2 + m^2 + n^2)^{1/2}}{(a^2l^2 + b^2m^2 + c^2n^2)^{1/2}}\left[1 - \frac{p^2}{a^2l^2 + b^2m^2 + c^2n^2}\right].$$

7. Find the area of the section of the ellipsoid $\dfrac{x^2}{a^2} + \dfrac{y^2}{b^2} + \dfrac{z^2}{c^2} = 1$ by the plane

$$\frac{x}{a} + \frac{y}{b} + \frac{z}{c} = 1. \qquad\qquad\qquad (Gorakhpur,\ 1996)$$

$$\left[\textbf{Ans. } \frac{2}{3}\,\frac{\pi}{\sqrt{3}}\,(b^2c^2 + c^2a^2 + a^2b^2)^{1/2}\right]$$

8. Show that the section of the ellipsoid $\dfrac{x^2}{a^2} + \dfrac{y^2}{b^2} + \dfrac{z^2}{c^2} = 1$ whose centre is the point

$\left(\dfrac{1}{3}a,\ \dfrac{1}{3}b,\ \dfrac{1}{3}c\right)$ passes through three of the extremities of its principal axes.

9. Show that the locus of the centres ot sections of the cone $ax^2 + by^2 + cz^2 = 0$ such that the sum of the squares of their axes is constant $(= k^2)$, is the conicoid

$$a\left(\frac{1}{b} + \frac{1}{c}\right)x^2 + b\left(\frac{1}{c} + \frac{1}{a}\right)y^2 + c\left(\frac{1}{a} + \frac{1}{b}\right)z^2 + k^2 = 0.$$

10. Prove that the areas of the sections of greatest and least areas of the ellipsoid $\dfrac{x^2}{a^2} + \dfrac{y^2}{b^2} + \dfrac{z^2}{c^2} = 1$ which pass through the fixed line $x/l = y/m = z/n$ are $\dfrac{\pi abc}{r_1},\ \dfrac{\pi abc}{r_2}$

where r_1 and r_2 are the axes of the section by the plane $\dfrac{lx}{a} + \dfrac{my}{b} + \dfrac{nz}{c} = 0.$

9.4. CIRCULAR SECTIONS

To determine the circular sections of the ellipsoid

$$\frac{x^2}{a^2} + \frac{y^2}{b^2} + \frac{z^2}{c^2} = 1 \qquad\qquad\qquad \dots(1)$$

We have to find the equations of the planes which cut the ellipsoid in circles. We suppose that $a^2 > b^2 > c^2$.

Writing the equation of the ellipsoid in the form

$$\frac{1}{b^2}(x^2 + y^2 + z^2 - b^2) + x^2\left(\frac{1}{a^2} - \frac{1}{b^2}\right) + z^2\left(\frac{1}{a^2} - \frac{1}{b^2}\right) = 0$$

$$\Leftrightarrow \qquad (x^2 + y^2 + z^2 - b^2) = \frac{a^2 - b^2}{a^2}x^2 - \frac{b^2 - c^2}{c^2}z^2$$

we see that the two planes

$$\frac{a^2 - b^2}{a^2}x^2 - \frac{b^2 - c^2}{c^2}z^2 = 0$$

meet the ellipsoid where they meet the sphere

$$x^2 + y^2 + z^2 = b^2$$

but as a plane necessarily cuts a sphere in a circle, we find that the planes (2) cut the ellipsoid (1) in circles.

Since parallel sections are similar, *the two systems of planes*

$$\frac{x}{a}\sqrt{a^2 - b^2} + \frac{z}{c}\sqrt{b^2 - c^2} = \lambda,$$

and

$$\frac{x}{a}\sqrt{a^2 - b^2} - \frac{z}{c}\sqrt{b^2 - c^2} = \mu$$

which are parallel to those given by the equations (5) *cut the ellipsoid in circles for all values of* λ *and* μ.

Note. If we rewrite the equation of the ellipsoid in the form

$$\frac{1}{a^2}(x^2 + y^2 + z^2 - a^2) + y^2\left(\frac{1}{b^2} - \frac{1}{a^2}\right) + z^2\left(\frac{1}{c^2} - \frac{1}{a^2}\right) = 0 \qquad \ldots(3)$$

$$\frac{1}{c^2}(x^2 + y^2 + z^2 - c^2) + x^2\left(\frac{1}{a^2} - \frac{1}{c^2}\right) + y^2\left(\frac{1}{b^2} - \frac{1}{c^2}\right) = 0 \qquad \ldots(4)$$

we find that the pairs of planes

$$y^2\left(\frac{1}{b^2} - \frac{1}{a^2}\right) + z^2\left(\frac{1}{c^2} - \frac{1}{a^2}\right) = 0$$

$$x^2\left(\frac{1}{a^2} - \frac{1}{c^2}\right) + y^2\left(\frac{1}{b^2} - \frac{1}{c^2}\right) = 0$$

also cut the ellipsoid in circles. It may be seen, however, that these pairs of planes are not real in that there are no points which satisfy these equations.

9.4.1. Any Two Circular Sections of an Ellipsoid of Opposite Systems Lie on a Sphere

Let

$$\frac{x}{a}\sqrt{a^2 - b^2} + \frac{z}{c}\sqrt{b^2 - c^2} = \lambda$$

and

$$\frac{x}{a}\sqrt{a^2 - b^2} - \frac{z}{c}\sqrt{b^2 - c^2} = \mu$$

be the equations of the planes of any two circular sections of opposite systems.

The conicoid

$$\frac{x^2}{a^2} + \frac{y^2}{b^2} + \frac{z^2}{c^2} - 1 + k\left[\frac{x}{a}\sqrt{a^2 - b^2} + \frac{z}{c}\sqrt{b^2 - c^2} - \lambda\right]$$

$$\times \left[\frac{x}{a}\sqrt{a^2 - b^2} - \frac{z}{c}\sqrt{b^2 - c^2} - \mu\right] = 0 \qquad \ldots(1)$$

which passes through the two circular sections for all values of k, will represent a sphere, if k satisfies the equations

$$\frac{1}{a^2} + \frac{k(a^2 - b^2)}{a^2} = \frac{1}{b^2} = \frac{1}{c^2} - \frac{k(b^2 - c^2)}{c^2}$$

Now, $k = 1/b^2$ clearly satisfies these two equations.

Substituting this value of k in (1), we get the equation

$$x^2 + y^2 + z^2 - \frac{(\lambda + \mu)\sqrt{a^2 - b^2}}{a}x + \frac{(\lambda - \mu)\sqrt{b^2 - c^2}}{c}z + \lambda\mu - b^2 = 0$$

representing the sphere through the two circular sections.

Hence, the proposition is proved.

9.4.2. Circular Sections of Any Central Conicoid

$$f(x, y, z) \equiv ax^2 + by^2 + cz^2 + 2fyz + 2gzx + 2hxy - 1 = 0$$

The given equation can be written in the following form

$$(ax^2 + by^2 + cz^2 + 2fyz + 2gzx + 2hxy) - \lambda(x^2 + y^2 + z^2)$$

$$+ \lambda\left(x^2 + y^2 + z^2 - \frac{1}{\lambda}\right) = 0 \qquad \ldots(1)$$

Hence if $(ax^2 + by^2 + cz^2 + 2fyz + 2gzx + 2hxy) - \lambda(x^2 + y^2 + z^2) = 0$ ...(2)
represents a pair of planes, they will cut the given conicoid in circles.

Obviously, (2) will represent a pair of planes, if

$$\begin{vmatrix} a - \lambda & h & g \\ h & b - \lambda & f \\ g & f & c - \lambda \end{vmatrix} = 0 \qquad \ldots(3)$$

The equation (3) being a cubic in λ gives three values of λ which are all real. But only one value of λ gives real sections.

EXAMPLES

1. *Prove that the sections of hyperboloid $x^2/a^2 - y^2/b^2 - z^2/c^2 = 1$ by the plane*

$$\frac{x}{a}\sqrt{a^2 + b^2} + \frac{z}{c}\sqrt{b^2 - c^2} = \lambda$$

is real if $\lambda^2 > a^2 + c^2$. *(Gorakhpur, 1999)*

Sol. Equation to a sphere through the section of given hyperboloid by the given plane is

$$b^2\left(-\frac{x^2}{a^2} + \frac{y^2}{b^2} + \frac{z^2}{c^2} + 1\right) + \left[\frac{x}{a}\sqrt{a^2 + b^2} - \frac{z}{c}\sqrt{b^2 - c^2}\right]$$

$$\times \left[\frac{x}{a}\sqrt{a^2 + b^2} + \frac{z}{c}\sqrt{b^2 - c^2} - \lambda\right] = 0$$

The centre C of this sphere is

$$\left[\frac{\lambda\sqrt{a^2 + b^2}}{2a}, \ 0, \ \frac{-\lambda\sqrt{b^2 - c^2}}{2c}\right]$$

and radius is given by

$$R^2 = \frac{\lambda^2(a^2 + b^2)}{4a^2} + \frac{\lambda^2(b^2 - c^2)}{4c^2} - b^2$$

$$\Rightarrow \qquad R^2 = \frac{\lambda^2 b^2(c^2 + a^2)}{4a^2 c^2} - b^2$$

If p be the distance of the section from the centre of the sphere, then

p = perpendicular from the centre C on the plane

$$= \frac{\dfrac{\lambda(a^2 + b^2)}{2a^2} - \dfrac{\lambda(b^2 - c^2)}{2c^2} - \lambda}{\left(\dfrac{a^2 + b^2}{a^2} + \dfrac{b^2 - c^2}{c^2}\right)^{1/2}} = \frac{\lambda b^2(c^2 - a^2)}{2ca\sqrt{b^2(a^2 + c^2)}}$$

Radius of the circular section, r, is given
$$r^2 = R^2 - p^2$$

It will be positive if $R^2 > p^2$

$$\Rightarrow \qquad \frac{\lambda^2 b^2 (a^2 + c^2)}{4a^2 c^2} - b^2 > \frac{\lambda^2 b^2 (c^2 - a^2)}{4c^2 a^2 (a^2 + c^2)}$$

$$\Rightarrow \qquad \frac{\lambda^2 b^2}{(a^2 + c^2)} > b^2$$

$$\Rightarrow \qquad \lambda^2 > (a^2 + c^2), \text{ since } b \neq 0.$$

2. *Show that the real central circular sections of the hyperboloids*

$$\frac{x^2}{a^2} + \frac{y^2}{b^2} - \frac{z^2}{c^2} = 1 \text{ and } \frac{x^2}{a^2} - \frac{y^2}{b^2} - \frac{z^2}{c^2} = 1$$

given by the plane

$$\frac{y}{b}\sqrt{a^2 - b^2} \pm \frac{z}{c}\sqrt{a^2 + c^2} = 0 \text{ and } \frac{x}{a}\sqrt{a^2 + b^2} \pm \frac{z}{c}\sqrt{b^2 - c^2} = 0.$$ *(Garhwal, 1995)*

Sol. The equation of the hyperboloid

$$\frac{x^2}{a^2} + \frac{y^2}{b^2} - \frac{z^2}{c^2} = 1 \qquad \qquad \dots(1)$$

can be written in the following three forms :

$$\left(\frac{x^2 + y^2 + z^2 - a^2}{a^2}\right) + y^2\left(\frac{1}{b^2} - \frac{1}{a^2}\right) - z^2\left(\frac{1}{c^2} + \frac{1}{a^2}\right) = 0 \qquad \dots(2)$$

$$\left(\frac{x^2 + y^2 + z^2 - b^2}{b^2}\right) + x^2\left(\frac{1}{a^2} - \frac{1}{b^2}\right) - z^2\left(\frac{1}{c^2} + \frac{1}{b^2}\right) = 0 \qquad \dots(3)$$

$$-\left(\frac{x^2 + y^2 + z^2 + c^2}{c^2}\right) + x^2\left(\frac{1}{a^2} + \frac{1}{c^2}\right) + y^2\left(\frac{1}{b^2} + \frac{1}{c^2}\right) = 0 \qquad \dots(4)$$

If $a > b > c$, then the only real central circular sections of (1) given by the planes

$$y^2\left(\frac{1}{b^2} - \frac{1}{a^2}\right) - z^2\left(\frac{1}{c^2} + \frac{1}{a^2}\right) = 0$$

It is of the form $Ay^2 - Bz^2 = 0$ in which A and B are positive.

or
$$\frac{y^2}{b^2}(a^2 - b^2) - \frac{z^2}{c^2}(a^2 + c^2) = 0$$

or
$$\frac{y}{b}\sqrt{a^2 - b^2} \pm \frac{z}{c}\sqrt{a^2 + c^2} = 0$$

Similarly the real central circular sections of

$$\frac{x^2}{a^2} - \frac{y^2}{b^2} - \frac{z^2}{c^2} = 1 \qquad \qquad \dots(5)$$

are
$$\frac{x}{a}\sqrt{a^2 + b^2} \pm \frac{z}{c}\sqrt{b^2 - c^2} = 0$$

since (5) can be written as

$$-\left(\frac{x^2+y^2+z^2+b^2}{b^2}\right)+x^2\left(\frac{1}{a^2}+\frac{1}{b^2}\right)-z^2\left(\frac{1}{c^2}-\frac{1}{b^2}\right)=0.$$

3. *Show that the circular sections of the ellipsoid $x^2/a^2 + y^2/b^2 + z^2/c^2 = 1$ passing through one extremity of x-axis are both of radius r, where*

$$\frac{r^2}{b^2}=\frac{(b^2-c^2)}{(a^2-c^2)}.$$ (Garhwal, 1994, 2001)

Sol. Real circular sections of the ellipsoid are

$$\frac{x}{a}\sqrt{a^2-b^2}+\frac{z}{c}\sqrt{b^2-c^2}=\lambda_1$$ ...(i)

and $$\frac{x}{a}\sqrt{a^2-b^2}-\frac{z}{c}\sqrt{b^2-c^2}=\lambda_2$$ ...(ii)

where $$a > b > c.$$

The radius r of the circle in which (i) cuts the ellipsoid is given by

$$r=b\left(1-\frac{\lambda_1^2}{a^2-c^2}\right)^{1/2}$$ ...(iii)

Similarly, the radius of the circle in which (ii) cuts the ellipsoid is

$$b\left(1-\frac{\lambda_2^2}{a^2-c^2}\right)^{1/2}$$

As plane (i) passes through $(a, 0, 0)$

$\therefore$ $$\lambda_1=\sqrt{a^2-b^2}$$

$\Rightarrow$ $$r^2=b^2\left(1-\frac{a^2-b^2}{a^2-c^2}\right)$$

$\Rightarrow$ $$\frac{r^2}{b^2}=\frac{b^2-c^2}{a^2-c^2}.$$

Similarly, we can show it for plane (ii) also.

4. *Chords of ellipse $x^2/a^2 + y^2/b^2 = 1$, z = 0 are drawn so as to make equal angles with its axes, and on them as diameters circles are described whose planes are parallel to OZ, prove that these circles generate the ellipsoid $2b^2x^2 + 2a^2y^2 + (a^2 + b^2) z^2 = 2a^2b^2$.*

Sol. Let $$y = x + k, z = 0$$ ...(i)

be any chord of the ellipse $$x^2/a^2 + y^2/b^2 = 1, z = 0$$ ...(ii)

which is equally inclined to the axes.

Let (i) cuts the ellipse (ii) in $D_1 (x_1, y_1, 0)$ and $D_2 (x_2, y_2, 0)$, where

$$\frac{x^2}{a^2}+\frac{(x+k)^2}{b^2}=1$$

or $$x^2 (a^2 + b^2) + 2kx^2 + a^2 (k^2 - b^2) = 0$$

$\Rightarrow$ $$x_1 + x_2 = \frac{2ka^2}{a^2+b^2} \text{ and } x_1x_2 = \frac{a^2 (k^2 - b^2)}{a^2 + b^2}$$

Similarly, $\qquad y_1 + y_2 = \dfrac{2kb^2}{a^2 + b^2}$ and $y_1 y_2 = \dfrac{b^2(k^2 - a^2)}{a^2 + b^2}$

Equation of sphere on $D_1 D_2$ as diameter will be

$$x^2 + y^2 + z^2 - x(x_1 + x_2) - y(y_1 + y_2) + x_1 x_2 + y_1 y_2 = 0$$

$$\Rightarrow \qquad (x^2 + y^2 + z^2)(a^2 + b^2) + 2k(a^2 x - b^2 y) + k^2(a^2 + b^2) - 2a^2 b^2 = 0 \qquad ...(iii)$$

And the circle on DD' as diameter and in a plane parallel to OZ is the section of the sphere (iii) by $y = x + k$.

To get the locus, remove k

$$\Rightarrow \qquad (x^2 + y^2 + z^2)(a^2 + b^2) + 2(y - x)(a^2 x - b^2 y) + (y - x)^2(a^2 + b^2) - 2a^2 b^2 = 0$$

$$\Rightarrow \qquad 2b^2 x^2 + 2a^2 y^2 + z^2(a^2 + b^2) = 2a^2 b^2.$$

5. *If p_1, p_2, p_3 be the lengths of the perpendiculars from the extremities P_1, P_2, P_3 of conjugate semi-diameters on one of the planes of central circular section of the ellipsoid $x^2/a^2 + y^2/b^2 + z^2/c^2 = 1$, then prove that $p_1^2 + p_2^2 + p_3^2 = a^2 c^2/b^2$.*

Sol. Let (x_1, y_1, z_1), (x_2, y_2, z_2) and (x_3, y_3, z_3) be the extremities of conjugate semi-diameters. One of the real central circular sections of

$$x^2/a^2 + y^2/b^2 + z^2/c^2 \qquad\qquad ...(i)$$

is $\qquad\qquad \dfrac{x}{a}\sqrt{a^2 - b^2} + \dfrac{z}{c}\sqrt{b^2 - c^2} = 0,\ a > b > c \qquad\qquad ...(ii)$

p_1 = perpendicular from (x_1, y_1, z_1) on (ii)

$$= \dfrac{(x_1/a)\sqrt{a^2 - b^2} + (z_1/c)\sqrt{b^2 - c^2}}{\sqrt{(a^2 - b^2)/a^2 + (b^2 - c^2)/c^2}} \qquad\qquad ...(iii)$$

$$\therefore\quad p_1^2 = \dfrac{(x_1^2/a^2)(a^2 - b^2) + (z_1^2/c^2)(b^2 - c^2) + (2x_1 z_1/ac)\sqrt{(a^2 - b^2)(b^2 - c^2)}}{b^2/c^2 - b^2/a^2}$$

$$= \dfrac{a^2 c^2}{b^2(a^2 - c^2)}\left[\left(\dfrac{a^2 - b^2}{a^2}\right)x_1^2 + \left(\dfrac{b^2 - c^2}{c^2}\right)z_1^2 + \dfrac{2x_1 z_1}{ac}\sqrt{(a^2 - b^2)(b^2 - c^2)}\right]$$

$$\therefore\quad p_1^2 + p_2^2 + p_3^2 = \dfrac{a^2 c^2}{b^2(a^2 - c^2)}\left[\left(\dfrac{a^2 - b^2}{a^2}\right)(\Sigma x_1^2) + \left(\dfrac{b^2 - c^2}{c^2}\right)(\Sigma z_1^2)\right.$$

$$\left. + \dfrac{2\sqrt{(a^2 - b^2)(b^2 - c^2)}}{ac}\times \Sigma(x_1 z_1)\right]$$

$$= \dfrac{a^2 c^2}{b^2(a^2 - c^2)}\left[\left(\dfrac{a^2 - b^2}{a^2}\right)a^2 + \left(\dfrac{b^2 - c^2}{c^2}\right)c^2\right]$$

$$[\text{since } \Sigma x_1^2 = a^2,\ \Sigma z_1^2 = c^2 \text{ and } \Sigma x_1 z_1 = 0]$$

$$= a^2 c^2/b^2.$$

6. *Find the equations to the sections of the circular conicoid*

$$yz\left(\dfrac{b}{c} + \dfrac{c}{b}\right) + zx\left(\dfrac{c}{a} + \dfrac{a}{c}\right) + xy\left(\dfrac{a}{b} + \dfrac{b}{a}\right) + 1 = 0.$$

Sol. The equation to the given conicoid may be written as

$$yz\left(\frac{b}{c}+\frac{c}{b}\right)+zx\left(\frac{c}{a}+\frac{a}{c}\right)+xy\left(\frac{a}{b}+\frac{b}{a}\right)$$

$$+\lambda\left[(x^2+y^2+z^2)-\lambda\left(x^2+y^2+z^2-\frac{1}{\lambda}\right)\right]=0 \quad ...(1)$$

If $\quad yz\left(\frac{b}{c}+\frac{c}{b}\right)+zx\left(\frac{c}{a}+\frac{a}{c}\right)+xy\left(\frac{a}{b}+\frac{b}{a}\right)+\lambda\,(x^2+y^2+z^2)=0 \quad ...(2)$

represents a pair of planes then they will cut the conicoid in circles.

Equation (2) will represent a pair of planes if

$$\begin{vmatrix} \lambda & \dfrac{a^2+b^2}{2ab} & \dfrac{c^2+a^2}{2ca} \\[2ex] \dfrac{a^2+b^2}{2ab} & \lambda & \dfrac{b^2+c^2}{2bc} \\[2ex] \dfrac{c^2+a^2}{2ca} & \dfrac{b^2+c^2}{2bc} & \lambda \end{vmatrix}=0$$

or $\quad \lambda^2+\dfrac{2\,(a^2+b^2)\,(b^2+c^2)\,(c^2+a^2)}{8a^2b^2c^2}-\lambda\left[\dfrac{(b^2+c^2)^2}{4b^2c^2}+\dfrac{(c^2+a^2)^2}{4c^2a^2}+\dfrac{(a^2+b^2)^2}{4a^2b^2}\right]=0$

or $\quad \lambda^2-\dfrac{\lambda}{4}\left[\dfrac{(a^2+b^2)\,(b^2+c^2)\,(c^2+a^2)+4a^2b^2c^2}{a^2b^2c^2}\right]$

$$+\dfrac{(a^2+b^2)\,(b^2+c^2)\,(c^2+a^2)}{4a^2b^2c^2}=0 \quad ...(3)$$

This equation is satisfied if $\lambda=1$.

Hence, putting $\lambda=1$ in (2), we have

$$(x^2+y^2+z^2)+yz\left(\frac{b}{c}+\frac{c}{b}\right)+zx\left(\frac{c}{a}+\frac{a}{c}\right)+xy\left(\frac{a}{b}+\frac{b}{a}\right)=0$$

or $\quad\left(\dfrac{x}{a}+\dfrac{y}{b}+\dfrac{z}{c}\right)(ax+by+cz)=0 \quad ...(4)$

which represents a pair of circular sections.

Hence, any circular sections being parallel to central circular sections are

$$\frac{x}{a}+\frac{y}{b}+\frac{z}{c}=\lambda_1 \text{ and } ax+by+cz=\lambda_2.$$

EXERCISES

1. Find the locus of the centres of spheres of constant radius k which cut ellipsoid $\dfrac{x^2}{a^2}+\dfrac{y^2}{b^2}+\dfrac{z^2}{c^2}=1$ in a pair of circles. $\left[\textbf{Ans. } \dfrac{x^2}{a^2-b^2}-\dfrac{z^2}{b^2-c^2}=1-\dfrac{k^2}{b^2},\ y=0\right]$

2. Find the condition that the section of the ellipsoid $\dfrac{x^2}{a^2} + \dfrac{y^2}{b^2} + \dfrac{z^2}{c^2} = 1$ by the plane

$lx + my + nz = p$ may be a circle. $\qquad\left[\textbf{Ans. } \dfrac{al}{\sqrt{a^2 - b^2}} = \dfrac{m}{0} = \dfrac{cn}{\pm\sqrt{b^2 - c^2}}\right]$

3. Show that the central circular sections of the hyperboloid

$$\frac{x^2}{a^2} + \frac{y^2}{b^2} + \frac{z^2}{c^2} = 1$$

are given by the planes

$$\frac{y}{b}\sqrt{a^2 - b^2} \pm \frac{z}{c}\sqrt{a^2 + c^2} = 0. \qquad\qquad (Garhwal,\ 1995)$$

Also show that any two circular sections of opposite systems in the case of either hyperboloid lie on a sphere.

4. Find the circular sections of the following conicoids:

   (i) $2x^2 + 11y^2 + z^2 = 1$;   (ii) $10x^2 - 2y^2 + z^2 + 2 = 0$;   (iii) $15x^2 + y^2 - 10z^2 + 4 = 0$.

      [**Ans.**   (i) $3y + z = \lambda$, $3y - z = \mu$;   (ii) $\sqrt{3}x + y = \lambda$, $\sqrt{3}x - y = \mu$;

            (iii) $4x + 3z = \lambda$, $4x - 3z = \mu$]

5. Find the equation of the sphere which contains the two circular sections of the ellipsoid $x^2 - 3y^2 + 2z = 4$ through the point $(1, 2, 3)$.   [**Ans.** $x^2 + y^2 + z^2 - 16y + 6z + 7 = 0$]

6. Find the radius of the circle in which the plane

$$\frac{x}{a}\sqrt{a^2 - b^2} + \frac{z}{a}\sqrt{b^2 - c^2} = \lambda$$

cuts the ellipsoid $\qquad \dfrac{x^2}{a^2} + \dfrac{y^2}{b^2} + \dfrac{z^2}{c^2} = 1.$ (Gorakhpur, 1996, 2003)

$$[\textbf{Ans. } b\sqrt{\{1 - \lambda^2 / (a^2 - c^2)\}}]$$

[**Hint.** Obtain the equation of the sphere which passes through the given circle and any circle of the opposite system and determine the radius of the circle in which the given plane cuts it.]

7. Prove that the radius of a circular section of the ellipsoid at a distance p from the centre is $b\sqrt{(1 - p^2 b^2 / a^2 c^2)}$.   (Gorakhpur, 1998)

8. Show that the locus of the centres of the spheres which pass through the origin and cut the ellipsoid

$$\frac{x^2}{a^2} + \frac{y^2}{b^2} + \frac{z^2}{c^2} = 1$$

in a pair of real circles is the hyperbola

$$\frac{a^2 x^2}{a^2 - b^2} - \frac{c^2 z^2}{b^2 - c^2} = b^2,\ y = 0.$$

9. Find the central circular sections of the conicoid $3x^2 + 5y^2 + 3z^2 + 2zx = 4$.

                                                         (Gorakhpur, 2000)

10. If p_1, p_2, p_3 and π_1, π_2, π_3 be perpendiculars from the extremities P_1, P_2, P_3 of conjugate semi-diameters on the two central sections of the ellipsoid $\dfrac{x^2}{a^2} + \dfrac{y^2}{b^2} + \dfrac{z^2}{c^2} = 1$, then show that

$$p_1\pi_1 + p_2\pi_2 + p_3\pi_3 = \frac{a^2c^2\,(a^2 + c^2 - 2b^2)}{b^2\,(a^2 - c^2)}.$$

11. A cone is drawn with its vertex at the centre of the ellipsoid $x^2/a^2 + y^2/b^2 + z^2/c^2 = 1$ and its base is a circular section of the ellipsoid. If the cone contains three mutually perpendicular generators, prove that the distance of the section from the centre of the ellipsoid is

$$\frac{abc}{\sqrt{b^2c^2 + c^2a^2 + a^2b^2}}.$$

9.4.2. Umbilics

Def. *A point on a quadric such that the planes parallel to the tangent plane at the point determine circular sections is called an* **umbilic.**

Clearly, an *umbilic* is a point-circle lying on a quadric.

The umbilics are the extremities of the diameters which pass through the centres of the system of circular sections.

To determine the umbilics of the ellipsoid,

$$\frac{x^2}{a^2} + \frac{y^2}{b^2} + \frac{z^2}{c^2} = 1.$$

If f, g, h be an umbilic, the tangent plane

$$\frac{fx}{a^2} + \frac{gy}{b^2} + \frac{hz}{c^2} = 1 \qquad \ldots(1)$$

t the point is parallel to either of the central circular sections

$$\frac{x}{a}\sqrt{a^2 - b^2} \pm \frac{z}{c}\sqrt{b^2 - c^2} = 0 \qquad \ldots(2)$$

From (1) and (2), we see that

$$g = 0 \text{ and } \frac{f}{a\sqrt{a^2 - b^2}} = \pm \frac{h}{c\sqrt{b^2 - c^2}}$$

Also

$$\frac{f^2}{a^2} + \frac{g^2}{b^2} + \frac{h^2}{c^2} = 1.$$

Hence,

$$f = \pm \frac{a\sqrt{a^2 - b^2}}{\sqrt{a^2 - c^2}},\ g = 0,\ h = \pm \frac{c\sqrt{b^2 - c^2}}{\sqrt{a^2 - c^2}}.$$

These are the co-ordinates of the four real umbilics.

EXAMPLES

1. *Prove that the perpendicular distance from the centre of the tangent planes at an umbilic of the ellipsoid $x^2/a^2 + y^2/b^2 + z^2/c^2 = 1$ is ac/b.*   (*Garhwal, 1995, 96; Gorakhpur, 2003*)

Sol. Let $P(\alpha, \beta, \gamma)$ be an umbilic. Tangent plane at P is

$$\alpha x/a^2 + \beta y/b^2 + \gamma z/c^2 - 1 = 0.$$

Its distance p from centre $(0, 0, 0)$ is given by

$$p = \frac{1}{\sqrt{(\alpha^2/a^4 + \beta^2/b^4 + \gamma^2/c^4)}} \qquad \qquad \ldots(i)$$

But

$$\alpha = \pm \frac{a\sqrt{a^2 - b^2}}{\sqrt{(a^2 - c^2)}}, \ \beta = 0, \ \gamma = \pm \frac{c\sqrt{(b^2 - c^2)}}{\sqrt{(a^2 - c^2)}}$$

Put the values in (i) and get the result.

2. *Prove that the umbilics of the conicoid $x^2/(a + b) + y^2/a + z^2/(a - b) = 1$ are the extremities of the equal conjugate diameters of the ellipse*

$$y = 0, \ \frac{x^2}{a+b} + \frac{z^2}{a-b} = 1. \quad \text{(Garhwal, 1994; Gorakhpur, 1998, 2001)}$$

Sol. Let $P(\alpha, \beta, \gamma)$ be an umbilic. Then

$$\alpha = \pm \frac{\sqrt{(a+b)\,[(a+b)-a]}}{\sqrt{(a+b)-(a-b)}} = \pm \sqrt{(a+b)/2}, \ \beta = 0 \ \text{and} \ \gamma = \pm \sqrt{(a-b)/2}$$

Let the extremities of equal conjugate diameters of the given ellipse be

$$\{\sqrt{a+b}\,\cos\phi, \ 0, \ \sqrt{a-b}\,\sin\phi\} \ \text{and} \ \{-\sqrt{a+b}\,\sin\phi, \ 0, \ \sqrt{a-b}\,\cos\phi\}.$$

These diameters are equal if

$$(a+b)\cos^2\phi + (a-b)\sin^2\phi = (a+b)\sin^2\phi + (a-b)\cos^2\phi$$

$$\Rightarrow \qquad \tan^2\phi = 1 \ \text{or} \ \phi = \pm\,\pi/4$$

$\therefore$ The extremities of equal conjugate diameters are

$$[\pm\sqrt{(a+b)/2}, \ 0, \ \pm\sqrt{(a-b)/2}].$$

3. *Prove that the central circular sections of the conicoid $(a - b)\,x^2 + ay^2 + (a + b)\,z^2 = 1$ are at right angles and that the umbilics are given by*

$$x = \pm\sqrt{\left(\frac{a+b}{2a\,(a-b)}\right)}, y = 0, z = \pm\sqrt{\left(\frac{a-b}{2a\,(a+b)}\right)}. \quad \text{(Gorakhpur, 2000)}$$

Sol. We can write the equation of the conicoid in the form

$$[a\,(x^2 + y^2 + z^2) - 1] + b\,(z^2 - x^2) = 0$$

and clearly circular sections are given by $z = \pm x$ which are at right angles.

If (α, β, γ) be an umbilic, then tangent plane at it is

$$(a - b)\,\alpha x + a\beta y + (a + b)\,\gamma z = 1;$$

which should be parallel to either of $x \pm z = 0$.

Hence the direction ratios of the normals are proportional

$$\therefore \qquad \frac{(a-b)\,\alpha}{1} = \frac{a\beta}{0} = \frac{(a+b)\,\gamma}{\pm 1} = k \ \text{(say)}$$

$$\alpha = \frac{k}{a-b}, \ \beta = 0, \ \gamma = \pm\frac{k}{a+b} \qquad \qquad \ldots(1)$$

But (α, β, γ) lies on conicoid.

$\therefore$ $(a - b)\alpha^2 + a\beta^2 + (a + b)\gamma^2 = 1$

or $(a - b)\cdot\dfrac{k^2}{(a - b)^2} + 0 + (a + b)\cdot\dfrac{k^2}{(a + b)^2} = 1$

or $k^2\left(\dfrac{1}{a - b} + \dfrac{1}{a + b}\right) = 1$

or $k = \pm\sqrt{\left(\dfrac{a^2 - b^2}{2a}\right)}$ ...(2)

Hence from (1) and (2) the required umbilics are

$$\alpha = \pm\sqrt{\left(\frac{a + b}{2a\,(a - b)}\right)},\ \beta = 0\ \text{and}\ \gamma = \pm\sqrt{\left(\frac{a - b}{2a\,(a + b)}\right)}.$$

EXERCISES

1. Show that the hyperboloid of one sheet has no real umbilics.

2. Find the real umbilics of the hyperboloid $\dfrac{x^2}{a^2} - \dfrac{y^2}{b^2} - \dfrac{z^2}{c^2} = 1$.

(*Garhwal, 2001; Avadh, 2006*) $\left[\text{Ans. } \dfrac{\pm\,a\,\sqrt{(a^2 + b^2)}}{\sqrt{(a^2 + c^2)}},\ 0,\ \dfrac{\pm\,c\,\sqrt{(b^2 - c^2)}}{\sqrt{(a^2 + c^2)}}\right]$

3. Find the umbilics of the ellipsoid $2x^2 + 3y^2 + 6z^2 = 6$. $\left[\text{Ans. } \left(\pm\,\dfrac{1}{2}\sqrt{6},\ 0,\ \pm\,\dfrac{1}{2}\sqrt{2}\right)\right]$

4. Show that the four real umbilics of an ellipsoid lie upon a circle.

9.5. SECTIONS OF PARABOLOIDS

To determine the nature of the sections of the paraboloid
$$ax^2 + by^2 = 2cz,$$
by the plane
$$lx + my + nz = p.$$

Let $l \neq 0$ so that the plane is not perpendicular to the YZ plane which is a plane of symmetry of the surfaces. As in § 9.3, the equation of the projection of the section on the YZ plane are
$$x = 0,$$
$$(am^2 + bl^2)\,y^2 + 2amnyz + an^2z^2 - 2apmy - 2\,(apn + cl^2)\,z + ap^2 = 0$$

The projection and, therefore, also the section is an ellipse, parabola or hyperbola according as

$$a^2m^2n^2 - an^2\,(am^2 + bl^2)\ \begin{cases}<\\=0\\>\end{cases} \Leftrightarrow\ abn^2l^2\ \begin{cases}>\\=0\\<\end{cases}$$

Thus, *for a parabola $n = 0$. If $n \neq 0$, the section will be an ellipse or hyperbola according as ab is positive or negative, that is, according as the paraboloid is elliptic or hyperbolic.*

If $l = 0$ and $m \neq 0$ then, by projecting on the XZ plane, we get a similar result.

If $l = m = 0$ then n cannot be equal to zero and the section is then clearly an ellipse or hyperbola according as ab is positive or negative.

Thus, we have proved the following :

All the sections of a paraboloid (elliptic or hyperbolic) which are parallel to the axis of the surface are parabolas; all other sections of an elliptic paraboloid are ellipses and of an hyperbolic paraboloid are hyperbolas.

9.5.1. Axes of Plane Sections of Paraboloids

To determine the lengths and the direction ratios of the section of the paraboloid
$$ax^2 + by^2 = 2cz \qquad \qquad ...(1)$$
by the plane
$$lx + my + nz = p \qquad \qquad ...(2)$$

(*Gorakhpur, 1997*)

Let (α, β, γ) be the centre of the section so that the plane (2) is also represented by the equation
$$a\alpha x + b\beta y - cz = a\alpha^2 + b\beta^2 - c\gamma$$

Comparison gives
$$\frac{a\alpha}{l} = \frac{b\beta}{m} = \frac{-c}{n} = \frac{a\alpha^2 + b\beta^2 + c\gamma^2}{p}$$

$$\Rightarrow \quad \begin{cases} \alpha = -\dfrac{lc}{an}, \ \beta = -\dfrac{mc}{bn} \\[2mm] c\gamma = a\alpha^2 + b\beta^2 + \dfrac{pc}{n} = \dfrac{c^2}{n^2}\left(\dfrac{l^2}{a} + \dfrac{m^2}{b} + \dfrac{np}{c}\right) \end{cases}$$

If we write
$$k = \frac{l^2}{a} + \frac{m^2}{b} + \frac{np}{c}$$

we find that the centre of the section is
$$\left(-\frac{lc}{an}, \ -\frac{mc}{bn}, \ \frac{kc}{n^2}\right)$$

The equation of the paraboloid referred to this point as the origin is
$$a\left(x - \frac{lc}{an}\right)^2 + b\left(y - \frac{mc}{bn}\right)^2 = 2c\left(z + \frac{kc}{n}\right)$$

$$\Leftrightarrow \quad ax^2 + by^2 - \frac{2c}{n}(lx + my + nz) - \frac{c\,(kc + np)}{n^2} = 0$$

Also, the equation of the plane (2) now becomes
$$lx + my + nz = 0$$

Now the conic
$$\left.\begin{array}{c} ax^2 + by^2 - \dfrac{2c}{n}(lx + my + nz) - \dfrac{c\,(kc + np)}{n^2} = 0 \\[3mm] lx + my + nz = 0 \end{array}\right\} \qquad ...(3)$$

is the same as the conic
$$ax^2 + by^2 = \frac{c\,(kc + np)}{n^2}, \ lx + my + nz = 0.$$

Let us write
$$p_0^2 = c\,(kc + np) = c\left(\frac{l^2 c}{a} + \frac{m^2 c}{b} + 2np\right)$$

The semi-diameters of length r of the conicoid

$$ax^2 + by^2 = \frac{p_0^2}{n^2}$$

are the generators of the cone

$$ax^2 + by^2 = \frac{p_0^2}{n^2} \cdot \frac{x^2 + y^2 + z^2}{r^2}$$

$$\Leftrightarrow \qquad x^2(an^2r^2 - p_0^2) + y^2(bn^2r^2 - p_0^2) - z^2 p_0^2 = 0 \qquad \qquad \qquad ...(4)$$

The plane

$$lx + my + nz = 0$$

will touch the cone if

$$\frac{l^2}{an^2r^2 - p_0^2} + \frac{m^2}{bn^2r^2 - p_0^2} - \frac{n^2}{p_0^2} = 0 \qquad \qquad ...(5)$$

$$\Leftrightarrow \qquad abn^6 r^4 - n^2 r^2 p_0^2 [(a+b)n^2 + am^2 + bl^2] + p_0^4(l^2 + m^2 + n^2) = 0$$

which is a quadratic equation in r^2 and has two roots r_1^2, r_2^2, which are the squares of the semi-axes of the section.

Also, if λ, μ, ν be the direction ratios of the axis of length $2r$, the plane (2) touches the cone (4) along the line

$$\frac{x}{\lambda} = \frac{y}{\mu} = \frac{z}{\nu}$$

and is, therefore, identical with

$$(an^2r^2 - p_0^2)\lambda x + (bn^2r^2 - p_0^2)\mu y - \nu p_0^2 z = 0$$

so that we have

$$\frac{(an^2r^2 - p_0^2)\lambda}{l} = \frac{(bn^2r^2 - p_0^2)\mu}{m} = \frac{-p_0^2\nu}{n} \qquad \qquad ...(6)$$

thus determining the direction ratios of the axis of length $2r$; r being given from the equation (5).

9.5.2. The section will be a rectangular hyperbola, if

$$r_1^2 + r_2^2 = 0 \implies (a+b)n^2 + am^2 + bl^2 = 0.$$

Ex. Obtain the conclusion of § 9.5 with the help of the equation (5) of this article.

9.5.3. Area of the Section

If the section be elliptic, its area $= \pi r_1 r_2 = \dfrac{\pi p_0^2}{n^3}\left[\dfrac{l^2 + m^2 + n^2}{ab}\right]^{1/2}$

$$= \frac{\pi c}{n^3}\left[\frac{l^2 c}{a} + \frac{m^2 c}{b} + 2np\right]\left[\frac{l^2 + m^2 + n^2}{ab}\right]^{1/2}$$

9.5.4. If θ be the angle between the asymptotes of the section, then as in Ex. 7, page 289

$$\tan^2\theta = \frac{-4r_1^2 r_2^2}{(r_1^2 + r_2^2)^2} = \frac{-4abn^2(l^2 + m^2 + n^2)}{[(a+b)n^2 + am^2 + bl^2]^2}$$

which being independent of p, we deduce that the angle between the asymptotes of parallel plane sections is the same.

Thus, we see *that parallel plane sections of a paraboloid are similar.*

EXAMPLES

1. *Find the locus of the centres of sections of the paraboloid $x^2/a^2 + y^2/b^2 = 2z$ which are of constant area πk^2.*   (*Rohilkhand, 1995; Gorakhpur, 1999*)

Sol. Let (α, β, γ) be the centre of the section of the paraboloid by the plane

$$lx + my + nz = p$$

By § 9.5.3, the area of the section is given by

$$\pi k^2 = \frac{\pi ab}{(-1)^2}\left[a^2\left(\frac{\alpha}{a^2}\right)^2 + b^2\left(\frac{\beta}{b}\right)^2 - 2\left(\frac{\alpha^2}{a^2} + \frac{\beta^2}{b^2} - \gamma\right)\right]\cdot\left(\frac{\alpha^2}{a^4} + \frac{\beta^2}{b^4} + 1\right)^{1/2}$$

$$\Rightarrow \qquad k^4 = a^2 b^2 \left(-\frac{\alpha^2}{a^2} - \frac{\beta^2}{b^2} + 2\gamma\right)^2 \cdot \left(\frac{\alpha^2}{a^4} + \frac{\beta^2}{b^4} + 1\right)$$

Hence, the locus is

$$a^2 b^2 \left(x^2/a^4 + y^2/b^4 + 1\right)\left(x^2/a^4 + y^2/b^2 - 2z\right)^2 = k^4.$$

2. *Planes are drawn through a fixed point (α, β, γ) so that their sections of the paraboloid $ax^2 + by^2 = 2z$ are rectangular hyperbolas. Prove that they touch the cone*

$$\frac{(x-\alpha)^2}{b} + \frac{(y-\beta)^2}{a} + \frac{(z-\gamma)^2}{a+b} = 0.$$ (*Gorakhpur, 2000*)

Sol. Any plane through (α, β, γ) is

$$l(x - \alpha) + m(y - \beta) + n(z - \gamma) = 0 \qquad\qquad \text{...(i)}$$

If r be the length of either semi-axis of the section of $ax^2 + by^2 = 2z$ by (i), then

$$abn^6 r^4 - n^2 p_0^2 r^2 \left[(a-b)\,n^2 + am^2 + bl^2\right] + p_0^4\left(l^2 + m^2 + n^2\right) = 0 \qquad \text{...(ii)}$$

where

$$p_0^2 = \frac{l^2}{a} + \frac{m^2}{b} + 2\alpha\,(l\alpha + m\beta + n\gamma)$$

If r_1 and r_2 are the lengths of the semi-axes of the section, then the section will be a rectangular hyperbola, if

$$r_1^2 + r_2^2 = 0$$

$$\Rightarrow \text{ if} \qquad\qquad (a+b)\,n^2 + am^2 + bl^2 = 0 \qquad\qquad \text{...(iii)}$$

Normal to (i) through (α, β, γ) is

$$\frac{x-\alpha}{l} = \frac{y-\beta}{m} = \frac{z-\gamma}{n}$$

The normal will generate the cone

$$(a+b)(z-\gamma)^2 + a(y-\beta)^2 + b(x-\alpha)^2 = 0 \qquad\qquad \text{...(iv)}$$

$\therefore$ The plane (i) will touch the reciprocal cone

$$\frac{(x-\alpha)^2}{b} = \frac{(y-\beta)^2}{a} = \frac{(z-\gamma)^2}{a+b} = 0.$$

EXERCISES

1. Show that the section of the paraboloid $ax^2 + by^2 = 2cz$, by a tangent plane to the cone

$$\frac{x^2}{b} + \frac{y^2}{a} + \frac{z^2}{a+b} = 0,$$

is a rectangular hyperbola.

2. Prove that the axis of the section of the conicoid $ax^2 + by^2 = 2z$ by the plane

$$lx + my + nz = 0$$

lie on the cone $\dfrac{bl}{x} - \dfrac{am}{y} + \dfrac{(a-b)n}{z} = 0.$

3. If the area of the section of $ax^2 + by^2 = 2cz$, be constant and equal to πk^2, the locus of the centre is $(a^2x^2 + b^2y^2 + c^2)(ax^2 - by^2 - 2cz)^2 = abc^2k^4.$

9.6. CIRCULAR SECTIONS OF PARABOLOIDS

To determine the circular sections of the paraboloid

$$ax^2 + by^2 = 2cz \qquad\qquad ...(1)$$

The equation (1) can be written in the forms :

$$a\left(x^2 + y^2 + z^2 - \frac{2cz}{a}\right) + y^2(b - a) - az^2 = 0$$

$$b\left(x^2 + y^2 + z^2 - \frac{2cz}{b}\right) + x^2(a - b) - bz^2 = 0$$

Therefore, as before, the two pairs of planes

$$y^2(b - a) - az^2 = 0 \text{ and } x^2(a - b) \, bz^2 = 0 \qquad\qquad ...(2)$$

determine circular sections through the origin.

If a or b is negative and the other positive, neither of the equations (2) give real planes.

Hence, *hyperbolic paraboloids have no real circular sections.*

Of the two pairs of planes (2), one will be real if a and b are of the same sign.

In case $a > b > 0$,

$$x^2(a - b) - bz^2 = 0,$$

gives real circular sections through the origin and the two real systems of circular sections are given by

$$x\sqrt{(a-b)} + \sqrt{b}z = \lambda, \ x\sqrt{(a-b)} - \sqrt{b}z = \mu.$$

EXERCISES

1. Show that any two circular sections of opposite systems of an elliptic paraboloid lie on a sphere.

2. Find the real circular sections of the paraboloid :

   (i) $13y^2 + 4z^2 = 2x$;   (ii) $x^2 + 5z^2 + 5y = 0$.

   [**Ans.** (i) $2x \pm 3y = \lambda$; (ii) $y \pm 2z = \lambda$]

9.6.1. Umbilics of a Paraboloid

To determine the umbilics of the paraboloid

$$ax^2 + by^2 = 2cz; \ a > b > 0.$$

Circular sections are determined by the planes

$$x\sqrt{(a-b)} + \sqrt{b}z = \lambda, \ x\sqrt{(a-b)} - \sqrt{b}z = \mu.$$

If f, g, h be an umbilic, the tangent plane

$$afx + bgy - c(z + h) = 0$$

thereat is parallel to either of the circular sections.

It follows that
$$g = 0 \text{ and } f = \pm \frac{c}{a}\left(\frac{a-b}{b}\right)^{1/2}$$

Also,
$$af^2 + bg^2 = 2ch$$

Therefore,
$$h = \frac{(a-b)c}{2ab}$$

Hence,
$$\left[\pm \frac{c}{a}\left(\frac{a-b}{b}\right)^{1/2}, \ 0, \ \frac{(a-b)c}{2ab}\right]$$

are two real umbilics of the paraboloid.

EXERCISES

1. Find the umbilics of the paraboloids
   (i) $4x^2 + 5y^2 = 40z$; (ii) $25x^2 + 16y^2 = 2z$.

   [**Ans.** (i) $(0, \pm 2, 1/2)$; (ii) $(\pm 3/100, 0, 9/800)$]

2. Prove that the umbilics of the paraboloid $x^2/a^2 + y^2/b^2 = 2cz$, $a > b$ are

$$[0, \pm \sqrt{a^2 - b^2}, \ c(a^2 - b^2)/2] \qquad \text{(Gorakhpur, 1997, 2002)}$$

OBJECTIVE QUESTIONS

I. Multiple Choice Questions

Note : *For each of the following questions, four alternatives are given for the answer. Only one of them is correct. Choose the correct alternative.*

1. Section of conic $ax^2 + by^2 + cz^2 = 1$ on the plane $lx + my + nz = p$ will be an ellipse if :
   (a) $bcl^2 + cam^2 + abn^2 = 0$ (b) $bcl^2 + cam^2 + abn^2 < 0$
   (c) $bcl^2 + cam^2 + abn^2 > 0$ (d) None of these.

2. If p be the length of the perpendicular from the origin to the tangent plane parallel to the central plane section to the conicoid $ax^2 + by^2 + cz^2 = 1$, then area of central section is :
   (a) $\dfrac{\pi p}{\sqrt{abc}}$ (b) $\pi p \sqrt{abc}$ (c) $\dfrac{\pi}{p\sqrt{abc}}$ (d) $\dfrac{p}{\pi\sqrt{abc}}$.

3. The area of the central plane section of the conicoid $ax^2 + by^2 + cz^2 = 1$ by the plane $lx + my + nz = p$ is :
   (a) $\dfrac{\pi}{\sqrt{abc}}$ (b) $\pi \sqrt{abc}$ (c) $\dfrac{\pi}{p\sqrt{abc}}$ (d) None of these.

4. The section of the conicoid $ax^2 + by^2 + cz^2 = 1$ by a tangent plane to the cone
$$\frac{x^2}{b+c} + \frac{y^2}{c+a} + \frac{z^2}{a+b} = 0 \text{ is :}$$
   (a) an ellipse (b) a parabola
   (c) a circle (d) a rectangular hyperbola.

5. All planes sections of the conicoid $ax^2 + by^2 + cz^2 = 1$ which pass through the point (α, β, γ) and are rectangular hyperbolas touch :
   (a) a sphere (b) a cone (c) a cylinder (d) None of these.

6. The centre of the section of the conicoid $ax^2 + by^2 + cz^2 = 1$ by the non-central plane $lx + my + nz = p$ is :

   (a) $\left(\dfrac{lp_0^2}{ap}, \dfrac{mp_0^2}{bp}, \dfrac{np_0^2}{cp} \right)$

   (b) $\left(\dfrac{lp^2}{ap_0}, \dfrac{mp^2}{bp_0}, \dfrac{np^2}{cp_0} \right)$

   (c) $\left(\dfrac{lp}{ap_0^2}, \dfrac{mp}{bp_0^2}, \dfrac{np}{cp_0^2} \right)$

   (d) None of these.

7. The co-ordinates of the centre of the section of the ellipsoid $3x^2 + 3y^2 + 6z^2 = 10$ by the plane $x + y + z = 1$ are :

   (a) $\left(\dfrac{2}{5}, \dfrac{2}{5}, \dfrac{1}{5} \right)$

   (b) $\left(\dfrac{2}{5}, -\dfrac{2}{5}, \dfrac{1}{5} \right)$

   (c) $\left(\dfrac{2}{5}, \dfrac{2}{5}, -\dfrac{1}{5} \right)$

   (d) $\left(-\dfrac{2}{5}, \dfrac{2}{5}, \dfrac{1}{5} \right)$.

8. The area of the section of the ellipsoid $\dfrac{x^2}{a^2} + \dfrac{y^2}{b^2} + \dfrac{z^2}{c^2} = 1$ by the plane $\dfrac{x}{a} + \dfrac{y}{b} + \dfrac{z}{c} = 1$ is :

   (a) $\dfrac{2\pi}{3\sqrt{3}} \sqrt{b^2c^2 + c^2a^2 + a^2b^2}$

   (b) $\dfrac{3\pi}{2\sqrt{2}} \sqrt{b^2c^2 + c^2a^2 + a^2b^2}$

   (c) $\pi \sqrt{b^2c^2 + c^2a^2 + a^2b^2}$

   (d) None of these.

9. The real central circular sections of the ellipsoid $x^2 + 2y^2 + 6z^2 = 8$ are given by :

   (a) $2x \pm z = 0$
   (b) $x \pm 2z = 0$
   (c) $2x \pm 3z = 0$
   (d) $3x \pm 2z = 0$.

10. The plane $x + y - z = 0$ cuts the conicoid $4x^2 + 2y^2 + z^2 + 3yz + 3x = 1$ in a circle, whose radius is :

    (a) $1/2$
    (b) $1/\sqrt{2}$
    (c) $1/3$
    (d) $1/\sqrt{3}$.

11. Section of the surface $yz + zx + xy = a^2$ by the plane $lx + my + nz = p$ will be a parabola, if :

    (a) $\sqrt{l} + \sqrt{m} + \sqrt{n} = 0$

    (b) $l + m + n = 0$

    (c) $\dfrac{1}{\sqrt{l}} + \dfrac{1}{\sqrt{m}} + \dfrac{1}{\sqrt{n}} = 0$

    (d) $\dfrac{1}{l} + \dfrac{1}{m} + \dfrac{1}{n} = 0$.

12. Any two circular sections of the ellipsoid of opposite systems lie on a :

    (a) plane
    (b) ellipsoid
    (c) paraboloid
    (d) sphere.

13. Section $ax^2 + by^2 = 2cz$, $lx + my + nz = 0$ is a rectangular hyperbola if :

    (a) $(a + b) l^2 + am^2 + bn^2 = 0$

    (b) $bl^2 + (a + b) m^2 + bn^2 = 0$

    (c) $bl^2 + am^2 + (a + b) n^2 = 0$

    (d) $al^2 + bm^2 + (a + b) n^2 = 0$.

14. All sections of the paraboloid $\dfrac{x^2}{a^2} + \dfrac{y^2}{b^2} = \dfrac{2z}{c}$ perpendicular to the axis of the surface are :

    (a) parabolas
    (b) hyperbolas
    (c) ellipses
    (d) None of these.

15. All sections of a paraboloid parallel to its axis are :

    (a) circles
    (b) parabolas
    (c) ellipses
    (d) None of these.

16. Number of real umbilics of a hyperboloid of one sheet is :

    (a) 4
    (b) 2
    (c) 1
    (d) None of these.

17. Number of real umbilics of an ellipsoid is :

    (a) 2   (b) 4   (c) 6   (d) 8.

18. Number of real umbilics of a paraboloid is :

    (a) 2   (b) 4   (c) 6   (d) 8.

19. The umbilics of the paraboloid $5x^2 + 4y^2 = 40z$ are :

    (a) $\left(0, \dfrac{1}{10}, \pm\dfrac{1}{40}\right)$ (b) $\left(0, \pm\dfrac{1}{10}, \dfrac{1}{40}\right)$

    (c) $\left(0, \pm\dfrac{1}{10}, \pm\dfrac{1}{40}\right)$ (d) None of these.

20. The perpendicular distance from centre of the tangent plane at an umbilic of the ellipsoid $\dfrac{x^2}{a^2} + \dfrac{y^2}{b^2} + \dfrac{z^2}{c^2} = 1$ is :

    (a) ab/c (b) bc/a (c) a/cb (d) None of these.

ANSWERS

1. (b)   2. (c)   3. (c)   4. (d)   5. (b)   6. (c)   7. (a)   8. (a)

9. (b)   10. (d)   11. (a)   12. (d)   13. (c)   14. (c)   15. (b)   16. (d)

17. (b)   18. (a)   19. (b)   20. (c)

II. Fill in the Blanks

Note : *Fill in the blanks "......." so that the following statements are complete and correct.*

1. Area of the central plane section of the conicoid $ax^2 + by^2 + cz^2 = 1$ by the plane $lx + my + nz = p$ is $\pi/$...... .

2. The plane section of the conicoid $ax^2 + by^2 + cz^2 = 1$ by the plane $lx + my + nz = p$ will be a hyperbola if $bcl^2 + cam^2 + abn^2$ ....

3. The condition for the section of the conicoid $ax^2 + by^2 + cz^2 = 1$ by the plane
$$lx + my + nz = p$$
to be a rectangular hyperbola is $bl^2 + am^2 + (.....) n^2 = 0$.

4. The real central circular sections of the ellipsoid $x^2 + 2y^2 + 6z^2 = 8$ are given by ..... $\pm 2z = 0$.

5. The condition for the central section of the conicoid $ax^2 + by^2 + cz^2$ by the plane $lx + my + nz = p$ to be a rectangular hyperbola is $(b + c) l^2 + (c + a) m^2 + ... = 0$.

6. The central section of an ellipsoid whose area is constant touches a ..... .

7. The co-ordinates of the centre of the non-central plane section of the conicoid $ax^2 + by^2 + cz^2 = 1$ by the plane $lx + my + nz = 0$ are $\left(\dfrac{lp}{ap_0^{\,2}}, \,....., \dfrac{np}{cp_0^{\,2}}\right)$.

8. An umbilic, if it exists, is a circular section of ..... radius on the surface of a conicoid.

9. A hyperboloid of two sheets has ..... umbilics.

10. A hyperboloid of one sheet has ..... real umbilic.

ANSWERS

1. $p\sqrt{abc}$;   2. < 0;   3. $a + b$;   4. x;   5. $(a + b) n^2$;

6. cone;   7. $\dfrac{mp}{bp_0^{\,2}}$;   8. zero;   9. four;   10. no.

III. True/False Statements

Note : *Write 'T' for true and 'F' for false statements.*

1. The condition for the central section of the conicoid $ax^2 + by^2 + cz^2 = 1$ by the plane $lx + my + nz = p$ to be a rectangular hyperbola is $bcl^2 + cam^2 + abn^2 = 0$.

2. The plane section of the conicoid $ax^2 + by^2 + cz^2 = 1$ by the plane $lx + my + nz = p$ will be an ellipse if $bcl^2 + cam^2 + abn^2 < 0$.

3. The central section of an ellipsoid whose area is constant touches a cone of second degree.

4. The co-ordinates of the centre of the section of the ellipsoid $3x^2 + 3y^2 + 6z^2 = 10$ by the plane $x + y + z = 1$ are (1/5, 2/5, 2/5).

5. The condition for the section of the ellipsoid $\dfrac{x^2}{a^2} + \dfrac{y^2}{b^2} + \dfrac{z^2}{c^2} = 1$ by the plane $lx + my$ $+ nz = p$ to be a circle is $\dfrac{al}{\sqrt{a^2 - b^2}} = \dfrac{m}{0} = \dfrac{n}{\pm\sqrt{b^2 - c^2}}$.

6. Area of the central plane section of the conicoid $ax^2 + by^2 + cz^2 = 1$ by the plane $lx + my + nz = p$ is $\pi / (p\sqrt{abc})$.

7. The condition for the section of the paraboloid $ax^2 + by^2 = 2cz$ by the plane $lx + my$ $+ nz = p$ to be a rectangular hyperbola is $bl^2 + am^2 + n^2 = 0$.

8. The section of the paraboloid $ax^2 + by^2 = 2cz$ by a tangent plane to the cone $(x^2/b) + (y^2/a) + [z^2/(a + b)] = 0$ is a rectangular hyperbola.

9. A hyperboloid of one sheet has no real umbilics.

10. An umbilic is a circular section of unit radius on the surface of a hyperboloid of two sheets.

ANSWERS

1. F	**2.** F	**3.** T	**4.** F	**5.** T
6. T	**7.** F	**8.** T	**9.** T	**10.** F

10
Generating Lines of Conicoids

10.1. RULED SURFACES

The surfaces which are generated by a moving straight line are called *ruled surfaces*. For example, cones, cylinders, the hyperboloids of one sheet and hyperbolic paraboloids are ruled surfaces. A ruled surface can also be defined as one through every point of which a straight line can be drawn so as to lie completely on it. The lines which lie on the surfaces are called its *generating lines*.

The ruled surfaces may be divided into two categories : (*i*) *developable surfaces*, (*ii*) *skew surfaces*. A developable surface is one on which the consecutive generators intersect while on a skew surface, the consecutive generating lines do not intersect. The cone is a developable surface as all the generators pass through a common vertex and the cylinder is also a developable surface as consecutive generators touch all along their length. The hyperboloid of one sheet and the hyperbolic paraboloid are skew surfaces.

10.1.1. Condition for a Line to be a Generator of the Conicoid   (*Kumaon, 2004*)

Let the equation of the line be
$$\frac{x - \alpha}{l} = \frac{y - \beta}{m} = \frac{z - \gamma}{n} = r \text{ (say)} \qquad \qquad ...(i)$$
and that on the conicoid be
$$ax^2 + by^2 + cz^2 = 1 \qquad \qquad ...(ii)$$
Any point on the line (*i*) is $(lr + \alpha, mr + \beta, nr + \gamma)$.

If it lies on the conicoid (*ii*), we have
$$r^2 (al^2 + bm^2 + cn^2) + 2r (al\alpha + bm\beta + cn\gamma) + (a\alpha^2 + b\beta^2 + c\gamma^2 - 1) = 0 \qquad ...(iii)$$
If the line (*i*) is a generator, then it lies wholly on the conicoid, the conditions for which are
$$al^2 + bm^2 + cn^2 = 0 \qquad \qquad ...(iv)$$
$$al\alpha + bm\beta + cn\gamma = 0 \qquad \qquad ...(v)$$
$$a\alpha^2 + b\beta^2 + c\gamma^2 = 1 \qquad \qquad ...(vi)$$
Now, condition (*iv*) shows that the lines through the centre of the conicoid, *i.e.*, (0, 0, 0) and parallel to the generating lines, *i.e.*, the lines $\dfrac{x}{l} = \dfrac{y}{m} = \dfrac{z}{n}$ are generators of the cone
$$ax^2 + by^2 + cz^2 = 0,$$
which is called *asymptotic cone*.

The condition (*v*) shows that the generating lines whose direction cosines are *l*, *m*, *n* should lie on the plane,
$$a\alpha x + b\beta y + c\gamma z = 1$$
which is the equation of ~~ent plane~~ of the conicoid at the point (α, β, γ).

Equations (*iv*) and (*v*) give the *direction ratios of generating lines*.

10.2. GENERATING LINES OF A HYPERBOLOID OF ONE SHEET

(Gorakhpur, 1997; Banglore, 2005)

It is interesting to see that a hyperboloid of one sheet is a ruled surface in as much it can be thought of as generated by straight lines. The consideration of this aspect of the surface will be taken up in this chapter.

We write the equation

$$\frac{x^2}{a^2} + \frac{y^2}{b^2} - \frac{z^2}{c^2} = 1, \qquad \qquad ...(1)$$

of a hyperboloid of one sheet in the form

$$\frac{x^2}{a^2} - \frac{z^2}{c^2} = 1 - \frac{y^2}{b^2},$$

$$\Leftrightarrow \qquad \left(\frac{x}{a} - \frac{z}{c}\right)\left(\frac{x}{a} + \frac{z}{c}\right) = \left(1 - \frac{y}{b}\right)\left(1 + \frac{y}{b}\right)$$

This may again be written in either of the two forms

$$\frac{\dfrac{x}{a} - \dfrac{z}{c}}{1 - \dfrac{y}{b}} = \frac{1 + \dfrac{y}{b}}{\dfrac{x}{a} + \dfrac{z}{c}} \qquad \qquad ...(2)$$

and

$$\frac{\dfrac{x}{a} - \dfrac{z}{c}}{1 + \dfrac{y}{b}} = \frac{1 - \dfrac{y}{b}}{\dfrac{x}{a} + \dfrac{z}{c}} \qquad \qquad ...(3)$$

We consider, now, the two *families* of lines obtained by putting the equal fractions (2) and (3) equal to *arbitrary constants* λ and μ respectively.

$$\frac{x}{a} - \frac{z}{c} = \lambda\left(1 - \frac{y}{b}\right), \quad 1 + \frac{y}{b} = \lambda\left(\frac{x}{a} + \frac{z}{c}\right) \qquad ...(A)$$

$$\frac{x}{a} - \frac{z}{c} = \mu\left(1 + \frac{y}{b}\right), \quad 1 - \frac{y}{b} = \mu\left(\frac{x}{a} + \frac{z}{c}\right) \qquad ...(B)$$

To each value of the constant λ, corresponds a member of the family of lines (A) and to each value of the constant μ, corresponds a member of the family of lines (B).

Now it will be shown that *every point of each of the lines* (A) *and* (B) *lies on the hyperboloid* (1).

If (x_0, y_0, z_0) be a point of a member of the family (A) obtained for some value λ_0 of λ, we have

$$\frac{x_0}{a} - \frac{z_0}{c} = \lambda_0\left(1 - \frac{y_0}{b}\right), \quad 1 + \frac{y_0}{b} = \lambda_0\left(\frac{x_0}{a} + \frac{z_0}{c}\right).$$

On eliminating λ_0 from these, we obtain

$$\frac{x_0^2}{a^2} - \frac{z_0^2}{c^2} = 1 - \frac{y_0^2}{b^2} \quad \Leftrightarrow \quad \frac{x_0^2}{a^2} + \frac{y_0^2}{b^2} - \frac{z_0^2}{c^2} = 1$$

which shows that (x_0, y_0, z_0) is a point of the hyperboloid (1).

A similar proof holds for the family of lines (B).

Thus, as λ and μ vary, we get two families of lines (A) and (B) each member of which lies wholly on the hyperboloid. These two families of lines are called *two systems of generating lines (or generators) of the hyperboloid.*

We shall now proceed to discuss some properties of these systems of generating lines.

10.2.1. *Through every point of the hyperboloid there passes one generator of each system.*

Let (x_0, y_0, z_0) be a point of the hyperboloid so that we have

$$\frac{x_0^2}{a^2} + \frac{y_0^2}{b^2} - \frac{z_0^2}{c^2} = 1 \qquad \qquad \text{...(4)}$$

Now the generator

$$\frac{x}{a} - \frac{z}{c} = \lambda\left(1 - \frac{y}{b}\right), \; 1 + \frac{y}{b} = \lambda\left(\frac{x}{a} + \frac{z}{c}\right)$$

will pass through the point (x_0, y_0, z_0) if and only if λ has a value equal to each of the two fractions

$$\left(\frac{x_0}{a} - \frac{z_0}{c}\right) \div \left(1 - \frac{y_0}{b}\right), \; \left(1 + \frac{y_0}{b}\right) \div \left(\frac{x_0}{a} + \frac{z_0}{c}\right) \qquad \text{...(5)}$$

Also by virtue of the relation (4), these two fractions are equal.

Thus, the member of the system (A) corresponding to either of the equal values (5) of λ will pass through the given point (x_0, y_0, z_0). Similarly it can be shown that the member of the system (B) corresponding to either of the equal values

$$\left(\frac{x_0}{a} - \frac{z_0}{c}\right) \div \left(1 + \frac{y_0}{b}\right), \; \left(1 - \frac{y_0}{b}\right) \div \left(\frac{x_0}{a} + \frac{z_0}{c}\right)$$

of μ passes through the given point (x_0, y_0, z_0).

10.2.2. *No two generators of the same system intersect.*

Let

I. (i) $\dfrac{x}{a} - \dfrac{z}{c} = \lambda_1\left(1 - \dfrac{y}{b}\right),$ (ii) $1 + \dfrac{y}{b} = \lambda_1\left(\dfrac{x}{a} + \dfrac{z}{c}\right)$

II. (iii) $\dfrac{x}{a} - \dfrac{z}{c} = \lambda_2\left(1 - \dfrac{y}{b}\right),$ (iv) $1 + \dfrac{y}{b} = \lambda_2\left(\dfrac{x}{a} + \dfrac{z}{c}\right)$

be any two different generators of the λ system.

It will be shown that these four equations in x, y, z are not consistent.

Subtracting (iii) from (i), we obtain

$$(\lambda_1 - \lambda_2)\left(1 - \frac{y}{b}\right) = 0 \; \Rightarrow \; y = b, \text{ for } \lambda_1 \neq \lambda_2$$

Again, from (ii) and (iv), we obtain

$$\left(\frac{1}{\lambda_1} - \frac{1}{\lambda_2}\right)\left(1 + \frac{y}{b}\right) = 0 \; \Rightarrow \; y = -b, \text{ for } \lambda_1 \neq \lambda_2$$

Thus, we see that these four equations are inconsistent and accordingly the two lines do not intersect.

10.2.3. *Any two generators belonging to different systems intersect.* (Gorakhpur, 2002)

Let

I. (i) $\dfrac{x}{a} - \dfrac{z}{c} = \lambda\left(1 - \dfrac{y}{b}\right),$ (ii) $1 + \dfrac{y}{b} = \lambda\left(\dfrac{x}{a} + \dfrac{z}{c}\right)$

II. (iii) $\dfrac{x}{a} - \dfrac{z}{c} = \mu\left(1 + \dfrac{y}{b}\right),$ (iv) $1 - \dfrac{y}{b} = \mu\left(\dfrac{x}{a} + \dfrac{z}{c}\right)$

be two generators, one of each system.

It will be shown that these four equations in x, y, z are not consistent. Firstly, we solve simultaneously the equations (i), (ii) and (iii). Now, (i) and (iii) give

$$\lambda\left(1 - \frac{y}{b}\right) = \mu\left(1 + \frac{y}{b}\right) \quad \Rightarrow \quad y = b\,\frac{\lambda - \mu}{\lambda + \mu}$$

Substituting this value of y in (i) and (ii), we obtain

$$\frac{x}{a} - \frac{z}{c} = \frac{2\lambda\mu}{\lambda + \mu},\ \frac{x}{a} + \frac{z}{c} = \frac{2}{\lambda + \mu}$$

These give, on adding and subtracting,

$$x = a\,\frac{1 + \lambda\mu}{\lambda + \mu},\ z = c\,\frac{1 - \lambda\mu}{\lambda + \mu}$$

Now, as may easily be seen, these values of x, y, z satisfy (iv) also. Thus, the two lines intersect and the point of intersection is

$$\left(a\,\frac{1 + \lambda\mu}{\lambda + \mu},\ b\,\frac{\lambda - \mu}{\lambda + \mu},\ c\,\frac{1 - \lambda\mu}{\lambda + \mu}\right) \qquad \dots(6)$$

Another method. The planes

$$\frac{x}{a} - \frac{z}{c} - \lambda\left(1 - \frac{y}{b}\right) - k\left[1 + \frac{y}{b} - \lambda\left(\frac{x}{a} + \frac{z}{c}\right)\right] = 0$$

$$\frac{x}{a} - \frac{z}{c} - \mu\left(1 + \frac{y}{b}\right) - k'\left[1 - \frac{y}{b} - \mu\left(\frac{x}{a} + \frac{z}{c}\right)\right] = 0$$

pass through the two lines respectively for all values of k and k'.

Now, obviously these equations becomes identical for $k = \mu$ and $k' = \lambda$.

Thus, the two lines are coplanar and as such they intersect. Also the plane through the two lines, obtained by putting $k = \mu$ or $k' = \lambda$ is

$$\frac{1 + \lambda\mu}{\lambda + \mu} \cdot \frac{x}{a} + \frac{\lambda - \mu}{\lambda + \mu} \cdot \frac{y}{b} - \frac{1 - \lambda\mu}{\lambda + \mu} \cdot \frac{z}{c} = 1 \qquad \dots(7)$$

Cor. 1. The plane (7) through two generators of the opposite systems is the tangent plane to the hyperboloid (1) at the point of intersection (6) of the two generators. Since also through every point of the hyperboloid there pass two generators, one of each system, we see that *the tangent plane at a point of hyperboloid meets the hyperboloid in the two generators through the point.*

Cor. 2. *A plane through a generating line is the tangent plane at some point of the generator.* Now like every plane section, the section of the hyperboloid by a plane through a generator is a conic of which the given generator is a part. Thus, the conic is degenerate and the residue must also be a line. At the point of intersection of the lines constituting this degenerate plane section, the plane will touch the hyperboloid.

Ex. Prove this result analytically also.

Cor. 3. Parametric equations of the hyperboloid. The co-ordinates (6) show that

$$x = a\,\frac{1 + \lambda\mu}{\lambda + \mu},\ y = b\,\frac{\lambda - \mu}{\lambda + \mu},\ z = c\,\frac{1 - \lambda\mu}{\lambda + \mu}$$

are the parametric equations of the hyperboloid; λ, μ being the two parameters. These co-ordinates satisfy the equation of the hyperboloid for all values of the parameters λ and μ.

EXAMPLES

1. *Find the lengths of the sides of the skew-quadrilateral formed by the four generators of the hyperboloid*

$$x^2/4 + y^2 - z^2 = 49,$$ *(Avadh, 2006)*

which pass through the two points (10, 5, 1), (14, 2, – 2).

Sol. Rewriting the given equation in the form

$$\left(\frac{x}{2} - z\right)\left(\frac{x}{2} + z\right) = (7 - y)(7 + y)$$

we see that the equations of the two systems of generating lines of the hyperboloid are

$$\frac{x}{2} - z = \lambda(7 - y), \quad \lambda\left[\frac{x}{2} + z\right] = 7 + y \qquad \ldots(i)$$

$$\frac{x}{2} - z = \mu(7 + y), \quad \mu\left[\frac{x}{2} + z\right] = 7 - y \qquad \ldots(ii)$$

The generators (*i*) and (*ii*) pass through the points

$$(10, 5, 1) \text{ and } (14, 2, -2)$$

for

$$\lambda = 2, \ \mu = \frac{1}{3} \text{ and } \lambda = \frac{2}{5}, \ \mu = 1$$

respectively.

The two pairs of generators through the two points, therefore, are

$$\begin{cases} \frac{x}{2} - z = 2(7 - y), \ 2\left[\frac{x}{2} + z\right] = 7 + y \end{cases} \qquad \ldots(iii)$$

$$\begin{cases} \frac{x}{2} - z = \frac{1}{3}(7 + y), \ \frac{1}{3}\left[\frac{x}{2} + z\right] = 7 - y \end{cases} \qquad \ldots(iv)$$

$$\begin{cases} \frac{x}{2} - z = \frac{9}{5}(7 - y), \ \frac{9}{5}\left[\frac{x}{2} + z\right] = 7 + y \end{cases} \qquad \ldots(v)$$

$$\begin{cases} \frac{x}{2} - z = 7 + y, \qquad \frac{x}{2} + z = 7 - y \end{cases} \qquad \ldots(vi)$$

Solving in pairs (*iii*), (*vi*) and (*iv*), (*v*), we see that the two other vertices of the skew-quadrilateral formed by the four generators are

$$\left(14, \frac{7}{3}, -\frac{7}{3}\right), \left(\frac{12}{2}, \frac{77}{16}, \frac{21}{16}\right)$$

The lengths of the sides are now easily seen to be

$$\sqrt{98/16}, \ \sqrt{308/3}, \ \sqrt{2/3}, \ \sqrt{7970/16}.$$

2. *Find the equation to the generating lines of the hyperboloid*

$$\frac{x^2}{4} + \frac{y^2}{9} - \frac{z^2}{16} = 1$$

which pass through the point (2, 3, – 4).

(Gorakhpur, 1998, 2001, 2003; Garhwal, 1995; Rohilkhand 2006)

Sol. Any line through (2, 3, – 4) is

$$\frac{x - 2}{l} = \frac{y - 3}{m} = \frac{z + 4}{n} = r \text{ (say)} \qquad \ldots(i)$$

Any point on this line is $(lr + 2, mr + 3, nr - 4)$ and it lies on the given hyperboloid if

$$\frac{(lr + 2)^2}{4} + \frac{(mr + 3)^2}{9} - \frac{(nr - 4)^2}{16} = 1$$

$$\Rightarrow \qquad r^2 \left[\frac{l^2}{4} + \frac{m^2}{9} - \frac{n^2}{16}\right] + 2r \left[\frac{2l}{4} + \frac{3m}{9} + \frac{4n}{16}\right] = 0 \qquad \qquad ...(ii)$$

If the line (i) is a generator of the given hyperboloid, then (i) lies wholly on the hyperboloid. The conditions for this are

$$\frac{l^2}{4} + \frac{m^2}{9} - \frac{n^2}{16} = 0 \text{ and } \frac{l}{2} + \frac{m}{3} + \frac{n}{4} = 0.$$

Eliminating n, we get

$$\frac{l^2}{4} + \frac{m^2}{9} - \left(\frac{l}{2} + \frac{m}{3}\right)^2 = 0$$

$$\Rightarrow \qquad -\frac{1}{3} lm = 0 \Rightarrow \text{ either } l = 0 \text{ or } m = 0.$$

When $l = 0$, $\dfrac{m}{3} = -\dfrac{n}{4}$. When $m = 0$, $\dfrac{l}{2} = -\dfrac{n}{4}$.

Hence equations of the required generator are

$$\frac{x - 2}{0} = \frac{y - 3}{3} = \frac{z + 4}{-4} \text{ and } \frac{x - 2}{1} = \frac{y - 3}{0} = \frac{z + 4}{-2}.$$

3. *Find the equations to the generators of the hyperboloid*

$$\frac{x^2}{a^2} + \frac{y^2}{b^2} - \frac{z^2}{c^2} = 1$$

which pass through the point $(a \cos \alpha, b \sin \alpha, 0)$.   *(Gorakhpur, 1996, 99)*

Sol. Any line through $(a \cos \alpha, b \sin \alpha, 0)$ is given by

$$\frac{x - a \cos \alpha}{l} = \frac{y - b \sin \alpha}{m} = \frac{z}{n} = r \text{ (say)} \qquad \qquad ...(i)$$

(i) will meet the hyperboloid

$$\frac{x^2}{a^2} + \frac{y^2}{b^2} - \frac{z^2}{c^2} = 1 \qquad \qquad ...(ii)$$

if

$$\frac{(a \cos \alpha + lr)^2}{a^2} + \frac{(b \sin \alpha + mr)^2}{b^2} - \frac{(nr)^2}{c^2} = 1$$

$$\Rightarrow \qquad r^2 \left(\frac{l^2}{a^2} + \frac{m^2}{b^2} - \frac{n^2}{c^2}\right) + 2r \left(\frac{l \cos \alpha}{a} + \frac{m \sin \alpha}{b}\right) = 0 \qquad \qquad ...(iii)$$

(ii) will be a generating line if (iii) is an identity, *i.e.*, if

$$\frac{l^2}{a^2} + \frac{m^2}{b^2} - \frac{n^2}{c^2} = 0 \qquad \qquad ...(iv)$$

and

$$\frac{l \cos \alpha}{a} + \frac{m \sin \alpha}{b} = 0 \qquad \qquad ...(v)$$

From (v),

$$\frac{l \cos \alpha}{a} = -\frac{m \sin \alpha}{b}$$

or
$$\frac{l/a}{\sin \alpha} = \frac{m/b}{-\cos \alpha} = \frac{\pm \sqrt{\dfrac{l^2}{a^2} + \dfrac{m^2}{b^2}}}{\sqrt{\sin^2 \alpha + \cos^2 \alpha}}$$

$\therefore$
$$\frac{l/a}{\sin \alpha} = \frac{m/b}{-\cos \alpha} = \pm \frac{n/c}{1} \quad [\text{from } (iv)] \qquad \qquad \dots(vi)$$

$\therefore$ Equations of the required generators are given by
$$\frac{x - a \cos \alpha}{a \sin \alpha} = \frac{y - b \sin \alpha}{-b \cos \alpha} = \frac{z}{\pm c}.$$

4. *Find the conditions that the line given by equations*
$$l_1 x + m_1 y + n_1 z + p_1 = 0, \, l_2 x + m_2 y + n_2 z + p_2 = 0$$
be a generator of the hyperboloid
$$\frac{x^2}{a^2} + \frac{y^2}{b^2} - \frac{z^2}{c^2} = 1.$$

Sol. Any plane through the line is
$$(l_1 x + m_1 y - n_1 z + p_1) - k \, (l_2 x + m_2 y + n_2 z + p_2) = 0$$
$$\Rightarrow \quad (l_1 - l_2 k) x + (m_1 - m_2 k) y + (n_1 - n_2 k) z + (p_1 - kp_2) = 0 \qquad \dots(i)$$

If the given line is a generator of the given conicoid, then (i) should be a tangent plane to the hyperboloid
$$\frac{x^2}{a^2} + \frac{y^2}{b^2} - \frac{z^2}{c^2} = 1$$

i.e.,
$$a^2 \, (l_1 - l_2 k)^2 + b^2 \, (m_1 - m_2 k)^2 - c^2 \, (n_1 - n_2 k)^2 = (p_1 - kp_2)^2$$
$$\Rightarrow \quad k^2 \, (a^2 l_2{}^2 + b^2 m_2{}^2 - c^2 n_2{}^2 - p_2{}^2) - 2k \, (a^2 l_1 l_2 + b^2 m_1 m_2 - c^2 n_1 n_2 - p_1 p_2)$$
$$+ \, (a^2 l_1{}^2 + b^2 m_1{}^2 - c^2 n_1{}^2 - p_1{}^2) = 0 \qquad \dots(ii)$$

Since (ii) holds for all values of k, (ii) should be identically satisfied

i.e.,
$$a^2 l_2{}^2 + b^2 m_2{}^2 = c^2 n_2{}^2 + p_1{}^2$$
$$a^2 l_1 l_2 + b^2 m_1 m_2 = c^2 n_1 n_2 + p_1 p_2$$
and
$$a^2 l_1{}^2 + b^2 m_1{}^2 = c^2 n_1{}^2 + p_1{}^2$$

These are the required conditions.

5. *CP, CQ are any conjugate diameters of the ellipse* $\dfrac{x^2}{a^2} + \dfrac{y^2}{b^2} = 1, \, z = c; \, C'P', \, C'Q'$ *are*

the conjugate diameters of the ellipse $\dfrac{x^2}{a^2} + \dfrac{y^2}{b^2} = 1, \, z = -c$ *drawn in the same direction as CP*

and CQ. Prove that hyperboloid $\dfrac{2x^2}{a^2} + \dfrac{2y^2}{b^2} - \dfrac{z^2}{c^2} = 1$ *is generated by either PQ' or P'Q.*

Sol. Let the co-ordinates of P, Q, P' and Q' are
$$P \, (a \cos \theta, \, b \sin \theta, \, c), \, Q \, (- a \sin \theta, \, b \cos \theta, - c),$$
$$P' \, (a \cos \theta, \, b \sin \theta, - c) \text{ and } Q' \, (- a \sin \theta, \, b \cos \theta, - c)$$

$\therefore$ Equation to PQ' is
$$\frac{x - a \cos \theta}{- a \sin \theta - a \cos \theta} = \frac{y - b \sin \theta}{b \cos \theta - b \sin \theta} = \frac{z - c}{- c - c} = r \, (\text{say})$$

$$\therefore \qquad \frac{x}{a} = \cos\theta - r\,(\sin\theta + \cos\theta)$$

$$\frac{y}{b} = \sin\theta + r\,(\cos\theta - \sin\theta)$$

and
$$\frac{z}{c} = -2r + 1.$$

Eliminating r, we get

$$\frac{x^2}{a^2} + \frac{y^2}{b^2} = r\,(1+1) + 1 - 2r\,(\sin\theta\cos\theta + \cos^2\theta - \sin\theta\cos\theta + \sin^2\theta)$$

$$= 2r^2 + 1 - 2r$$

$$\Rightarrow \qquad \frac{2x^2}{a^2} + \frac{2y^2}{b^2} = 4r^2 - 4r + 1 + 1 = (1-2r)^2 + 1 = \frac{z^2}{c^2} + 1$$

$$\Rightarrow \qquad \frac{2x^2}{a^2} + \frac{2y^2}{b^2} - \frac{z^2}{c^2} = 1.$$

EXERCISES

1. Write down the equations of the systems of generating lines of the following hyperboloids and determine the pairs of lines of the systems which pass through the given point.

   (i) $x^2 + 9y^2 - z^2 = 9$, $(3, 1/3, -1)$ (ii) $x^2/9 - y^2/16 + z^2/4 = 1$, $(-1, 4/3, 2)$

   [**Ans.** (i) $x + 3\mu y - z = 3\lambda$, $\lambda x - 3y + \lambda z = 3$; $x + 6y - z = 6$, $2x - 3y + 2z = 3$

   $x - 3\mu y - z = 3\mu$, $\mu x + 3y + \mu z = 3$; $x - 3y - z = 3$, $x + 3y + z = 3$

   (ii) $4x - 3y + 6\lambda z = 12\lambda$, $4\lambda x + 3\lambda y - 6z = 12$; $z = 2$, $4x + 3y = 0$

   $4x - 3y - 6\mu z = 12\mu$, $4\mu x + 3\mu y - 6z = 12$;

   $4x - 3y + 2z + 4 = 0$, $4x + 3y - 8z + 36 = 0$]

2. Find the equations to the generating lines of the hyperboloid $yz + 2zx - 3xy + 6 = 0$ which pass through the point $(-1, 0, 3)$.

   $$\left[\textbf{Ans. } \frac{x+1}{0} = \frac{y-0}{1} = \frac{z-3}{0} \text{ and } \frac{x+1}{1} = \frac{y-0}{-1} = \frac{z-3}{3}\right]$$

3. Find equations to the generating lines of hyperboloid $(x + y + z)(2x + y + z) = 6z$, which pass through the point $(1, 1, 1)$.

   $$\left[\textbf{Ans. } \frac{x-1}{4} = \frac{y-1}{-5} = \frac{z-1}{1} \text{ and } \frac{x-1}{1} = \frac{y-1}{-3} = \frac{z-1}{-1}\right]$$

4. A point 'm' on the parabola $y = 0$, $cx^2 = 2a^2y$ is $(2am, 0, 2cm^2)$ and a point 'n' on the parabola $x = 0$, $cy^2 = -2b^2z$ is $(0, 2bn, -2cn^2)$. Find the locus of the line joining the points for which (i) $m = n$, (ii) $m = -n$.

   $$\left[\textbf{Ans. } \frac{x^2}{a^2} - \frac{y^2}{b^2} = \frac{2z}{c}\right]$$

10.3. *To find the equations of the two generating lines through any point $(a\cos\theta,\ b\sin\theta,\ 0)$, of the principal elliptic section*

$$x^2/a^2 + y^2/b^2 = 1,\ z = 0,$$

of the hyperboloid by the plane $z = 0$.

Let

$$\frac{x - a\cos\theta}{l} = \frac{y - b\sin\theta}{m} = \frac{z - 0}{n}$$

be a generator through the point $(a\cos\theta, b\sin\theta, 0)$.

The point

$$(lr + a\cos\theta,\ mr + b\sin\theta,\ nr)$$

on the generator is a point of the hyperboloid for all values of r so that the equation

$$\frac{(lr + a\cos\theta)^2}{a^2} + \frac{(mr + b\sin\theta)^2}{b^2} - \frac{n^2 r^2}{c^2} = 1$$

$$\Leftrightarrow \quad \left[\frac{l^2}{a^2} + \frac{m^2}{b^2} - \frac{n^2}{c^2}\right]r^2 + 2r\left[\frac{l\cos\theta}{a} + \frac{m\sin\theta}{b}\right] = 0$$

is true for all values of r. This will be so if

$$\frac{l^2}{a^2} + \frac{m^2}{b^2} - \frac{n^2}{c^2} = 0 \text{ and } \frac{l\cos\theta}{b} + \frac{m\sin\theta}{b} = 0$$

These give

$$\frac{l}{a\sin\theta} = \frac{m}{-b\cos\theta} = \frac{n}{\pm c}$$

Thus, we obtain

$$\frac{x - a\cos\theta}{a\sin\theta} = \frac{y - b\sin\theta}{-b\cos\theta} = \frac{z}{\pm c} \qquad \ldots(C)$$

as the two required generators.

Note. Since every generator of either system meets the plane $z = 0$ at a point of the principal elliptic section, we see that the two systems of lines obtained from (C) as θ varies from 0 to 2π are the two systems of generators of the hyperboloid. The form (C) of the equations of two systems of generators is often found more useful than the forms (A) and (B) obtained in § 10.2.

Ex. Show that the equations (A) and (B) are equivalent to the equations (C) for

$$\lambda = \tan\left(\frac{1}{4}\pi - \frac{1}{2}\theta\right),\ \mu = \cot\left(\frac{1}{4}\pi - \frac{1}{2}\theta\right).$$

10.4. *To show that the projections of the generators of a hyperboloid on any principal plane are tangents to the section of the hyperboloid by the principal plane.*

Consider a generator

$$\frac{x - a\cos\theta}{a\sin\theta} = \frac{y - b\sin\theta}{-b\cos\theta} = \frac{z}{c}$$

The equation

$$\frac{x - a\cos\theta}{a\sin\theta} = \frac{y - b\sin\theta}{-b\cos\theta}$$

represents the plane through the generator perpendicular to the *XOY* plane so that the projection of the generator on the *XOY* plane is

$$\frac{x - a\cos\theta}{a\sin\theta} = \frac{y - b\sin\theta}{-b\cos\theta},\ z = 0 \ \Leftrightarrow \ \frac{x\cos\theta}{a} + \frac{y\sin\theta}{b} = 1,\ z = 0$$

which is clearly the tangent line to the section

$$x^2/a^2 + y^2/b^2 = 1, z = 0$$

of the hyperboloid by the principal plane $z = 0$ at the point $(a \cos \theta, b \sin \theta, 0)$.

Again

$$\frac{x - a \cos \theta}{a \sin \theta} = \frac{z}{c}$$

is the plane through the generator perpendicular to the *XOZ* plane so that the projection of the generator on the *XOZ* plane is

$$\frac{x - a \cos \theta}{a \sin \theta} = \frac{z}{c}, y = 0 \Leftrightarrow \frac{x \sec \theta}{a} - \frac{z}{c} \tan \theta = 1, y = 0$$

which is clearly the tangent to the section

$$\frac{x^2}{a^2} - \frac{z^2}{c^2} = 1, y = 0$$

of the hyperboloid by the principal plane $y = 0$ at the point $(a \sec \theta, c \tan \theta)$.

Similarly we may show that the projections of the generators on the principal plane $x = 0$ are tangents to the corresponding section.

EXAMPLES

1. *Show that the points of intersection R, S of the generators of opposite systems drawn through the points*

$$(a \cos \theta, b \sin \theta, 0), (a \cos \phi, b \sin \phi, 0)$$

of the principal elliptic section of the hyperboloid

$$\frac{x^2}{a^2} + \frac{y^2}{b^2} - \frac{z^2}{c^2} = 1$$

are

$$\left[a \frac{\cos \frac{1}{2}(\theta + \phi)}{\cos \frac{1}{2}(\theta - \phi)}, b \frac{\sin \frac{1}{2}(\theta + \phi)}{\cos \frac{1}{2}(\theta - \phi)}, \pm c \frac{\sin \frac{1}{2}(\theta - \phi)}{\cos \frac{1}{2}(\theta - \phi)} \right].$$

Sol. The question can, of course, be solved by solving simultaneously the equations of the generators obtained by § 10.2, but we shall give another method which is perhaps simpler.

Let $R(x_1, y_1, z_1)$ be either of the two points of intersection of the generators.

The tangent plane

$$\frac{xx_1}{a^2} + \frac{yy_1}{b^2} + \frac{zz_1}{c^2} = 1$$

at *R* meets the plane $z = 0$ of the principal elliptic section in the line

$$\frac{xx_1}{a^2} + \frac{yy_1}{b^2} - 1 = 0, z = 0$$

which is the line joining the points *P*, *Q* whose equation is known to be

$$\frac{x \cos \frac{1}{2}(\theta + \phi)}{a} + \frac{y \sin \frac{1}{2}(\theta + \phi)}{b} = \cos \frac{1}{2}(\theta - \phi), z = 0.$$

Comparing these equations, we obtain

$$x_1 = a\,\frac{\cos\dfrac{1}{2}(\theta+\phi)}{\cos\dfrac{1}{2}(\theta-\phi)},\; y_1 = b\,\frac{\sin\dfrac{1}{2}(\theta+\phi)}{\cos\dfrac{1}{2}(\theta-\phi)}$$

Also, we have $x_1^2/a^2 + y_1^2/b^2 - z_1^2/c^2 = 1$.

Substituting these values of x_1 and y_1 in this relation, we obtain

$$z_1 = \pm\, c\tan\frac{1}{2}(\theta-\phi) = \pm\, c\,\frac{\sin\dfrac{1}{2}(\theta-\phi)}{\cos\dfrac{1}{2}(\theta-\phi)}$$

Hence, the result.

2. *Prove that the equations to the generating lines through the hyperboloid of one sheet are*

$$\frac{x - a\cos\theta\sec\phi}{a\sin(\theta\pm\phi)} = \frac{y - b\sin\theta\sec\phi}{-b\cos(\theta\pm\phi)} = \frac{z - c\tan\theta}{\pm\, c}. \quad (\textit{Gorakhpur, 1997})$$

Sol. Let P ("θ,ϕ") be any point on the hyperboloid

$$\frac{x^2}{a^2} + \frac{y^2}{b^2} - \frac{z^2}{c^2} = 1. \qquad \qquad ...(i)$$

Hence co-ordinates of P would be ($a\cos\theta\sec\phi$, $b\sin\theta\sec\phi$, $c\tan\phi$).

Let equation of tangent plane at this point be

$$\frac{x}{a}\cos\theta\sec\phi + \frac{y}{b}\sin\theta\sec\phi - \frac{z}{c}\tan\phi = 1 \qquad \qquad ...(ii)$$

This plane meets the plane $z = 0$ in the line given by

$$\frac{x}{a}\cos\theta + \frac{y}{b}\sin\theta = \cos\phi,\; z = 0 \qquad \qquad ...(iii)$$

If this line meets the section of the surface by $z = 0$ in points A and B whose eccentric angles are α and β respectively, then

$$\frac{a\cos\alpha\cos\theta}{a} + \frac{b\sin\alpha\sin\theta}{b} = \cos\phi$$

or $\qquad \cos(\theta-\alpha) = \cos\phi$

and $\qquad \dfrac{a\cos\beta\cos\theta}{a} + \dfrac{b\sin\beta\sin\theta}{b} = \cos\phi$

or $\qquad \cos(\theta-\beta) = \cos\phi$

$\therefore \qquad \theta-\alpha = -\phi$ and $\theta-\beta = \phi$

so that $\qquad \theta = \dfrac{\alpha+\beta}{2}$ and $\phi = \dfrac{\alpha-\beta}{2}$,

i.e., $\qquad \alpha = \theta+\phi$ and $\beta = \theta-\phi$ $\qquad \qquad ...(iv)$

Since the two generating lines through P are the lines of intersection of the surface and the tangent plane P, AP and BP will be the generators through P such that $\theta + \phi = \alpha$, a constant for all points on the generator AP and $\theta - \phi = \beta$, a constant for all points on the generator BP.

Also, the direction cosines of AP are proportional to

$$a\,(\cos\alpha - \cos\theta\sec\phi),\; b\,(\sin\alpha - \sin\theta\sec\phi),\; -c\tan\phi$$

$$\Rightarrow \qquad \frac{a\,(\cos\alpha\,\cos\phi - \cos\theta)}{\sin\phi}, \ \frac{b\,(\sin\alpha\,\cos\phi - \sin\theta)}{\sin\phi}, \ -c$$

$$\Rightarrow \qquad a\left\{\frac{\cos(\theta+\phi)\cos\phi - \cos\theta}{\sin\phi}\right\}, \ b\left\{\frac{\sin(\theta+\phi)\cos\phi - \sin\theta}{\sin\phi}\right\}, \ -c$$

$$\Rightarrow \qquad a\left\{\frac{\cos(\theta+\phi)\cos\phi - \sin(\theta+\phi-\phi)}{\sin\phi}\right\}, \ b\left\{\frac{\sin(\theta+\phi)\cos\phi - \sin(\theta+\phi-\phi)}{\sin\phi}\right\}, \ -c$$

$$\Rightarrow \qquad a\sin(\theta+\phi), \ -b\cos(\theta+\phi), \ c$$

∴ Equation to the generator AP are

$$\frac{x - a\cos\theta\,\sec\phi}{a\sin(\theta+\phi)} = \frac{y - b\sin\theta\,\sec\phi}{-b\cos(\theta+\phi)} = \frac{z - c\tan\phi}{c} \qquad \qquad ...(v)$$

Similarly the generator BP will be

$$\frac{x - a\cos\theta\,\sec\phi}{a\sin(\theta-\phi)} = \frac{y - b\sin\theta\,\sec\phi}{-b\cos(\theta+\phi)} = \frac{z - c\tan\phi}{c} \qquad \qquad ...(vi)$$

3. *If the generators through P, a point on the hyperboloid* $\dfrac{x^2}{a^2} + \dfrac{y^2}{b^2} - \dfrac{z^2}{c^2} = 1$ *whose centre is O, meet the plane z = 0 in A and B and the volume of the tetrahedron OAPB is constant and equal to* $\dfrac{abc}{6}$, *P lies on one of the planes z = ± c.*

Sol. Let the co-ordinates of the points A and B on the principal elliptic section

$$z = 0, \ \frac{x^2}{a^2} + \frac{y^2}{b^2} = 1$$

be $(a\cos\alpha,\ b\sin\alpha,\ 0)$ and $(a\cos\beta,\ b\sin\beta,\ 0)$.

The λ-generator through A intersects the μ-generator through B at a point (x, y, z) on the hyperboloid such that

$$x = \frac{a\cos\frac{1}{2}(\beta+\alpha)}{\cos\frac{1}{2}(\beta-\alpha)}, \ y = \frac{b\sin\frac{1}{2}(\beta+\alpha)}{\cos\frac{1}{2}(\beta-\alpha)}, \ z = c\tan\left(\frac{\beta-\alpha}{2}\right) \qquad ...(1)$$

∴ Volume of tetrahedron $OAPB$

$$= \frac{1}{6}\begin{vmatrix} 0 & 0 & 0 & 1 \\[2mm] a\cos\alpha & b\sin\beta & 0 & 1 \\[2mm] \dfrac{a\cos\frac{1}{2}(\beta+\alpha)}{\cos\frac{1}{2}(\beta-\alpha)} & \dfrac{b\sin\frac{1}{2}(\beta+\alpha)}{\cos\frac{1}{2}(\beta-\alpha)} & c\tan\frac{1}{2}(\beta-\alpha) & 1 \\[4mm] a\cos\beta & b\sin\beta & 0 & 1 \end{vmatrix}$$

$$= \frac{abc}{6} \ \text{(given)}$$

$$\Rightarrow \quad -ab \begin{vmatrix} \cos\alpha & \sin\alpha & 0 \\ \dfrac{\cos\frac{1}{2}(\alpha+\beta)}{\cos\frac{1}{2}(\beta-\alpha)} & \dfrac{\sin\frac{1}{2}(\beta+\alpha)}{\cos\frac{1}{2}(\beta-\alpha)} & c\tan\left(\dfrac{\beta-\alpha}{2}\right) \\ \cos\beta & \sin\beta & 0 \end{vmatrix} = abc$$

$$\Rightarrow \quad c\tan\left(\frac{\beta-\alpha}{2}\right)\sin(\beta-\alpha) = c$$

$$\Rightarrow \quad 2\sin^2\left(\frac{\beta-\alpha}{2}\right) = 1$$

$$\Rightarrow \quad 2\left[1-\cos^2\frac{1}{2}(\beta-\alpha)\right] = 1$$

$$\Rightarrow \quad 2\cos^2\frac{1}{2}(\beta-\alpha) = 1$$

$$\Rightarrow \quad \sec^2\frac{1}{2}(\beta-\alpha) = 2$$

$$\Rightarrow \quad \tan^2(\beta-\alpha) = 1$$

$$\Rightarrow \quad (z/c)^2 = 1$$

$$\Rightarrow \quad z = \pm c.$$

4. *Prove that the angle between the generators through any point P on the hyperboloid*

$$\frac{x^2}{a^2}+\frac{y^2}{b^2}-\frac{z^2}{c^2} = 1$$

is given by

$$\tan\theta = \frac{2abc}{p\,(a^2+b^2+c^2-r^2)},$$

where p is the perpendicular from the centre to the tangent plane at P and r is the distance of P from the centre. Hence or otherwise, find the locus of the point of intersection of perpendicular generators.

Sol. The co-ordinates of P are $(a\cos\theta\sec\phi,\, b\sin\theta\sec\phi,\, \tan\phi)$.

$$\therefore \qquad OP^2 = \frac{a^2\cos^2\theta+b^2\sin^2\theta+c^2\sin^2\phi}{\cos^2\phi}$$

Tangent plane at P is

$$\frac{x}{a}\cos\theta\sec\phi + \frac{y}{b}\sin\theta\sec\phi - \frac{z}{c}\sin\phi\sec\phi = 1.$$

If p be the length of perpendicular from origin on the above tangent plane, then

$$\frac{1}{p} = \left[\frac{\cos^2\theta\sec^2\phi}{a^2}+\frac{\sin^2\theta\sec^2\phi}{b^2}+\frac{\sin^2\phi\sec^2\phi}{c^2}\right]^{1/2}$$

$$\therefore \qquad \frac{abc\cos\phi}{p} = (b^2c^2\cos^2\theta+c^2a^2\sin^2\theta+a^2b^2\sin^2\phi)^{1/2} \qquad \dots(1)$$

Now, we have the direction ratios of two generators through P are

$$a \sin (\theta + \phi), - b \cos (\theta + \phi), c; a \sin (\theta - \phi), - b \cos (\theta - \phi), - c$$

If α be the angle between them, then

$$\tan \alpha = \sqrt{\frac{\left\{\begin{array}{l}[- ab \{\sin (\theta + \phi) \cos (\theta - \phi) - \cos (\theta + \phi) \sin (\theta - \phi)\}]^2 \\ + [bc \{\cos (\theta + \phi) + \cos (\theta - \phi)\}]^2 + [ca \{\sin (\theta - \phi) + \sin (\theta + \phi)\}]^2\end{array}\right\}}{[a^2 \sin (\theta + \phi) \sin (\theta - \phi) + b^2 \cos (\theta + \phi)(\theta - \phi)] - c^2}}$$

Now,

$$Nr. = [a^2 b^2 (2 \sin \phi \cos \phi)^2 + b^2 c^2 (2 \cos \theta \cos \phi)^2 + c^2 a^2 (2 \sin \theta \cos \phi)^2]^{1/2}$$

$$= 2 \cos \phi [(a^2 c^2 \sin^2 \phi + b^2 c^2 \cos^2 \theta + c^2 a^2 \sin^2 \theta)]^{1/2}$$

$$= 2 \cos \phi \cdot \frac{abc \cos \phi}{p} = \frac{2}{p} abc \cos^2 \phi \qquad \text{[from (1)]}$$

$$Dr. = a^2 (\sin^2 \theta - \sin^2 \phi) + b^2 (\cos^2 \theta - \sin^2 \phi) - c^2$$

$$= a^2 (\cos^2 \phi - \cos^2 \theta) + b^2 (\cos^2 \phi - \sin^2 \theta) - c^2$$

$$= \cos^2 \phi (a^2 + b^2 - c^2 \sec^2 \phi) - a^2 (\cos^2 \theta \sec^2 \phi + b^2 \sin^2 \theta \sec^2 \phi)$$

$$= \cos^2 \phi [a^2 + b^2 - c^2 - (a^2 \cos^2 \theta \sec^2 \phi + b^2 \sin^2 \theta \sec^2 \phi + c^2 \tan^2 \phi)]$$

$$= \cos^2 \phi (a^2 + b^2 - c^2 - r^2)$$

$$\therefore \qquad \tan \alpha = \frac{2}{p} \frac{abc \cos^2 \phi}{\cos^2 \phi (a^2 + b^2 - c^2 - r^2)} = \frac{2abc}{p (a^2 + b^2 - c^2 - r^2)}$$

In case $\alpha = 90°$, then $\tan 90° = \infty$

$$\therefore \qquad a^2 + b^2 - c^2 = r^2$$

or

$$x^2 + y^2 + z^2 = a^2 + b^2 - c^2$$

This is the required locus.

5. *The normals to* $\dfrac{x^2}{a^2} + \dfrac{y^2}{b^2} - \dfrac{z^2}{c^2} = 1$ *at points of a generator meet the plane* $z = 0$ *at points lying on a straight line, and for different generators of the same system this line touches a fixed conic.*

Sol. Any generator through

$$(a \cos \theta \sec \phi, b \sin \theta \sec \phi, c \tan \phi)$$

is

$$\frac{x - a \cos \theta \sec \phi}{a \sin (\theta + \phi)} = \frac{y - b \sin \theta \sec \phi}{- b \cos (\theta + \phi)} = \frac{z - c \tan \phi}{c} \qquad \qquad ...(i)$$

which shows that

$$(\theta + \phi) = \alpha \qquad \qquad ...(ii)$$

a constant for a given generator.

Now, the tangent plane at the point "θ, ϕ" is

$$\frac{x}{a} \cos \theta \sec \phi + \frac{y}{b} \sin \theta \sec \phi - \frac{z}{c} \tan \phi = 1$$

$$\Rightarrow \qquad \frac{x}{a} \cos \theta + \frac{y}{b} \sin \theta - \frac{z}{c} \sin \phi = \cos \phi \qquad \qquad ...(iii)$$

And the normal at "θ, ϕ" is

$$\frac{x - a\cos\theta\sec\phi}{\dfrac{\cos\theta}{a}} = \frac{y - b\sin\theta\sec\phi}{\dfrac{\sin\theta}{b}} = \frac{z - c\tan\phi}{-\dfrac{\sin\phi}{c}} \qquad \ldots(iv)$$

which meets the plane $z = 0$ in the point.

$$z = 0, \ x = a\cos\theta\sec\phi + \frac{c^2}{a}\sec\phi\cos\theta = \frac{\cos\theta\sec\phi}{a}(c^2 + a^2)$$

$$y = b\sin\theta\sec\phi + \frac{c^2}{b}\sec\phi\sin\theta = \frac{\sin\theta\sec\phi}{b}(b^2 + c^2)$$

$$\Rightarrow \quad x = \left(\frac{a^2 + c^2}{a}\right)\frac{\cos(\alpha - \phi)}{\cos\phi} = \left(\frac{a^2 + c^2}{a}\right)(\cos\alpha + \sin\alpha\tan\phi)$$

$$[\text{since } \theta + \phi = \alpha, \text{ a constant, by } (ii)]$$

$$y = \left(\frac{b^2 + c^2}{b}\right)\frac{\sin(\alpha + \phi)}{\cos\phi} = \left(\frac{b^2 + c^2}{b}\right)(\sin\alpha - \cos\alpha\tan\phi),$$

$$z = 0$$

$$\Rightarrow \quad \frac{x}{a^2 + c^2} - \cos\alpha = \sin\alpha\tan\phi$$

$$\frac{by}{b^2 + c^2} - \sin\alpha = -\cos\alpha\tan\phi \qquad \ldots(v)$$

Eliminating ϕ, we get

$$\frac{ax\cos\alpha}{a^2 + c^2} - \cos^2\alpha + \frac{by\sin\alpha}{b^2 + c^2} - \sin^2\alpha = 0, \ z = 0$$

$$\Rightarrow \quad \frac{ax\cos\alpha}{a^2 + c^2} + \frac{by\sin\alpha}{b^2 + c^2} = 1, \ z = 0 \qquad \ldots(vi)$$

which is a fixed straight line since α is constant.

Again for different generators of the same system, α varies.

$\therefore$ Differentiating (vi) w.r.t. α, we get

$$\frac{-ax\sin\alpha}{a^2 + c^2} + \frac{by\cos\alpha}{b^2 + c^2} = 0, \ z = 0 \qquad \ldots(vii)$$

Squaring and adding (vi) and (vii), we get the envelope of (vi) as

$$\frac{a^2 x^2}{(a^2 + c^2)^2} + \frac{b^2 y^2}{(b^2 + c^2)^2} = 1, \ z = 0,$$

which is a fixed conic.

6. *Show that the generators through points on the principal elliptic section of*

$$\frac{x^2}{a^2} + \frac{y^2}{b^2} - \frac{z^2}{c^2} = 1$$

such that the eccentric angle of one is double the eccentric angle of the other intersect on the curve given by

$$x = \frac{a(1 - 3t^2)}{1 + t^2}, \ y = \frac{bt(3 - t^2)}{1 + t^2}, \ z = \pm ct.$$

Sol. Let A $(a \cos \theta, b \sin \theta, 0)$ and B $(a \cos \phi, b \sin \phi, 0)$ be the two points on the principal elliptic section by the plane $z = 0$. The points of intersection P and ϕ of the generators of opposite system through them are given by

$$\frac{x}{a} = \frac{\cos\left(\dfrac{\theta + \phi}{2}\right)}{\cos\left(\dfrac{\theta - \phi}{2}\right)}, \quad \frac{y}{b} = -\frac{\sin\left(\dfrac{\theta + \phi}{2}\right)}{\cos\left(\dfrac{\theta - \phi}{2}\right)}, \quad \frac{z}{c} = \pm \frac{\sin\left(\dfrac{\theta - \phi}{2}\right)}{\cos\left(\dfrac{\theta - \phi}{2}\right)}$$

Now, we are given that $\phi = 2\theta$.

$$\therefore \quad \frac{z}{c} = \pm \tan\frac{-\theta}{2} \text{ or } z = \pm ct.$$

If we take $t = \tan\dfrac{\theta}{2}$.

$$x = a \cdot \frac{\cos 3\theta/2}{\cos\theta/2} = a \cdot \frac{4\cos^3\theta/2 - 3\cos\theta/2}{\cos\theta/2}$$

$$= a(4\cos^2\theta/2 - 3) = a \cdot \frac{4 - 3\sec^2\theta/2}{\sec^2\theta/2}$$

$$= a \cdot \frac{4 - 3(1 + \tan^2\theta/2)}{1 + \tan^2\theta/2} = a \cdot \frac{1 - 3t^2}{1 + t^2}$$

$$y = b \cdot \frac{\sin 3\theta/2}{\cos\theta/2} = b \cdot \frac{3\sin\theta/2 - 4\sin^3\theta/2}{\cos\theta/2}$$

$$= b(3\tan\theta/2 - 4 \cdot \sin^2\theta/2\tan\theta/2)$$

$$= b\tan\theta/2\left(\frac{3\sec^2\theta/2 - 4\sin^2\theta/2\sec^2\theta/2}{1 + \tan^2\theta/2}\right)$$

$$= b\tan\theta/2\left[\frac{3(1 + \tan^2\theta/2) - 4\tan^2\theta/2}{1 + \tan^2\theta/2}\right] = \frac{bt(1 - t^2)}{1 + t^2}$$

Hence the generators intersect on the curve

$$x = \frac{a(1 - 3t^2)}{1 + t^2}, \quad y = \frac{bt(3 - t^2)}{1 + t^2}, \quad z = \pm ct.$$

7. *Show that the shortest distance between generators of the same system drawn at the ends of diameters of the principal elliptic section of the hyperboloid* $\dfrac{x^2}{a^2} + \dfrac{y^2}{b^2} - \dfrac{z^2}{c^2} = 1$ *lie on the surface whose equations are* $\dfrac{cxy}{x^2 + y^2} = \pm \dfrac{abz}{a^2 - b^2}$.

Sol. Let P $(a \cos \alpha, b \sin \alpha, 0)$; Q $(-a \cos \alpha, -b \sin \alpha, 0)$ be the extremities of any diameter of the principal elliptic section

$$z = 0, \quad \frac{x^2}{a^2} + \frac{y^2}{b^2} = 1.$$

The generator of the same system through these points are

$$\frac{x - a\cos\alpha}{a\sin\alpha} = \frac{y - b\sin\alpha}{-b\cos\alpha} = \frac{z}{c} \qquad \ldots(i)$$

and

$$\frac{x + a\cos\alpha}{-a\sin\alpha} = \frac{y + b\sin\alpha}{b\cos\alpha} = \frac{z}{c} \qquad \ldots(ii)$$

If L, M, N be the d.c.'s of the shortest distance between (i) and (ii), then

$$La\sin\alpha - Mb\cos\alpha + Nc = 0,$$
$$-La\sin\alpha + Mb\cos\alpha + Nc = 0.$$

$\therefore \qquad \dfrac{L}{-2bc\cos\alpha} = \dfrac{M}{-2ac\sin\alpha} = \dfrac{N}{0}. \qquad \ldots(iii)$

$\therefore$ Equations to the S.D. are

$$\begin{vmatrix} x - a\cos\alpha & y - b\sin\alpha & z \\ a\sin\alpha & -b\cos\alpha & c \\ L & M & N \end{vmatrix} = 0,$$

$$\begin{vmatrix} x + a\cos\alpha & y + b\sin\alpha & z \\ -a\sin\alpha & b\cos\alpha & c \\ L & M & N \end{vmatrix} = 0$$

$\Rightarrow -(x - a\cos\alpha)(ca\sin\alpha) + (y - b\sin\alpha)bc\cos\alpha$
$$+ z(a^2\sin^2\alpha + b^2\cos^2\alpha) = 0 \quad \ldots(iv)$$

and $\quad -(x + a\cos\alpha)ca\sin\alpha + (y + b\sin\alpha)bc\cos\alpha - z(a^2\sin^2\alpha + b^2\cos^2\alpha) \quad \ldots(v)$

To eliminate α, adding (iv) and (v),

$$-xca\sin\alpha + ybc\cos\alpha = 0$$

$\Rightarrow \qquad \tan\alpha \parallel \dfrac{by}{ax} \qquad \ldots(vi)$

Again subtracting (v) from (iv),

$$a^2c\sin\alpha\cos\alpha - b^2c\sin\alpha\cos\alpha + z(a^2\sin^2\alpha + b^2\cos^2\alpha) = 0$$

$\therefore \quad (a^2 - b^2)\, c\tan\alpha + z(a^2\tan^2\alpha + b^2) = 0$

$\Rightarrow \quad (a^2 - b^2)\cdot c\, \dfrac{by}{ax} = -z\left(\dfrac{b^2 y^2}{x^2} + b^2\right)$

$\Rightarrow \quad \dfrac{abz}{a^2 - b^2} = -\dfrac{cxy}{x^2 + y^2}$

Similarly, the locus of the S.D. between the generators of the other system will be

$$\frac{abz}{a^2 - b^2} = \frac{cxy}{x^2 + y^2}$$

$\therefore$ The required locus of S.D. is

$$\frac{cxy}{x^2 + y^2} = \pm\frac{abz}{a^2 - b^2}.$$

EXERCISES

1. R, S are the points of intersection of generators of opposite systems drawn at the extremities P, Q of semi-conjugate diameters of the principal elliptic section; show that

   (i) the locus of the points R, S are the ellipses $x^2/a^2 + y^2/b^2 = 2$, $z = \pm c$;

   (ii) the perimeter of the skew-quadrilateral $PSQR$ taken in order, is constant and equal to $2(a^2 + b^2 + 2c^2)$;

   (iii) $\cot^2 \alpha + \cot^2 \beta = (a^2 + b^2)/c^2$, where $\angle RPS = 2\alpha$ and $\angle RQS = 2\beta$;

   (iv) the volume of the tetrahedron $PSQR$ is constant and equal to $\dfrac{1}{3} abc$.

2. The generators through a point P on the hyperboloid $x^2/a^2 + y^2/b^2 - z^2/c^2 = 1$ meet the principal elliptic section in points whose eccentric angles differ by a constant 2α; show that the locus of P is the curve of intersection of the hyperboloid with the cone

   $$x^2/a^2 + y^2/b^2 = z^2/c^2 \cos^2 \alpha.$$

3. If the generators through a point P on the hyperboloid $x^2/a^2 + y^2/b^2 - z^2/c^2 = 1$ meet the principal elliptic section in two points such that eccentric angle of one is three times that of the other. Prove that P lies on the curve of intersection of the hyperboloid with the cylinder

   $$y^2 (z^2 + c^2) = 4b^2z^2.$$

4. Show that the generators through any one of the ends of an equi-conjugate diameter of the principal elliptic section of the hyperboloid $x^2/a^2 + y^2/b^2 - z^2/c^2 = 1$ are inclined to each other at an angle $60°$ if $a^2 + b^2 = 6c^2$. Find also the condition for the generators to be perpendicular to each other.   **[Ans. $a^2 + b^2 = 2c^2$]**

5. A variable generator of the hyperboloid $x^2/a^2 + y^2/b^2 - z^2/c^2 = 1$ intersects generators of the same system through the extremities of a diameter of the principal elliptic section in points P and P'; show that

   $$x_P\, x_{P'} /a^2 = y_P\, y_{P'} /b^2 z_P\, z_{P'} = -c^2.$$

6. Show that the shortest distance between generators of the same system drawn at one end of each of the major and minor axes of the principal elliptic section of the hyperboloid $x^2/a^2 + y^2/b^2 - z^2/c^2 = 1$ is

   $$2abc /\sqrt{a^2b^2 + b^2c^2 + c^2a^2}.$$

7. Show that the shortest distance between the generators of the same system drawn at the extremities of the diameters of the principal elliptic section of the hyperboloid $x^2/a^2 + y^2/b^2 - z^2/c^2 = 1$, are parallel to the XOY plane and lie on the surface

   $$abz (x^2 + y^2) = \pm (a^2 - b^2)\, cxy.$$

8. Show that the lines through the origin drawn parallel to the line of shortest distance between generators of the same system through the ends of semi-conjugate diameters of the principal elliptic section of the hyperboloid $x^2/a^2 + y^2/b^2 - z^2/c^2 = 1$ generate the cone

   $$a^2x^2 + b^2y^2 - 2c^2z^2 = 0.$$

9. A variable generator meets two generators of the system through the extremities B and B' of the minor axis of the principal elliptic section of the hyperboloid

   $$x^2/a^2 + y^2/b^2 - z^2/c^2 = 1,$$

   in P and P', prove that

   $$BP \cdot B'P' = b^2 + c^2.$$

10. Q is a point on a generator at any point P of the principal circular section of the hyperboloid $c^2 (x^2 + y^2) - a^2z^2 = a^2c^2$, such that $PQ = r$; show that the angle between the tangent plane at P and Q is $\tan^{-1} (r/c)$.

11. The generators through a point P on the hyperboloid $x^2/a^2 + y^2/b^2 - z^2/c^2 = 1$ meet the plane $z = 0$ in A, B and the volume of the tetrahedron formed by the generators through A and B is constant and equal to $abc/4$; show that the locus of P is either of the ellipses

$$x^2/a^2 + y^2/b^2 = 4, \quad z = \pm \sqrt{3}c.$$

10.5. *To find the locus of the points of intersection of perpendicular generators of the hyperboloid*
$$x^2/a^2 + y^2/b^2 - z^2/c^2 = 1 \qquad \qquad \text{...(1)}$$

(Gorakhpur, 1997, 2000)

Let (x_1, y_1, z_1) be a point the generators through which are perpendicular.
The generators are the lines in which the tangent plane

$$\frac{xx_1}{a^2} + \frac{yy_1}{b^2} - \frac{zz_1}{c^2} = 1 \qquad \qquad \text{...(2)}$$

at the point meets the surface. On making (1) homogeneous with the help of (2), we obtain the equation

$$\frac{x^2}{a^2} + \frac{y^2}{b^2} - \frac{z^2}{c^2} = \left(\frac{xx_1}{a^2} + \frac{yy_1}{b^2} - \frac{zz_1}{c^2} \right)^2 \qquad \qquad \text{...(3)}$$

The curve of intersection of (1) and (2) being a pair of lines, the cone with its vertex at the origin and with the curve of intersection of (1) and (2), as the guiding curve, represented by the equation (3), reduces to a pair of planes.

If l, m, n be the direction ratios of either of the two generators, we have, since they lie on the planes (2) and (3),

$$\frac{lx_1}{a^2} + \frac{my_1}{b^2} - \frac{nz_1}{c^2} = 0 \qquad \qquad \text{...(4)}$$

and
$$\frac{l^2}{a^2} + \frac{m^2}{b^2} - \frac{n^2}{c^2} = \left(\frac{lx_1}{a^2} + \frac{my_1}{b^2} - \frac{nz_1}{c^2} \right)^2 \qquad \qquad \text{...(5)}$$

Now the equation (5) with the help of the equation (4) reduces to

$$\frac{l^2}{a^2} + \frac{m^2}{b^2} - \frac{n^2}{c^2} = 0 \qquad \qquad \text{...(6)}$$

Eliminating n from (4) and (5), we obtain

$$\frac{l^2}{a^4} (a^2z_1^2 - c^2x_1^2) - \frac{2lmc^2x_1y_1}{a^2b^2} + \frac{m^2}{b^4} (b^2z_1^2 - c^2y_1^2) = 0$$

If $l_1, m_1, n_1; l_2, m_2, n_2$ be the direction ratios of the two generators, this gives

$$\frac{l_1}{m_1} \cdot \frac{l_2}{m_2} = \frac{b^2z_1^2 - c^2y_1^2}{b^4} \cdot \frac{a^4}{a^2z_1^2 - c^2x_1^2}$$

$$\Leftrightarrow \qquad \frac{l_1l_2}{a^4 (b^2z_1^2 - c^2y_1^2)} = \frac{m_1m_2}{b^4 (a^2z_1^2 - c^2x_1^2)} = \frac{n_1n_2}{c^4 (a^2y_1^2 + c^2x_1^2)}$$

Since $l_1l_2 + m_1m_2 = 0$, we obtain
$$a^4 (b^2z_1^2 - c^2y_1^2) + b^4 (a^2z_1^2 - c^2x_1^2) + c^4 (a^2y_1^2 + b^2x_1^2) = 0$$

$$\Rightarrow \qquad b^2c^2x_1^{\,2}\,(c^2 - b^2) + a^2c^2y_1^{\,2}\,(c^2 - a^2) + a^2b^2z_1^{\,2}\,(a^2 + b^2) = 0$$

$$\Leftrightarrow \qquad (b^2 - c^2)\,\frac{x_1^{\,2}}{a^2} + (a^2 - c^2)\,\frac{y_1^{\,2}}{b^2} - (a^2 + b^2)\,\frac{z_1^{\,2}}{c^2} = 0$$

We rewrite it as

$$(a^2 + b^2 - c^2)\,\frac{x_1^{\,2}}{a^2} + (a^2 + b^2 - c^2)\,\frac{y_1^{\,2}}{b^2} - (a^2 + b^2 - c^2)\,\frac{z_1^{\,2}}{c^2} = x_1^{\,2} + y_1^{\,2} + z_1^{\,2}$$

$$\Leftrightarrow \qquad (a^2 + b^2 - c^2)\left(\frac{x_1^{\,2}}{a^2} + \frac{y_1^{\,2}}{b^2} + \frac{z_1^{\,2}}{c^2}\right) = x_1^{\,2} + y_1^{\,2} + z_1^{\,2}$$

Since now the point (x_1, y_1, z_1) lies on the hyperboloid, this reduces to

$$x_1^{\,2} + y_1^{\,2} + z_1^{\,2} = a^2 + b^2 - c^2$$

Thus, we see that the point of intersection of pairs of perpendicular generators lies on the curve of intersection of the hyperboloid and the director sphere

$$x^2 + y^2 + z^2 = a^2 + b^2 - c^2.$$

Another method. Let PA, PB be two perpendicular generators through P and PC be the normal at P so that it is perpendicular to the tangent plane determined by PA and PB. The lines PA, PB, PC are mutually perpendicular and as such the three planes CPA, APB, BPC determined by them, taken in pairs, are also mutually perpendicular.

The plane CPA through the generator PA is the tangent plane at some point of PA and the plane CPB through the generator PB is the tangent plane at some point of PB. Also the plane APB is the tangent plane at P.

Thus, the three planes CPA, APB and BPC are mutually perpendicular tangent planes and as such their point of intersection P lies on the director sphere. It follows that the locus of P is the curve of intersection of the hyperboloid with its director sphere.

EXAMPLE

Show that the angle θ between the generators through any point P of the hyperboloid is given by

$$\cot \theta = p\,(r^2 - a^2 - b^2 + c^2)/\,2abc$$

where p is the perpendicular from the centre to the tangent plane at P and r is the distance of P from the centre.

Sol. The tangent plane at $P\,(x_1, y_1, z_1)$ is

$$\frac{xx_1}{a^2} + \frac{yy_1}{b^2} - \frac{zz_1}{c^2} = 1 \qquad\qquad\qquad ...(1)$$

As in § 10.5 it can be shown that the direction ratios l, m, n of the two generators through this point are given by the equations

$$\frac{lx_1}{a^2} + \frac{my_1}{b^2} - \frac{nz_1}{c^2} = 0, \qquad \frac{l^2}{a^2} + \frac{m^2}{b^2} + \frac{n^2}{c^2} = 0.$$

Proceeding as in Example 1, on page ???, we can show that angle θ between the lines is given by

$$\tan \theta = \frac{\left[-4\left(\dfrac{x_1^{\,2}}{a^4} + \dfrac{y_1^{\,2}}{b^4} + \dfrac{z_1^{\,2}}{c^4}\right)\left(\dfrac{x_1^{\,2}}{a^4b^2c^2} - \dfrac{y_1^{\,2}}{b^4c^2a^2} + \dfrac{z_1^{\,2}}{c^4a^2b^2}\right)\right]^{1/2}}{\dfrac{1}{a^2}\left(\dfrac{y_1^{\,2}}{b^4} + \dfrac{z_1^{\,2}}{c^4}\right) + \dfrac{1}{b^2}\left(\dfrac{z_1^{\,2}}{c^4} + \dfrac{x_1^{\,2}}{a^4}\right) - \dfrac{1}{c^2}\left(\dfrac{x_1^{\,2}}{a^4} + \dfrac{y_1^{\,2}}{b^4}\right)}$$

Now, p, the length of perpendicular from the centre to the tangent plane (1) at (x_1, y_1, z_1), is given by

$$p = \frac{1}{\left[\sum \frac{x_1^2}{a^4}\right]^{1/2}} \Rightarrow \frac{1}{p^2} = \sum \frac{x_1^2}{a^4}$$

Also the denominator of the expression for $\tan \theta$

$$= \frac{1}{a^2 b^2 c^2}\left[\frac{x_1^2}{a^2}(c^2 - b^2) + \frac{y_1^2}{b^2}(c^2 - a^2) + \frac{z_1^2}{c^2}(a^2 + b^2)\right]$$

$$= \frac{1}{a^2 b^2 c^2}\left[\frac{x_1^2}{a^2}(c^2 - b^2 - a^2) + \frac{y_1^2}{b^2}(c^2 - a^2 - b^2) + \frac{z_1^2}{c^2}(a^2 + b^2 - c^2)\right.$$

$$\left. + (x_1^2 + y_1^2 + z_1^2)\right]$$

$$= \frac{1}{a^2 b^2 c^2}\left[r^2 - (a^2 + b^2 - c^2)\left(\frac{x_1^2}{a^2} + \frac{y_1^2}{b^2} - \frac{z_1^2}{c^2}\right)\right]$$

$$= \frac{1}{a^2 b^2 c^2}(r^2 - a^2 - b^2 + c^2)$$

$$\therefore \quad \tan \theta = \frac{\left[-\frac{4}{p^2}\left(-\frac{1}{a^2 b^2 c^2}\right)\left(\frac{x_1^2}{a^2} + \frac{y_1^2}{b^2} - \frac{z_1^2}{c^2}\right)\right]^{1/2}}{(r^2 - a^2 - b^2 + c^2)/a^2 b^2 c^2} = 2abc / p(r^2 - a^2 - b^2 + c^2).$$

10.6. CENTRAL POINT. LINE OF STRICTION. PARAMETER OF DISTRIBUTION OF A GENERATOR

Def. 1. *The **central point** of a given generator, l, is the limiting position of its point of intersection with the line of shortest distance between it and another generator, m, of the same system; the limit being taken when, m, tends to coincide with l.*

With some sacrifice of precision, one may say that the central point of a given generator is the point of intersection of the generator and the line of shortest distance between the generator and a consecutive generator of the system.

Def. 2. *The locus of the central points of generators of a hyperboloid is called its **line of striction**.*

Def. 3. *The **parameter of distribution** of a generator, l is*

$$lim \left(\frac{\Delta s}{\Delta \psi}\right)$$

where, Δs, is the shortest distance and, $\Delta \psi$, the angle between l, and another generator m of the same system, the limit being taken when the generator m tends to coincide with the generator l.

10.6.1. *To determine the central point of a generator.*

We consider generators of the system

$$\frac{x - a \cos \theta}{a \sin \theta} = \frac{y - b \sin \theta}{-b \cos \theta} = \frac{z}{c}$$

Let any generator, l, of the system be

$$\frac{x - a\cos\varphi}{a\sin\varphi} = \frac{y - b\sin\varphi}{-b\cos\varphi} = \frac{z}{c} \qquad \ldots(1)$$

We, now, consider any other generator, m

$$\frac{x - a\cos\varphi'}{a\sin\varphi'} = \frac{y - b\sin\varphi'}{-b\cos\varphi'} = \frac{z}{c} \qquad \ldots(2)$$

of the same system.

Let the shortest distance between these generators meet them in P and Q respectively so that we have to find the limiting position of the point P on the generator l when $\varphi' \to \varphi$. Let C be the limit of P.

Since PQ is a chord of the hyperboloid, its limit will be a tangent line CD at the point C. Let l, m, n be the direction ratios of the shortest distance PQ and l_0, m_0, n_0 those of its limit. We have

$$\begin{cases} al\sin\varphi - bm\cos\varphi + cn = 0. \\ al\sin\varphi' - bm\cos\varphi' + cn = 0. \end{cases}$$

$$\Rightarrow \qquad \frac{al}{\cos\varphi' - \cos\varphi} = \frac{bm}{\sin\varphi' - \sin\varphi} = \frac{cn}{\sin(\varphi' - \varphi)}$$

$$\Rightarrow \qquad \frac{al}{-\sin\dfrac{1}{2}(\varphi' + \varphi)} = \frac{bm}{\cos\dfrac{1}{2}(\varphi' + \varphi)} = \frac{cn}{\cos\dfrac{1}{2}(\varphi' + \varphi)}$$

Let $\varphi' \to \varphi$.

Thus, we obtain

$$\frac{al_0}{-\sin\varphi} = \frac{bm_0}{\cos\varphi} = \frac{cn_0}{1}$$

Let $\qquad [a\,(r\sin\varphi + \cos\varphi),\ b\,(\sin\varphi - r\cos\varphi),\ cr] \qquad \ldots(3)$

be the central point C on the generator (1). The equation of the tangent plane at C is

$$\frac{x\,(r\sin\varphi + \cos\varphi)}{a} + \frac{y\,(\sin\varphi - r\cos\varphi)}{b} - \frac{zr}{c} = 1$$

Since the line CD with direction ratios l_0, m_0, n_0, lies on this tangent plane, we have

$$-\frac{\sin\varphi\,(r\sin\varphi + \cos\varphi)}{a^2} + \frac{\cos\varphi\,(\sin\varphi - r\cos\varphi)}{b^2} - \frac{r}{c^2} = 0$$

$$\Rightarrow \qquad r\left(\frac{\sin^2\varphi}{a^2} + \frac{\cos^2\varphi}{b^2} + \frac{1}{c^2}\right) = \left(\frac{1}{b^2} - \frac{1}{c^2}\right)\sin\varphi\cos\varphi$$

$$\Rightarrow \qquad r = \frac{c^2\,(a^2 - b^2)\sin\varphi\cos\varphi}{(a^2b^2 + a^2c^2\cos^2\varphi + b^2c^2\sin^2\varphi)}$$

so that we have obtained r.

Substituting this value of r in (3), we see that the co-ordinates of the central point $C\,(x, y, z)$ are given by

$$r = \frac{a^3\,(b^2 + c^2)\cos\varphi}{k}, \quad y = \frac{b^3\,(c^2 + a^2)\sin\varphi}{k}, \quad z = \frac{c^3\,(a^2 - b^2)\sin\varphi\cos\varphi}{k}$$

where $\qquad k = a^2b^2 + a^2c^2\cos^2\varphi + b^2c^2\sin^2\varphi$

Eliminating φ, we see that the *line of striction* is the curve of intersection of the hyperboloid with the cone

$$\frac{a^6(b^2+c^2)^2}{x^2} + \frac{b^6(c^2+a^2)^2}{y^2} - \frac{c^6(b^2-a^2)^2}{z^2} = 0$$

Ex. Find the central point for a generator of the second system and show that the line of striction is the same for either system.

10.6.2. *To determine the parameter of distribution of the generator, l.*

If $\Delta\psi$ be the angle between the generators (1) and (2) of § 10.5.1, we have

$$\tan\Delta\psi = \frac{\sqrt{[b^2c^2(\cos\varphi'-\cos\varphi)^2 + c^2a^2(\sin\varphi'-\sin\varphi)^2 + a^2b^2\sin^2(\varphi'-\varphi)]}}{a^2\sin\varphi\sin\varphi' + b^2\cos\varphi\cos\varphi' + c^2}$$

$$= 2\sin\frac{1}{2}(\varphi'-\varphi)\frac{\sqrt{\left[b^2c^2\sin^2\frac{1}{2}(\varphi'+\varphi) + c^2a^2\cos^2\frac{1}{2}(\varphi'+\varphi) + a^2b^2\cos^2\frac{1}{2}(\varphi'-\varphi)\right]}}{a^2\sin\varphi\sin\varphi' + b^2\cos\varphi\cos\varphi' + c^2}$$

We write $\varphi' = \varphi + \Delta\varphi$ so that $\Delta\varphi \to 0$ as $\varphi' \to \varphi$. Then, from above, we obtain

$$\frac{d\psi}{d\varphi} = \frac{\sqrt{b^2c^2\sin^2\varphi + a^2c^2\cos^2\varphi + a^2b^2}}{a^2\sin^2\varphi + b^2\cos^2\varphi + c^2}$$

Again we shall now find the S.D., Δs between the two generators. Now the equation of the plane through (1) parallel to (2) is

$$\begin{vmatrix} x - a\cos\varphi & y - b\sin\varphi & z \\ a\sin\varphi & -b\cos\varphi & c \\ a\sin\varphi' & -b\cos\varphi' & c \end{vmatrix} = 0$$

so that cancelling a common factor $\sin\frac{1}{2}(\varphi'-\varphi)$, we obtain

$$-bcx\sin\frac{1}{2}(\varphi'+\varphi) + cay\cos\frac{1}{2}(\varphi'+\varphi) + abz\cos\frac{1}{2}(\varphi'-\varphi) + abc\sin\frac{1}{2}(\varphi'-\varphi) = 0$$

The S.D., Δs, which is the distance of the point $(a\cos\varphi', b\sin\varphi', 0)$ from this plane is given by

$$\Delta s = \frac{2abc\sin\frac{1}{2}(\varphi'-\varphi)}{\sqrt{b^2c^2\sin^2\frac{1}{2}(\varphi'+\varphi) + c^2a^2\cos^2\frac{1}{2}(\varphi'+\varphi) + a^2b^2\cos^2\frac{1}{2}(\varphi'-\varphi)}}$$

Again putting $\varphi' = \varphi + \Delta\varphi$, we obtain

$$\frac{ds}{d\varphi} = \frac{abc}{\sqrt{b^2c^2\sin^2\varphi + c^2a^2\cos^2\varphi + a^2b^2}}$$

$$\Rightarrow \qquad \frac{ds}{d\psi} = \frac{ds/d\varphi}{d\psi/d\varphi} = \frac{abc(a^2\sin^2\varphi + b^2\cos^2\varphi + c^2)}{b^2c^2\sin^2\varphi + c^2a^2\cos^2\varphi + a^2b^2}$$

10.7. HYPERBOLIC PARABOLOID

We rewrite the equation

$$x^2/a^2 - y^2/b^2 = 2z/c \qquad \qquad ...(1)$$

of a hyperbolic paraboloid in the form

$$\left[\frac{x}{a} - \frac{y}{b}\right]\left[\frac{x}{a} + \frac{y}{b}\right] = \frac{2z}{c}$$

which may again be rewritten in either of the two forms

$$\frac{\dfrac{x}{a} - \dfrac{y}{b}}{\dfrac{z}{c}} = \frac{2}{\dfrac{x}{a} + \dfrac{y}{b}}, \qquad \frac{\dfrac{x}{a} - \dfrac{y}{b}}{2} = \frac{\dfrac{z}{c}}{\dfrac{x}{a} + \dfrac{y}{b}}$$

Now, as in § 10.2 it can be shown that as λ and μ vary; each member of each of the systems of lines

$$\frac{x}{a} - \frac{y}{b} = \frac{\lambda z}{c}, \quad 2 = \lambda\left[\frac{x}{a} + \frac{y}{b}\right] \qquad \qquad ...(A)$$

$$\frac{x}{a} - \frac{y}{b} = 2\mu, \quad \frac{z}{c} = \mu\left[\frac{x}{a} + \frac{y}{b}\right] \qquad \qquad ...(B)$$

lies wholly on the hyperbolic paraboloid (1).

Thus, we see that a *hyperbolic paraboloid also admits of two systems of generating lines.*

As in the case of hyperboloid of one sheet, it can be shown that the following results hold good for the two systems of generating lines of a hyperbolic paraboloid also.

1. *Through every point of a hyperbolic paraboloid, there passes a member of each system.*
2. *No two members of the same system intersect.*
3. *Any two generators belonging to the two different systems intersect and the plane through them is the tangent plane at their point of intersection.*
4. *The tangent plane at a point meets the paraboloid in two generators through the point.*
5. *The locus of the point of intersection of perpendicular generator is the curve of intersection of the paraboloid with the plane $2cz + a^2 - b^2 = 0$.*

An Important Note. Since the generator

$$\frac{x}{a} - \frac{y}{b} = \frac{\lambda z}{c}, \quad 2 = \lambda\left[\frac{x}{a} + \frac{y}{b}\right]$$

lies in the plane

$$2 = \lambda\left[\frac{x}{a} + \frac{y}{b}\right]$$

which is parallel to the plane

$$\frac{x}{a} + \frac{y}{b} = 0$$

whatever value λ may have, we deduce that all the generators belonging to one system of the hyperbolic paraboloid

$$x^2/a^2 - y^2/b^2 = 2z/c$$

are parallel to the plane

$$x/a + y/b = 0$$

It may similarly be seen that the generators of the second system are also parallel to a plane, *viz.,*

$$x/a - y/b = 0.$$

10.7.1. *Tangent plane at any point meets the paraboloid in two generators through the point.*

The planes passing through the two generators of different systems λ and μ of a hyperbolic paraboloid may be given as

$$\left(\frac{x}{a} - \frac{y}{b} - 2\lambda\right) + k\left(\frac{x}{a} + \frac{y}{b} - \frac{z}{c\lambda}\right) = 0 \qquad \text{...}(i)$$

and

$$\left(\frac{x}{a} + \frac{y}{b} - 2\mu\right) + k'\left(\frac{x}{a} - \frac{y}{b} - \frac{z}{c\mu}\right) = 0 \qquad \text{...}(ii)$$

for all values of k and k'.

These planes become identical if $k = \dfrac{1}{k'} = \dfrac{\lambda}{\mu}$.

This shows that the two generators, one of each system, are coplanar and such they intersect. The plane through them being given as [putting $k = 1/k' = \lambda/\mu$ in (i) and (ii)]

$$\mu\left(\frac{x}{a} - \frac{y}{b} - 2\lambda\right) + \lambda\left(\frac{x}{a} + \frac{y}{b} - \frac{z}{c\lambda}\right) = 0$$

$$\Rightarrow \qquad \frac{x}{a}(\mu + \lambda) - \frac{y}{b}(\mu - \lambda) = \frac{1}{c}(z + 2c\lambda\mu) \qquad \text{...}(iii)$$

which is a tangent plane to the hyperbolic paraboloid at the point of intersection of the two generators. Thus the tangent plane at a point of hyperbolic paraboloid meets it in two generators through the point, the two generators being of different systems λ and μ and the point, their common point of intersection.

So we have shown that any plane through a generating line of a hyperbolic paraboloid is a tangent plane at some point of the generator.

10.7.2. *Direction cosines of the generators of the two systems given by*

$$\frac{x}{a} - \frac{y}{b} = 2\lambda, \; \frac{x}{a} + \frac{y}{b} = \frac{z}{c\lambda} \qquad \text{...}(i)$$

$$\frac{x}{a} + \frac{y}{b} = 2\mu, \; \frac{x}{a} - \frac{y}{b} = \frac{z}{c\mu} \qquad \text{...}(ii)$$

If l_1, m_1, n_1 and l_2, m_2, n_2 are the d.c.'s of (i) and (ii), then we have

$$\frac{l_1}{\dfrac{1}{bc\lambda}} = \frac{m_1}{\dfrac{1}{ac\lambda}} = \frac{n_1}{\dfrac{2}{ab\lambda}},$$

since this generator is the line of intersection of the planes

$$\frac{x}{a} - \frac{y}{b} + 0 \cdot z = 2\lambda \text{ and } \frac{x}{a} + \frac{y}{b} - \frac{z}{c\lambda} = 0$$

$$\Rightarrow \qquad \frac{l_1}{a} = \frac{m_1}{b} = \frac{n_1}{2c\lambda} \qquad \text{...}(iii)$$

Similarly,

$$\frac{l_2}{\dfrac{1}{bc\mu}} = \frac{m_2}{\dfrac{1}{ca\mu}} = \frac{n_2}{\dfrac{-2}{ab}}$$

$$\Rightarrow \qquad \frac{l_2}{a} = \frac{m_2}{-b} = \frac{n_2}{2c\mu} \qquad \text{...}(iv)$$

EXAMPLES

1. *Planes are drawn through the origin O and the generators through any point P of the paraboloid given by $x^2 - y^2 = az$. Prove that the angle between them is $\tan^{-1}(2r/a)$, where r is the length of OP.* (*Gorakhpur, 2000, 03*)

Sol. The two systems of generators of the paraboloid

$$x^2 - y^2 = az \qquad \qquad ...(i)$$

are given as $\qquad\qquad x - y = a\lambda, \; x + y = z/\lambda \qquad \qquad ...(ii)$

and $\qquad\qquad x + y = a\mu, \; x - y = z/\mu \qquad \qquad ...(iii)$

Plane through the λ-generator and the origin is

$$x + y = z/\lambda \qquad \qquad ...(iv)$$

Plane through the origin and the μ-generator is

$$x - y = z/\mu \qquad \qquad ...(v)$$

If θ is the angle between these planes (*iv*) and (*v*), then

$$\cos \theta = \frac{1 - 1 + 1/(\lambda\mu)}{\sqrt{1 + 1 + 1/\lambda^2}\;\sqrt{1 + 1 + 1/\mu^2}}$$

$\Rightarrow \qquad \sec^2 \theta = (2\lambda^2 + 1)(2\mu^2 + 1)$

$\Rightarrow \qquad \tan \theta = \sqrt{2\lambda^2 + 2\mu^2 + 4\lambda^2\mu^2} \qquad \qquad ...(vi)$

Also P, the point of intersection of the generators (*ii*) and (*iii*) is,

$$\left[a\left(\frac{\lambda + \mu}{2}\right), \; a\left(\frac{\mu - \lambda}{2}\right), \; a\lambda\mu \right]$$

Then $\qquad OP = r = \dfrac{1}{2} a \sqrt{(\lambda + \mu)^2 + (\mu - \lambda)^2 + 4\lambda^2\mu^2}$

$$= \frac{1}{2} a \sqrt{2\lambda^2 + 2\mu^2 + 4\lambda^2\mu^2} = \frac{1}{2} a \tan \theta, \qquad \text{[from (vi)]}$$

$\therefore \qquad \tan \theta = \dfrac{2r}{a} \;\Rightarrow\; \theta = \tan^{-1}(2r/a).$

2. *Prove that the equations $4x = a(1 + \cos 2\theta)$, $y = b \cosh \phi \cos \theta$, $z = c \sinh \phi \cos \theta$ determine a hyperbolic paraboloid and that the angle between the generating lines through "θ, ϕ" is given by*

$$\sec \psi = \frac{[(b^2 + c^2)^2 + a^4 \cos^4 \theta + 2a^2 (b^2 + c^2) \cos^2 \theta + \cosh 2\phi]^{1/2}}{b^2 - c^2 + a^2 \cos^2 \theta}.$$

Sol. Any point on the given surface is

$$4x = a(1 + \cos 2\theta), \; y = b \cosh \phi \cos \theta, \; z = c \sinh \phi \cos \theta \qquad \qquad ...(i)$$

Then $\qquad \left(\dfrac{y}{b}\right)^2 - \left(\dfrac{z}{c}\right)^2 = \cos^2 \theta (\cosh^2 \phi - \sinh^2 \phi) = \cos^2 \theta = \dfrac{1}{2}(1 + \cos 2\theta) = \dfrac{2x}{a}$

$\therefore$ Required surface is

$$\frac{y^2}{b^2} - \frac{z^2}{c^2} = \frac{2x}{a} \qquad \qquad ...(ii)$$

which is a hyperbolic paraboloid.

Let any line through (α, β, γ) be

$$\frac{x - \alpha}{l} = \frac{y - \beta}{m} = \frac{z - \gamma}{n} = r \text{ (say)} \qquad \qquad ...(iii)$$

It meets the surface (ii), where

$$\frac{(\beta + mr)^2}{b^2} - \frac{(\gamma + nr)^2}{c^2} = \frac{2(\alpha + lr)}{a}$$

$$\Rightarrow \qquad r^2\left(\frac{m^2}{b^2} - \frac{n^2}{c^2}\right) + 2r\left(\frac{\beta m}{b^2} - \frac{\gamma n}{c^2} - \frac{l}{a}\right) + \frac{\beta^2}{b^2} - \frac{\gamma^2}{c^2} - \frac{2\alpha}{a} = 0 \qquad \qquad ...(iv)$$

If (iii) were a generator of (ii), then we have

$$\frac{m^2}{b^2} - \frac{n^2}{c^2} = 0 \qquad \qquad ...(v)$$

$$\frac{\beta m}{b^2} - \frac{\gamma n}{c^2} - \frac{1}{a} = 0 \qquad \qquad ...(vi)$$

and

$$\frac{\beta^2}{b^2} - \frac{\gamma^2}{c^2} - \frac{2\alpha}{a} = 0 \qquad \qquad ...(vii)$$

From (v) $\qquad \dfrac{m}{b} = \dfrac{n}{\pm c}$

$$\Rightarrow \qquad \frac{\dfrac{m}{b}}{1} = \frac{\dfrac{n}{c}}{\pm 1} = \frac{\dfrac{m\beta}{b^2} - \dfrac{\gamma n}{c^2}}{\dfrac{\beta}{b} \mp \dfrac{\gamma}{c}} = \frac{\dfrac{1}{a}}{\dfrac{\beta}{b} \mp \dfrac{\gamma}{c}} \qquad \qquad \text{[from } (vi)\text{]}$$

$$\therefore \qquad \frac{l_1}{a\left(\dfrac{\beta}{b} - \dfrac{\gamma}{c}\right)} = \frac{m_1}{b} = \frac{n_1}{c} = \frac{1}{\left[a^2\left(\dfrac{\beta}{b} - \dfrac{\gamma}{c}\right)^2 + b^2 + c^2\right]^{1/2}} \qquad \qquad ...(viii)$$

$$\frac{l_2}{a\left(\dfrac{\beta}{b} + \dfrac{\gamma}{c}\right)} = \frac{m_2}{b} = \frac{n_2}{c} = \mp \frac{1}{\left[a^2\left(\dfrac{\beta}{b} + \dfrac{\gamma}{c}\right)^2 + b^2 + c^2\right]^{1/2}} \qquad \qquad ...(ix)$$

where l_1, m_1, n_1 and l_2, m_2, n_2 are d.c.'s of the two generators.

$$\therefore \qquad \sec\phi = \frac{1}{l_1 l_2 + m_1 m_2 + n_1 n_2}$$

$$= \frac{\left[b^2 + c^2 + a^2\left(\dfrac{\beta}{b} - \dfrac{\gamma}{c}\right)^2\right]^{1/2}\left[b^2 + c^2 + a^2\left(\dfrac{\beta}{b} + \dfrac{\gamma}{c}\right)^2\right]^{1/2}}{a^2\left(\dfrac{\beta^2}{b^2} - \dfrac{\gamma^2}{c^2}\right) + b^2 - c^2}$$

$$= \frac{\left[(b^2+c^2)^2 + 2a^2\left(\dfrac{\beta^2}{b^2}+\dfrac{\gamma^2}{c^2}\right)(b^2+c^2) + a^4\left(\dfrac{\beta^2}{b^2}-\dfrac{\gamma^2}{c^2}\right)^2\right]^{1/2}}{a^2\left(\dfrac{2\alpha}{a}\right) + b^2 - c^2} \qquad \text{[by } (viii)]$$

$$= \frac{\left[(b^2+c^2)^2 + 2a^2 + (a^2+c^2)(\cosh^2\phi\cos^2\phi + \sinh^2\phi\cos^2\theta) + a^4 + \dfrac{\alpha^2}{a^2}\right]^{1/2}}{a^2\left(\dfrac{1+\cos 2\theta}{2}\right) + b^2 - c^2}$$

$$= \frac{\left[(b^2+c^2)^2 + 2a^2(b^2+c^2)\cos^2\theta\cosh 2\phi + 4a^4\left(\dfrac{\cos^2\theta}{2}\right)^2\right]^{1/2}}{b^2 - c^2 + a^2\cos^2\theta}$$

$$= \frac{[(b^2+c^2)^2 + 2a^2(b^2+c^2)\cos^2\theta\cosh 2\phi + a^4\cos^4\theta]^{1/2}}{b^2 - c^2 + a^2\cos^2\theta}.$$

3. *Prove that the equation* $2x = ae^{2\phi}$, $y = be^{\phi}\cosh\theta$, $z = ce^{\phi}\sinh\theta$ *determines a hyperbolic paraboloid and that* $(\theta+\phi)$ *is constant for points of a given generator of one system and* $(\theta-\phi)$ *is constant for a given generator of the other.* (Gorakhpur, 1996)

Sol. The parametric equations of the surface are

$$2x = ae^{2\phi},\ y = be^{\phi}\cosh\theta,\ z = ce^{\phi}\sinh\theta \qquad \ldots(i)$$

$$\therefore \qquad \left(\frac{y}{b}\right)^2 - \left(\frac{z}{c}\right)^2 = e^{2\phi} = \frac{2x}{a}$$

$$\Rightarrow \qquad \frac{y^2}{b^2} - \frac{z^2}{c^2} = \frac{2x}{a}, \qquad \ldots(ii)$$

which is a hyperbolic paraboloid.

The different systems of generators of (ii) are given as

$$\frac{y}{b} + \frac{z}{c} = 2\lambda,\ \frac{y}{b} - \frac{z}{c} = \frac{x}{a\lambda} \qquad \ldots(iii)$$

$$\frac{y}{b} - \frac{z}{c} = 2\mu,\ \frac{y}{b} + \frac{z}{c} = \frac{x}{a\mu} \qquad \ldots(iv)$$

Since both the generators pass through the given point, we have

$$e^{\phi}(\cosh\theta + \sinh\theta) = 2\lambda,\ e^{\phi}(\cosh\theta - \sinh\theta) = \frac{e^{2\phi}}{2\lambda} \qquad \ldots(v)$$

From the second of the relation in (v), we have

$$\cosh\theta - \sinh\theta = \frac{e^{\phi}}{2\lambda} \Rightarrow e^{-\theta} = \frac{e^{\phi}}{2\lambda}$$

$$\lambda = \frac{e^{(\theta+\phi)}}{2} \qquad \ldots(vi)$$

Also from (v),

$$e^\phi (\cosh \theta + \sinh \theta) = \frac{e^{2\phi}}{2\mu}$$

$$\Rightarrow \qquad \mu = \frac{e^{(\phi - \theta)}}{2} \qquad\qquad\qquad ...(vii)$$

Relations (vi) and (vii) show that $(\theta + \phi)$ is constant for points of a given generator of the λ-system (since λ was constant for a given generator of the λ-system) and $(\theta - \phi)$ is constant for a given generator of the μ-system.

4. *Show that the polar lines with respect to the sphere $x^2 + y^2 + z^2 = a^2$ of the generators of the quadric $x^2 + y^2 = 2az$ are the generators of the quadric $x^2 - y^2 = -2az$.*

Sol. Rewriting the equation

$$x^2 - y^2 = 2az$$

as

$$(x - y)(x + y) = 2az$$

we see that the two systems of generators of this quadric are

$$\begin{matrix} x - y = 2\lambda a \\ x + y = z/\lambda \end{matrix}\Bigg\}, \qquad \begin{matrix} x - y = 2\mu z \\ x + y = a/\mu \end{matrix}\Bigg\}$$

Symmetric form of the λ-generator is

$$\frac{x - \lambda a}{1} = \frac{y + \lambda a}{1} = \frac{z}{2\lambda}$$

The polar plane of any point

$$(r + \lambda a, r - \lambda a, 2r\lambda),$$

on the λ-generator w.r.t. the sphere

$$x^2 + y^2 + z^2 = a^2$$

is

$$(r + \lambda a) x + (r - \lambda a) y + 2r\lambda z = a^2$$

$$\Leftrightarrow \qquad r (x + y + 2\lambda z) + a (\lambda x - \lambda y - a) = 0$$

so that the polar line of the λ-generator is

$$x + y + 2\lambda z = 0, \quad \lambda x - \lambda y - a = 0$$

Eliminating λ between these, we see that these polar lines are the generators of the quadric

$$x^2 - y^2 = -2az.$$

We may similarly treat the μ-generators.

5. *Show that the angle between the generating lines of $\dfrac{x^2}{a^2} - \dfrac{y^2}{b^2} = 2z$ through (x, y, z) is given by*

$$\tan \theta = ab \left(1 + \frac{x^2}{a^4} + \frac{y^2}{b^4} \right)^{1/2} \left(z + \frac{a^2 - b^2}{2} \right)^{-1} \qquad (Gorakhpur, 1999)$$

Sol. The d.r.'s of different systems of generators are $a, b, 2c\lambda$ and $a, -b, 2c\mu$ respectively. Hence,

$$\tan \theta = \frac{[(2b\mu + 2b\lambda)^2 + (2\lambda a - 2\mu a)^2 + (-2ab)^2]^{1/2}}{a^2 - b^2 + 4\lambda\mu}$$

$$- \frac{[4b^2 (\mu + \lambda)^2 + 4a^2 (\mu - \lambda)^2 + 4a^2b^2]^{1/2}}{a^2 - b^2 + 4\lambda\mu}$$

$$= \frac{\left[4b^2 \left(\frac{x}{a}\right)^2 + 4a^2 \left(\frac{y}{b}\right)^2 + 4a^2 b^2 \right]^{1/2}}{a^2 - b^2 + 2z} = ab \left(1 + \frac{z^2}{a^4} + \frac{y^2}{b^4}\right)^{1/2} \left(z + \frac{a^2 - b^2}{2}\right)^{-1}$$

6. *Find the locus of the point of intersection of perpendicular generators of hyperbolic paraboloid.*

Sol. The d.r.'s of different systems of generators are $a, b, 2c\lambda$ and $a, -b, 2c\mu$ respectively.

Two generators of λ and μ-systems intersect at right angles if

$$l_1 l_2 + m_1 m_2 + n_1 n_2 = 0$$

$\Rightarrow$

$$a^2 - b^2 + 4c^2 \lambda \mu = 0$$

The point of intersection of generators of λ and μ-systems are given by

$$x = a \frac{\lambda + \mu}{\lambda \mu}, \ y = b \frac{\mu - \lambda}{\mu \lambda}, \ z = \frac{2c}{\lambda \mu}$$

$\therefore$

$$(a^2 - b^2) \frac{2c}{z} + 4c^2 = 0$$

or

$$(a^2 - b^2) + 2cz = 0$$

Hence, the required locus is the curve of intersection of the hyperbolic paraboloid and the plane $a^2 - b^2 + 2cz = 0$.

7. *Prove that the shortest distance of any two perpendicular members of the system of generators of the paraboloid $y (ax + by) = z$, which is perpendicular to the y-axis, lies in the plane $a^2 z = b$.*

Sol. The given paraboloid is

$$y (ax + by) = z \qquad \qquad \dots(i)$$

The systems of generators (perpendicular to the axis) is given by

$$y = \lambda, \ ax + by = \frac{z}{\lambda} \qquad \qquad \dots(ii)$$

Let any two members of the λ-system of generators be given from (ii) by taking λ_1 and λ_2 n succession for λ.

Let a point on the λ_1-generator be $[-b\lambda_1 / a, \lambda, 0]$.

The d.r.'s of the generator are $1, 0, a\lambda_1$, since the equation can be written as

$$\frac{x + b\lambda_1 / a}{1} = \frac{y - \lambda_1}{0} = \frac{z}{a\lambda_1} \qquad \qquad \dots(iii)$$

Similarly the other member for λ_2 will be

$$\frac{x + b\lambda_2 / a}{1} = \frac{y - \lambda_2}{0} = \frac{z}{a\lambda_2} \qquad \qquad \dots(iv)$$

The d.c.'s of the shortest distance between (iii) and (iv) are proportional to $0, 1, 0$.

$\therefore$ Equations to shortest distance will become

$$\begin{vmatrix} x + b\lambda_1 / a & y - \lambda_1 & z \\ 1 & 0 & a\lambda_1 \\ 0 & 1 & 0 \end{vmatrix} = 0 = \begin{vmatrix} x + b\lambda_2 / a & y - \lambda_2 & z \\ 1 & 0 & a\lambda_2 \\ 0 & 1 & 0 \end{vmatrix}$$

or
$$z = a\lambda_1 \left(x + \frac{b\lambda_1}{a} \right) = a\lambda_2 \left(x + \frac{b\lambda_2}{a} \right) \qquad \ldots(v)$$

By subtraction and addition, we get

$$ax(\lambda_1 - \lambda_2) + b(\lambda_1^2 - \lambda_2^2) = 0$$

or
$$\lambda_1 + \lambda_2 = -\frac{ax}{b} \qquad \ldots(vi)$$

since
$$\lambda_1 \neq \lambda_2$$

and
$$ax(\lambda_1 + \lambda_2) + b(\lambda_1^2 + \lambda_2^2) = 2z \qquad \ldots(vii)$$

Also, as the two generators (iii) and (iv) are mutually perpendicular,

$$1 + a^2\lambda_1\lambda_2 = 0 \qquad \ldots(viii)$$

Eliminating λ_1 and λ_2 from (vi), (vii) and (viii), we get

$$ax\left(-\frac{ax}{b} \right) + b\left[\left(\frac{ax}{b} \right)^2 + \frac{2}{a^2} \right] = 2z$$

or
$$a^2 z = b.$$

EXERCISES

1. Obtain equations for the two systems of generating lines on the hyperbolic paraboloid $x^2/a^2 - y^2/b^2 = 4z$, and hence express the co-ordinates of a point on the surface as functions of two parameters. Find the direction cosines of the generators through $(\alpha, 0, \gamma)$ and show that the cosines of the angle between them is $(a^2 - b^2 + \gamma)/(a^2 + b^2 + \gamma)$.

2. Show that the projections of the generators of a hyperbolic paraboloid on any principal plane are tangents to the section by the plane.

3. Find the locus of the perpendiculars from the vertex at the paraboloid
$$x^2/a^2 - y^2/b^2 = 2z/c$$
to the generators of one system.   [**Ans.** $x^2 + y^2 + 2z^2 \mp (a^2 + b^2) \, xy/ab = 0$]

4. Show that the points of intersection of generators $xy = az$ which are inclined at a constant angle α lie on the curve of intersection of the paraboloid and the hyperboloid
$$x^2 + y^2 - z^2 \tan^2 \alpha + a^2 = 0.$$

5. Through a variable generator $x - y = \lambda$, $x + y = \dfrac{2z}{\lambda}$ of the paraboloid $x^2 - y^2 = 2z$ a plane is drawn making a constant angle α with the plane $x = y$. Find the locus of the point at which it touches the paraboloid.

   [**Ans.** Curve of intersection of the above surface and paraboloid is $x^2 - y^2 = 2z$.]

6. Show that the equations to the generators through the point "r, θ" on the hyperbolic paraboloid
$$\frac{x^2}{a^2} - \frac{y^2}{b^2} = 2z$$
are
$$\frac{x - ar\cos\theta}{a} = \frac{y - br\sin\theta}{\pm b} = \frac{z - \dfrac{1}{2}r^2 \cos 2\theta}{r(\cos\theta \mp \sin\theta)}.$$

7. Prove that the projections of the generators of the hyperboloid on any principal plane are tangent to the section by the plane.

10.8. CENTRAL POINT. LINE OF STRICTION. PARAMETER OF DISTRIBUTION

10.8.1. *To determine the central point of any generator of the system of generators.*

$$\frac{x}{a} - \frac{y}{b} = \frac{\lambda z}{c}, \quad 2 = \lambda\left(\frac{x}{a} - \frac{y}{b}\right).$$

Let a generator, l, of this system be

$$\frac{x}{a} - \frac{y}{b} = \frac{pz}{c}, \quad 2 = p\left(\frac{x}{a} + \frac{y}{b}\right) \qquad \qquad \ldots(1)$$

We, now, consider a generator, m, of the same system

$$\frac{x}{a} - \frac{y}{b} = \frac{p'z}{c}, \quad 2 = p'\left(\frac{x}{a} + \frac{y}{b}\right) \qquad \qquad \ldots(2)$$

The direction ratios of these generators are $a, -b, 2c/p; \ a, -b, 2c/p'$.

If l, m, n be the direction ratios of the line of S.D., between (1) and (2), we have

$$al - bm + 2cn/p = 0, \quad al - bm + 2cn/p' = 0$$

These give $1/a, 1/b, 0$ as the direction ratios of the line of S.D., being independent of p and p', we see that the line of S.D., is parallel to a fixed line.

Let (x_1, y_1, z_1) be the central point of the generator (1). As in § 10.5.1, the limiting position of the line of S.D., is a line contained in the tangent plane

$$\frac{xx_1}{a^2} - \frac{yy_1}{b^2} = \frac{1}{c}(z + z_1)$$

at (x_1, y_1, z_1).

Thus, we have

$$\frac{x_1}{a^3} - \frac{y_1}{b^3} = 0 \qquad \qquad \ldots(3)$$

Also, since (x_1, y_1, z_1) lies on (1), we have

$$\frac{x_1}{a} - \frac{y_1}{b} = \frac{pz_1}{c}, \quad 2 = p\left(\frac{x_1}{a} + \frac{y_1}{b}\right) \qquad \qquad \ldots(4)$$

Solving (3) and (4), we obtain

$$x_1 = \frac{2a^3}{p(a^2 + b^2)}, \quad y_1 = \frac{2b^3}{p(a^2 + b^2)}, \quad z_1 = \frac{2c(a^2 - b^2)}{p(a^2 + b^2)}.$$

Eliminating p, we see that the line of striction is the curve of intersection of the surface with the plane

$$x/a^3 + y/b^3 = 0.$$

Ex. Find the central point of a generator of the second system and show that the corresponding line of striction is the curve of intersection of the surface with the plane

$$x/a^3 + y/b^3 = 0.$$

10.8.2. *To determine the parameter of distribution.*

Let $\Delta \psi$ and Δs be the angle of S.D., respectively between the generators (1) and (2).

We have

$$\tan \Delta \psi = \frac{2c\sqrt{(a^2 + b^2)(p' - p)}}{pp'(a^2 + b^2) + 4c^2}$$

Let $p' = p + \Delta p$ so that $\Delta p \to 0$ as $p' \to p$. We have

$$\frac{d\psi}{dp} = \frac{2c\sqrt{a^2+b^2}}{p^2(a^2+b^2)+4c^2} \qquad \qquad ...(5)$$

Now the plane through the generator (1) and parallel to the generator (2) is

$$\frac{x}{a} + \frac{y}{b} = \frac{2}{p}.$$

Also taking $z = 0$, we see that $(a/p', b/p', 0)$ is a point on the generator (2).

$$\therefore \qquad \Delta s = \frac{\dfrac{2}{p} - \dfrac{2}{p'}}{\left(\dfrac{1}{a^2} + \dfrac{1}{b^2}\right)^{1/2}} = \frac{2(p'-p)ab}{pp'\sqrt{a^2+b^2}} \qquad \qquad ...(6)$$

Thus, as before

$$\frac{ds}{dp} = \frac{2ab}{p^2\sqrt{a^2+b^2}},$$

$$\Rightarrow \qquad \frac{ds}{d\psi} = \frac{ab\,[p^2(a^2+b^2)+4c^2]}{cp^2(a^2+b^2)}$$

which is the parameter of distribution.

Ex. For the generator of the paraboloid $x^2/a^2 - y^2/b^2 = 2z$ given by

$$\frac{x}{a} - \frac{y}{b} = 2\lambda, \; \frac{x}{a} + \frac{y}{b} = \frac{z}{\lambda},$$

prove that the parameter of distribution is

$$ab\,(a^2 + b^2 + 4\lambda^2)/(a^2 + b^2)$$

and the central point is

$$\left[\frac{2a^3\lambda}{a^2+b^2}, \frac{-2b^3\lambda}{a^2+b^2}, \frac{2(a^2-b^2)\lambda^2}{a^2+b^2}\right].$$

Prove that the central points of the systems of generators lie on the planes

$$x/a^3 \pm y/b^3 = 0.$$

10.9. GENERAL CONSIDERATION

We have seen that hyperboloid of one sheet and hyperbolic paraboloid each admit of two systems of generators such that through each point of the surface there passes one member of each system and that two members of opposite systems intersect but no two members of the same system intersect. Also we know that through each point of a cone or a cylinder there passes one generator. Thus, hyperboloids of one sheet, hyperbolic paraboloids, cones and cylinders are *ruled surfaces* in as much as they can be generated by straight lines.

We now proceed to examine the case of the general quadric in relation to the existence of generators.

10.9.1. Condition for a Line to be a Generator

A straight line will be a generator of a quadric if three points of the line lie on the quadric.

(*Kumaon*, 2004)

Let the quadric be

$$ax^2 + by^2 + cz^2 + 2fyz + 2gzx + 2hxy + 2ux + 2vy + 2wz + d = 0 \qquad ...(1)$$

The line
$$\frac{x-\alpha}{l} = \frac{y-\beta}{m} = \frac{z-\gamma}{n}$$
will be a generator of the quadric, if the point $(lr + \alpha, mr + \beta, nr + \gamma)$ on the line lies on the quadric for all values of r, *i.e.*, the equation obtained on substituting these co-ordinates for x, y, z in (1) is an identity. As this equation is a quadric in r, it will be an identity if it is satisfied for three values of r, *i.e.*, if three points of the line lie on the quadric.

Cor. 1. The quadric equation in r obtained above will be an identity if the coefficients of r^2, r and the constant term are separately zero. This gives

$$al^2 + bm^2 + cn^2 + 2fmn + 2gnl + 2hlm = 0 \qquad ...(2)$$

$$l(a\alpha + h\beta + g\gamma) + m(h\alpha + b\beta + f\gamma) + n(g\alpha + f\beta + c\gamma) = 0 \qquad ...(3)$$

$$a\alpha^2 + b\beta^2 + c\gamma^2 + 2f\beta\gamma + 2g\gamma\alpha + 2h\alpha\beta + 2u\alpha + 2v\beta + 2w\gamma + d = 0 \qquad ...(4)$$

The condition (4) simply means that the point (α, β, γ) lies on the quadric.

Since (2) is a homogeneous quadric equation and (3) is a homogeneous linear equation in l, m, n, these two equations will determine *two* sets of values of l, m, n. Thus, we deduce that *through every point on a quadric there pass two lines, real, coincident or imaginary lying wholly on the quadric.*

Cor. 2. A quadric can be drawn so as to contain **three** mutually skew lines as generators, for the quadric determined by nine points, three on each line, will contain the three lines as generators.

10.10. QUADRICS WITH REAL AND DISTINCT PAIRS OF GENERATING LINES

10.10.1. *Of all real central quadrics, hyperboloid of one sheet only possesses two real and distinct generators through a point.*

Let
$$ax^2 + by^2 + cz^2 = 1$$
be any central quadric.

The direction ratios, l, m, n of any generator
$$\frac{x-\alpha}{l} = \frac{y-\beta}{m} = \frac{z-\gamma}{n}$$
of the quadric through the point (α, β, γ) are given by the equations
$$al^2 + bm^2 + cn^2 = 0, \quad al\alpha + bm\beta + cn\gamma = 0$$

Eliminating n from these, we obtain
$$a(a\alpha^2 + c\gamma^2) l^2 + 2ab\alpha\beta lm + b(b\beta^2 + c\gamma^2) m^2 = 0$$

Its roots will be real and distinct if, and only if
$$4a^2b^2\alpha^2\beta^2 - 4ab(a\alpha^2 + c\gamma^2)(b\beta^2 + c\gamma^2) > 0$$
$$\Leftrightarrow \qquad\qquad - 4abc\gamma^2(a\alpha^2 + b\beta^2 + c\gamma^2) > 0$$

Since $a\alpha^2 + b\beta^2 + c\gamma^2 = 1$, we see that the roots will be real and distinct, if and only if, abc is negative.

Now this will be the case if a, b, c are all negative or one negative and two positive. In the former case the quadric itself is imaginary and in the latter it is a hyperboloid of one sheet.

10.10.2. *Of the two paraboloids, hyperbolic paraboloid only possesses two real and distinct generators through a point.*

In the case of the paraboloid
$$ax^2 + by^2 = 2cz$$
the direction ratios, l, m, n of the generating lines through a point (α, β, γ) of the surface are given by

$$al^2 + bm^2 = 0 \qquad ...(1)$$

$$al\alpha + bm\beta = 0 \qquad ...(2)$$

The equation (1) shows that for real values of l and m, we must have a and b with opposite signs, *i.e.*, the paraboloid must be hyperbolic.

10.11. LINES INTERSECTING THREE LINES

An infinite number of lines can be drawn meeting three given mutually skew lines. For the quadric through the three given mutually skew lines a, b, c, the three lines will be generators of one system and all the other generators of the other system will intersect a, b and c.

In fact the quadric through three given mutually skew lines can be determined as the locus of lines which intersect the three given lines.

Thus, the locus determined in § 4.4.1 on page ??? is really the equation of the quadric through the three lines

$$u_r = 0 = v_r; \; r = 1, 2, 3.$$

EXAMPLES

1. *Find the equations of the quadric containing the three lines*

$$y = b, z = -c; \; z = c, x = -a; \; x = a, y = -b.$$

Also obtain the equations of its two systems of generators.

Sol. Any line which intersects the first two lines is given by

$$\left. \begin{array}{l} y - b + \lambda_1 (z + c) = 0, \\ z - c + \lambda_2 (x + a) = 0, \end{array} \right\} \qquad \qquad ...(i)$$

for all values of λ_1, λ_2.

This will intersect the third line $x = a$, $y = -b$ if

$$z = c - 2a\lambda_2 = \frac{2b}{\lambda_1} - c$$

$$\Rightarrow \qquad\qquad c = \frac{b}{\lambda_1} + a\lambda_2, \qquad\qquad ...(ii)$$

which is $f(\lambda_1, \lambda_2) = 0$.

Eliminating λ_1, λ_2 from (*i*) and (*ii*), we get

$$c = -\frac{b(z+c)}{y-b} - \frac{a(z-c)}{x+a}.$$

$$\Rightarrow \qquad c(xy - bx + ay - ab) + b(xz + cx + az + ca) + a(yz - cy - bz + bc) = 0$$

$$\Rightarrow \qquad ayz + bzx + cxy + abc = 0 \qquad\qquad ...(iii)$$

which is the required quadric containing the three given lines.

To get the two systems of generators of (*iii*), rewrite (*iii*) as

$$y(az + cx) + b(zx + ca) = 0$$

$$\Rightarrow \qquad y(az + cx) + b[(x + a)(z + c) - (az + cx)] = 0$$

$$\Rightarrow \qquad (y - b)(az + cx) + b(x + a)(z + c) = 0 \qquad\qquad ...(iv)$$

which may again be written in either of the two forms

$$\frac{b(x+a)}{(az+cx)} = \frac{-(y-b)}{(z+c)} = \lambda \text{ (say)} \qquad\qquad ...(v)$$

and

$$\frac{-(y-b)}{b(x+a)} = \frac{z+c}{(az+cx)} = \mu \text{ (say)} \qquad\qquad ...(vi)$$

where λ and μ are arbitrary constants.

Relations (v) and (vi) give system of generators as

$$y - b + \lambda (z + c) = 0, \ b (x + a) - \lambda (az + cx) = 0,$$
$$\mu (az + cx) - (z + c) = 0, \ \mu b (x + a) + (y - b) = 0.$$

2. *Find the locus of the perpendicular from a point on a hyperboloid to the generators of one system.*

Sol. Let the given point O be taken as origin and a generator through O as OX, the x-axis.

Let OZ, the normal at O be taken as the z-axis. Then XOY is the tangent plane at Q, OY being the y-axis.

Then the equation of the hyperboloid of which the x-axis is a generator and the z-axis is the normal, is of the form

$$by^2 + cz^2 + 2fyz + 2gzx + 2hxy + 2wz = 0$$
$$\Rightarrow \qquad y (by + 2hx) + z (cz + 2gx + 2fy + 2w) = 0 \qquad \qquad ...(i)$$

The system of generators of (i) are given by

$$\lambda y = z, (by + 2hx) + \lambda (cz + 2gx + 2fy + 2w) = 0 \qquad \qquad ...(ii)$$
$$y = \mu, (cz + 2gx + 2fy + 2w) z + \mu (by + 2hx) = 0 \qquad \qquad ...(iii)$$

Again let any line through origin O and perpendicular to the λ-generator be

$$\frac{x}{L} = \frac{y}{M} = \frac{z}{N} = k. \qquad \qquad ...(iv)$$

Also the λ-generator is the line of intersection of the plane

$$\lambda y - z = 0$$
and $$2 (h + g\lambda) x + (b + 2\lambda f) y + c\lambda z = - 2w$$

$\therefore$ The d.c.'s of the λ-generator are proportional to

$$(c\lambda^2 + b + 2\lambda f), - 2 (h + g\lambda), - 2\lambda (h + g\lambda).$$

Since (iv) is perpendicular to the generator (ii), we have

$$L (c\lambda^2 + b + 2\lambda f) - 2M (h + g\lambda) - 2\lambda N (h + g\lambda) = 0 \qquad \qquad ...(v)$$

Eliminating L, M, N and λ between (ii), (iv) and (v), we get

$$\frac{x}{k}\left[c\left(\frac{z}{y}\right)^2 + b + 2\frac{z}{y} f\right] - 2\frac{y}{k}\left(h + g\frac{z}{y}\right) - 2\frac{z}{k}\cdot\frac{z}{y}\left(h + g\cdot\frac{z}{y}\right) = 0$$

$$\Rightarrow \qquad x (cz^2 + 2fyz + by^2) - 2y^2 (hy + gz) - 2z^2 (hy + gz) = 0$$

$$\Rightarrow \qquad x (cz^2 + 2fyz + by^2) - 2 (y^2 + z^2) (hy + gz) = 0,$$

which is the required locus.

EXERCISES

1. Find the equations of the hyperboloid through the three lines

$$y - z = 1, x = 0; \ z - x = 1, y = 0; \ x - y = 1, z = 0.$$

Also obtain the equations of its two systems of generators.

[**Ans.** $x^2 + y^2 + z^2 - 2xy - 2yz - 2zx = 1; \ x - y - 1 = \lambda z, \ \lambda (x - y + 1) = 2x + 2y - z,$
$$x - y - 1 = \lambda (2x + 2y - z), \ \lambda (x - y + 1) = z]$$

2. The generators of one system of a hyperbolic paraboloid are parallel to the plane

$$lx + my + nz = 0$$

and the lines $ax + by = 0 = z + c; \ ax - by = 0 = z - c$

are two members of the same system.

Show that the equation of the paraboloid is

$$abc (lx + my + nz) = c (a^2nx + b^2ly + abcn). \qquad \text{(See Ex. 2, p. ???)}$$

3. Show that two straight lines can be drawn intersecting four given mutually skew lines.

MISCELLANEOUS EXAMPLES

1. *From a fixed point A (f, g, h) perpendiculars are let fall on three conjugate diameters of the ellipsoid*

$$\frac{x^2}{a^2} + \frac{y^2}{b^2} + \frac{z^2}{c^2} = 1;$$

prove that the plane passing through the three feet of the perpendiculars goes through the fixed point

$$\left(\frac{a^2 f}{a^2 + b^2 + c^2}, \frac{b^2 g}{a^2 + b^2 + c^2}, \frac{c^2 h}{a^2 + b^2 + c^2} \right).$$

Sol. Let $P(x_1, y_1, z_1)$, $Q(x_2, y_2, z_2)$, $R(x_3, y_3, z_3)$, be the extremities of their conjugate semi-diameters.

Equations of the line *OP* are

$$\frac{x}{x_1} = \frac{y}{y_1} = \frac{z}{z_1}$$

so that (rx_1, ry_1, rz_1) are the general co-ordinates of a point on this line. The line joining the points (f, g, h) and (rx_1, ry_1, rz_1) will be perpendicular to the line *OP*, if

$$(rx_1 - f) x_1 + (ry_1 - g) y_1 + (rz_1 - h) z_1 = 0$$

$$\Rightarrow \qquad r = \frac{fx_1 + gy_1 + hz_1}{x_1^2 + y_1^2 + z_1^2}$$

Therefore, the foot of the perpendicular *L* from the point (f, g, h) on the line *OP* is

$$\left(\frac{\Sigma fx_1}{\Sigma x_1^2} x_1, \frac{\Sigma fx_1}{\Sigma x_1^2} y_1, \frac{\Sigma fx_1}{\Sigma x_1^2} z_1 \right)$$

Similarly, the feet *M, N* of the perpendiculars to the line *OQ, OR* are

$$\left(\frac{\Sigma fx_2}{\Sigma x_2^2} x_2, \frac{\Sigma fx_2}{\Sigma x_2^2} y_2, \frac{\Sigma fx_2}{\Sigma x_2^2} z_2 \right) \text{ and } \left(\frac{\Sigma fx_3}{\Sigma x_3^3} x_3, \frac{\Sigma fx_3}{\Sigma x_3^3} y_3, \frac{\Sigma fx_3}{\Sigma x_3^3} z_3 \right)$$

The plane *LMN* is

$$\begin{vmatrix} x & y & z & 1 \\ \dfrac{\Sigma fx_1}{\Sigma x_1^2} x_1 & \dfrac{\Sigma fx_1}{\Sigma x_1^2} y_1 & \dfrac{\Sigma fx_1}{\Sigma x_1^2} z_1 & 1 \\ \dfrac{\Sigma fx_2}{\Sigma x_2^2} x_2 & \dfrac{\Sigma fx_2}{\Sigma x_2^2} y_2 & \dfrac{\Sigma fx_2}{\Sigma x_2^2} z_2 & 1 \\ \dfrac{\Sigma fx_3}{\Sigma x_3^3} x_3 & \dfrac{\Sigma fx_3}{\Sigma x_3^3} y_3 & \dfrac{\Sigma fx_3}{\Sigma x_3^3} z_3 & 1 \end{vmatrix} = 0$$

$$\Rightarrow \qquad \begin{vmatrix} x & y & z & 1 \\ x_1 \Sigma fx_1 & y_1 \Sigma fx_1 & z_1 \Sigma fx_1 & \Sigma x_1^2 \\ x_2 \Sigma fx_2 & y_2 \Sigma fx_2 & z_2 \Sigma fx_2 & \Sigma x_2^2 \\ x_3 \Sigma fx_3 & y_3 \Sigma fx_3 & z_3 \Sigma fx_3 & \Sigma x_3^2 \end{vmatrix} = 0$$

Adding third and fourth rows to the second and making use of the relation in § 8.8, this becomes

$$\begin{vmatrix} x & y & z & 1 \\ a^2 f & b^2 g & c^2 h & \Sigma a^2 \\ x_2 \Sigma fx_2 & y_2 \Sigma fx_2 & z_2 \Sigma fx_2 & \Sigma x_2{}^2 \\ x_3 \Sigma fx_3 & y_3 \Sigma fx_3 & z_3 \Sigma fx_3 & \Sigma x_3{}^2 \end{vmatrix} = 0$$

$$\Leftrightarrow \begin{vmatrix} x & y & z & 1 \\ a^2 f / \Sigma a^2 & b^2 g / \Sigma a^2 & c^2 h / \Sigma a^2 & 1 \\ x_2 \Sigma fx_2 & y_2 \Sigma fx_2 & z_2 \Sigma fx_2 & \Sigma x_2{}^2 \\ x_3 \Sigma fx_3 & y_3' \Sigma fx_3 & z_3 \Sigma fx_3 & \Sigma x_3{}^2 \end{vmatrix} = 0$$

This form of the equation of the plane clearly shows that it passes through the point

$$\left(\frac{a^2 f}{\Sigma a^2}, \frac{b^2 g}{\Sigma a^2}, \frac{c^2 h}{\Sigma a^2} \right).$$

2. *Show that the normals to the ellipsoid*

$$\frac{x^2}{a^2} + \frac{y^2}{b^2} + \frac{z^2}{c^2} = 1$$

at all points of a central circular section are parallel to a fixed plane. Find the angle which this plane makes with the plane of the section.

Sol. Consider the central circular section

$$\frac{x^2}{a^2} + \frac{y^2}{b^2} + \frac{z^2}{c^2} = 1, \quad \frac{\sqrt{(a^2 - b^2)}}{a} x + \frac{\sqrt{(b^2 - c^2)}}{c} z = 0$$

The direction ratios of the normal to the ellipsoid at any point (f, g, h) of the section are

$$f / a^2, g / b^2, h / c^2$$

Also we have the relation

$$\frac{\sqrt{(a^2 - b^2)}}{a} f + \frac{\sqrt{(b^2 - c^2)}}{c} h = 0$$

which we rewrite as

$$a \sqrt{(a^2 - b^2)} \cdot \frac{f}{a^2} + 0 \cdot \frac{g}{b^2} + c \sqrt{(b^2 - c^2)} \cdot \frac{h}{c^2} = 0$$

This relation shows that the normals are parallel to the fixed plane

$$a \sqrt{(a^2 - b^2)} x + 0y + c \sqrt{(b^2 - c^2)} z = 0,$$

If, θ, be the angle between this plane and the plane of the section, we have

$$\cos \theta = \frac{(a^2 - b^2) + (b^2 - c^2)}{\left(\dfrac{a^2 - b^2}{a^2} + \dfrac{b^2 - c^2}{c^2} \right)^{1/2} [a^2 (a^2 - b^2) + c^2 (b^2 - c^2)]^{1/2}}$$

$$= \frac{a^2 - c^2}{\left[b^2 \left(\dfrac{1}{c^2} - \dfrac{1}{a^2} \right)(a^2 - c^2)(a^2 + c^2 - b^2) \right]^{1/2}} = \frac{ac}{b\sqrt{(a^2 + c^2 - b^2)}}$$

$$\Leftrightarrow \qquad \theta = \cos^{-1}[ac/b\sqrt{(a^2 + c^2 - b^2)}].$$

3. *The generators through a point P on the hyperboloid*
$$x^2/a^2 + y^2/b^2 - z^2/c^2 = 1$$
meet the principal plane z = 0 in points A and B such that the median of the triangle PAB through the point P is parallel to the fixed plane
$$lx + my + nz = 0;$$
show that the point P lies on the curve of the intersection of the hyperboloid with the surface
$$z(lx + my) + n(c^2 + z^2) = 0.$$

Sol. The equations of the line AB where the tangent plane
$$\frac{xx_1}{a^2} + \frac{yy_1}{b^2} - \frac{zz_1}{c^2} = 1$$

at $P(x_1, y_1, z_1)$ of the hyperboloid, containing as it does the generators through P, meets the plane $z = 0$ are

$$\frac{xx_1}{a^2} + \frac{yy_1}{b^2} = 1, \quad z = 0 \qquad \qquad \ldots(1)$$

Let $(f, g, 0)$ be the mid-point of AB. The equations of the chord of the principal elliptical section
$$x^2/a^2 + y^2/b^2 = 1, \quad z = 0$$
with $(f, g, 0)$ as its middle point is

$$\frac{fx}{a^2} + \frac{gy}{b^2} = \frac{f^2}{a^2} + \frac{g^2}{b^2}, \quad z = 0 \qquad \qquad \ldots(2)$$

Comparing (1) and (2), we have

$$x_1 = \frac{f}{f^2/a^2 + g^2/b^2}, \quad y_1 = \frac{g}{f^2/a^2 + g^2/b^2}$$

These give

$$f = \frac{x_1}{x_1^2/a^2 + y_1^2/b^2} = \frac{x_1}{1 + z_1^2/c^2} \qquad \qquad \ldots(3)$$

$$g = \frac{y_1}{x_1^2/a^2 + y_1^2/b^2} = \frac{y_1}{1 + z_1^2/c^2} \qquad \qquad \ldots(4)$$

Also the median of the triangle PAB through the point P being parallel to the plane
$$lx + my + nz = 0$$
we have
$$l(x_1 - f) + m(y_1 - g) + nz_1 = 0 \qquad \qquad \ldots(5)$$

Eliminating f, g from (3), (4) and (5), we obtain
$$z_1(lx_1 + my_1) + n(c^2 + z_1^2) = 0.$$

Thus, we have the result as required.

4. *If A and B are the extremities of conjugate diameters of the principal elliptic section, prove that the median through P of the $\triangle PAB$ lies on the cone*

$$\frac{2x^2}{a^2} + \frac{2y^2}{b^2} = \left(\frac{z}{c} \pm 1\right)^2.$$

Sol. Let A and B, the extremities of conjugate diameters, be

$$(a \cos \alpha, \ b \sin \alpha, \ 0), \ (- a \sin \alpha, \ b \cos \alpha, \ 0)$$

and P be

$$(a \cos \theta \sec \phi, \ b \sin \theta \sec \phi, \ c \tan \phi)$$

where

$$\theta + \phi = \alpha, \ \theta - \phi = \alpha + \frac{\pi}{2}.$$

$$\therefore \qquad \theta = \alpha + \frac{\pi}{4}, \ \phi = -\frac{\pi}{4}$$

$\therefore$ The co-ordinates of P are

$$[a (\cos \alpha - \sin \alpha), \ b (\sin \alpha + \cos \alpha), \ - c]$$

and C the middle point of AB is

$$\left[\frac{a}{2} (\cos \alpha - \sin \alpha), \ \frac{b}{2} (\cos \alpha + \sin \alpha), \ 0\right]$$

Equations of the median PC of $\triangle PAB$ are given by

$$\frac{x - a (\cos \alpha - \sin \alpha)}{\frac{1}{2} a (\cos \alpha - \sin \alpha)} = \frac{y - b (\sin \alpha + \cos \alpha)}{\frac{1}{2} b (\sin \alpha + \cos \alpha)} = \frac{z + c}{- c}$$

$$\Rightarrow \quad \frac{2x}{a (\cos \alpha - \sin \alpha)} = \frac{- 2y}{b (\cos \alpha + \sin \alpha)} = \frac{z + c}{- c} + 2 = -\frac{z}{c} + 1 = k \text{ (say)} \quad ...(i)$$

To get the envelope of the median PC, eliminate α between the equation (i).

$$\therefore \quad \left(\frac{2x}{a}\right)^2 + \left(\frac{2y}{b}\right)^2 = k^2 \left[(\cos \alpha - \sin \alpha)^2 + (\cos \alpha + \sin \alpha)^2\right] = 2k^2$$

$$= 2 \left(1 - \frac{z}{c}\right)^2, \qquad\qquad\qquad\qquad \text{[from } (i)\text{]}$$

$$\therefore \quad \frac{2x^2}{a^2} + \frac{2y^2}{b^2} = \left(\frac{z}{c} - 1\right)^2 \qquad\qquad\qquad\qquad ...(ii)$$

Also, let the other extremities of the conjugate diameter be A' and B', so that A' is

$$[a \cos (\alpha + \pi), \ b \sin (\alpha + \pi), \ 0]$$

and B' is

$$\left[a \cos \left(\alpha + \frac{3\pi}{2}\right), \ b \sin \left(\alpha + \frac{3\pi}{2}\right), \ 0\right]$$

i.e., A' is $(- a \cos \alpha, \ - b \sin \alpha, \ 0)$

and B' is $(a \sin \alpha, \ - b \cos \alpha, \ 0)$

And P' is $(a \cos \theta \sec \phi, \ b \sin \theta \sec \phi, \ c \tan \phi)$,

where

$$\theta + \phi = \alpha + \frac{3\pi}{2}; \ \theta = \phi - \alpha + \pi$$

$$\Rightarrow \qquad \theta = \alpha + \frac{5\pi}{4}, \ \phi = \frac{\pi}{4}.$$

$$\therefore \qquad P' \text{ is } \left[a \cos\left(\alpha + \frac{5\pi}{4}\right) \sec\frac{\pi}{4}, \ b \sin\left(\alpha + \frac{5\pi}{4}\right) \sec\frac{\pi}{4}, \ c \tan\frac{\pi}{4} \right],$$

i.e., $\qquad P'$ is $[- a\ (\cos\alpha - \sin\alpha), - b\ (\sin\alpha + \cos\alpha), c]$

Hence on changing the signs of x, y, z in (*ii*) we get the envelope of the median $P'C$ as

$$\frac{2\ (-x)^2}{a^2} + \frac{2\ (-y)^2}{b^2} = \left(-\frac{z}{c} - 1\right)^2$$

$$\Rightarrow \qquad \frac{2x^2}{a^2} + \frac{2y^2}{b^2} = \left(\frac{z}{c} + 1\right)^2 \qquad \qquad \qquad ...(iii)$$

Hence from (*ii*) and (*iii*) the required envelope is

$$\frac{2x^2}{a^2} + \frac{2y^2}{b^2} = \left(\frac{z}{c} \pm 1\right)^2.$$

5. *If four generators of the hyperboloid form a skew-quadrilateral whose vertices are "θ_r, ϕ_r", $r = 1, 2, 3, 4$, prove that*

$$\theta_1 + \theta_3 = \theta_2 + \theta_4, \ \phi_1 + \phi_3 = \phi_2 + \phi_4.$$

Sol. Let $PQRS$ be the skew-quadrilateral whose vertices are (θ_r, ϕ_r), $r = 1, 2, 3, 4$ respectively.

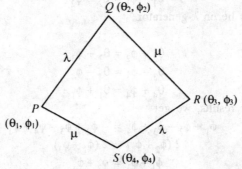

Fig. 48

Since the generators of the opposite systems of a hyperboloid intersect, the generators of λ- and μ-systems pass through each of the vertices as shown in the figure.

Again if a λ-generator

$$\frac{x}{a} + \frac{z}{c} = \lambda\left(1 + \frac{y}{b}\right); \ \frac{x}{a} - \frac{z}{c} = \frac{1}{\lambda}\left(1 - \frac{y}{b}\right) \qquad \qquad ...(i)$$

passes through the point "θ, ϕ", *i.e.*, $(a \cos\theta \sec\phi, b \sin\theta \sec\phi, c \tan\phi)$, then

$$\cos\theta \sec\phi + \tan\phi = \lambda\ (1 + \sin\theta \sec\phi)$$

$$\Rightarrow \qquad \frac{\lambda}{1} = \frac{\cos\theta + \sin\phi}{\cos\phi + \sin\theta}$$

$$\Rightarrow \qquad \frac{1 - \lambda}{1 + \lambda} = \frac{(\cos\phi + \sin\theta) - (\cos\theta + \sin\phi)}{(\cos\phi + \sin\theta) + (\cos\theta + \sin\phi)}$$

$$= \frac{(\cos\phi - \cos\theta) + (\sin\theta - \sin\phi)}{(\cos\phi + \cos\theta) + (\sin\theta + \sin\phi)} = \tan\left(\frac{\theta - \phi}{2}\right)$$

i.e., $\qquad \frac{1 - \lambda}{1 + \lambda} = \tan\left(\frac{\theta - \phi}{2}\right) \qquad \qquad \qquad ...(ii)$

$\Rightarrow$ for points of a given generator of the λ-system, $(\theta - \phi)$ is constant.

Similarly if a μ-generator

$$\frac{x}{a} - \frac{z}{c} = \mu\left(1 + \frac{y}{b}\right); \quad \frac{x}{a} + \frac{z}{c} = \frac{1}{\mu}\left(1 - \frac{y}{b}\right) \qquad \ldots(iii)$$

passes through "θ, ϕ", we have

$$(\cos\theta - \sec\phi - \tan\phi) = \mu\,(1 + \sin\theta\sec\phi)$$

$$\Rightarrow \qquad \mu = \frac{\cos\theta - \sin\phi}{\cos\phi + \sin\theta}$$

$$\frac{\mu - 1}{\mu + 1} = \frac{(\cos\theta - \sin\phi) - (\cos\phi + \sin\theta)}{(\cos\theta - \sin\phi) + (\cos\phi + \sin\theta)}$$

$$= \frac{(\cos\theta - \cos\phi) - (\sin\theta + \sin\phi)}{(\cos\theta + \cos\phi) - (\sin\phi - \sin\theta)} = -\tan\left(\frac{\theta + \phi}{2}\right)$$

$$\Rightarrow \qquad \tan\left(\frac{\theta + \phi}{2}\right) = \frac{1 - \mu}{1 + \mu} \qquad \ldots(iv)$$

which shows that for points of a given generator of the μ-system, μ is constant and as such $(\theta + \phi)$ is constant.

Hence, we have

$$\theta_1 - \phi_1 = \theta_2 - \phi_2 \qquad \ldots(v)$$

by (ii), for P and Q both lie on λ-generator.

Similarly,

$$\theta_2 + \phi_2 = \theta_3 + \phi_3 \qquad \ldots(vi)$$
$$\theta_3 - \phi_3 = \theta_4 - \phi_4 \qquad \ldots(vii)$$
$$\theta_4 + \phi_4 = \theta_1 + \phi_1 \qquad \ldots(viii)$$

Adding the last four results, we get

$$-\phi_1 + \phi_2 - \phi_3 + \phi_4 = -\phi_2 + \phi_3 - \phi_4 + \phi_1$$

$$\Rightarrow \qquad 2\,(\phi_2 + \phi_4) = 2\,(\phi_1 + \phi_3)$$

$$\Rightarrow \qquad \phi_1 + \phi_3 = \phi_2 + \phi_4.$$

Also adding (v) and (vii) and subtracting the sum of (vii) and (viii), we get

$$(\theta_1 - \phi_1) - (\theta_2 + \phi_2) + (\theta_3 - \phi_3) - (\theta_4 + \phi_4) = (\theta_2 - \phi_2) - (\theta_3 + \phi_3) + (\theta_4 - \phi_4) - (\theta_1 + \phi_1)$$

$$\Rightarrow \qquad 2\,(\theta_1 + \theta_3) = 2\,(\theta_2 + \theta_4)$$

$$\Rightarrow \qquad \theta_1 + \theta_3 = \theta_2 + \theta_4.$$

6. *Tangent planes to*

$$\frac{x^2}{a^2} + \frac{y^2}{b^2} - \frac{z^2}{c^2} = 1$$

which are parallel to tangent planes to

$$\frac{b^2 c^2 x^2}{c^2 - b^2} + \frac{c^2 a^2 y^2}{c^2 - a^2} + \frac{a^2 b^2 z^2}{a^2 + b^2} = 0$$

cut the surface in perpendicular generators.

Sol. Tangent at any point "θ, ϕ" to

$$\frac{x^2}{a^2} + \frac{y^2}{b^2} - \frac{z^2}{c^2} = 1$$

is
$$\frac{x}{a}\cos\theta\sec\phi + \frac{y}{b}\sin\theta\sec\phi - \frac{z}{c}\tan\phi = 1 \qquad \ldots(i)$$

The plane parallel to (*i*) and passing through the origin is

$$\frac{x}{a}\cos\theta\sec\phi + \frac{y}{b}\sin\theta\sec\phi - \frac{z}{c}\tan\phi = 0 \qquad \ldots(ii)$$

Now (*ii*) will be a tangent plane to the cone

$$\frac{b^2c^2x^2}{c^2-b^2} + \frac{c^2a^2y^2}{c^2-a^2} + \frac{a^2b^2z^2}{a^2+b^2} = 0, \qquad \ldots(iii)$$

if

$$\frac{\cos^2\theta\sec^2\phi}{a^2}\left(\frac{c^2-b^2}{b^2c^2}\right) + \frac{\sin^2\theta\sec^2\phi}{b^2}\left(\frac{c^2-a^2}{c^2a^2}\right) + \frac{\tan^2\phi}{c^2}\left(\frac{a^2+b^2}{a^2b^2}\right) = 0$$

or if $\quad\cos^2\theta\sec^2\phi\,(c^2-b^2) + \sin^2\theta\sec^2\phi\,(c^2-a^2) + \tan^2\phi\,(a^2+b^2) = 0$

or if $\quad a^2(\tan^2\phi - \sin^2\theta\sec^2\phi) + b^2(\tan^2\phi - \cos^2\theta\sec^2\phi)$
$$+ c^2(\cos^2\theta + \sin^2\theta)\sec^2\phi = 0$$

or if $\quad a^2(\sec^2\phi - \sin^2\theta\sec^2\phi - 1) + b^2(\sec^2\phi - 1 - \cos^2\theta\sec^2\phi) + c^2\sec^2\phi = 0$

or if $\quad a^2\cos^2\theta\sec^2\phi + b^2\sin^2\theta\sec^2\phi + c^2\tan^2\phi = a^2 + b^2 - c^2 \qquad \ldots(iv)$

which shows that the point ($a\cos\theta\sec\phi$, $b\sin\theta\sec\phi$, $c\tan\phi$) (which is the point of intersection of the generators) lies on the director sphere $x^2 + y^2 + z^2 = a^2 + b^2 - c^2$ which is the locus of the point of intersection of perpendicular generators.

7. *A and B are the extremities of the principal elliptic section of the hyperboloid*

$$\frac{x^2}{a^2} + \frac{y^2}{b^2} - \frac{z^2}{c^2} = 1 \text{ and T is any line in the plane of the section, } G_1,\ G_2 \text{ are generators of the}$$

same system; G_1 passing through A and G_2 through B. Two hyperboloids are drawn, one through T, G_1, OZ and the other through T, G_2, OZ. Show that the other common generators of these hyperboloids lie on the surface

$$\frac{x^2}{a^2} + \frac{y^2}{b^2} \pm \frac{z}{c}\left(\frac{x}{a} - \frac{y}{b}\right) - \frac{x}{a} - \frac{y}{b} = 0.$$

Sol. *A* and *B* being the extremities of the axes of the principal elliptic section $\dfrac{x^2}{a^2} + \dfrac{y^2}{b^2} = 1$,

$z = 0$ are (a, 0, 0) and (0, b, 0).

Generators of the λ-system are given by

$$\frac{x}{a} + \frac{z}{c} = \lambda\left(1 + \frac{y}{b}\right); \quad \frac{x}{a} - \frac{z}{c} = \frac{1}{\lambda}\left(1 - \frac{y}{b}\right).$$

If the generator passes through *A* (a, 0, 0), then $\lambda = 1$,

∴ The λ-generator through *A* is given by

$$\frac{x}{a} + \frac{z}{c} = 1 + \frac{y}{b}, \quad \frac{x}{a} - \frac{z}{c} = 1 - \frac{y}{b}$$

⇒ $\qquad \dfrac{x}{a} = 1; \quad \dfrac{y}{b} = \dfrac{z}{c}.$

Again if (*i*) passes through *B* (0, b, 0), $\lambda\left(1 + \dfrac{b}{b}\right) = 0 \Rightarrow \lambda = 0$.

Hence the generator through *B* is given by

$$\frac{x}{a} + \frac{z}{c} = 0; \quad \frac{y}{b} = 1 \qquad \ldots(i)$$

∴   The generator G_1 is $\qquad \dfrac{x}{a} - 1 = 0 = \dfrac{y}{b} - \dfrac{z}{c}$ $\qquad\qquad\qquad$ ...(ii)

and   the generator G_2 is $\qquad \dfrac{y}{b} - 1 = 0 = \dfrac{z}{c} + \dfrac{x}{a}$ $\qquad\qquad\qquad$ ...(iii)

Let T be any line in the plane $z = 0$ given by

$$y - mx - k = 0, \; z = 0 \qquad\qquad\qquad ...(iv)$$

Also, equations of OZ are $\qquad\qquad x = 0 = y$ $\qquad\qquad\qquad$ ...(v)

Now, any hyperboloid through G_1 and T is

$$\alpha\left(\frac{x}{a} - 1\right)(y - mx - k) + \beta\left(\frac{x}{a} - 1\right)z + \gamma\left(\frac{y}{b} - \frac{z}{c}\right)(y - mx - k) + \delta\left(\frac{y}{b} - \frac{z}{c}\right)z = 0, \quad ...(vi)$$

where $\alpha, \beta, \gamma, \delta$ are arbitrary constants.

If (vi) passes through OZ, then

$$\alpha k - \beta z + \gamma\,\frac{kz}{c} - \frac{\delta z^2}{c} = 0, \qquad\qquad\qquad ...(vii)$$

For every value of z, i.e., (vii) should be identically true.

$\Rightarrow \qquad\qquad\qquad\qquad \alpha = 0 = \delta$ and $\beta = \dfrac{\gamma k}{c}$.

∴   The hyperboloid passing through G_1, T and OZ is

$$k\left(\frac{x}{a} - 1\right)z + c\left(\frac{y}{b} - \frac{z}{c}\right)(y - mx - k) = 0 \qquad\qquad ...(viii)$$

Again hyperboloid through G_1 and T is

$$\alpha'\left(\frac{y}{b} - 1\right)(y - mx - k) + \beta'\left(\frac{y}{b} - 1\right)z + \gamma'\left(\frac{z}{c} + \frac{x}{a}\right)(y - mx - k) + \delta'\left(\frac{z}{c} + \frac{x}{a}\right)z = 0,$$

where $\alpha', \beta', \gamma', \delta'$ are arbitrary constants.

If it passes through OZ, then

$$\alpha' k - \beta' z - \gamma'\,\frac{zk}{b} + \delta'\,\frac{z^2}{c} = 0$$

for every value of z.

∴ $\qquad\qquad\qquad\qquad \alpha' = \delta' = 0,\; \beta' = \dfrac{\gamma' k}{c}$.

∴   The hyperboloid through G_2, T and OZ is

$$k\left(\frac{y}{b} - 1\right)z - c\left(\frac{z}{c} + \frac{x}{a}\right)(y - mx - k) = 0 \qquad\qquad ...(ix)$$

Now the common generator (other than OZ) of (viii) and (ix) is

$$z = 0 = y - mx - k \qquad\qquad\qquad ...(x)$$

Eliminating m and k between the equations (viii) and (ix), the locus of T is

$$\frac{\dfrac{x}{a} - 1}{\dfrac{y}{b} - 1} = \frac{\dfrac{y}{b} - \dfrac{z}{c}}{\dfrac{z}{c} + \dfrac{x}{a}} \qquad\qquad \text{[by division]}$$

$\Rightarrow \qquad \left(\dfrac{x}{a} - 1\right)\left(\dfrac{z}{c} + \dfrac{x}{a}\right) + \left(\dfrac{y}{b} - 1\right)\left(\dfrac{y}{b} - \dfrac{z}{c}\right) = 0$

$\Rightarrow \qquad \dfrac{x^2}{a^2} + \dfrac{y^2}{b^2} + \dfrac{z}{c}\left(\dfrac{x}{a} - \dfrac{y}{b}\right) - \dfrac{x}{a} - \dfrac{y}{b} = 0 \qquad \qquad \dots(xi)$

Similarly taking the generators of μ-system through A and B the corresponding surface can be shown to be

$$\dfrac{x^2}{a^2} + \dfrac{y^2}{b^2} - \dfrac{z}{c}\left(\dfrac{x}{a} - \dfrac{y}{b}\right) - \dfrac{x}{a} - \dfrac{y}{b} = 0 \qquad \qquad \dots(xii)$$

Hence the required surface is given by

$$\dfrac{x^2}{a^2} + \dfrac{y^2}{b^2} + \dfrac{z}{c}\left(\dfrac{x}{a} - \dfrac{y}{b}\right) - \dfrac{x}{a} - \dfrac{y}{b} = 0.$$

8. *Prove that the equation to the conicoid through the lines* $u = 0 = v$, $u' = 0 = v'$, $\lambda u + \mu v + \lambda' u' + \mu' v' = 0 = lu + mv + l'u' + m'v'$ *is*

$$\dfrac{\lambda u + \mu v}{\lambda' u' + \mu' v'} = \dfrac{lu + mv}{l'u' + m'v'}.$$

Sol. The three given lines are

$$u = 0 = v, \qquad \qquad \dots(i)$$
$$u' = 0 = v' \qquad \qquad \dots(ii)$$

and $\qquad \lambda u + \mu v + \lambda' u' + \mu' v' = 0 = lu + mv + l'u' + m'v' \qquad \dots(iii)$

From (iii), we have

$$\dfrac{\lambda u + \mu v}{\lambda' u' + \mu' v'} = -1 = \dfrac{lu + mv}{l'u' + m'v'}$$

$$\therefore \qquad \dfrac{\lambda u + \mu v}{\lambda' u' + \mu' v'} = \dfrac{lu + mv}{l'u' + m'v'} \qquad \qquad \dots(iv)$$

which represents a conicoid through the line (iii).

Also (iv) is satisfied if (i) or (ii) hold. Hence (iv) represents the conicoids through the lines (i), (ii) and (iii).

OBJECTIVE QUESTIONS

I. Multiple Choice Questions

Note : *For each of the following questions, four alternatives are given for the answer. Only one of them is correct. Choose the correct alternative.*

1. No two generators of the same system of a hyperboloid of one sheet :
   - (a) are parallel
   - (b) intersect
   - (c) coincide
   - (d) None of these.
2. One generator of λ-system and one of μ-system of a hyperboloid :
   - (a) are parallel
   - (b) intersect
   - (c) coincide
   - (d) None of these.
3. How many systems of generators are there for a hyperboloid of one sheet ?
   - (a) one
   - (b) two
   - (c) three
   - (d) four.
4. Two generators of the same system of hyperboloid of one sheet :
   - (a) intersect at a point
   - (b) never intersect
   - (c) intersect on the hyperboloid
   - (d) None of these.
5. Locus of the point of intersection of perpendicular generators of a hyperboloid of one sheet is :
   - (a) Sphere
   - (b) Paraboloid
   - (c) Hyperboloid of one sheet
   - (d) Hyperboloid of two sheets.
6. Number of systems of generating lines in a hyperbolic paraboloid is :
   - (a) 1
   - (b) 2
   - (c) 4
   - (d) ∞.

7. Generators of the λ- and μ-systems of the hyperbolic paraboloid $\dfrac{x^2}{a^2} - \dfrac{y^2}{b^2} = \dfrac{2z}{c}$ are

parallel to the planes :

    (a) $x = 0,\, y = 0$ (b) $ax \pm by = 0$ (c) $x/a \pm y/b = 0$ (d) $y = \pm\, mx.$

8. The locus of the point of intersection of perpendicular generators of the hyperbolic

paraboloid $\dfrac{x^2}{a^2} - \dfrac{y^2}{b^2} = 2z$ is given by $a^2 - b^2 =$

    (a) $2z$ (b) $2y$ (c) $2x$ (d) $- 2z.$

ANSWERS

  1. (b)   **2.** (b)   **3.** (b)   **4.** (b)   **5.** (a)   **6.** (b)   **7.** (c)   **8.** (d)

II. Fill in the Blanks

Note : *Fill in the blanks "........" so that the following statements are complete and correct.*

1. One generator of each system passes through every ..... of a hyperboloid.

2. The locus of the point of intersection of perpendicular generator of $\dfrac{x^2}{a^2} + \dfrac{y^2}{b^2} - \dfrac{z^2}{c^2} = 1$

is $x^2 + y^2 + z^2 =$ ......

3. No two generators of the same system of a hyperboloid ..... .

4. If three points of any straight line lie on the conicoid $F(x, y, z) = 0$, then the line ..... on the conicoid.

5. The locus of the point of intersection of perpendicular generator of the hyperbolic

paraboloid $\dfrac{x^2}{a^2} - \dfrac{y^2}{b^2} = 2z$ is ..... $+ 2z = 0.$

6. Any two generators of different systems of a hyperbolic paraboloid ..... .

7. The locus of the central points of generators of a hyperboloid is called its line of ..... .

8. A straight line will be a generator of a quadric if ..... points of the line lie on the quadric.

ANSWERS

  1. point;   **2.** $a^2 + b^2 + c^2$;   **3.** intersect;   **4.** wholly lies;

  5. $a^2 - b^2$;   **6.** intersect;   **7.** striction;   **8.** three.

III. True/False Statements

Note : *Write 'T' for true and 'F' for false statements.*

1. Any two generators of different systems of a hyperbolic paraboloid do not intersect.

2. Two generators of the same system of a hyperboloid of one sheet always intersect.

3. One generator of each system passes through every point of hyperboloid of one sheet.

4. The locus of the central points of generators of a hyperboloid is called its line of striction.

5. The locus of the point of intersection of perpendicular generators of hyperboloid of one

sheet, *viz.*, $\dfrac{x^2}{a^2} + \dfrac{y^2}{b^2} - \dfrac{z^2}{c^2} = 1$ is $x^2 + y^2 + z^2 = ab + bc + ca.$

6. If three points of any straight line lie on a hyperboloid of one sheet then the line wholly lies on it.

ANSWERS

1. F   **2.** F   **3.** T   **4.** T   **5.** F   **6.** T

REVISION EXERCISES III

1. Prove that if θ is the angle between the central radius to the point $P(x, y, z)$ on the ellipsoid $x^2/a^2 + y^2/b^2 + z^2/c^2 = 1$ and the normal at P, then

$$\tan^2 \theta = \Sigma \, y^2 z^2 \left(\frac{1}{b^2} - \frac{1}{c^2} \right).$$

2. Prove that the common tangents of the three ellipsoids

$$\frac{x^2}{a^2} + \frac{y^2}{b^2} + \frac{z^2}{c^2} = 1, \quad \frac{x^2}{b^2} + \frac{y^2}{c^2} + \frac{z^2}{a^2} = 1, \quad \frac{x^2}{c^2} + \frac{y^2}{a^2} + \frac{z^2}{b^2} = 1,$$

touch a sphere of radius

$$\left(\frac{a^2 + b^2 + c^2}{3} \right)^{1/2}$$

and that the points of contact of the planes lie on a sphere of radius

$$\left(\frac{a^4 + b^4 + c^4}{a^2 + b^2 + c^2} \right)^{1/2}$$

3. Show that if three central radii of an ellipsoid be mutually perpendicular, the plane passing through their extremities will envelope a sphere.

4. Prove that six normals can be drawn from any point P to a central quadric surface and that these six normals are generators of a quadric cone with vertex at P.

Prove that the conic in which the cone meets any one of the principal planes of the quadric surface remains fixed when P moves along a straight line perpendicular to that plane.

5. Show that the length of the normal chord at any point (x, y, z) of the ellipsoid

$$x^2/a^2 + y^2/b^2 + z^2/c^2 = 1$$

is

$$2q^4 4p^2,$$

where

$$\frac{1}{p^2} = \frac{x^2}{a^4} + \frac{y^2}{b^4} + \frac{z^2}{c^4}; \quad \frac{1}{q^4} = \frac{x^2}{a^6} + \frac{y^2}{b^6} + \frac{z^2}{c^6}.$$

6. If p_1, p_2, p_3 and π_1, π_2, π_3 be the perpendiculars from the extremities P_1, P_2, P_3 of conjugate semi-diameters on the two central circular sections of the ellipsoid

$$x^2/a^2 + y^2/b^2 + z^2/c^2 = 1,$$

then

$$p_1\pi_1 + p_2\pi_2 + p_3\pi_3 = \frac{a^2 c^2 (a^2 + c^2 + 2b^2)}{a^2 - c^2}.$$

7. Show that the locus of points on the quadric $ax^2 + by^2 + cz^2 = 1$, the normals at which intersect the straight line

$$\frac{x - \alpha}{l} = \frac{y - \beta}{m} = \frac{z - \gamma}{n}$$

is the curve of intersection with the quadric

$$l(b - c) yz + m(c - a) zx + n(a - b) xy - (n\beta - m\gamma) ax$$
$$- (l\gamma - n\alpha) by - (m\alpha - l\beta) cz = 0.$$

8. If $r_1, r_2, r_3, r_4, r_5, r_6$ are the lengths of the normals drawn from any point to a central conicoid and $p_1, p_2, p_3, p_4, p_5, p_6$ are the lengths of the perpendiculars from its centre to the tangent planes at their feet, then $p_1r_1 + p_2r_2 + p_3r_3 + p_4r_4 + p_5r_5 + p_6r_6$ is constant.

9. Two planes are drawn through the six feet of the normals drawn to the ellipsoid $x^2/a^2 + y^2/b^2 + z^2/c^2 = 1$ from a given point (f, g, h); each plane containing three; prove that if (α, β, γ), $(\alpha', \beta', \gamma')$ be the poles of these planes with respect to the ellipsoid, then,

$$\alpha\alpha' + a^2 = \beta\beta' + b^2 = \gamma\gamma' + c^2$$

and $$f(\alpha + \alpha') + g(\beta + \beta') + h(\gamma + \gamma') = 0.$$

10. If three of the feet of the normals from a point to the ellipsoid $x^2/a^2 + y^2/b^2 + z^2/c^2 = 1$ lie on the plane $lx + my + nz = p$, show that the equation of the plane through the other three is

$$\frac{x}{a^2 l} + \frac{y}{b^2 m} + \frac{z}{c^2 n} + \frac{1}{p} = 0.$$

Also, show that if one of the planes contains the extremities of three conjugate semi-diameters, the other plane cuts co-ordinate planes in triangle whose centroid lies on a coaxial ellipsoid.

11. Pairs of planes are drawn which are conjugate with respect to the ellipsoid

$$x^2/a^2 + y^2/b^2 + z^2/c^2 = 1,$$

the first member of each pair passing through the line

$$y = mz, \quad z = k$$

and the second member of each pair passing through the line

$$y = -mx, \quad z = -k;$$

prove that the line of intersection of the two members of any pair lie on the surface

$$(b^2 - a^2m^2)(z^2 - k^2) + (y^2 - m^2x^2)(c^2 + k^2) = 0.$$

12. The normal to the ellipsoid $x^2/a^2 + y^2/b^2 + z^2/c^2 = 1$, at a point P meets the plane $z = 0$ at G and GQ is drawn perpendicular to this plane and equal to CP. Show that the locus of Q is the surface

$$\frac{x^2}{a^2 - c^2} + \frac{y^2}{b^2 - c^2} + \frac{z^2}{c^2} = 1.$$

Show also that if N is the foot of the perpendicular from P to the principal plane on which G lies and the normal at Q to its locus meets this plane at K, then G is the mid-point of KN.

13. Through a given point (α, β, γ) planes are drawn parallel to three conjugate diametral planes of the ellipsoid $x^2/a^2 + y^2/b^2 + z^2/c^2 = 1$. Show that the sum of the ratios of the areas of the sections by these planes to the areas of the parallel central planes is

$$3 - \frac{\alpha^2}{a^2} - \frac{\beta^2}{b^2} - \frac{\gamma^2}{c^2}.$$

14. If A_1, A_2, A_3 are the areas of the sections of the ellipsoid $x^2/a^2 + y^2/b^2 + z^2/c^2 = 1$ be the diametral planes of three mutually perpendicular semi-diameters of lengths r_1, r_2, r_3, show that

$$\frac{A_1^2}{r_1^2} + \frac{A_2^2}{r_2^2} + \frac{A_3^2}{r_3^2} = \pi^2 \left(\frac{b^2c^2}{a^2} + \frac{c^2a^2}{b^2} + \frac{a^2b^2}{c^2} \right).$$

15. If through a given point (f, g, h) lines be drawn each of which is an axis of some plane section of $ax^2 + by^2 + cz^2 = 1$, such lines describe the cone

$$\frac{af(b-c)}{x-f} + \frac{bg(c-a)}{y-g} + \frac{ch(a-b)}{z-h} = 0.$$

16. If a plane $lx + my + nz = p$ cuts the surface $ax^2 + by^2 + cz^2 = 1$ in a parabolic section, prove that the direction cosines of its axis are proportional to l/a, m/b, n/c and the co-ordinates of the vertex of the parabola satisfy the equation

$$\frac{ax}{l}\left(\frac{1}{b} - \frac{1}{c}\right) + \frac{by}{m}\left(\frac{1}{c} - \frac{1}{a}\right) + \frac{cz}{n}\left(\frac{1}{a} - \frac{1}{b}\right) = 0.$$

17. Prove that the generating lines through any point P on the section $z = c$ of the hyperboloid $x^2/a^2 + y^2/b^2 - z^2/c^2 = 1$ meet the principal section by the plane $z = 0$ at the ends of a pair of conjugate diameters.

18. The generators of opposite systems drawn through the extremities A, B of semi-conjugate diameters of the principal elliptic section of the hyperboloid $x^2/a^2 + y^2/b^2 - z^2/c^2 = 1$ meet in P; show that the median through P of the triangle PAB lies on the cone

$$\frac{2x^2}{a^2} + \frac{2y^2}{b^2} = \left(\frac{z}{c} \pm 1\right)^2.$$

19. Prove that tangent planes to $x^2/a^2 + y^2/b^2 - z^2/c^2 = 1$ which are parallel to the tangent planes to

$$\frac{x^2}{\dfrac{1}{b^2} - \dfrac{1}{c^2}} + \frac{y^2}{\dfrac{1}{a^2} - \dfrac{1}{c^2}} + \frac{z^2}{\dfrac{1}{a^2} - \dfrac{1}{b^2}} = 0$$

meet the surface in perpendicular generators.

20. Show that the generators of the surface $x^2 + y^2 - z^2 = 1$ which intersect on XOY plane are at right angles.

21. Show that the points on the quadric $ax^2 + by^2 + cz^2 + d = 0$, at which the generators are perpendicular lie on the cylinder

$$(b - a) x^2 + (c - b) y^2 + cd(a + b)/ab = 0.$$

22. If $(a \cos \theta \sec \varphi,\ b \sin \theta \sec \varphi,\ c \tan \varphi)$ is a point on the generating line

$$\frac{x}{a} + \frac{z}{c} = \lambda\left(1 + \frac{y}{b}\right),\quad \frac{x}{a} - \frac{z}{c} = \frac{1}{\lambda}\left(1 - \frac{y}{b}\right)$$

of the hyperboloid $x^2/a^2 + y^2/b^2 - z^2/c^2 = 1$, prove that for points along the generator, $(\theta - \varphi)$ is constant.

23. Generators through P of $\dfrac{x^2}{a^2} + \dfrac{y^2}{b^2} - \dfrac{z^2}{c^2} = 1$ meet the principal elliptic section in A and B. If the median of the triangle APB through P is parallel to a fixed plane $\alpha x + \beta y + \gamma z = 0$, show that P lies on the surface

$$z(\alpha x + \beta y) + \gamma(c^2 + z^2) = 0.$$

24. Prove that if the generators of $\dfrac{x^2}{a^2} + \dfrac{y^2}{b^2} - \dfrac{z^2}{c^2} = 1$ be drawn through the points where it is met by a tangent to $z = 0$, $\dfrac{x^2}{a^2(a^2 + c^2)} + \dfrac{y^2}{b^2(b^2 + c^2)} = \dfrac{1}{a^2 + b^2}$ they form a

skew-quadrilateral with two opposite angles, right angles and the other diagonal of which is a generator of the cylinder

$$\frac{x^2 (a^2 + c^2)}{a^2} + \frac{y^2 (b^2 + c^2)}{b^2} = (a^2 + b^2).$$

25. Prove that the perpendicular from the origin on the generators of the hyperboloid

$$\frac{x^2}{a^2} + \frac{y^2}{b^2} - \frac{z^2}{c^2} = 1$$

lies on the cone

$$\frac{a^2 (b^2 + c^2)^2}{x^2} + \frac{b^2 (a^2 + c^2)^2}{y^2} = \frac{c^2 (a^2 - b^2)^2}{z^2}.$$

26. Show that the most general quadric surface which has the lines

$$x = 0, y = 0; \ x = 0, z = c; \ y = 0, z = -c$$

as generators is

$$fy (z - c) + gx (z + c) + hxy = 0$$

where f, g, h are arbitrary constants.

27. Find equations in symmetrical form for the line of intersection of the two planes whose equations are

$$x + y = 2 (\lambda + \mu) (z - 1), \ (x - y) = 2 (\lambda - \mu) (z - 1),$$

where λ and μ are constants. Find also the co-ordinates of the point in which this line meets the plane $z = 0$.

If now λ and μ are taken to be variable parameters connected by the relation $\lambda^2 + \mu^2 = 1$, show that the line traces out a right circular cone.

11

General Equation of the Second Degree

11.1. REDUCTION TO CANONICAL FORMS AND CLASSIFICATION

A quadric has been defined as the locus of a point satisfying an equation of the second degree. Thus, a quadric is the locus of a point satisfying an equation of the type

$$F(x, y, z) \equiv ax^2 + by^2 + cz^2 + 2fyz + 2gzx + 2hxy + 2ux + 2vy + 2wz + d = 0$$

which we may rewrite as

$$\Sigma (ax^2 + 2fyz) + 2\Sigma ux + d = 0 \qquad \text{...(1)}$$

splitting the set of all terms into three homogeneous subsets.

We have considered so far special forms of the equations of the second degree in order to discuss *geometrical* properties of the various types of quadrics. In this chapter we shall see how the general equation of a second degree by means of an appropriate change of co-ordinate system can be reduced to simpler forms and also thus classify the types of quadrics.

Equations of various loci connected with a given quadric. We proceed to determine the equations of various loci associated with a quadric given by a general second degree equation. In this connection, we shall start obtaining a quadric in r, which will play a very important role in connection with the determination of the equations of these loci.

Consider a point (α, β, γ) and a line through the same with direction cosines (l, m, n). The co-ordinates of the point on this line at a distance r from (α, β, γ) are

$$(lr + \alpha, \ mr + \beta, \ nr + \gamma).$$

This point will lie on the quadric

$$F(x, y, z) \equiv \Sigma (ax^2 + 2fyz) + 2\Sigma ux + d = 0$$

for values of r satisfying the equation

$$\Sigma [a (lr + \alpha)^2 + 2f (mr + \beta) (nr + \gamma)] + 2\Sigma u (lr + \alpha) + d = 0$$

$$\Leftrightarrow \quad r^2 \Sigma (al^2 + 2fmn) + 2r [l (a\alpha + h\beta + g\gamma + u) + m (h\alpha + b\beta + f\gamma + v)$$
$$+ n (g\alpha + f\beta + c\gamma + w) + F (\alpha, \beta, \gamma) = 0 \qquad \text{...(2)}$$

which is a quadric in r. Thus, if r_1, r_2 be the roots of this quadric, the two points of intersection of the line with the quadric are

$$(lr_1 + \alpha, \ mr_1 + \beta, \ nr_1 + \gamma), \ (lr_2 + \alpha, \ mr_2 + \beta, \ nr_2 + \gamma).$$

Note. It may be noted that the equation (2) can be rewritten as

$$r^2 \Sigma (al^2 + 2fmn) + r \left(l \frac{\partial F}{\partial \alpha} + m \frac{\partial F}{\partial \beta} + n \frac{\partial F}{\partial \gamma} \right) + F (\alpha, \beta, \gamma) = 0$$

where $\partial F/\partial \alpha$, $\partial F/\partial \beta$, $\partial F/\partial \gamma$ denote the values of the partial derivatives of F, w.r.t. x, y, z respectively at the point (α, β, γ).

11.1.1. The tangent plane at a point.

Suppose that the point (α, β, γ) lies on the quadric so that we have

$$F(\alpha, \beta, \gamma) = 0$$

and one root of the quadric equation (2) is zero. The vanishing of value of r is also a simple consequence of the fact that one of the two points of intersection of the quadric with every line through a point of the quadric coincides with the point in question.

A line through the point (α, β, γ) on the quadric with direction cosines (l, m, n) will be a tangent line if the second point of intersection also coincides with (α, β, γ), *i.e.*, if the second value of r, as given by (2) is also zero. This will be so if the coefficient of r is also zero, *i.e.*, if

$$l(a\alpha + h\beta + g\gamma + u) + m(h\alpha + b\beta + f\gamma + v) + n(g\alpha + f\beta + c\gamma + w) = 0 \qquad ...(3)$$

which is thus the condition for the line

$$\frac{x - \alpha}{l} = \frac{y - \beta}{m} = \frac{z - \gamma}{n} \qquad ...(4)$$

to be a tangent line at the point (α, β, γ). The locus of the tangent lines through (α, β, γ), obtained on eliminating l, m, n between (3) and (4) is

$$\Sigma(x - a)(a\alpha + h\beta + g\gamma + u) = 0$$

$$\Leftrightarrow \qquad \Sigma x(a\alpha + h\beta + g\gamma + u) = \Sigma\alpha(a\alpha + h\beta + g\gamma + u)$$

Adding $u\alpha + v\beta + w\gamma + d$ to both sides, we get

$$\Sigma x(a\alpha + h\beta + g\gamma + u) + (u\alpha + v\beta + g\gamma + d) = F(\alpha, \beta, \gamma) = 0$$

Thus, the locus of the tangent lines (α, β, γ) is

$$\Sigma x(a\alpha + h\beta + g\gamma + u) + (u\alpha + v\beta + w\gamma + d) = 0$$

which is a plane called the *tangent plane* at (α, β, γ).

11.1.2. The normal at a point

The line through (α, β, γ), perpendicular to the tangent plane thereat, *viz.*,

$$\frac{x - \alpha}{a\alpha + h\beta + g\gamma + u} = \frac{y - \beta}{h\alpha + b\beta + f\gamma + v} = \frac{z - \gamma}{g\alpha + f\beta + c\gamma + w}$$

is the normal at the point (α, β, γ).

11.1.3. Enveloping cone from a point

Suppose now that (α, β, γ) is a point not necessarily on the quadric. Then any line through (α, β, γ) with direction cosines (l, m, n) will touch the quadric, *i.e.*, meet the same in two coincident points, if the two roots of the quadric equation in r, are equal. The condition for this is

$$[\Sigma l(a\alpha + h\beta + g\gamma + u)]^2 = \Sigma(al^2 + 2fmn)F(\alpha, \beta, \gamma) \qquad ...(5)$$

The locus of the line

$$\frac{x - \alpha}{l} = \frac{y - \beta}{m} = \frac{z - \gamma}{n} \qquad ...(6)$$

through (α, β, γ) touching the quadric, obtained on eliminating l, m, n between (5) and (6), is

$$[\Sigma(x - \alpha)(a\alpha + h\beta + g\gamma + u)]^2 = [\Sigma a(x - \alpha)^2 + 2f(y - \beta)(z - \gamma)]F(\alpha, \beta, \gamma) \qquad ...(7)$$

To put this equation in a convenient form, we write

$$S = F(x, y, z), \ S_1 = F(\alpha, \beta, \gamma), \ T = \Sigma x(a\alpha + h\beta + g\gamma + u) + (u\alpha + v\beta + w\gamma + d)$$

Then (7) can be written as

$$(T - S_1)^2 = S_1(S + S_1 - 2T)$$

$$\Leftrightarrow \qquad SS_1 = T^2$$

which is the *equation of the Enveloping cone of the quadric $S = 0$ with the point (α, β, γ) as its vertex*.

11.1.4. Enveloping cylinder

Suppose now that (l, m, n) are given and we require the locus of tangent lines with direction cosines (l, m, n). If (α, β, γ) be a point on any such tangent line, we have the condition

$$[\Sigma l (a\alpha + h\beta + g\gamma + u)]^2 = [\Sigma (al^2 + 2fmn)] F (\alpha, \beta, \gamma)$$

as obtained in § 11.1.3 above. Thus, the required locus is

$$[\Sigma l (ax + hy + gz + u)]^2 = \Sigma (al^2 + 2fmn) F (x, y, z)$$

known as Enveloping Cylinder.

This is the equation of the enveloping cylinder of the quadric $F (x, y, z) = 0$ with generators parallel to the line with direction cosines (l, m, n).

11.1.5. Section with a given centre

Suppose now that (α, β, γ) is a given point. Then a chord with direction cosines (l, m, n) through the point (α, β, γ) will be bisected thereat if the sum of the two roots of the r-quadratic (2) is zero. This will be so, if and only if

$$\Sigma l (a\alpha + h\beta + g\gamma + u) = 0 \qquad \qquad ...(8)$$

so that the locus of the chord

$$\frac{x - \alpha}{l} = \frac{y - \beta}{m} = \frac{z - \gamma}{n} \qquad \qquad ...(9)$$

through the point (α, β, γ) and bisected thereat, obtained on eliminating l, m, n from the relations (8) and (9) is

$$\Sigma (x - \alpha) (a\alpha + h\beta + g\gamma + u) = 0$$

which, we may rewrite as,

$$T = S_1.$$

The *plane* $T = S_1$, *meets the quadric in a conic with its centre at* (α, β, γ).

11.2. POLAR PLANE OF A POINT

If a line through a point $A (\alpha, \beta, \gamma)$ meets the quadric in points Q, R and a point P is taken on the line such that the points A and P divide the segment QR internally and externally in the same ratio, then the locus of P for different lines through A is a plane called the *Polar plane* of the point A with respect to the quadric. It is easily seen that if the points A and P divide the segment QR internally and externally in the same ratio, then the points Q and R also divide the segment AP internally and externally in the same ratio.

Consider a line through the point $A (\alpha, \beta, \gamma)$ and let P be the point (x, y, z). The point dividing the segment AP in the ratio $\lambda : 1$ is

$$\left(\frac{\lambda x + \alpha}{\lambda + 1}, \frac{\lambda y + \beta}{\lambda + 1}, \frac{\lambda z + \gamma}{\lambda + 1} \right).$$

This point will lie on the quadric

$$\Sigma (ax^2 + 2fyz) + 2\Sigma ux + d = 0$$

if

$$\Sigma \left[a \left(\frac{\lambda x + \alpha}{\lambda + 1} \right)^2 + 2f \left(\frac{\lambda y + \beta}{\lambda + 1} \right) \left(\frac{\lambda z + \gamma}{\lambda + 1} \right) \right] + 2\Sigma u \left(\frac{\lambda x + \alpha}{\lambda + 1} \right) + d = 0$$

$\Leftrightarrow$
$$\lambda^2 F (x, y, z) + 2\lambda [x (a\alpha + h\beta + g\gamma + u) + y (h\alpha + b\beta + f\gamma + v)$$
$$+ z (g\alpha + f\beta + c\gamma + w) + (u\alpha + v\beta + w\gamma + d)] + F (\alpha, \beta, \gamma) = 0$$

The two values of λ give the two ratios in which the points Q and R divide the segment AP. In order that the points Q and R may divide the segment AP internally and externally in the same ratio, the sum of the two values of λ should be zero, *i.e.*,

$$x (a\alpha + h\beta + g\gamma + u) + y (h\alpha + b\beta + f\gamma + v) + z (g\alpha + f\beta + c\gamma + w)$$
$$+ (u\alpha + v\beta + w\gamma + d) = 0 \quad ...(10)$$

which is the required locus of the point $P (x, y, z)$.

Thus, (10) is the required equation of the polar plane.

Note. The notions of *Conjugate points*, *Conjugate planes*, *Conjugate lines* and *Polar lines* can be introduced as in the case of particular forms of equations in the preceding chapters.

11.3. DIAMETRAL PLANE CONJUGATE TO A GIVEN DIRECTION

We know [Refer equation (2), page 307] that if (l, m, n) be the direction cosines of a chord and (x, y, z) the mid-point of the same, then we have

$$l \frac{\partial F}{\partial x} + m \frac{\partial F}{\partial y} + n \frac{\partial F}{\partial z} = 0 \qquad ...(1)$$

Thus, if l, m, n be supposed to be given, then the equation of the locus of the mid-point (x, y, z) of parallel chords with direction cosines (l, m, n) is given by (1) above. This locus is a plane called the *Diametral plane conjugate to the direction cosines* (l, m, n). We can rewrite *the equation* (1) *of the diametral plane conjugate to* l, m, n *as*

$$x (al + hm + gn) + y (hl + bm + fn) + z (gl + fm + cn) + (ul + vm + wn) = 0 \quad ...(2)$$

Note. In this connection we should remember that there does not necessarily correspond a diametral plane conjugate to *every* given direction. Thus, we see from above that there is no diametral plane conjugate to the direction cosines (l, m, n) if l, m, n are such that the coefficients of x, y, z in the equation (2) are all zero. Thus, there will be no diametral plane corresponding to a direction whose direction cosines (l, m, n) satisfy the three relations

$$al + hm + gn = 0$$
$$hl + bm + fn = 0$$
$$gl + fm + cn = 0$$

These three homogeneous linear equations in l, m, n will have a non-zero solution, if and only if

$$D = \begin{vmatrix} a & h & g \\ h & b & f \\ g & f & c \end{vmatrix} = 0.$$

We also denote by A, B, C, the co-factors of a, b, c in this determinant so that we have $A = bc - f^2, B = ca - g^2, C = ab - h^2$.

11.4. PRINCIPAL DIRECTIONS AND PRINCIPAL PLANES

A direction l, m, n is said to be a *Principal direction*, if it is perpendicular to the diametral plane conjugate to the same. Also then the corresponding conjugate diametral plane is called a *Principal plane* in that the chords perpendicular to itself are bisected by it.

Thus, l, m, n will be a principal direction if and only if the direction ratios

$$al + hm + gn, \ hl + bm + fn, \ gl + fm + cn$$

of the normal to the corresponding conjugate diametral plane are proportional to l, m, n, *i.e.*, if and only if there exists a number λ such that

$$al + hm + gn = l\lambda$$
$$hl + bm + fn = m\lambda$$
$$gl + fm + cn = n\lambda$$

We rewrite these as

$$(a - \lambda)\, l + hm + gn = 0 \qquad\qquad ...(1)$$
$$hl + (b - \lambda)\, m + fn = 0 \qquad\qquad ...(2)$$
$$gl + fm + (c - \lambda)\, n = 0 \qquad\qquad ...(3)$$

These three linear homogeneous equations in l, m, n will possess a non-zero solution in l, m, n, if and only if

$$\begin{vmatrix} a - \lambda & h & g \\ h & b - \lambda & f \\ g & f & c - \lambda \end{vmatrix} = 0.$$

On expanding this determinant, we see that λ must be a root of the cubic

$$\lambda^3 - \lambda^2 (a + b + c) + \lambda (A + B + C) - D = 0 \qquad\qquad ...(4)$$

This cubic is known as the **Discriminating cubic** and each root of the same is called a **Characteristic root.**

The eqn. (4) has three roots which may not all be real or distinct. Also to each real root of (4) corresponds at least one principal direction l, m, n obtained on solving any two of the eqns. (1), (2) and (3).

Note 1. If l, m, n be a principal direction corresponding to a real root λ of the discriminating cubic, then we may easily see that the equation of the corresponding principal plane takes the form

$$\lambda\, (lx + my + nz) + (ul + vm + wn) = 0.$$

This equation shows that we shall have no principal plane corresponding to $\lambda = 0$ if $\lambda = 0$ is a root of the discriminating cubic. In spite of this, however, we shall find it useful to say that l, m, n is a principal direction corresponding to $\lambda = 0$. Thus, every direction l, m, n satisfying the eqns. (1), (2), (3) corresponding to a root λ of the discriminating cubic (4) will be called a *Principal direction*.

Note 2. In the following, we shall prove some important results concerning the nature of the roots of the discriminating cubic and the **existence** of principal directions and principal planes.

Before taking up this consideration, we give a few preliminary results of algebraic character in the following section.

11.5. SOME PRELIMINARIES TO REDUCTION AND CLASSIFICATION

In this section we shall state some points which will prove useful in relation to the problem of reduction and classification.

In the following discussion, the determinant

$$\begin{vmatrix} a & h & g \\ h & b & f \\ g & f & c \end{vmatrix}$$

to be denoted by D will play an important part.

We may verify that

$$D = abc + 2fgh - af^2 - bg^2 - ch^2.$$

As usual, A, B, C, F, G, H will denote the co-factors of a, b, c, f, g, h respectively in the determinant D, so that we have

$$A = bc - f^2, \quad B = ca - g^2, \quad C = ab - h^2;$$
$$F = gh - af, \quad G = hf - bg, \quad H = fg - ch$$

It can be easily verified that

$$\left. \begin{array}{l} BC - F^2 = aD, \quad CA - G^2 = bD, \quad AB - H^2 = cD; \\ GH - AF = fD, \quad HF - BG = gD, \quad FG - CH = hD \end{array} \right\} \qquad \text{...}(i)$$

Also we have

$$aA + bH + gG = D, \quad hA + bH + fG = 0, \quad gA + fH + cG = 0;$$
$$aH + hB + gF = 0, \quad hH + bB + fF = D, \quad gH + fB + cF = 0;$$
$$aG + hF + gC = 0, \quad hG + bF + fC = 0, \quad gG + fF + cC = D.$$

11.5.1. If $D = 0$, then from (i), we have

$$BC = F^2, \qquad\qquad CA = G^2, \qquad\qquad AB = H^2,$$
$$GH = AF, \qquad\qquad HF = BG, \qquad\qquad FG = CH.$$

Ex. Show that

(i) $D = 0$ and $A = 0 \implies H = 0$, $G = 0$,

(ii) $D = 0$ and $H = 0 \implies A = 0$, $H = 0$, $C = 0$ or $H = 0$, $B = 0$, $F = 0$.

Further prove that if $D = 0$, $A = 0$, $B = 0$, then F, G, H must all be zero but G may or may not be zero.

11.5.2. If $D = 0$ and $A + B + C = 0$, then

$$A, B, C, F, G, H$$

are all zero.

Now $D = 0 \implies BC = F^2$, $CA = G^2$, $AB = H^2$

$\implies$ A, B, C are all of the same sign.

Now A, B, C being all of the same sign,

$$A + B + C = 0 \implies A = 0, B = 0, C = 0.$$

Further A, B, C being zero

$$F^2 = BC, B = 0, C = 0$$

$\implies$ $F = 0$

Similarly $G = 0, H = 0.$

Note. Three homogeneous linear equations

$$a_1x + b_1y + c_1z = 0, \ a_2x + b_2y + c_2z = 0, \ a_3x + b_3y + c_3z = 0$$

will possess a non-zero solution, *i.e.*, a solution wherefor x, y, z are not all zero, if and only if

$$\begin{vmatrix} a_1 & b_1 & c_1 \\ a_2 & b_2 & c_2 \\ a_3 & b_3 & c_3 \end{vmatrix} = 0.$$

11.6. THEOREM I

The roots of the discriminating cubic are all real.

We, of course, suppose that the coefficients of the equation $F(x, y, z) = 0$ are all real.

Suppose that λ is a root of the discriminating cubic (4), page 363, and l, m, n is any non-zero set of values satisfying the corresponding eqns. (1), (2), (3), page 363.

Here it should be remembered that we cannot regard l, m, n as real, for λ is not yet proved to be real.

In the following, the complex conjugate of any number will be expressed by putting a bar over the same. Thus, $\bar{l}$, $\bar{m}$, $\bar{n}$ will denote the complex conjugate of the numbers l, m, n respectively.

Now, we have

$$al + hm + gn = l\lambda, \quad hl + bm + fn = m\lambda, \quad gl + fm + cn = n\lambda.$$

Multiplying these by $\bar{l}$, $\bar{m}$, $\bar{n}$ respectively and adding, we obtain

$$\Sigma al\bar{l} + \Sigma f\,(\bar{m}n + m\bar{n}) = \lambda \Sigma l\bar{l} \qquad \text{...(1)}$$

Now, a, b, c, f, g, h are real. Also

$$l\bar{l}, \; m\bar{m}, \; n\bar{n}$$

being the products of pairs of conjugate complex numbers, are real.

Also we notice that $m\bar{n}$ is the conjugate complex of $\bar{m}n$ so that

$$m\bar{n} + \bar{m}n$$

is real.

Similarly

$$n\bar{l} + \bar{n}l, \; l\bar{m} + \bar{l}m$$

are real.

Finally $\Sigma l\bar{l}$ is a non-zero real number.

Thus, λ, being the ratio of two real numbers from (1), is necessarily a real number.

Hence, the roots of the discriminating cubic are all real. Also, therefore, the numbers l, m, n corresponding to each λ are real.

11.6.1. Theorem II

The two principal directions corresponding to any two distinct roots of the discriminating cubic are perpendicular.

Suppose that λ_1, λ_2 are two distinct roots of the discriminating cubic, and

$$l_1, \; m_1, \; n_1; \; l_2, \; m_2, \; n_2$$

are the two corresponding principal directions.

We then have

(2) $al_1 + hm_1 + gn_1 = \lambda_1 l_1$,   (5) $al_2 + hm_2 + gn_2 = \lambda_2 l_2$,

(3) $hl_1 + bm_1 + fn_1 = \lambda_1 m_1$,   (6) $hl_2 + bm_2 + fn_2 = \lambda_2 m_2$,

(4) $gl_1 + fm_1 + cn_1 = \lambda_1 n_1$,   (7) $gl_2 + fm_2 + cn_2 = \lambda_2 n_2$.

Multiplying (2), (3), (4) by l_2, m_2, n_2 respectively and adding, we obtain

$$\Sigma al_1 l_2 + \Sigma f\,(m_1 n_2 + m_2 n_1) = \lambda_1 \Sigma l_1 l_2 \qquad \text{...(8)}$$

Also multiplying (5), (6), (7) by l_1, m_1, n_1 respectively and adding, we obtain

$$\Sigma al_1 l_2 + \Sigma f\,(m_1 n_2 + m_2 n_1) = \lambda_2 \Sigma l_1 l_2 \qquad \text{...(9)}$$

From (8) and (9), we obtain

$$\lambda_1 \Sigma l_1 l_2 = \lambda_2 \Sigma l_1 l_2$$

$$\Rightarrow \qquad (\lambda_1 - \lambda_2)\, \Sigma l_1 l_2 = 0$$

$$\Rightarrow \qquad \Sigma l_1 l_2 = 0, \text{ for } \lambda_1 - \lambda_2 \neq 0.$$

Thus, the two directions are perpendicular. Hence, the theorem.

11.6.2. Theorem III

For every quadric, there exists at least one set of three mutually perpendicular principal directions.

We have to consider the following three cases :

(A) The roots of the discriminating cubic are all distinct.

(B) Two of the roots are equal and the third is different from these.

(C) The three roots are all equal.

These three cases will be considered one by one.

(A) **Case of three distinct roots.** The roots being distinct, there will correspond a principal direction l, m, n satisfying the equation (1), (2), (3) on page 312 to each of these.

Also by Theorem II, these three directions will be mutually perpendicular. The three principal directions are unique in this case.

Thus, there exist three principal directions in this case. Moreover, these directions are as well unique in this case.

(B) **Case of two equal roots.** Let the discriminating cubic have two equal roots and let the third root be different from the same.

Suppose λ is a root of the D-cubic repeated twice so that λ satisfies the equation

$$\lambda^3 - \lambda^2 (a + b + c) + \lambda (A + B + C) - D = 0 \qquad \text{...(10)}$$

and the equation $\qquad 3\lambda^2 - 2\lambda (a + b + c) + (A + B + C) = 0 \qquad \text{...(11)}$

obtained on differentiating the cubic (10) with respect to λ. We write these as

$$(a - \lambda) (b - \lambda) (c - \lambda) + 2fgh - (a - \lambda) f^2 - (b - \lambda) g^2 - (c - \lambda) h^2 = 0$$

$$[(b - \lambda) (c - \lambda) - f^2] + [(c - \lambda) (a - \lambda) - g^2] [(a + \lambda) (b - \lambda) - h^2] = 0$$

Here we have two relations corresponding to

$$D = 0, A + B + C = 0$$

obtained on replacing $\qquad a, b, c$ by $a - \lambda, b - \lambda, c - \lambda$

respectively.

Thus, we conclude that (Refer § 11.5.2, page 313)

$$\begin{cases} (b - \lambda)(c - \lambda) = f^2, \ (c - \lambda)(a - \lambda) = g^2, \ (a - \lambda)(b - \lambda) = h^2 \\ (a - \lambda) f - gh, \qquad (b - \lambda) g = hf, \qquad (c - \lambda) h = fg \end{cases} \qquad \text{...(12)}$$

corresponding to $A \equiv 0, B = 0, C = 0; F = 0, G = 0, H = 0$. These relations show that the equation

$$(a - \lambda) l + hm + gn = 0$$

$$hl + (b - \lambda) m + fn = 0$$

$$gl + fm + (c - \lambda) n = 0$$

for the determination of l, m, n are all equivalent.

Thus, we see that if λ is a twice repeated root, the direction cosines (l, m, n) satisfy the single relation

$$(a - \lambda) l + hm + gn = 0 \qquad \text{...(13)}$$

Suppose now that l_1, m_1, n_1 is any direction satisfying equation (13).* Further we determine a direction l_2, m_2, n_2 satisfying equation (13) and perpendicular to the direction l_1, m_1, n_1. Thus, l_2, m_2, n_2 are determined from

$$(a - \lambda) l_2 + hm_2 + gn_2 = 0$$

$$l_1 l_2 + m_1 m_2 + n_1 n_2 = 0$$

---

* If desired, l_1, m_1, n_1 may be selected further so as to satisfy some additional suitable condition.

The principal direction corresponding to the third root of the discriminating cubic will, of course, be perpendicular to each of the two principal directions

$$l_1, m_1, n_1; l_2, m_2, n_2.$$

Thus, in this case also we have a set of three mutually perpendicular principal directions. Of course, they are not unique in this case.

(C) **Case of all three roots equal.** Suppose now that all the three roots are equal to λ. The root λ satisfies the three equations

$$\lambda^3 - \lambda^2 (a + b + c) \lambda (A + B + C) - D = 0 \qquad \text{[by eqn. (10)]}$$
$$3\lambda^2 - 2\lambda (a + b + c) + (A + B + C) = 0 \qquad \text{[by eqn. (11)]}$$
$$3\lambda - (a + b + c) = 0 \qquad \qquad ...(14)$$

In this case also the relation (12), page 366 as deduced from (10) and (11) are true.

We rewrite (14) as

$$(a - \lambda) + (b - \lambda) + (c - \lambda) = 0 \qquad \qquad ...(15)$$

Also, we have

$$(b - \lambda)(c - \lambda) = f^2, (c - \lambda)(a - \lambda) = g^2, (a - \lambda)(b - \lambda) = h^2 \qquad ...(16)$$

From (16), we see that

$$a - \lambda, b - \lambda, c - \lambda$$

must all have the same sign so that with the help of (15), it follows that

$$a - \lambda = 0, b - \lambda = 0, c - \lambda = 0$$
$$\Rightarrow \qquad \qquad \lambda = a = b = c.$$

Also then it follows that $f = 0$, $g = 0$, $h = 0$.

We now see that in thisj case the equations

$$(a - \lambda) l + hm + gn = 0, hl + (b - \lambda) m + fn = 0, gl + fm + (c - \lambda) n = 0$$

for the determination of the principal directions are identically satisfied, *i.e.*, they are true for arbitrary values of l, m, n, so that *every direction is a principal direction* in this case.

Thus, in this case also a quadric has a set of three mutually perpendicular principal directions. In fact, any set of three mutually perpendicular directions is a set of three mutually perpendicular principal directions in this case.

The reader may observe that the quadric is a sphere in the last case.

EXAMPLE

Find a set of three mutually perpendicular principal directions for the following conicoids :
1. $3x^2 + 5y^2 + 3z^2 - 2yz + 2zx - 2xy + 2z = 0.$
2. $8x^2 + 7y^2 + 3z^2 - 8yz + 4zx - 12xy + 2x - 8y + 1 = 0.$
3. $6x^2 + 3y^2 + 3z^2 - 2yz + 4zx - 4xy - 3y + 5z = 0.$

Sol. 1. We have $a = 3$, $b = 5$, $c = 3$, $f = -1$, $g = 1$, $h = -1$.

Therefore, the discriminating cubic is

$$\begin{vmatrix} 3 - \lambda & -1 & 1 \\ -1 & 5 - \lambda & -1 \\ 1 & -1 & 3 - \lambda \end{vmatrix} = 0$$

$$\Leftrightarrow \qquad -\lambda^3 + 11\lambda^2 - 36\lambda + 36 = 0$$

Its root are $\qquad\qquad\qquad\qquad \lambda = 2, 3, 6$

so that the characteristic roots are all different.

The principal direction corresponding to $\lambda = 2$ is given by

$$l - m + n = 0$$
$$-l + 3m - n = 0$$
$$l - m + n = 0$$

$\Rightarrow \qquad\qquad\qquad\qquad l : m : n = 1 : 0 : -1$

Thus, the principal direction corresponding to $\lambda = 2$ is given by

$$1/\sqrt{2}, \, 0, \, -1/\sqrt{2}.$$

Again the principal direction corresponding to $\lambda = 3$ is given by

$$0 \cdot l - m + n = 0,$$
$$-l + 2m - n = 0,$$
$$l - m + 0 \cdot n = 0.$$

$\Rightarrow \qquad\qquad\qquad\qquad l : m : n = 1 : 1 : 1$

and we have the corresponding principal direction

$$1/\sqrt{3}, \, 1/\sqrt{3}, \, 1/\sqrt{3}.$$

Finally the principal direction corresponding to $\lambda = 6$ is given by

$$-3l - m + n = 0$$
$$-l - m - n = 0$$
$$l - m - 3n = 0$$

wherefrom we may see that this principal direction is

$$1/\sqrt{6}, \, -2/\sqrt{6}, \, 1/\sqrt{6}.$$

The principal planes corresponding to the characteristic root λ being

$$\lambda \, (lx + my + nz) + (ul + vm + wn) = 0.$$

We see that the three principal planes are

$$2x - 2z - 1 = 0, \, 3x + 3y + 3z + 1 = 0, \, 6x - 12y + 6z + 1 = 0.$$

2. We have $a = 8, \, b = 7, \, c = 3, \, f = -4, \, g = 2, \, h = -6$.

Therefore, the discriminating cubic is

$$\begin{vmatrix} 8 - \lambda & -6 & 2 \\ -6 & 7 - \lambda & -4 \\ 2 & -4 & 3 - \lambda \end{vmatrix} = 0$$

$\Rightarrow \qquad -\lambda^3 + 18\lambda^2 - 45\lambda = 0$

$\Rightarrow \qquad\qquad\qquad\qquad \lambda = 0, \, 3, \, 15.$

Thus, 0, 3, 15 are three **distinct** characteristic roots.

The principal direction $l, \, m, \, n$ corresponding to $\lambda = 0$ is given by

$$8l - 6m + 2n = 0$$
$$-6l + 7m - 4n = 0$$
$$2l - 4m + 3n = 0$$

Solving these, we see that $\qquad\qquad l : m : n = 1 : 2 : 2.$

Thus, the principal direction corresponding to $\lambda = 0$ is given by

$$1/3, \, 2/3, \, 2/3.$$

Again the principal direction corresponding to $\lambda = 3$ is given by

$$5l - 6m + 2n = 0$$
$$- 6l + 4m - 4n = 0$$
$$2l - 4m + 0 \cdot n = 0$$

These give $\qquad\qquad l : m : n = 2 : 1 : - 2$

so that the corresponding principal direction is given by

$$2/3, 1/3, -2/3.$$

Finally the principal direction corresponding to $\lambda = 15$ is given by

$$- 7l - 6m + 2n = 0$$
$$- 6l - 8m - 4n = 0$$
$$2l - 4m - 12n = 0$$

which give $\qquad\qquad l : m : n = 2 : - 2 : 1$

so that the corresponding principal direction is given by

$$2/3, -2/3, 1/3.$$

The reader may verify that the three directions are mutually perpendicular.

The principal plane corresponding to the characteristic root λ being

$$\lambda (lx + my + nz) + (ul + vm + wn) = 0$$

we may see that the two principal planes corresponding to the non-zero values 3, 15 of λ are

$$3 (2x + y - 2z) + (- 2) = 0 \iff 6x + 3y - 6z - 2 = 0$$

and $\qquad\qquad 15 (2x - 2y + z) + 10 = 0 \iff 6x - 6y + 3z + 2 = 0.$

3. We have $a = 6, b = 3, c = 3, f = - 1, g = 2, h = - 2.$

The discriminating cubic is

$$\begin{vmatrix} 6 - \lambda & - 2 & 2 \\ - 2 & 3 - \lambda & - 1 \\ 2 & - 1 & 3 - \lambda \end{vmatrix} = 0$$

$$\Rightarrow \qquad - \lambda^3 + 12\lambda^2 - 36\lambda + 32 = 0$$

whose roots are 2, 2, 8. Thus, two of the characteristic roots are equal. Firstly we consider the non-repeated root 8. The principal direction corresponding to this is given by

$$- 2l - 2m + 2n = 0$$
$$- 2l - 5m - 2n = 0$$
$$2l - m - 5n = 0$$

$$\Rightarrow \qquad\qquad l : m : n = 2 : - 1 : 1$$

so that the principal direction corresponding to $\lambda = 8$ is given by

$$2/\sqrt{6}, -2/\sqrt{6}, 1/\sqrt{6}.$$

Again the principal direction corresponding to $\lambda = 2$ is given by

$$4l - 2m + 2n = 0$$
$$- 2l + m - n = 0$$
$$2l - m + n = 0$$

These three equations for the determination of l, m, n are all equivalent as has been shown for the general case.

Thus, every l, m, n satisfying the single equation

$$2l - m + n = 0 \qquad \qquad ...(1)$$

determines a principal direction. Consider any set of values of l, m, n satisfying (1), say

$$-1, -1, 1$$

We write $\qquad\qquad\qquad l_1 : m_1 : n_1 = -1 : -1 : 1.$

Then we determine l_2, m_2, n_2 satisfying (1) and perpendicular to l_1, m_1, n_1.

Thus,

$$-2l_2 - m_2 + n_2 = 0$$
$$-l_2 - m_2 + n_2 = 0$$
$$\Rightarrow \qquad\qquad l_2 : m_2 : n_2 = 0 : 1 : 1$$

Thus, we have obtained a set of three mutually perpendicular principal directions given by

$$1/\sqrt{6}, -1/\sqrt{6}, 1/\sqrt{6}; \; 1/\sqrt{3}, -1/\sqrt{3}, 1/\sqrt{3}; \; 0, 1/\sqrt{2}, 1/\sqrt{2}.$$

The choice of principal directions is **not** unique in the present case as two of the characteristic roots are equal.

Note. It may be verified that every direction perpendicular to the principal direction corresponding to the non-repeated root 8 is a principal direction for the twice repeated root 2.

EXERCISES

Examine the following quadrics for principal directions and principal planes :

1. $4x^2 - y^2 - z^2 + 2yz - 8x - 4y + 8z = 0.$
2. $x^2 + 2yz - 4x + 6y + 2z = 0.$
3. $4y^2 - 4yz - 4zx - 4xy - 2x + 2y - 1 = 0.$
4. $3x^2 - y^2 - z^2 + 6yz - 6x + 6y - 2z - 2 = 0.$

ANSWERS

1. Principal directions : $1, 0, 0; \; 0, 1/\sqrt{2}, -1/\sqrt{2}; \; 0, 1/\sqrt{2}, 1/\sqrt{2}.$

   Principal planes : $x = 1, \; y - z + 3 = 0.$

2. Principal directions : $0, 1/\sqrt{2}, -1/\sqrt{2}$ and every direction perpendicular to it.

   Principal planes : $y - z - 2 = 0$ and every plane through the line, $y + z + 4 = 0, \; x = 2.$

3. Principal directions : $1/\sqrt{3}, 1/\sqrt{3}, 1/\sqrt{3}; \; 1/\sqrt{6}, -2/\sqrt{6}, 1/\sqrt{6}; \; 1/\sqrt{2}, 0, -1/\sqrt{2}.$

   Principal planes : Any plane at right angle to $x = y = z - 1/2$, $2\,(x - 2y + z) = 1$, $2\,(x - z) + 1 = 0.$

4. Principal directions : $0, 1/\sqrt{2}, 1/\sqrt{2}; \; 1, 0, 0; \; 0, 1/\sqrt{2}, -1/\sqrt{2}.$

   Principal planes : $y + z + 1 = 0, \; x = 1, \; y - z = 1.$

11.6.3. Centre

We know that if a point (x, y, z) is the mid-point of a chord with direction cosines (l, m, n) of a quadric

$$F(x, y, z) = 0$$

then we have

$$l\frac{\partial F}{\partial x} + m\frac{\partial F}{\partial y} + n\frac{\partial F}{\partial z} = 0 \qquad\qquad ...(1)$$

This shows that if (x, y, z) is such that

$$\frac{\partial F}{\partial x} = 0, \frac{\partial F}{\partial y} = 0, \frac{\partial F}{\partial z} = 0$$

then the condition (1) is satisfied, whatever values l, m, n may have, implying that every chord through (x, y, z) is bisected thereat. Such a point is known as a **Centre** of the quadric. We can rewrite these equations as

$$ax + hy + gz + u = 0 \qquad\qquad\qquad ...(2)$$
$$hx + by + fz + v = 0 \qquad\qquad\qquad ...(3)$$
$$gx + fy + cz + w = 0 \qquad\qquad\qquad ...(4)$$

It should be remembered that a quadric may or may not have a centre; also it may have more than one centre — *a line of centres* or *a plane of centres*, depending upon the nature of the solutions of the three equations (2), (3), (4).

In the following, we shall consider the different cases regarding the possible solutions of these equations. This discussion will be facilitated a good deal, if regarding x, y, z as variables, we consider the three planes represented by these equations. We have thus to examine the nature of the points of intersection, if any, of these three planes to be called *Central planes*.

Before we proceed to consider the problem of the existence of the centre of a quadric, we state a preliminary result.

11.6.4. The two planes

$$p_1x + q_1y + r_1z + s_1 = 0$$
$$p_2x + q_2y + r_2z + s_2 = 0$$

will be

(*i*) same if

$$\begin{vmatrix} p_1 & q_1 \\ p_2 & q_2 \end{vmatrix} = 0, \begin{vmatrix} q_1 & r_1 \\ q_2 & r_2 \end{vmatrix} = 0, \begin{vmatrix} r_1 & s_1 \\ r_2 & s_2 \end{vmatrix} = 0$$

(*ii*) parallel but not same if

$$\begin{vmatrix} p_1 & q_1 \\ p_2 & q_2 \end{vmatrix} = 0, \begin{vmatrix} q_1 & r_1 \\ q_2 & r_2 \end{vmatrix} = 0, \begin{vmatrix} r_1 & s_1 \\ r_2 & s_2 \end{vmatrix} \neq 0$$

(*iii*) neither parallel nor same, *i.e.*, will intersect in a straight line if

$$\begin{vmatrix} p_1 & q_1 \\ p_2 & q_2 \end{vmatrix} \neq 0 \text{ or } \begin{vmatrix} q_1 & r_1 \\ q_2 & r_2 \end{vmatrix} \neq 0.$$

11.7. CASE OF A UNIQUE CENTRE

Multiplying the equations (2), (3), (4) by A, H, G respectively and adding, we obtain

$$Dx + (Au + Hv + Gw) = 0 \qquad\qquad \text{(Refer § 11.5.2, page 313)}$$

Again, on multiplying (2), (3), (4) by H, B, F and by G, F, C and adding separately, we obtain

$$Dy + (Hu + Bv + Fw) = 0$$
$$Dz + (Gu + Fv + Cw) = 0$$

If $D \neq 0$, we obtain from these

$$x = -(Au + Hv + Gw)/D, \ y = -(Hu + Bv + Fw)/D, \ z = -(Gu + Fv + Cw)/D$$

Substituting these in (2), (3), (4) we may easily verify that the same are satisfied.

Thus, if $D \neq 0$, the quadric has a unique centre (x, y, z) where (x, y, z) have the values given above.

11.7.1. Case of No Centre

Now suppose that D = 0. Then, we have

$$A(ax + hy + gz + u) + H(hx + by + fz + y) + G(gx + fy + cz + w) \equiv Au + Hv + Gw$$

(Refer § 11.5.1, page 364)

This shows that the three equations cannot have a common solution, *i.e.*, the quadric will not have a centre if

$$Au + Hv + Gw \neq 0.$$

Considering H, B, F and G, F, C as sets of multipliers instead of A, H, G, we may similarly see that the quadric will not have a centre if

$$Hu + Bv + Fw \neq 0 \text{ or if } Gu + Fv + Cw \neq 0.$$

Thus, we see that *the quadric will* **not** *have a centre if D = 0 and any one of*

$$Au + Hv + Gw, \; Hu + Bv + Fw, \; Gu + Fv + Cw$$

is not zero.

11.7.2. Case of a Line of Centres

We now suppose that D = 0 as well as Au + Hv + Gw = 0.

Then we have

$$A(ax + hy + gz + u) + H(hx + by + fz + v) + G(gx + fy + cz + w) = 0.$$

(*i*) Thus, if $A \neq 0$, we have

$$ax + hy + gz + u = -\frac{H}{A}(hx + by + fz + v) - \frac{G}{A}(gx + fy + cz + w)$$

(*ii*) Also, if $A \neq 0$, the two planes

$$hx + by + fz + v = 0$$
$$gx + fy + cz + w = 0$$

are neither the same nor parallel so that they intersect in a line. This is because

$$\begin{vmatrix} b & f \\ f & c \end{vmatrix} = A \neq 0 \qquad \text{[Refer § 11.6.4, page 371]}$$

From (*i*) and (*ii*), we deduce that the plane

$$ax + hy + gz + u = 0$$

passes through the line of intersection of the two intersecting planes

$$hx + by + fz + v = 0, \; gx + fy + cz + w = 0$$

Thus, in case

$$D = 0, \; Au + Hv + Gw = 0, \; A \neq 0$$

the three central planes all pass through one line so that we have a line of centres.

We may similarly see that the quadric will have a line of centres if

$$D = 0, \; Hu + Bv + Fw = 0, \; B \neq 0$$

or if

$$D = 0, \; Gu + Fv + Cw = 0, \; C \neq 0$$

Note 1. We can show that if $D = 0$, and $A \neq 0$ and $Au + Hv + Gw = 0$, then we must also simultaneously have

$$Hu + Bv + Fw = 0, \; Gu + Fv + Cw = 0$$

In fact we have

$$A(Hu + Bv + Fw) \equiv H(Au + Hv + Gw)$$

and

$$A(Gu + Fv + Cw) \equiv G(Au + Hv + Gw)$$

the equalities holding for all values of u, v and w. Thus, if $A \neq 0$, we have

$$Hu + Bv + Fw = \frac{H}{A}(Au + Hv + Gw)$$

$$Gu + Fv + Cw = \frac{G}{A}(Au + Hv + Cw)$$

The result stated now follows.

It may be remembered that if $A = 0$ then also $H = 0$, $G = 0$, so that $Au + Hv + Gw \equiv 0$. In this case when $A = 0$, $H = 0$, $G = 0$, we may not have

$$Hu + Bv + Fw = 0 \text{ or } Gu + Fv + Cw = 0.$$

For example, consider

$$x^2 + 2y^2 + 2xy + 2x + y + 2z + 3 = 0$$

Here $a = 1$, $b = 2$, $c = 0$, $f = 0$, $g = 0$, $h = 1$, $u = 1$, $v = 1/2$, $w = 1$,

so that $\qquad A = 0$, $B = 0$, $C = 1$, $F = 0$, $G = 0$, $H = 0$, $D = 0$.

Thus, we have $Au + Hv + Gw = 0$ but $Gu + Fv + Cw \neq 0$.

Note 2. The cases treated above cover the cases when $D = 0$ and one at least of A, B, C is not zero.

If we suppose that A, B, C are all zero, then it follows that F, G, H are also all zero, for

$$F^2 = BC, \quad G^2 = CA, \quad H^2 = AB$$

In the next sub-section we consider the case when A, B, C, F, G, H are all zero. The vanishing of D then follows from the vanishing of these co-factors in as much as we have

$$D = Aa + Hh + Gg,$$

so that $D = 0$ even if A, H, G only are known to be zero.

11.7.3. Case of no centre

Suppose now that A, B, C, F, G, H are all zero, so that $D = 0$ also.

We have in this case,

(1) $\begin{cases} f(ax + hy + gz + u) - g(hx + by + fz + v) = fu - gv \\ f(ax + hy + gz + u) - h(gx + fy + cz + w) = fu - hw \end{cases}$

These show that if

$$fu - gv \neq 0 \text{ or } fu - hw \neq 0,$$

then the quadric cannot have a centre.

11.7.4. Case of a plane of centres

Suppose now that

$$fu - gv = 0 \text{ and } fu - hw = 0$$

$\Leftrightarrow \qquad fu = gv = hw.$

Then if $g \neq 0$, $h \neq 0$, we have from (1) above in § 11.7.3 that

$$hx + by + fz + v = \frac{f}{g}(ax + hy + gz + u)$$

$$gx + fy + cz + w = \frac{f}{h}(ax + hy + gz + u)$$

so that every point of the plane

$$ax + hy + gz + u = 0$$

is also a point of the other two central planes. Thus, we have a plane of centres in this case.

Similarly we may show that if

$$fu = gv = hw$$

and some two of f, g, h are not zero, then the quadric has a plane of centres.

Note. It can be easily seen that if A, B, C, F, G, H are zero and one of f, g, h is known to be zero, then one more of f, g, h must also be zero. For instance, suppose that $f = 0$. Then, because

$$0 = F = gh - af$$

it follows that either g or h must also be zero. Thus, the case treated here can be stated as follows :

If A, B, C, F, G, H are all zero, none of f, g, h is zero and $fu = gv = hw$, then the quadric has a line of centres.

The case where one and, therefore, two of f, g, h are zero is treated below here.

11.7.5. Now *suppose that two of f, g, h are zero in addition to A, B, C, F, G, H being all zero and $fu = gv = hw$.*

Let $g = 0 = h$ and $f \neq 0$. In this case we see from (1) above, § 11.7.3, page 325 that

$$ax + hy + gz + u = 0$$

so that $a = 0, h = 0, g = 0, u = 0$.

The vanishing of u also follows from the fact that

$$fu = gv = hw \text{ and } g = 0, h = 0, f \neq 0.$$

Consider now the two central planes

$$hx + by + fz + v = 0$$
$$gx + fy + cz + w = 0$$

the coefficients of the third central plane being all zero. As h and g are both zero, we can rewrite these as

$$by + fz + v = 0$$
$$fy + cz + w = 0$$

Here
$$\begin{vmatrix} b & f \\ f & c \end{vmatrix} = bc - f^2 = A = 0, \qquad \begin{vmatrix} f & v \\ c & w \end{vmatrix} = fw - cv$$

Thus, if $fw - cv \neq 0$, the quadric has no centre and if $fw - cv = 0$, the quadric has a plane of centres.

We can obtain similar conditions, when

$$f = 0 = h, g \neq 0$$

or when
$$f = 0 = g, h \neq 0.$$

11.7.6. Now *suppose* that f, g, h are all zero in addition to the vanishing of A, B, C, F, G, H.

In this case two of a, b, c must be zero. Suppose that $b = c = 0$ and $a \neq 0$. Then the first of the three central planes is

$$ax + u = 0$$

and the other two are

$$0x + 0y + 0z + v = 0$$
$$0x + 0y + 0z + w = 0$$

Thus, if $v \neq 0$ or $w \neq 0$ the quadric has no centre and if $v = 0 = w$, the quadric has a plane of centres.

SUMMARY OF THE VARIOUS CASES

1. $D \neq 0$. Unique centre.

2. $\begin{cases} D = 0, \ Au + Hv + Gw \neq 0. \text{ No centre.} \\ D = 0, \ Hu + Bv + Fw \neq 0. \text{ No centre.} \\ D = 0, \ Gu + Fv + Cw \neq 0. \text{ No centre.} \end{cases}$

3. $\begin{cases} D = 0, \ Au + Hv + Fw = 0, \ A \neq 0. \text{ Line of centres.} \\ D = 0, \ Hu + Bv + Gw = 0, \ B \neq 0. \text{ Line of centres.} \\ D = 0, \ Gu + Fv + Cw = 0, \ C \neq 0. \text{ Line of centres.} \end{cases}$

4. A, B, C, F, G, H all zero, $fu \neq gv$ or $gv \neq hw$. No centre.

5. A, B, C, F, G, H all zero, $fu = gv = hw, f \neq 0, g \neq 0, h \neq 0$. Plane of centres.

6. A, B, C, F, G, H all zero, $fu = gv = hw, g = 0, h = 0, f \neq 0, fw - cv \neq 0$. No centre.

7. A, B, C, F, G, H all zero, $fu = gv = hw, g = 0, h = 0, f \neq 0, fw - cv = 0$. Plane of centres.

   We may have results similar to (6) and (7), when $f = 0, g = 0, h \neq 0$ or when $h = 0, f = 0$, $g \neq 0$.

8. A, B, C, F, G, H all zero, f, g, h all zero. Then two of a, b, c must be zero and one non-zero. Then we have no centre if

$$a \neq 0, \ v \neq 0 \text{ or } w \neq 0$$

and a plane of centres if

$$a \neq 0, \ v = 0 = w.$$

We have similar results when $b \neq 0$ or $c \neq 0$.

Note. The results given above need not be committed to memory.

EXERCISE

Examine the following quadrics for centres :

1. $z^2 - yz + zx + xy - 2y + 2z + 2 = 0$.   [**Ans.** Unique centre; $(1, 1, -1)$]

2. $2z^2 - 2yz - 2zx + 2xy + 3x - y - 2z + 1 = 0$.

$$\left[\textbf{Ans. } \text{Line of centres; } \frac{x}{1} = \frac{y+2}{1} = \frac{2z+1}{2} \right]$$

3. $4x^2 + 9y^2 + 4z^2 + 12xy + 12yz + 8zx + 3x + 4y + z = 0$.   [**Ans.** No centre]

4. $x^2 + y^2 + z^2 - 2xy - 2yz + 2zx + x - y + z = 0$.

     [**Ans.** Plane of centres; $2x - 2y + 2z + 1 = 0$]

5. $4x^2 - 2y^2 - 2z^2 + 5yz + 2zx + 2xy - x + 2y + 2z - 1 = 0$.   [**Ans.** No centre]

6. $2x^2 + 2y^2 + 5z^2 - 2yz - 2zx - 4xy - 14x - 14y + 16z + 6 = 0$.

     [**Ans.** Line of centres; $x = 3 - y, z + 1 = 0$]

7. $18x^2 + 2y^2 + 20z^2 - 12zx + 12yz + x - 22y - 6z + 1 = 0$.   [**Ans.** No centre]

8. $4x^2 - y^2 + 2z^2 + 2xy - 3yz + 12x - 11y + 6z + 4 = 0$.

     [**Ans.** Unique centre; $(-1, -2, -3)$]

11.8. TRANSFORMATION OF CO-ORDINATES

Before we take up the problem of actual reduction and classification, we shall consider two important cases of transformation of co-ordinates.

11.8.1. The Form of the Equation of a Quadric Referred to a Centre as Origin

We suppose that the given quadric has a centre.

Let (α, β, γ) be a centre of the quadric with equation

$$F(x, y, z) \equiv \Sigma(ax^2 + 2fyz) + 2\Sigma ux + d = 0$$

Consider now a new system of co-ordinate axes parallel to the given system and with its origin at (α, β, γ). The equation of the quadric, w.r.t. the new system, obtained on replacing x, y, z by $x + \alpha, y + \beta, z + \gamma$ respectively is

$$\Sigma[a(x + \alpha)^2 + 2f(y + \beta)(z + \gamma)] + 2\Sigma u(x + \alpha) + d = 0$$

$$\Leftrightarrow \quad \Sigma(ax^2 + 2fyz) + 2x(a\alpha + h\beta + g\gamma + u) + 2y(h\alpha + b\beta + f\gamma + v)$$
$$+ 2z(g\alpha + f\beta + c\gamma + w) + F(\alpha, \beta, \gamma) = 0$$

As (α, β, γ) is a centre, we have

$$a\alpha + h\beta + g\gamma + u = 0, \ h\alpha + b\beta + f\gamma + v = 0, \ g\alpha + f\beta + c\gamma + w = 0$$

Further, as may be easily seen

$$F(\alpha, \beta, \gamma) = \alpha(a\alpha + h\beta + g\gamma + u) + \beta(h\alpha + b\beta + f\gamma + v) + \gamma(g\alpha + f\beta + c\gamma + w)$$
$$+ (u\alpha + v\beta + w\gamma + d)$$

$$= u\alpha + v\beta + w\gamma + d$$

Thus, the required new equation is

$$\Sigma(ax^2 + 2fyz) + (u\alpha + v\beta + w\gamma + d) = 0.$$

It will be seen that the second degree homogeneous part of the equation has remained unchanged and the first degree terms have disappeared.

Note 1. The discussion above is applicable whether the quadric has one centre, a line of centres or a plane of centres. In case the quadric has more than one centre, (α, β, γ) may denote any one of them.

Note 2. The co-ordinates, w.r.t. the old as well as the new system of axes have both been denoted by the same symbols, x, y, z.

11.8.2. The Form of the Equation of a Quadric, When the Co-ordinate Axes are Parallel to a Set of Three Mutually Perpendicular Principal Directions

Suppose that

$$(l_1, m_1, n_1); \ (l_2, m_2, n_2); \ (l_3, m_3, n_3) \qquad \qquad ...(1)$$

are the direction cosines of three mutually perpendicular principal directions corresponding to the three roots

$$\lambda_1, \lambda_2, \lambda_3$$

of the discriminating cubic. These roots may not be all different.

We take now a new co-ordinate system through the same origin such that the axes of the new system are parallel to the directions given by (1) above.

The equation referred to the new system of axes is obtained on replacing

$$x, y, z$$

by $\qquad \qquad l_1x + l_2y + l_3z, \ m_1x + m_2y + m_3z, \ n_1x + n_2y + n_3z$

respectively.

As homogeneous linear expressions are to be substituted for x, y, z, we may note that a homogeneous expression of any degree will be transformed to a homogeneous expression of the same degree.

Thus, we may separately consider the transforms of the homogeneous parts

$$\Sigma(ax^2 + 2fyz) \text{ and } 2\Sigma ux.$$

We shall show that the transform of the second degree homogeneous part

$$\Sigma\,(ax^2 + 2fyz) \qquad\qquad ...(2)$$
$$\lambda_1 x^2 + \lambda_2 y^2 + \lambda_3 z^2.$$

On direct substitution, we may see that the coefficient of x^2 in the transform of (2) is

$$al_1^2 + bm_1^2 + cn_1^2 + 2fm_1 n_1 + 2gn_1 l_1 + 2hl_1 m_1$$
$$= l_1\,(al_1 + hm_1 + gn_1) + m_1\,(hl_1 + bm_1 + fn_1) + n_1\,(gl_1 + fm_1 + cn_1)$$
$$= l_1\,(\lambda_1 l_1) + m_1\,(\lambda_1 m_1) + n_1\,(\lambda_1 n_1) = \lambda_1\,(l_1^2 + m_1^2 + n_1^2) = \lambda_1.$$

Similarly the coefficients of y^2 and z^2 in the transform can be shown to be

$$\cdot\lambda_2 \text{ and } \lambda_3$$

respectively.

Again the coefficient of $2yz$ in the transform of (1) is

$$= al_2 l_3 + bm_2 m_3 + cn_2 n_3 + f\,(m_2 n_3 + m_3 n_2) + g\,(n_2 l_3 + n_3 l_2) + h\,(l_2 m_3 + l_3 m_2)$$
$$= l_2\,(al_3 + hm_3 + gn_3) + m_2\,(hl_3 + bm_3 + fn_3) + n_2\,(gl_3 + fm_3 + cn_3)$$
$$= \lambda_3\,(l_2 l_3 + m_2 m_3 + n_2 n_3) = 0.$$

Similarly the coefficients of zx and xy in the transform can be seen to be zero.

Thus, the transform of

$$\Sigma\,(ax^2 + 2fyz)$$

is
$$\lambda_1 x^2 + \lambda_2 y^2 + \lambda_3 z^2$$

Finally, we see that the transform of

$$\Sigma\,(ax^2 + 2fyz) + 2\Sigma ux + d$$

is $\lambda_1 x^2 + \lambda_2 y^2 + \lambda_3 z^2 + 2u\,(l_1 x + l_2 y + l_3 z) + 2y\,(m_1 x + m_2 y + m_3 z) + 2w\,(n_1 x + n_2 y + n_3 z) +$
d

$$= \lambda_1 x^2 + \lambda_2 y^2 + \lambda_3 z^2 + 2x\,(ul_1 + vm_1 + wn_1) + 2y\,(ul_2 + vm_2 + wn_2)$$
$$+ 2z\,(ul_3 + vm_3 + wn_3) + d$$

11.9. REDUCTION TO CANONICAL FORMS AND CLASSIFICATION

We shall now consider the several cases one by one.

11.9.1. Case I. *When $D \neq 0$.* In this case the quadric has a unique centre and no root of the discriminating cubic is zero.

Shifting the origin to the centre (α, β, γ), the equation takes the form

$$\Sigma\,(ax^2 + 2fyz) + (u\alpha + v\beta + w\gamma + d) = 0 \qquad\qquad (\S\,11.8.1, \text{page } 376)$$

Now rotating the axes so that the axes of the new system are parallel to the set of three mutually perpendicular principal directions, we see that the equation becomes

$$\lambda_1 x^2 + \lambda_2 y^2 + \lambda_3 z^2 + (u\alpha + v\beta + w\gamma + d) = 0$$

which is the required canonical form.

Below we find an elegant form for the constant term.

We have

$$a\alpha + h\beta + g\gamma + u = 0 \qquad\qquad ...(1)$$
$$h\alpha + b\beta + f\gamma + v = 0 \qquad\qquad ...(2)$$
$$g\alpha + f\beta + c\gamma + w = 0 \qquad\qquad ...(3)$$

Also we write

$$u\alpha + v\beta + w\gamma + d = k$$

$$\Leftrightarrow \qquad u\alpha + v\beta + w\gamma + (d - k) = 0 \qquad \qquad ...(4)$$

Eliminating α, β, γ from (1), (2), (3) and (4), we obtain

$$\begin{vmatrix} a & h & g & u \\ h & b & f & v \\ g & f & c & w \\ u & v & w & (d-k) \end{vmatrix} = 0$$

$$\Leftrightarrow \qquad \begin{vmatrix} a & h & g & u \\ h & b & f & v \\ g & f & c & w \\ u & v & w & d \end{vmatrix} - \begin{vmatrix} a & h & g \\ h & b & f \\ g & f & c \end{vmatrix} k = 0$$

$$\Leftrightarrow \qquad k = \frac{\Delta}{D}, \ (D \neq 0)$$

where we have represented the fourth order determinant on the left by Δ.

We thus see that the new equation assumes the form

$$\lambda_1 x^2 + \lambda_2 y^2 + \lambda_3 z^2 + \Delta/D = 0.$$

The equation represents various types of surfaces as shown in the following table. It may be remembered that the word 'roots' refers to the characteristic roots :

	Given	*Conclusion*
$\Delta = 0$	Roots all > 0 or < 0	Imaginary cone.
$\Delta = 0$	Two roots > 0 and one < 0	Real cone.
$\Delta = 0$	Two roots < 0 and one > 0	Real cone.
$\Delta/D > 0$	Roots all > 0	Imaginary ellipsoid.
$\Delta/D > 0$	Roots all < 0	Real ellipsoid.
$\Delta/D > 0$	Two roots > 0 and one < 0	Hyperboloid of two sheets.
$\Delta/D > 0$	Two roots < 0 and one > 0	Hyperboloid of one sheet.
$\Delta/D < 0$	Roots all > 0	Real ellipsoid.
$\Delta/D < 0$	Roots all < 0	Imaginary ellipsoid.
$\Delta/D < 0$	Two roots > 0 and one < 0	Hyperboloid of one sheet.
$\Delta/D < 0$	Two roots < 0 and one > 0	Hyperboloid of two sheets.

11.9.2. Case II. *When $D = 0$, $Au + Hv + Gw \neq 0$.* In this case the quadric has no centre and the discriminating cubic has one zero root and two non-zero roots.

We denote the non-zero roots by λ_1, λ_2. The third root λ_3 is 0.

We rotate the co-ordinate axes through the same origin so that new axes are parallel to the set of three mutually perpendicular principal directions.

The new equation takes the form

$$\lambda_1 x^2 + \lambda_2 y^2 + 2x \, (ul_1 + vm_1 + wn_1) + 2y \, (ul_2 + vm_2 + wn_2) + 2z \, (ul_3 + vm_3 + wn_3) + d = 0$$
$$...(1)$$

where l_3, m_3, n_3 correspond to $\lambda_3 = 0$.

Here we notice that $\qquad\qquad ul_3 + vm_3 + wn_3 \neq 0$

If possible, let $ul_3 + vm_3 + wn_3 = 0$ ...(2)

We also have

$$hl_3 + bm_3 + fn_3 = 0$$ ...(3)

$$gl_3 + fm_3 + cn_3 = 0$$

As l_3, m_3, n_3 are not all zero, we have from (2), (3), (4)

$$\begin{vmatrix} u & v & w \\ h & b & f \\ g & f & c \end{vmatrix} = 0$$

$\Leftrightarrow$ $Au + Hv + Gw = 0$

which is contradictory to the given condition.

Denoting the coefficients of x, y, z by p, q, r, we rewrite (1) as

$\lambda_1 x^2 + \lambda_2 y^2 + 2px + 2qy + 2rz + d = 0$, where $r \neq 0$.

$$\Leftrightarrow \quad \lambda_1 \left(x + \frac{p}{\lambda_1} \right)^2 + \lambda_2 \left(y + \frac{q}{\lambda_2} \right)^2 + 2r \left[z + \frac{1}{2r} \left(d - \frac{p^2}{\lambda_1} - \frac{q^2}{\lambda_2} \right) \right] = 0$$

so that shifting the origin to the point

$$\left[-\frac{p}{\lambda_1}, -\frac{q}{\lambda_2}, -\frac{1}{2r} \left(d - \frac{p^2}{\lambda_1} - \frac{q^2}{\lambda_2} \right) \right],$$

we see that the equation takes the form

$$\lambda_1 x^2 + \lambda_2 y^2 + 2rz = 0$$

where $r = ul_3 + vm_3 + wn_3 \neq 0$.

This is the required canonical form in the present case.

This equation represents an elliptic or hyperbolic paraboloid according as λ_1, λ_2 are of the same or opposite signs.

Cor. Axis and vertex of the paraboloid. It is known that Z-axis is the axis and $(0, 0, 0)$ is the vertex of the paraboloid

$$\lambda_1 x^2 + \lambda_2 y^2 + 2rz = 0.$$

Also the principal directions of the paraboloid are those of the co-ordinate axes; the principal direction corresponding to the characteristic root zero being that of Z-axis and the principal direction corresponding to the non-zero roots λ_1, λ_2 being those of X-axis and Y-axis respectively. Further, it can be easily seen that the principal planes corresponding to the non-zero characteristic roots are the planes $x = 0$, $y = 0$ whose intersection Z-axis is the axis of the paraboloid. Thus, we have the following important and useful result :

The line of intersection of the principal planes corresponding to the non-zero characteristic roots is the axis and the point where the axis meets the paraboloid is the vertex. Also the axis is the line through the vertex parallel to the principal direction corresponding to the characteristic root zero.

11.9.3. Case III. *When $D = 0$, $Au + Hv + Gw = 0$, $A \neq 0$.* In this case the quadric has a line of centres and the discriminating cubic has one zero and two non-zero roots.

We may see that $A + B + C \neq 0$, for if it were so, then we would have A, B, C all zero and the condition $A \neq 0$, would be contradicted. Since $D = 0$ and $A + B + C \neq 0$, the discriminating cubic would have only one zero root.

Let (α, β, γ) be a centre. Shifting the origin to (α, β, γ) and rotating the axes so that the new axes are parallel to the set of mutually perpendicular principal directions, we see that the equation becomes

$$\lambda_1 x^2 + \lambda_2 y^2 + (u\alpha + v\beta + w\gamma + d) = 0$$

which is the required canonical form.

We may, as follows, obtain an expression for the constant term in a form free from α, β, γ. In this case the central planes all pass through one line.

*We select the following two equations of the centre giving

$$hx + by + fz + v = 0$$
$$gx + fy + cz + w = 0$$

so that they are different.

Now (α, β, γ) is a point satisfying these two equations. Taking $\alpha = 0$, we have

$$b\beta + f\gamma + v = 0$$
$$f\beta + c\gamma + w = 0$$

Also we write $v\beta + w\gamma + (d - k) = 0.$

These give

$$\begin{vmatrix} b & f & v \\ f & c & w \\ v & w & (d-k) \end{vmatrix} = 0 \implies k = \frac{1}{A}\begin{vmatrix} b & f & v \\ f & c & w \\ v & w & d \end{vmatrix}$$

Thus, the required canonical form is

$$\lambda_1 x^2 + \lambda_2 y^2 + k = 0.$$

The equation represents various types of surfaces as shown in the following table :

	Given	*Conclusion*
$k = 0$	Roots both > 0 or < 0	Imaginary pair of planes.
$k = 0$	One root > 0 and other < 0	Pair of intersecting planes.
$k > 0$	Roots both > 0	Imaginary cylinder.
$k > 0$	Roots both < 0	Elliptic cylinder.
$k > 0$	One root > 0 and other < 0	Hyperbolic cylinder.
$k < 0$	Roots both > 0	Elliptic cylinder.
$k < 0$	Roots both < 0	Imaginary cylinder.
$k < 0$	One root > 0 and other < 0	Hyperbolic cylinder.

Cor. 2. Axis of the Cylinder. The Z-axis is known to be the axis of the cylinder.

$$\lambda_1 x^2 + \lambda_2 y^2 + k = 0, \, k \neq 0.$$

As in the case of the paraboloid, we have the following result regarding the axis of the cylinder.

The axis of the cylinder is the line of intersection of the principal planes corresponding to the non-zero characteristic roots. Also, it is parallel to the principal direction corresponding to the characteristic root zero. The axis is also the line of centres.

Cor. 3. Planes bisecting the angles between two planes. It may be seen that planes bisecting the angles between the two planes

$$\lambda_1 x^2 + \lambda_2 y^2 = 0$$

are $x = 0, y = 0.$

---

* These are so selected that they are not the same. The condition $A \neq 0$ ensures the non-sameness of these two planes.

Thus, we see that *the two principal planes corresponding to the two non-zero characteristic roots are the two bisecting planes.*

Cor. 4. The homogeneous second degree equation

$$\Sigma\,(ax^2 + 2fyz) = 0$$

will represent a pair of planes if $D = 0$.

11.9.4. Case IV. *When A, B, C, F, G, H are all zero and $fu \neq gv$.*

In this case the quadric has no centre and two roots of the discriminating cubic are zero and one non-zero.

We rotate the axes so that the new axes are parallel to the three mutually perpendicular principal directions. The new equation takes the form

$$\lambda_1 x^2 + 2x\,(ul_1 + vm_1 + wn_1) + 2y\,(ul_2 + vm_2 + wn_2) + 2z\,(ul_3 + vm_3 + wn_3) + d = 0$$

As the two roots λ_2, λ_3 are equal, both being zero, we know that l_2, m_2, n_2 is *any* direction satisfying

$$al + hm + gn = 0 \qquad\qquad\qquad ...(1)$$

We suppose that l_2, m_2, n_2 are so chosen that these satisfy (1) and

$$ul_2 + vm_2 + wn_2 = 0 \qquad\qquad\qquad ...(2)$$

Then l_3, m_3, n_3 are chosen so as to satisfy (1) and

$$l_3 l_2 + m_3 m_2 + n_3 n_2 = 0$$

Denoting the coefficients of x and z by p, r, we rewrite the equation as

$$\lambda_1 x^2 + 2px + 2rz + d = 0 \qquad\qquad\qquad ...(3)$$

the coefficient of y being zero by (2).

Again we rewrite (3) as

$$\lambda_1 \left(x + \frac{p}{\lambda_1} \right)^2 + 2rz + \left(d - \frac{p^2}{\lambda_1} \right) = 0 \qquad\qquad ...(4)$$

Also we may see that $r \neq 0$, for otherwise the quadric will have a centre. Again, we rewrite (4) as

$$\lambda_1 \left(x + \frac{p}{\lambda_1} \right)^2 + 2r \left[z + \frac{1}{2r} \left(d - \frac{p^2}{\lambda_1} \right) \right] = 0$$

Shifting the origin to

$$\left[-\frac{p}{\lambda_1},\ 0,\ -\frac{1}{2r} \left(d - \frac{p^2}{\lambda_1} \right) \right]$$

we see that the equation becomes

$$\lambda_1 x^2 + 2rz = 0$$

which is the required canonical form.

The equation represents a parabolic cylinder in this case.

11.9.5. Case V. *When A, B, C, F, G, H are all zero, $fu = gv = hw$, and no one of f, g, h is zero.*

In this case the quadric has a plane of centres and the discriminating cubic has two zero and one non-zero root.

Let (α, β, γ) be a centre. Shifting the origin to (α, β, γ) and rotating the axes so that the axes of the new system are parallel to a set of three mutually perpendicular principal directions, we see that the equation becomes

$$\lambda_1 x^2 + (u\alpha + v\beta + w\gamma + d) = 0$$

The equation represents a pair of parallel or coincident planes.

Note. The case when any two or all of f, g, h are zero can be easily considered and it can be shown that we shall have a parabolic cylinder in case the quadric does not have a centre and a pair of parallel planes if the quadric has a plane of centres.

11.10. QUADRICS OF REVOLUTION

Firstly, we shall prove a lemma concerning surfaces of revolution obtained on revolving a plane curve about an axis of co-ordinates.

Lemma. *The equation of a surface of revolution obtained on revolving a plane curve about X-axis is of the form*

$$\sqrt{y^2 + z^2} = f(x)$$

Consider the surface of revolution on revolving a curve about X-axis. Let the equations of the section of this surface by the plane $z = 0$ be

$$y = f(x), z = 0$$

...(1)

If P be a point on the curve and M the foot of the perpendicular from P on X-axis, we have

$$OM = x, MP = y$$

so that we can rewrite

$$y = f(x) \text{ as } MP = f(OM). \qquad ...(2)$$

Now this relation remains unchanged as the curve revolves about the X-axis so that the point P describes a circle with M as its centre.

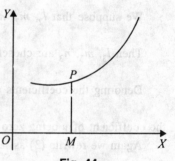

Fig. 44

In terms of the co-ordinates (x, y, z) of the point P in any position, we have

$$MP = \sqrt{y^2 + z^2}, OM = x$$

so that we can rewrite (2) as

$$\sqrt{y^2 + z^2} = f(x)$$

Hence, the result.

Similarly the equations of the surfaces of revolution obtained on revolving plane curves about Y-axis and Z-axis are of the form

$$\sqrt{z^2 + x^2} = \phi(y), \sqrt{x^2 + y^2} = \psi(z)$$

respectively.

Cor. *A quadric is a surface of revolution, if and only if, it has equal non-zero characteristic roots.* To see the truth of this result, we examine the various canonical forms which we have obtained. These are as follows :

Case I	$\lambda_1 x^2 + \lambda_2 y^2 + \lambda_3 z^2 + \Delta/D = 0$	...(1)
Case II	$\lambda_1 x^2 + \lambda_2 y^2 + 2rz = 0$	...(2)
Case III	$\lambda_1 x^2 + \lambda_2 y^2 + k = 0$	...(3)
Case IV	$\lambda_1 x^2 + 2rz = 0$	...(4)
Case V	$\lambda_1 x^2 + k = 0$	...(5)

On comparison with the equations of the surfaces of revolution we see that for the surface (1) to be that of revolution we must have two of λ_1, λ_2, λ_3 equal and for the surfaces (2) and (3) to be of revolution we must have $\lambda_1 = \lambda_2$. The quadrics (4) and (5) cannot be surfaces of revolution.

It will be seen that a necessary condition for a quadric to be a surface of revolution is that two of the characteristic roots are equal.

Clearly the equations (1) will represent a sphere if the characteristic roots λ_1, λ_2, λ_3 are all equal.

Hence, the result.

11.10.1. Condition for the general equation of the second degree to represent a quadric of revolution

Let the equation $\qquad \Sigma\,(ax^2 + 2fyz) + 2\Sigma ux + d = 0$
represent a surface of revolution so that two of the characteristic roots are equal, so that as shown in § 11.6.2 (B), page 315, we have the following two sets of necessary conditions :

$$(b - \lambda)\,(c - \lambda) = f^2,\ (c - \lambda)\,(a - \lambda) = g^2,\ (a - \lambda)\,(b - \lambda) = h^2 \qquad \text{...(I)}$$
$$gh = (a - \lambda)\,f,\ hf = (b - \lambda)\,g,\ fg = (c - \lambda)\,h. \qquad \text{...(II)}$$

λ denoting the twice repeated root.

11.10.2. Case I. *Firstly, suppose that none of f, g, h is zero.*

We show that in this case the set of conditions I and deducible from the Set II so that the Set I is not an independent set of conditions and can as such be ignored. Let us assume the Set II. Now

$$gh = (a - \lambda)\,f,\ hf = (b - \lambda)\,g$$
$$\Rightarrow \qquad fgh^2 = (a - \lambda)\,(b - \lambda)\,fg$$
$$\Rightarrow \qquad (a - \lambda)\,(b - \lambda) = h^2;\ fg\ \text{being not equal to zero.}$$

We may similarly deduce the other two conditions of the Set I from the set of conditions II.

Thus, if the given equation represents a surface of revolution and none of *f, g, h* is zero, we have

$$\lambda = a - \frac{gh}{f} = b - \frac{hf}{g} = c - \frac{fg}{h}$$

$$\Rightarrow \qquad a - \frac{gh}{f} = b - \frac{hf}{g} = c - \frac{fg}{h}$$

$$\Leftrightarrow \qquad \frac{F}{f} = \frac{G}{g} = \frac{H}{h} \qquad\qquad\qquad \text{...(III)}$$

Now we suppose that the conditions III are satisfied and show that the quadric is a surface of revolution.

Let $\qquad \dfrac{F}{f} = \dfrac{G}{g} = \dfrac{H}{h} = k$ (say)

$$\Leftrightarrow \qquad \frac{gh - af}{f} = \frac{hf - bg}{g} = \frac{fg - ch}{h} = k$$

$$\Leftrightarrow \qquad a = \frac{gh}{f} - k,\ b = \frac{hf}{g} - k,\ c = \frac{fg}{h} - k$$

Replacing *a, b, c* by $\dfrac{gh}{f} - k,\ \dfrac{hf}{g} - k,\ \dfrac{fg}{h} - k$, we get

$$F\,(x,\,y,\,z) = -\,k\,(x^2 + y^2 + z^2) + fgh\left(\frac{x}{f} + \frac{y}{g} + \frac{z}{h}\right) + 2ux + 2vy + 2wz + d$$

$$= -\,k\,(x^2 + y^2 + z^2) + 2ux + 2wz + d + fgh\left(\frac{x}{f} + \frac{y}{g} + \frac{z}{h}\right)^2$$

This form of the equation shows that every plane parallel to the plane

$$\frac{x}{f} + \frac{y}{g} + \frac{z}{h} = 0 \qquad \dots(1)$$

cuts the surface in a circle. Thus, the equation represents a surface of revolution and the axis of revolution, being the locus of the centres of the circular sections, is the line through the centre of the sphere

$$- k (x^2 + y^2 + z^2) + 2ux + 2vy + 2wz + d = 0$$

perpendicular to the plane (1). Thus, the axis of revolution is

$$\frac{x + \dfrac{u}{\lambda}}{1/f} = \frac{y + \dfrac{v}{\lambda}}{1/g} = \frac{z + \dfrac{w}{\lambda}}{1/h}.$$

We have thus shown that *if no one of f, g, h is zero, the necessary and sufficient condition for the equation*

$$\Sigma (ax^2 + 2fyz) + 2\Sigma ux + d = 0$$

to be a surface of revolution is

$$\frac{F}{f} = \frac{G}{g} = \frac{H}{h}.$$

11.10.3. Case II. *When any one of f, g, h is zero and not each one of f, g, h is zero.*

Suppose that $f = 0$.

Now $\qquad gh = (a - \lambda) f$ and $f = 0$

$\Rightarrow \qquad gh = 0 \Rightarrow g = 0$ or $h = 0$.

Since we have supposed that not each one of f, g, h is 0, both of g, h are not zero.

Let $g = 0$ and $h \neq 0$.

Now $\qquad f = 0, g = 0, h \neq 0$ and $fg = (c - \lambda) h$

$\Rightarrow \qquad \lambda = c$.

Also $\qquad (a - \lambda) (b - \lambda) = h^2$ and $\lambda = c$

$\Rightarrow \qquad (a - c) (b - c) = h^2$.

We have thus shown that if the given quadric is a surface of revolution and

$$f = 0, g = 0, h \neq 0$$

then we necessarily have the relation

$$(a - c) (b - c) = h^2$$

We now show that this condition is also sufficient.

Since $\qquad\qquad (a - c) (b - c) = h^2$

$a - c$ and $b - c$ must both be of the same sign. Suppose that they are both positive.

We have in this case

$$ax^2 + by^2 + cz^2 + 2fyz + 2gzx + 2hxy = (a - c) x^2 + (b - c) y^2$$

$$+ c (x^2 + y^2 + z^2) \pm \sqrt{2 (a - c) (b - c)}\, xy$$

$$= (\sqrt{a - c}\, x \pm \sqrt{b - c}\, y)^2 + c (x^2 + y^2 + z^2)$$

where actually we have no ambiguity of sign in that the sign is positive or negative according as h is positive or negative.

Thus, we see that planes parallel to the plane

$$\sqrt{(a - c)}\, x \pm \sqrt{(b - c)}\, y = 0$$

cut the surface in circular sections. Thus, the quadric is a surface of revolution, the axis of revolution being the line through the centre

$$(- u/c, - v/c, - w/c)$$

of the sphere

$$c\,(x^2 + y^2 + z^2) + 2ux + 2vy + 2wz + d = 0$$

perpendicular to the plane (4); viz., the line

$$\frac{x + u/c}{\sqrt{(a - c)}} = \pm \frac{y + v/c}{\sqrt{(b - c)}}, \; z + \frac{w}{c} = 0$$

We have thus shown *that if*

$$f = 0,\; g = 0,\; h \neq 0,$$

the necessary and sufficient condition for the equation

$$\Sigma\,(ax^2 + 2fyz) + 2\Sigma ux + d = 0$$

to represent a surface of revolution is

$$(a - c)\,(b - c) = h^2.$$

We may similarly consider the cases $g = 0$, $h = 0$, $f \neq 0$; and $f = 0$, $h = 0$, $g \neq 0$.

11.10.4. Case III. *When f, g, h are all zero.*

We have in this case from Set I,

$$(b - \lambda)\,(c - \lambda) = 0,\; (c - \lambda)\,(a - \lambda) = 0,\; (a - \lambda)\,(b - \lambda) = 0$$

These relations imply that we necessarily have

$$a = b \text{ or } b = c \text{ or } c = a$$

This can also be seen as follows. The three conditions imply that the three equations

$$\lambda^2 - \lambda\,(b + c) + bc = 0$$
$$\lambda^2 - \lambda\,(c + a) + ca = 0$$
$$\lambda^2 - \lambda\,(a + b) + ab = 0$$

are consistent. This means that we have the relations

$$\begin{vmatrix} 1 & b + c & bc \\ 1 & c + a & ca \\ 1 & a + b & ab \end{vmatrix} = 0$$

$\Rightarrow \qquad (a - b)\,(b - c)\; c - a) = 0$

$\Rightarrow \qquad a = b \text{ or } b = c \text{ or } c = a$

Thus, we see that if $f = g = h = 0$ and the given equation represents a surface of revolution, we necessarily have

$$a = b \text{ or } b = c \text{ or } c = a$$

We now show that the condition is as well sufficient

Let $a = b$.

We have in this case

$$\Sigma\,(ax^2 + 2fyz) + 2\Sigma ux + d = 0$$

$\Rightarrow \qquad [a\,(x^2 + y^2 + z^2) + 2\Sigma ux + d] + (c - a)\, z^2 = 0$

so that planes parallel to $z = 0$ cut the surface in circles implying that the given quadric is a surface of revolution.

The equations of the axis of revolution may now be easily obtained.

The cases $b = c$, $c = a$ may now be similarly discussed.

We have thus shown that if f, g, h are all zero, a necessary and sufficient condition for the quadric to be a surface of revolution is that

$$a = b \text{ or } b = c \text{ or } c = a.$$

11.11. REDUCTION OF EQUATIONS WITH NUMERICAL COEFFICIENTS

The manner in which we actually proceed in any given case depends upon whether the second degree terms do or do not form a perfect square.

Case I. *Suppose that the second degree terms form a perfect square.*

Thus, the given equation is of the form

$$(px + qy + rz)^2 + 2(ux + vy + wz) + d = 0 \qquad \ldots(1)$$

We rewrite it as

$$(px + qy + rz + t)^2 + 2(u - pt)x + 2(v - gt)y + 2(w - rt)z + (d - t^2) = 0 \qquad \ldots(2)$$

t, being any number whatsoever. Consider now the two planes

$$px + qy + rz = 0$$

$$(u - pt)x + (v - pt)y + (w - rt)z = 0$$

We so choose t that these planes are perpendicular to each other. Thus, t is given by

$$p(u - pt) + q(v - qt) + r(w - rt) = 0$$
$$\Rightarrow \qquad (pu + qv + rw) = (p^2 + q^2 + r^2)t$$
$$\Rightarrow \qquad t = (pu + qv + rw)/(p^2 + q^2 + r^2)$$

Having thus chosen t, we rewrite (2) as

$$\left(\frac{px + qy + rz + t}{\sqrt{p^2 + q^2 + r^2}}\right)^2 = k\,\frac{2(u - pt)x + 2(v - qt)y + 2(w - rt)z + (d - t^2)}{2\sqrt{(u - pt)^2 + (v - qt)^2 + (w - rt)^2}}$$

where $k = -\dfrac{2\sqrt{(u - pt)^2 + (v - qt)^2 + (w - rt)^2}}{\sqrt{p^2 + q^2 + r^2}}$

Taking

$$\frac{px + qy + rz + t}{\sqrt{p^2 + q^2 + r^2}} = Y$$

$$\frac{2(u - pt)x + 2(v - qt)y + 2(w - rt)z + (d - t^2)}{2\sqrt{(u - pt)^2 + (v - qt)^2 + (w - rt)^2}} = X$$

we see that the given equation takes the form

$$Y^2 = kX$$

so that the surface is a parabolic cylinder.

Ex. Show that the second degree terms form a perfect square if A, B, C, F, G, H are all zero.

Case II. The following procedure is suggested for the reduction of numerical equations when the second degree terms do not form a perfect square.

1. Find the discriminating cubic and solve the same.

2. If no characteristic root is zero, then put down the centre-giving equations and solve them.

If (α, β, γ) is a centre and $\lambda_1, \lambda_2, \lambda_3$ are the characteristics roots, then the reduced equation is
$$\lambda_1 x^2 + \lambda_2 y^2 + \lambda_3 z^2 + (u\alpha + v\beta + w\gamma + d) = 0$$

3. If one characteristic root is zero, find the principal direction l, m, n corresponding to the zero characteristic root by solving two of the three equations
$$al + hm + gn = 0, \; hl + bm + fn = 0, \; gl + fm + cn = 0$$
Then find $ul + vm + wn$. If this is not zero, the reduced equation is
$$\lambda_1 x^2 + \lambda_2 y^2 + 2 (ul + vm + wn) z = 0;$$
λ_1, λ_2 being the non-zero characteristic roots.

4. If $ul + vm + wn = 0$, find the centre-giving equations. In this case we have a line of centres and only two of the three centres-giving equations will be independent. Find any point (α, β, γ) satisfying two of the three equations. Then
$$\lambda_1 x^2 + \lambda_2 y^2 + (u\alpha + v\beta + w\gamma + d) = 0$$
is the required reduced equation.

Note. If one characteristic root is zero and two non-zero, then the line of intersection of the two principal planes corresponding to the non-zero roots is the axis, if the quadric is a parabolic or an elliptic or hyperbolic cylinder and the line of intersection of the planes, if the quadric is a pair of intersecting planes.

In the case of elliptic and hyperbolic cylinders, and a pair of intersecting planes, the line of centres is also the axis.

EXAMPLES

1. *Reduce the equation $2x^2 + 7y^2 - 10yz - 8zx - 10xy + 6x + 12y - 6z + 2 = 0$ to a canonical form.*

Sol. The discriminating cubic is $\lambda^3 + 3\lambda^2 - 90\lambda + 216 = 0$.

This shows that $D = -216 \neq 0$. The roots of the discriminating cubic are $3, 6, -12$.

Again the centre-giving equations are
$$2x - 5y - 4z + 3 = 0, \; 5x + 7y + 5z - 6 = 0, \; 4x + 5y - 2z + 3 = 0.$$
Solving these we see that the centre is
$$\left(\frac{1}{3}, -\frac{1}{3}, \frac{4}{3} \right).$$
Denoting this by (α, β, γ), we have
$$u\alpha + v\beta + w\gamma + d = -3$$
Thus, the canonical form of the equation is
$$3x^2 + 6y^2 - 12z^2 - 3 = 0 \; \Leftrightarrow \; x^2 + 2y^2 - 4z^2 - 1 = 0 \qquad \qquad ...(1)$$
which shows that the given quadric is a hyperboloid of one sheet.

The equation (1) represents the given quadric when the origin of co-ordinates is its centre and the co-ordinate axes are parallel to the principal directions, *i.e.*, (1) is an equation referred to principal axes as co-ordinate axes.

2. *Reduce to canonical form the equation $x^2 - y^2 + 4yz - 4xz - 3 = 0$ of a quadric.*

Sol. The discriminating cubic is
$$\lambda^3 - 9\lambda = 0$$
so that the characteristic roots are
$$0, 3, -3$$
Thus, $D = 0$.

The direction cosines (l, m, n) of the principal direction corresponding to $\lambda = 0$ are given by

$$2l + 4n = 0, - 2m + 4n = 0, 4l + 4m = 0$$

These give

$$l : m : n = 2 : - 2 : - 1$$

Thus, in this case we have

$$ul + vm + wn = 0$$

so that we proceed to find the centre-giving equations.

These are

$$2x + 4z = 0, - 2y + 4z = 0, 4y + 4x = 0.$$

These three planes meet in the line. Clearly $(0, 0, 0)$ is a point on it. Denoting this by (α, β, γ), we have

$$u\alpha + v\beta + w\gamma + d = - 3$$

Thus, the required canonical form of the equation is

$$3x^2 - 3y^2 = 0 \iff x^2 - y^2 = 0.$$

The given equation, therefore, represents a pair of intersecting planes.

Note. The fact that the given equation is free from first degree terms also shows that $(0, 0, 0)$ is a centre of the given quadric.

3. *Show that* $2x^2 + 2y^2 + z^2 + 2yz - 2zx - 4xy + x + y = 0$ *represents a paraboloid. Obtain its reduced equation.*

Sol. The discriminating cubic is $\lambda^3 - 5\lambda^2 + 2\lambda = 0.$

Its roots are $0, \dfrac{5+\sqrt{21}}{2}, \dfrac{5-\sqrt{21}}{2}.$

This shows that $D = 0$. The direction cosines (l, m, n) of the principal direction corresponding o $\lambda = 0$ are given by

$$4l - 4m - 2n = 0 \qquad\qquad ...(1)$$
$$- 4l + 4m + 2n = 0 \qquad\qquad ...(2)$$
$$- 2l + 2m + 2n = 0 \qquad\qquad ...(3)$$

Clearly (1) and (2) are the same. Solving (2) and (3), we obtain

$$l = \frac{1}{\sqrt{2}}, m = \frac{1}{\sqrt{2}}, n = 0$$

$$\Rightarrow \qquad ul + vm + wn = \frac{1}{\sqrt{2}} \neq 0$$

Thus, the reduced equation is

$$\frac{5+\sqrt{21}}{2} x^2 + \frac{5-\sqrt{21}}{2} y^2 + \sqrt{2}\, z = 0.$$

4. *Discuss the nature of the surface whose equation is*

$$4x^2 - y^2 - z^2 + 2yz + 3z - 4y + 8z - 2 = 0$$

and find the co-ordinates of its vertex and equations to its axis.

Sol. It may be shown that the roots of the discriminating cubic are $0, - 2, 4.$

The direction cosines (l, m, n) of the principal direction corresponding to the root 0, are given by

$$8l = 0, - 2m + 2n = 0, - 2m + 2n = 0$$

These give

$$l = 0, m = 1/\sqrt{2}, n = 1/\sqrt{2}$$

Then $\qquad\qquad ul + vm + wn = 2/\sqrt{2} \neq 0$

Thus, the quadric is a paraboloid.

We now proceed to find the axis and the vertex.

The direction cosines (l, m, n) of the principal direction corresponding to $\lambda = -2$ are given by
$$6l + 0 \cdot m + 0 \cdot n = 0,\ 0 \cdot l + m + n = 0,\ 0 \cdot l + m + n = 0$$

These give $\qquad\qquad l = 0,\ m = 1/\sqrt{2},\ n = -1/\sqrt{2}$

so that the corresponding principal plane is
$$- 2\,(y - z) + (- 2 - 4) = 0,\ y - z + 3 = 0 \qquad\qquad\text{...(1)}$$

Again the direction cosines of the principal direction corresponding to $\lambda = 4$ are given by
$$0 \cdot l + 0 \cdot m + 0 \cdot n = 0,\ 0 \cdot l - 5m + n = 0,\ 0 \cdot l + m - 5n = 0$$

These give $\qquad\qquad l : m : n = 1 : 0 : 0$

so that the corresponding principal plane is
$$4x - 4 = 0,\ x = 1 \qquad\qquad\text{...(2)}$$

Thus, $\qquad\qquad y - z + 3 = 0,\ x = 1$

is the required axis of the paraboloid.

The vertex is the point where the axis meets the paraboloid. Rewriting the equations of the axis in the form
$$x = 1,\ \frac{y + 3}{1} = \frac{z}{1}$$

we see that $\qquad\qquad (1, r - 3, r)$

are the co-ordinates of a point on this line; r being the parameter.

This point will lie on the surface for $r = 3/4$ so that *the vertex is the point*
$$\left(1, -\frac{9}{4}, \frac{3}{4}\right).$$

5. *Prove that* $5x^2 + 5y^2 + 8z^2 + 8yz + 8zx - 2xy + 12x - 12y + 6 = 0$ *represents a cylinder whose cross-section is an ellipse of eccentricity* $1/\sqrt{2}$. $\qquad$ *(Garhwal, 1995)*

Find also the equations of the axis of the cylinder.

Sol. The discriminating cubic is
$$\lambda^3 - 18\lambda^2 + 72\lambda = 0$$

so that the values of λ are
$$0,\ 6,\ 12$$

The direction cosines (l, m, n) of the principal direction corresponding to $\lambda = 0$ are given by
$$l - 5m - 4n = 0$$
$$5l - m + 4n = 0$$

$\Leftrightarrow \qquad\qquad l = 1/\sqrt{3},\ m = 1/\sqrt{3},\ n = -1/\sqrt{3}$

Thus, $\qquad\qquad ul + vm + wn = 6/\sqrt{3} - 6/\sqrt{3} - 0/\sqrt{3} = 0$

We have, therefore, to proceed to put down the centre-giving equations. These are
$$10x - 2y + 8z + 12 = 0 \qquad\qquad\text{...(1)}$$
$$- 2x + 10y + 8z - 12 = 0 \qquad\qquad\text{...(2)}$$
$$8x + 8y + 16z = 0 \qquad\qquad\text{...(3)}$$

Clearly (3) can be obtained on adding (1) and (2) so that as expected, these three equations are equivalent to only two. Putting $z = 0$ in (1) and (2), we obtain
$$x = -1,\ y = 1,\ z = 0$$

so that $(-1, 1, 0)$ is a centre. Thus,

$$u\alpha + v\beta + w\gamma + d = -6 - 6 + 6 = -6$$

Hence, the reduced equation is

$$12x^2 + 6y^2 - 6 = 0 \iff 2x^2 + y^2 = 1$$

The cross-section is $2x^2 + y^2 = 1$, $z = 0$.

Its eccentricity is now easily seen to be $1/\sqrt{2}$.

The line of centres is the axis of the cylinder so that the equations of the axis are

$$5x - y + 4z + 6 = 0, \ x + y + 2z = 0.$$

6. *Show that the equation $x^2 + 2yz = 1$ represents a quadric of revolution. Also find the axis of revolution.*

Sol. The discriminating cubic is

$$(1 - \lambda)(\lambda^2 - 1) = 0 \iff (\lambda + 1)(\lambda - 1)^2 = 0$$

so that the characteristic roots are

$$-1, 1, 1$$

Two of the characteristic roots being equal and non-zero, we see that the given equation represents a quadric of revolution.

Further rewriting the given equation as

$$(x^2 + y^2 + z^2) - (y - z)^2 = 1$$
$$\iff \qquad (x^2 + y^2 + z^2 - 1) - (y - z)^2 = 0$$

we see that the planes parallel to the plane

$$y - z = 0 \qquad\qquad\qquad ...(1)$$

cut the quadric in circles. Thus, the axis of revolution which is the line through the centre of the sphere

$$x^2 + y^2 + z^2 = 1$$

perpendicular to the line (1) is

$$x = 0, \ y = z.$$

7. *Prove that $x^2 + y^2 + z^2 - yz - zx - zy - 3x - 6y - 9z + 21 = 0$ represents a paraboloid of revolution and find the co-ordinates of its focus.*   (Garhwal, 1997, 2000)

Sol. The discriminating cubic is

$$-4\lambda^3 + 12\lambda^2 - 9\lambda = 0$$

so that the characteristic roots are

$$0, 3/2, 3/2$$

Two values of λ being equal, the given quadric is a surface of revolution.

The direction cosines (l, m, n) of the principal direction corresponding to $\lambda = 0$ are given by any two of the three equations

$$l - \frac{1}{2}m - \frac{1}{2}n = 0$$

$$-\frac{1}{2}l + m - \frac{1}{2}n = 0$$

$$-\frac{1}{2}l - \frac{1}{2}m + n = 0$$

These give

$$l : m : n = 1 : 1 : 1$$

$$\therefore \qquad l = 1/\sqrt{3},\ m = 1/\sqrt{3},\ n = 1/\sqrt{3}$$

Now we have

$$ul + vm + wn = -\frac{3}{2}\cdot\frac{1}{\sqrt{3}} - 3,\ \frac{1}{\sqrt{3}} - \frac{9}{2}\cdot\frac{1}{\sqrt{3}} = -\frac{9}{\sqrt{3}} \ne 0$$

Thus, the quadric is a paraboloid of revolution and the reduced equation is

$$\frac{3}{2}x^2 + \frac{3}{2}y^2 - 2\cdot\frac{9}{\sqrt{3}}z = 0 \iff x^2 + y^2 = 4\sqrt{3}\,z.$$

This form of the equation shows that the latus rectum of the generating parabola is $4\sqrt{3}$.

With respect to the given system of co-ordinate axes, the direction ratios of the axis of the paraboloid which is also the axis of revolution are 1, 1, 1.

We rewrite the given equations in the form

$$x^2 + y^2 + z^2 - \frac{1}{2}[(x + y + z)^2 - (x^2 + y^2 + z^2)] - 3x - 6y - 9z + 21 = 0$$

$$\iff \qquad \frac{3}{2}(x^2 + y^2 + z^2) - 3x - 6y - 9z + 21 - \frac{1}{2}(x + y + z)^2 = 0$$

$$\iff \qquad x^2 + y^2 + z^2 - 2x - 4y - 6z + 14 - \frac{1}{3}(x + y + z)^2 = 0$$

Thus, the axis of revolution, being the line through the centre of the sphere

$$x^2 + y^2 + z^2 - 2x - 4y - 6z + 14 = 0$$

and perpendicular to the plane

$$x + y + z = 0$$

is

$$\frac{x - 1}{1} = \frac{y - 2}{1} = \frac{z - 3}{1} \qquad \qquad \dots(1)$$

which is the axis of the paraboloid.

The vertex is the point where this axis meets the paraboloid. It can be shown that any point

$$(r + 1, r + 2, r + 3)$$

on the axis will be on the paraboloid if $r = -1$.

Thus, $(0, 1, 2)$ is the vertex of the paraboloid.

The required focus is the point on the axis (1) at a distance $\sqrt{3}$ from $(0, 1, 2)$. Rewriting the equations of the axis in the form

$$\frac{x - 0}{1/\sqrt{3}} = \frac{y - 1}{1/\sqrt{3}} = \frac{z - 2}{1/\sqrt{3}}$$

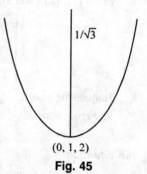

$1/\sqrt{3}$

$(0, 1, 2)$

Fig. 45

we see that the point on the axis at a distance $\sqrt{3}$ from $(0, 1, 2)$ is

$$(1, 2, 3)$$

Thus, $(1, 2, 3)$ is the required focus.

8. If $ax^2 + by^2 + cz^2 + 2fyz + 2gzx + 2hxy = 0$ represents a pair of planes, prove that the planes bisecting the angles between them are

$$\begin{vmatrix} ax + hy + gz & hx + by + fz & gx + fy + cz \\ x & y & z \\ F^{-1} & G^{-1} & H^{-1} \end{vmatrix} = 0.$$

Sol. As the given equation represents a pair of planes, we must have $D = 0$.

The line of intersection of the two planes is parallel to the principal direction corresponding to the characteristic root 0 so that if (l, m, n) be the direction cosines of this line, we have

$$al + hm + gn = 0$$
$$hl + bm + fn = 0$$

These give

$$\frac{l}{G} = \frac{m}{F} = \frac{n}{C}$$

As $FG = CH$, we see on replacing C by FG/H, that l, m, n are proportional to F^{-1}, G^{-1}, H^{-1}.

The result can also be obtained if we regard the line of intersection as the line of centres.

Now we know that the two bisecting planes are the principal planes corresponding to the two non-zero characteristic roots.

Suppose that (x, y, z) is any point on either bisecting plane. Let this bisecting plane, as a principal plane, bisect chords with direction cosines (l_1, m_1, n_1) and perpendicular to the plane. The equation of the plane being

$$l_1 (ax + hy + gz) + m_1 (hx + by + fz) + n_1 (gx + fy + cz) = 0 \qquad ...(1)$$

we see that any point (x, y, z) on the bisecting plane satisfies this equation.

Further the plane being normal to the line with direction cosines (l_1, m_1, n_1), its equation is also

$$l_1 x + m_1 y + n_1 z = 0 \qquad ...(2)$$

so that (x, y, z) satisfies (2) also.

Finally, the principal direction l_1, m_1, n_1 corresponding to a non-zero characteristic root being perpendicular to that corresponding to the zero characteristic root, we have

$$l_1 F^{-1} + m_1 G^{-1} + n_1 H^{-1} = 0 \qquad ...(3)$$

From (1), (2) and (3), we have

$$\begin{vmatrix} ax + hy + gz & hx + by + fz & gx + fy + cz \\ x & y & z \\ F^{-1} & G^{-1} & H^{-1} \end{vmatrix} = 0$$

Hence, the result.

9. *Prove that if*

$$a^3 + b^3 + c^3 = 3abc \ and \ u + v + w \neq 0$$

the equation

$$ax^2 + by^2 + cz^2 + 2ayz + 2bzx + 2cxy + 2ux + 2vy + 2wz + d = 0$$

represents either a parabolic cylinder or a hyperbolic paraboloid.

Sol. The discriminating cubic of the given quadric is

$$\lambda^3 - \lambda^2 (a + b + c) + \lambda (ab + bc + ca - a^2 - b^2 - c^2) - (3abc - a^3 - b^3 - c^3) = 0$$

so that under one of the given conditions, one root of the cubic is zero.

We have

$$0 = a^3 + b^3 + c^3 - 3abc = (a + b + c) (a^2 + b^2 + c^2 - ab - bc - ca)$$

so that either

$$a + b + c = 0 \qquad ...(1)$$

or

$$a^2 + b^2 + c^2 - ab - bc - ca = 0 \qquad ...(2)$$

The condition (2) is equivalent to

$$(a - b)^2 + (b - c)^2 + (c - a)^2 = 0 \Rightarrow a = b = c. \qquad ...(3)$$

Assuming (2) to be satisfied, we see that the given equation takes the form

$$a (x + y + z)^2 + 2 (ux + vy + wz) + d = 0$$

which is a parabolic cylinder, if $u \neq v$ or $v \neq w$.

Suppose now that the condition (1) is satisfied so that only one root of the discriminating cubic is zero.

The direction cosines (l, m, n) of the principal direction corresponding to the zero root are given by

$$al + cm + bn = 0$$
$$cl + bm + an = 0$$

so that

$$\frac{l}{ac - b^2} = \frac{m}{bc - a^2} = \frac{n}{ab - c^2}$$

As
$$a + b + c = 0,$$
we may see that
$$ac - b^2 = bc - a^2 = ab - c^2$$

Thus, the principal direction corresponding to the zero root is given by

$$\frac{1}{\sqrt{3}}, \frac{1}{\sqrt{3}}, \frac{1}{\sqrt{3}}$$

Also
$$ul + vm + wn = \frac{1}{\sqrt{3}}(u + v + w) \neq 0$$

Thus, in this case the quadric is a paraboloid. This paraboloid is hyperbolic for the two non-zero characteristic roots given by

$$\lambda^2 + (ab + bc + ca - a^2 - b^2 - c^2) = 0$$

are of opposite signs.

EXERCISES

1. Show that $4x^2 - y^2 - z^2 + 2yz - 8x - 4y + 8z - 2 = 0$ represents a paraboloid. Find the reduced equation and the co-ordinates of the vertex.

2. Reduce to its principal axes $2y^2 - 2yz + 2zx - 2xy - x - 2y + 3z - 2 = 0$ and state the nature of the surface represented by the equation.

3. Find the nature of the surface represented by the equation
$$x^2 + 2y^2 - 3z^2 - 4yz + 8zx - 12xy + 1 = 0.$$

4. Find the reduced equation of
    (i) $x^2 + 2yz - 4x + 6y + 2z = 0.$
    (ii) $x^2 - y^2 + 2yz - 2xz - x - y + z = 0.$
    (iii) $yz + zx + xy - 7x - 6y - 5z - 25 = 0.$
    (iv) $4y^2 - 4yz + 4zx - 4xy - 2x + 2y - 1 = 0.$
    (v) $2x^2 + 2y^2 + z^2 + 2yz - 2zx - 4xy + x + v + z = 0.$
    (vi) $(x \cos \alpha - y \sin \alpha)^2 + (y \cos \alpha + z \sin \alpha)^2 + 2y = 1.$
    (vii) $3x^2 + 6yz - y^2 - z^2 - 6x + 6y - 2z - 2 = 0.$ *(Avadh, 2006)*
    (viii) $4x^2 + y^2 + z^2 - 4xy - 2yz + 4zx - 12x + 6y - 6z + 8 = 0.$
    (ix) $x^2 + y^2 + z^2 - 2xy - 2yz + 2zx + x - 4y + z + 1 = 0.$

5. Show that the equation

$$a (z - x) (x - y) + b (x - y) (y - z) + c (y - z) (z - x) = 0$$

represents two planes whose line of intersection is equally inclined to the three co-ordinate axes.

6. Show that the equation $2yz + 2zx + 2xy = 1$ represents a hyperboloid of revolution. Is this a hyperboloid of one or two sheets ?

7. Show that the quadric $2y^2 + 4zx - 6x - 8y + 2z + 5 = 0$ is a cone and obtain its reduced equation. Show further that this is a right circular cone with its axis of revolution parallel to the line $x + z = 0 = y$.

8. Show that the quadric with generators

$$y = 1, z = -1; z = 1, x = -1; x = 1, y = -1$$

is a hyperboloid of revolution.

9. Find the reduced equation of the quadric with generators

$$x - 1 = 0 = y - 1; x = 0 = y - z, x - 2 = 0 = z.$$

10. Prove that every quadric of the linear system determined by the two equations

$$y^2 - zx + x = 0, x^2 + y^2 + 2xz = 0$$

is a cone.

11. Discuss the nature of the quadrics represented by the equation

$$2x^2 + (m^2 + 2) (y^2 + z^2) - 4 (yz + zx + xy) = m^2 - 2m + 2$$

as m varies from $-\infty$ to $+\infty$.

Obtain the reduced equation of the quadric corresponding to $m = 1$.

12. Show that there is only one paraboloid in the system of quadrics

$$\Sigma (ax^2 + 2fyz) + 2\Sigma ux + d + \lambda (lx + my + nz + p)^2 = 0.$$

In particular, show that if f, g, h, u, v, w are all zero, the equation of this paraboloid is

$$ax^2 + by^2 + cz^2 + d \left(\frac{l^2}{a} + \frac{m^2}{b} + \frac{n^2}{c} \right) - (lx + my + nz + p)^2 = 0$$

Further prove that its axis is parallel to the line

$$\frac{ax}{l} = \frac{by}{m} = \frac{cz}{n}.$$

13. If the general equation $\Sigma (ax^2 + 2fyz) + 2\Sigma ux + d = 0$ represents a right circular cylinder, prove that

$$\frac{a}{f} + \frac{h}{g} + \frac{g}{h} = 0; \frac{h}{f} + \frac{b}{g} + \frac{f}{h} = 0; \frac{g}{f} + \frac{f}{g} + \frac{c}{h} = 0; \frac{u}{f} + \frac{v}{g} + \frac{w}{h} = 0.$$

14. Show that the condition for the equation

$$(x - \alpha)^2 + (y - \beta)^2 + (z - \gamma)^2 + \left(\frac{x^2}{a^2} + \frac{y^2}{b^2} + \frac{z^2}{c^2} - 1 \right) = 0$$

to represent a cone is

$$\frac{\alpha^2}{a^2 + \lambda} + \frac{\beta^2}{b^2 + \lambda} + \frac{\gamma^2}{c^2 + \lambda} = 1.$$

15. Prove that the principal axes of the conicoid $ax^2 + by^2 + cz^2 + 2fyz + 2gzx + 2hxy = 1$ are given by the equations

$$x (f\lambda_r + F) = y (g\lambda_r + G) = z (h\lambda_r + H), (r = 1, 2, 3)$$

where $\lambda_1, \lambda_2, \lambda_3$ are the roots of the equation

$$\begin{vmatrix} a - \lambda & h & g \\ h & b - \lambda & f \\ g & f & c - \lambda \end{vmatrix} = 0$$

and $F = gh - af, G = hf - bg, H = fg - ch$.

Also show that the cone which touches the co-ordinate planes and the principal planes of the above conicoid is

$$\sqrt{[(gH - hG)\, x]} + \sqrt{[(hF - f H)\, y]} + \sqrt{[(f G - gF)\, z]} = 0.$$

16. If the feet of the six normals from P to the ellipsoid $\dfrac{x^2}{a^2} + \dfrac{y^2}{b^2} + \dfrac{z^2}{c^2} = 1$ lie upon a concentric conicoid of revolution, prove that the locus of P is the cone

$$\frac{y^2 z^2}{a^2 (b^2 - c^2)} + \frac{z^2 x^2}{b^2 (c^2 - a^2)} + \frac{x^2 y^2}{c^2 (a^2 - b^2)} = 0$$

and that the axes of symmetry of the conicoids lie on the cone

$$a^2 (b^2 - c^2)\, x^2 + b^2 (c^2 - a^2)\, y^2 + c^2 (a^2 - b^2)\, z^2 = 0.$$

17. Prove that the equation $ax^2 + by^2 + cz^2 + 2fyz + 2gzx + 2hxy = 0$ will represent a right circular cone with vertical angle θ provided that

$$\frac{af - gh}{f} = \frac{bg - hf}{g} = \frac{ch - fg}{h} = \frac{(a + b + c)(1 + \cos \theta)}{(1 + 3 \cos \theta)}.$$

18. Given the ellipsoid of revolution $\dfrac{x^2}{a^2} + \dfrac{y^2 + z^2}{b^2} = 1, (a^2 < b^2)$, show that the cone whose vertex is one of the foci of the ellipse $z = 0, \dfrac{x^2}{a^2} + \dfrac{y^2}{b^2} = 1$ and whose base is any plane section of the ellipsoid is a surface of revolution.

19. Prove that if $F (x, y, z) \equiv \Sigma (ax^2 + 2fyz) + 2\Sigma ux + d = 0$ represents a paraboloid of revolution, we have

$$agh + f (g^2 + h^2) = bhf + g (h^2 + f^2) = cfg + h (f^2 + g^2) = 0$$

and that if it represents a right circular cylinder, we have also

$$\frac{u}{f} + \frac{v}{g} + \frac{w}{h} = 0.$$

ANSWERS

1. $2x^2 - y^2 + \sqrt{2}z = 0, \left(1, -\dfrac{9}{4}, \dfrac{3}{4}\right).$ **2.** $3x^2 - y^2 = \dfrac{1}{2}.$ Hyperbolic cylinder.

3. $3x^2 + 6y^2 - 9z^2 + 1 = 0.$ Hyperboloid of two sheets.

4. (i) $x^2 + y^2 - z^2 = 10.$ (ii) $3x^2 - 3y^2 = z.$ (iii) $2x^2 - y^2 - z^2 = 102.$

(iv) $6x^2 - 2y^2 = 1.$ (v) $\dfrac{5 + \sqrt{17}}{2} x^2 + \dfrac{5 - \sqrt{17}}{2} y^2 + \sqrt{2}z = 0.$

(vi) $(1 + \sin \alpha \cos \alpha) x^2 + (1 - \sin \alpha \cos \alpha) y^2 + z \sin 2\alpha / \sqrt{1 - \sin^2 \alpha \cos^2 \alpha} = 0$

if $\sin \alpha \neq 0$, $\cos \alpha \neq 0$; $x^2 + y^2 = 2$ if $\sin \alpha = 0$ and $y^2 + z^2 = 2$ if $\cos \alpha = 0$.

(vii) $2x^2 + 3y^2 - 4z^2 = 4$.   (viii) $3x^2 - 3\sqrt{6} x + 4 = 0$.   (ix) $3y^2 = \sqrt{6} x$.

6. Hyperboloid of two sheets.   **7.** $x^2 = y^2 + z^2$.

9. $\dfrac{\sqrt{6}+1}{2} x^2 - \dfrac{\sqrt{6}-1}{2} y^2 + \dfrac{2}{\sqrt{5}} z = 0$.

11. For $m > 2$, ellipsoid.   For $m < -2$, ellipsoid.

For $m = 2$, pair of imaginary planes.   For $m = -2$, elliptic cylinder.

For $1 < m < 2$, hyperboloid of two sheets.   For $-2 < m < 1$, hyperboloid of one sheet.

For $m = 1$, cone.

The reduced equation for the last case is

$$10x^2 + (3 + \sqrt{33}) y^2 = (\sqrt{33} - 3) z^2.$$

OBJECTIVE QUESTIONS

I. Multiple Choice Questions

Note : *For each of the following questions, four alternatives are given for the answer. Only one of them is correct. Choose the correct alternative.*

1. Centre of surface $F(x, y, z)$ is :

(a) $\dfrac{\partial F}{\partial x} = 0$, $\dfrac{\partial F}{\partial y} = 0$, $\dfrac{\partial F}{\partial z} = 0$ (b) $\dfrac{\partial F}{\partial x} = 0$, $\dfrac{\partial F}{\partial y} = 0$, $\dfrac{\partial F}{\partial z} \neq 0$

(c) $\dfrac{\partial F}{\partial x} = 0$, $\dfrac{\partial F}{\partial y} \neq 0$, $\dfrac{\partial F}{\partial z} = 0$ (d) $\dfrac{\partial F}{\partial x} \neq 0$, $\dfrac{\partial F}{\partial y} = 0$, $\dfrac{\partial F}{\partial z} = 0$.

2. Centre of the surface $3x^2 - y^2 - z^2 + 6yz - 6x + 6y - 2z - 2 = 0$ is :

(a) $(0, 1, -1)$ (b) $(1, 0, -1)$ (c) $(1, -1, 0)$ (d) $(1, 1, -1)$.

3. Surface represented by $2x^2 + 5y^2 + 3z^2 + 2yz + 2zx + 2xy - 4x - 8z + 5 = 0$ is :

(a) Ellipsoid   (b) Cone

(c) Hyperboloid of one sheet   (d) Hyperboloid of two sheets.

4. Standard form of the surface $5x^2 - 16y^2 + 5z^2 + 8yz - 14zx + 8xy + 4x + 20y + 4z - 24 = 0$ is :

(a) $14x^2 - 26y^2 = 3$ (b) $2x^2 - 3y^2 + 2z = 0$

(c) $3x^2 + y^2 - 2z = 0$ (d) None of these.

5. The surface $2y^2 - 2yz + 2zx - 2xy - x - 2y + 3z - 2 = 0$ represents :

(a) elliptic cylinder   (b) parabolic cylinder

(c) hyperbolic cylinder   (d) pair of planes.

6. Surface represented by the equation

$$2x^2 + 5y^2 + 2z^2 - 2yz + 4zx - 2xy + 14x - 16y + 14z + 26 = 0$$

represents :

(a) an elliptic cylinder   (b) a parabolic cylinder

(c) a hyperbolic cylinder   (d) a pair of planes.

7. Surface represented by the equation $x^2 - y^2 + 4yz + 4zx - 6x - 2y - 8z + 5 = 0$ is :

(a) Elliptic cylinder   (b) Hyperbolic cylinder

(c) Pair of planes   (d) Cone.

8. Surface represented by the equation
$$x^2 + 4y^2 + z^2 + 2zx - 4yz - 4xy - 2x + 4y - 2z - 3 = 0$$
is :

(a) Parabolic cylinder   (b) Pair of planes

(c) Cone   (d) None of these.

9. Surface represented by the equation $x^2 + 2y^2 + 3z^2 - 4xz - 4xy + d = 0$ will be a cone if :

(a) d is $-$ve   (b) d is $+$ve

(c) $d = 0$ (d) Never represents a cone.

10. The standard form of the surface. $\sqrt{x} + \sqrt{y} + \sqrt{z} = 0$ is :

(a) $x^2 + y^2 + z^2 = 0$ (b) $2(x^2 + y^2) - z^2 = 0$

(c) $x^2 + y^2 - 2z^2 = 0$ (d) None of these.

ANSWERS

1. (a)   **2.** (b)   **3.** (a)   **4.** (b)   **5.** (c)

6. (a)   **7.** (a)   **8.** (b)   **9.** (c)   **10.** (b)

II. Fill in the Blanks

Note : *Fill in the blanks "........", so that the following statements are complete and correct.*

1. The equation $Ax^2 - By^2 - Cz^2 = 1$ represents a ....

2. The centre of the surface $F(x, y, z) = 0$ is obtained by solving x, y, z the equations ....

3. The planes $a_1x + b_1y + c_1z + d_1 = 0$ and $a_2x + b_2y + c_2z + d_2 = 0$ will be parallel but

not ..... provided $\dfrac{a_1}{a_2} = \dfrac{b_1}{b_2} = \dfrac{c_1}{c_2} \neq \dfrac{d_1}{d_2}$.

4. The equation of the ..... of the conicoid $F(x, y, z) = 0$ is $l\dfrac{\partial F}{\partial x} + m\dfrac{\partial F}{\partial y} + n\dfrac{\partial F}{\partial z} = 0$.

5. The equation $y^2 = Ax$ represents a ..... cylinder.

6. The equation $x^2 + z^2 = a^2$ represents a ....., whose axis is parallel to y-axis.

7. The equation $A(x^2 + y^2) + Bz = 0$ represents a ..... of revolution.

8. The equation $5x^2 - 4y^2 + 5z^2 + 4yz - 14zx + 4xy + 16x + 16y + 32z + 8 = 0$ represents a ....

ANSWERS

1. hyperboloid of two sheets;   **2.** $\dfrac{\partial F}{\partial x} = \dfrac{\partial F}{\partial y} = \dfrac{\partial F}{\partial z} = 0$;   **3.** the same;

4. diametral plane;   **5.** parabolic;   **6.** circular cylinder;

7. paraboloid;   **8.** pair of planes.

III. True/False Statements

Note : *Write 'T' for true and 'F' for false statements.*

1. The equation $Ax^2 + By^2 + C = 0$ represents an elliptic cylinder.

2. The equation $A(x^2 + y^2) + Bz^2 = 1$ represents a paraboloid of revolution.

3. The planes $a_1x + b_1y + c_1z + d_1 = 0$ and $a_2x + b_2y + c_2z + d_2 = 0$ will be parallel but

not the same, if $\dfrac{a_1}{a_2} = \dfrac{b_1}{b_2} = \dfrac{c_1}{c_2} = \dfrac{d_1}{d_2}$.

4. The centre of the surface $F(x, y, z) = 0$ is obtained by solving $\dfrac{\partial F}{\partial x} = 0$, $\dfrac{\partial F}{\partial y} = 0$, $\dfrac{\partial F}{\partial z} = 0$ for x, y, z.

5. The equation $x^2 + z^2 = a^2$ represents a circular cylinder whose axis is parallel to y-axis.

6. By rotation of axes, the expression $f(x, y, z) \equiv ax^2 + by^2 + cz^2 + 2fyz + 2gzx + 2hxy$ transforms to $\lambda_1 x^2 + \lambda_2 y^2 + \lambda_3 z^2 = 0$, where λ's are the roots of the equation

$$\begin{vmatrix} a - \lambda & h & f \\ h & b - \lambda & g \\ b & g & c - \lambda \end{vmatrix} = 0.$$

7. The equation of a diametral plane of the conicoid $F(x, y, z) = 0$ is

$$l\,\frac{\partial F}{\partial x} + m\,\frac{\partial F}{\partial y} + n\,\frac{\partial F}{\partial z} = 0.$$

8. The equation $2y^2 - 2yz + 2zx - 2xy - x - 2y + 3z = 2$ represents a hyperbolic cylinder.

ANSWERS

| 1. T | 2. F | 3. F | 4. T |
| 5. T | 6. F | 7. T | 8. T |

12

Confocal Conicoids

12.1. DEFINITION

The conicoids whose principal sections are confocal conics, i.e., the conics having same foci, are called **confocal conicoids.** Thus,

$$\frac{x^2}{a^2 - \lambda} + \frac{y^2}{b^2 - \lambda} + \frac{z^2}{c^2 - \lambda} = 1 \qquad \ldots(i)$$

represents, for all values of λ, the general equation of a system of conicoids confocal with the ellipsoid

$$x^2/a^2 + y^2/b^2 + z^2/c^2 = 1$$

λ is known as the *parameter* of the confocal.

12.1.1. Principal Sections

The principal sections of (i) are confocal conics. Suppose $a > b > c$ and λ varies from $-\infty$ to $+\infty$.

(*a*) When λ is negative, the surface (i) is an ellipsoid. As λ increases, *i.e.*, as $\lambda \to \infty$, the principal axes of the surface increase and their ratio tends to unity. Thus, a sphere of infinite radius is a limiting case of the confocals.

(*b*) When λ is positive and less than c^2, the surface is an ellipsoid, but the ellipsoid becomes more and more flat as λ approaches c^2. Thus, as $z \to c^2$, the ellipsoid tends to coincide with the ellipse

$$z = 0, \ x^2/(a^2 - c^2) + y^2/(b^2 - c^2) = 1 \qquad \ldots(ii)$$

on the *xy*-plane.

(*c*) When λ lies between c^2 and b^2, the surface is a hyperboloid of one sheet. As $\lambda \to c^2$ from the right, the hyperboloid tends to coincide with the ellipse (ii), and as $\lambda \to b^2$ from the left, the hyperboloid tends to coincide with the hyperbola

$$y = 0, \ x^2/(a^2 - b^2) - z^2/(b^2 - c^2) = 1 \qquad \ldots(iii)$$

in the *zx*-plane.

(*d*) When λ lies between b^2 and a^2, the surface is a hyperboloid of two sheets. As $\lambda \to b^2$ from the right, the hyperboloid tends to coincide with the hyperbola (iii), and as $\lambda \to a^2$ from the left, the surface tends to reduce to the imaginary ellipse

$$x = 0, \ y^2/(a^2 - b^2) + z^2/(a^2 - c^2) = -1.$$

When $\lambda > a^2$, the surface is always imaginary.

The conics (ii) and (iii) which are the boundaries of limiting cases of confocal conicoids, are called *focal conics*, the conic (ii) is known as the *focal ellipse* and the conic (iii) as the *focal hyperbola*.

In the same way, since the principal section of the paraboloids

$$\frac{x^2}{a^2 - \lambda} + \frac{y^2}{b^2 - \lambda} = 2z - \lambda \qquad \ldots(iv)$$

and

$$\frac{x^2}{a^2} + \frac{y^2}{b^2} = 2z$$

by the planes $x = 0$ and $y = 0$ are confocal parabolas, the eqn. (iv) represents a system of *confocal paraboloids*.

12.1.2. Confocals Through a Given Point

To prove that three conicoids confocal with a given central conicoid will pass through a given point; and one of the three is an ellipsoid, one a hyperboloid of one sheet and one a hyperboloid of two sheets.   (*Gorakhpur, 1997, 2003; Avadh, 1996*)

Let the equation of the given conicoid be

$$x^2/a^2 + y^2/b^2 + z^2/c^2 = 1 \ (a > b > c) \qquad \ldots(i)$$

and the equation of a conicoid confocal to it be

$$\sim x^2/(a^2 - \lambda) + y^2/(b^2 - \lambda) + z^2/(c^2 - \lambda) = 1 \qquad \ldots(ii)$$

If it passes through the given point (α, β, γ), then

$$\alpha^2/(a^2 - \lambda) + \beta^2/(b^2 - \lambda) + \gamma^2/(c^2 - \lambda) = 1$$

$$\Rightarrow \quad f(\lambda) \equiv \alpha^2 (b^2 - \lambda)(c^2 - \lambda) + \beta^2 (c^2 - \lambda)(a^2 - \lambda) + \gamma^2 (a^2 - \lambda)(b^2 - \lambda)$$
$$- (a^2 - \lambda)(b^2 - \lambda)(c^2 - \lambda) = 0 \quad \ldots(iii)$$

This being cubic in λ, gives the parameters of three confocals which pass through the given point. By giving different values of λ, we have

λ	$=$	∞,	a^2,	b^2,	c^2,	$-\infty$
$f(x)$	is	$+$,	$+$,	$-$,	$+$,	$-$

Hence, $f(\lambda) = 0$ has three real roots, such that

$$a^2 > \lambda_1 > b^2 > \lambda_2 > c^2 > \lambda_3.$$

When $\lambda = \lambda_3$, the surface is an ellipsoid; when $\lambda = \lambda_2$, it is a hyperboloid of one sheet; and when $\lambda = \lambda_1$, it is a hyperboloid of two sheets.

12.2. CONFOCALS TOUCHING A GIVEN PLANE

To prove that the conicoids confocal with a given conicoid touch a given plane.
(*Avadh, 2006*)

The given plane is $lx + my + nz = p$ $\ldots(i)$

The condition that the plane touches the conicoid

$$x^2/(a^2 + \lambda) + y^2/(b^2 + \lambda) + z^2/(c^2 + \lambda) = 1 \qquad \ldots(ii)$$

is $l^2(a^2 + \lambda) + m^2(b^2 + \lambda) + n^2(c^2 + \lambda) = p^2 \qquad \ldots(iii)$

This is a linear equation in λ and hence gives one and only one value of λ. Hence, it follows that one conicoid of a given confocal system touches any given plane.

12.2.1. Confocals Touching a Given Line

To prove that two conicoids confocal with a given conicoid touch a given straight line.
(*Gorakhpur, 1998, 2000*)

Let the given line be

$$lx + my + nz + p = 0 = l'x + m'y + n'z + p'$$

A plane through this line is

$$(lx + my + nz + p) + k(l'x + m'y + n'z + p') = 0$$

$$\Rightarrow \qquad (l + kl')x + (m + km')y + (n + kn')z + (p + kp') = 0$$

This plane touches the conicoid

$$x^2/(a^2 + \lambda) + y^2/(b^2 + \lambda) + z^2/(c^2 + \lambda) = 1$$

if $\qquad (a^2 + \lambda)(l + kl')^2 + (b^2 + \lambda)(m + km')^2 + (c^2 + \lambda)(n + kn')^2 = (p + kp')^2$

If given line is a tangent line of the conicoid, the two tangent planes through it coincide. Hence, roots of the above equation in k are equal.

$$\Rightarrow \quad [(a^2 + \lambda)l^2 + (b^2 + \lambda)m^2 + (c^2 + \lambda)n^2 - p^2]$$
$$\times [(a^2 + \lambda)l'^2 + (b^2 + \lambda)m'^2 + (c^2 + \lambda)n'^2 - p'^2]$$
$$= [(a^2 + \lambda)ll' + (b^2 + \lambda)mm' + (c^2 + \lambda)nn' - pp']^2$$

This is quadratic in λ. Hence, gives two confocals which touch the given line.

12.2.2. Confocals Cut at Right Angles

To prove that the confocal conicoids cut one another at right angles at all their common points, i.e., the tangent planes at any common point are at right angles.

(Gorakhpur, 1998, 2000, 01)

Let (x_1, y_1, z_1) be a common point of confocals.

$$\frac{x^2}{a^2 + \lambda_1} + \frac{y^2}{b^2 + \lambda_1} + \frac{z^2}{c^2 + \lambda_1} = 1 \qquad \qquad ...(i)$$

and

$$\frac{x^2}{a^2 + \lambda_2} + \frac{y^2}{b^2 + \lambda_2} + \frac{z^2}{c^2 + \lambda_2} = 1 \qquad \qquad ...(ii)$$

Hence,

$$\frac{x_1^2}{a^2 + \lambda_1} + \frac{y_1^2}{b^2 + \lambda_1} + \frac{z_1^2}{c^2 + \lambda_1} = 1 \qquad \qquad ...(iii)$$

and

$$\frac{x_1^2}{a^2 + \lambda_2} + \frac{y_1^2}{b^2 + \lambda_2} + \frac{z_1^2}{c^2 + \lambda_2} = 1 \qquad \qquad ...(iv)$$

Equations of tangent planes at (x_1, y_1, z_1) to (i) and (ii) are

$$\frac{xx_1}{a^2 + \lambda_1} + \frac{yy_1}{b^2 + \lambda_1} + \frac{zz_1}{c^2 + \lambda_1} = 1 \qquad \qquad ...(v)$$

and

$$\frac{xx_1}{a^2 + \lambda_2} + \frac{yy_1}{b^2 + \lambda_2} + \frac{zz_1}{c^2 + \lambda_2} = 1 \qquad \qquad ...(vi)$$

Subtracting (iv) from (iii), we get

$$\frac{x_1^2}{(a^2 + \lambda_1)(a^2 + \lambda_2)} + \frac{y_1^2}{(b^2 + \lambda_1)(b^2 + \lambda_2)} + \frac{z_1^2}{(c^2 + \lambda_1)(c^2 + \lambda_2)} = 0$$

which is the condition that the tangent planes (v) and (vi) are at right angles.

12.3. ELLIPTIC CO-ORDINATES

From eqn. (iii), § 12.1.2, we have

$$f(\lambda) \equiv \alpha^2(b^2 - \lambda)(c^2 - \lambda) + \beta^2(a^2 - \lambda)(c^2 - \lambda) + \gamma^2(a^2 - \lambda)(b^2 - \lambda)$$
$$- (a^2 - \lambda)(b^2 - \lambda)(c^2 - \lambda) = 0 \qquad ...(i)$$

If the roots of this equation are λ_1, λ_2, λ_3, then

$$f(\lambda) = (\lambda - \lambda_1)(\lambda - \lambda_2)(\lambda - \lambda_3) \qquad \qquad ...(ii)$$

Dividing (i) by $(a^2 - \lambda)(b^2 - \lambda)(c^2 - \lambda)$, we have

$$1 - \frac{\alpha^2}{a^2 - \lambda} - \frac{\beta^2}{b^2 - \lambda} - \frac{\gamma^2}{c^2 - \lambda} = \frac{-f(\lambda)}{(a^2 - \lambda)(b^2 - \lambda)(c^2 - \lambda)}$$

$$\Rightarrow \quad 1 - \frac{\alpha^2}{a^2 - \lambda} - \frac{\beta^2}{b^2 - \lambda} - \frac{\gamma^2}{c^2 - \lambda} = \frac{-(\lambda - \lambda_1)(\lambda - \lambda_2)(\lambda - \lambda_3)}{(a^2 - \lambda)(b^2 - \lambda)(c^2 - \lambda)} \qquad ...(iii)$$

$$\Rightarrow \quad 1 - \frac{\alpha^2}{a^2 - \lambda} - \frac{\beta^2}{b^2 - \lambda} - \frac{\gamma^2}{c^2 - \lambda} - \frac{(a^2 - \lambda_1)(a^2 - \lambda_2)(a^2 - \lambda_3)}{(b^2 - a^2)(c^2 - a^2)(a^2 - \lambda)}$$

$$- \frac{(b^2 - \lambda_1)(b^2 - \lambda_2)(b^2 - \lambda_3)}{(c^2 - b^2)(a^2 - b^2)(b^2 - \lambda)} - \frac{(c^2 - \lambda_1)(c^2 - \lambda_2)(c^2 - \lambda_3)}{(a^2 - c^2)(b^2 - c^2)(c^2 - \lambda)}.$$

Comparing the coefficients of $1/(a^2 - \lambda)$, $1/(b^2 - \lambda)$ and $1/(c^2 - \lambda)$ on either side, we have :

$$\alpha^2 = \frac{(a^2 - \lambda_1)(a^2 - \lambda_2)(a^2 - \lambda_3)}{(b^2 - a^2)(c^2 - a^2)}, \quad \beta^2 = \frac{(b^2 - \lambda_1)(b^2 - \lambda_2)(b^2 - \lambda_3)}{(c^2 - b^2)(a^2 - b^2)},$$

$$\gamma^2 = \frac{(c^2 - \lambda_1)(c^2 - \lambda_2)(c^2 - \lambda_3)}{(a^2 - c^2)(b^2 - c^2)}.$$

These express the co-ordinates of the point $P(\alpha, \beta, \gamma)$ in terms of the parameters of the three confocal conicoids through the point P, i.e, if the parameters λ_1, λ_2, λ_3 are given, the position of the point P can be uniquely determined. Co-ordinates λ_1, λ_2, λ_3 are called the *elliptic co-ordinates* of the point (α, β, γ) with respect to the conicoid.

EXAMPLES

1. *Prove that three paraboloids confocal with a given paraboloid pass through a given point — two elliptic and one hyperbolic.*

Sol. Let the equation of the paraboloid be

$$x^2/a^2 + y^2/b^2 = 2z \qquad \qquad ...(i)$$

Any paraboloid confocal to (i) is

$$x^2/(a^2 - \lambda) + y^2/(b^2 - \lambda) = 2z - \lambda \qquad \qquad ...(ii)$$

Let (ii) pass through the given point (α, β, γ), then we have

$$\alpha^2/(a^2 - \lambda) + \beta^2/(b^2 - \lambda) = 2\gamma - \lambda$$

$$\Rightarrow \quad f(\lambda) = \alpha^2(b^2 - \lambda) + \beta^2(a^2 - \lambda) - 2\gamma(a^2 - \lambda)(b^2 - \lambda) + \lambda(a^2 - \lambda)(b^2 - \lambda) = 0 \quad ...(iii)$$

(iii) is a cubic in λ. Hence, corresponding to these three values of λ, three paraboloids confocal to (i) pass through the given point. Let $a > b$, then

λ	=	∞,	a^2,	b^2,	$-\infty$
$f(\lambda)$	is	+,	−,	+,	−

Since $f(\lambda)$ has three changes of signs, the eqn. (iii) has three real roots λ_1, λ_2, λ_3 and are such that

$$\lambda_1 > a^2 > \lambda_2 > b^2 > \lambda_3$$

When $\lambda = \lambda_1$ and $\lambda = \lambda_3$, the eqn. (ii) will represent elliptic paraboloids, while for $\lambda = \lambda_2$, it will represent a hyperbolic paraboloid.

2. *Prove that the equation to the confocal which has a system of circular sections parallel to the plane* $x = y$ *is*

$$\frac{x^2}{(c^2 - a^2)(a^2 - b^2)} + \frac{y^2}{(b^2 - c^2)(a^2 - b^2)} - \frac{z^2}{2(b^2 - c^2)(c^2 - a^2)} = \frac{1}{2c^2 - (a^2 + b^2)}.$$

(*Avadh, 1995; Garhwal, 1996; Gorakhpur, 2001*)

Sol. Let the equation of confocal be

$$\frac{x^2}{(a^2 - \lambda)} + \frac{y^2}{(b^2 - \lambda)} + \frac{z^2}{(c^2 - \lambda)} = 1 \qquad \ldots(i)$$

It can be rewritten as

$$\frac{1}{(c^2 - \lambda)} + [x^2 + y^2 + z^2 - (c^2 - \lambda)] + x^2\left(\frac{1}{a^2 - \lambda} - \frac{1}{c^2 - \lambda}\right) + y^2\left(\frac{1}{b^2 - \lambda} - \frac{1}{c^2 - \lambda}\right) = 0$$

$$\ldots(ii)$$

It will represent a sphere if

$$x^2\left(\frac{1}{a^2 - \lambda} - \frac{1}{c^2 - \lambda}\right) + y^2\left(\frac{1}{b^2 - \lambda} - \frac{1}{c^2 - \lambda}\right) = 0$$

$$\Rightarrow \qquad x^2(b^2 - \lambda)(c^2 - a^2) = y^2(b^2 - c^2)(a^2 - \lambda) \qquad \ldots(iii)$$

Equation (*ii*) represents a pair of planes ($a^2 > b^2 > c^2$), and hence the central circular sections are given by (*iii*). The central circular section (*ii*) will be parallel to the plane $x = y$ if

$$(b^2 - \lambda)(c^2 - a^2) = (b^2 - c^2)(a^2 - \lambda)$$

$$\Rightarrow \qquad \lambda = \frac{2a^2b^2 - b^2c^2 - c^2a^2}{a^2 + b^2 - 2c^2}$$

Putting this value of λ in (*i*), the required confocal is

$$\frac{x^2}{a^2 - \dfrac{2a^2b^2 - b^2c^2 - c^2a^2}{a^2 + b^2 - 2c^2}} + \frac{y^2}{b^2 - \dfrac{2a^2b^2 - b^2c^2 - c^2a^2}{a^2 + b^2 - 2c^2}}$$

$$+ \frac{z^2}{c^2 - \dfrac{2a^2b^2 - b^2c^2 - c^2a^2}{a^2 + b^2 + c^2}} = 1$$

$$\Rightarrow \qquad \frac{x^2}{(b^2 - a^2)(a^2 - b^2)} + \frac{y^2}{(b^2 - c^2)(a^2 - b^2)} - \frac{z^2}{2(b^2 - c^2)(c^2 - a^2)} = \frac{1}{2c^2 - a^2 - b^2}.$$

3. *If* a_1, a_2, a_3 *are the primary semi-axes of the confocals to* $x^2/a^2 + y^2/b^2 + z^2/c^2 = 1$ *which pass through a point* (α, β, γ), *then show that*

$$\alpha^2 = \frac{a_1^2 a_2^2 a_3^2}{(b^2 - a^2)(c^2 - a)^2}, \quad \beta^2 = \frac{(b^2 - a^2 + a_1^2)(b^2 + a^2 + a_2^2)(b^2 - a^2 + a_3^2)}{(c^2 - b^2)(a^2 - b^2)},$$

$$\gamma^2 = \frac{(c^2 - a^2 + a_1^2)(c^2 - a^2 + a_2^2)(c^2 - a^2 + a_3^2)}{(a^2 - e^2)(b^2 - c^2)}.$$

Sol. from § 12.1.2, $\qquad f(\lambda) = (\lambda - \lambda_1)(\lambda - \lambda_2)(\lambda - \lambda_3).$

Thus, $\dfrac{\alpha^2}{(a^2 - \lambda)} + \dfrac{\beta^2}{(b^2 - \lambda)} + \dfrac{\gamma^2}{(c^2 - \lambda)} - 1 \equiv \dfrac{f(\lambda)}{(a^2 - \lambda)(b^2 - \lambda)(c^2 - \lambda)}$

$$\equiv \dfrac{(\lambda - \lambda_1)(\lambda - \lambda_2)(\lambda - \lambda_3)}{(a^2 - \lambda)(b^2 - \lambda)(c^2 - \lambda)}$$

By the rule of partial fractions

$$\alpha^2 = \dfrac{(a^2 - \lambda_1)(a^2 - \lambda_2)(a^2 - \lambda_3)}{(b^2 - a^2)(c^2 - a^2)}, \quad \beta^2 = \dfrac{(b^2 - \lambda_1)(b^2 - \lambda_2)(b^2 - \lambda_3)}{(a^2 - b^2)(c^2 - b^2)},$$

and $\quad \gamma^2 = \dfrac{(c^2 - \lambda_1)(c^2 - \lambda_2)(c^2 - \lambda_3)}{(a^2 - c^2)(b^2 - c^2)}.$

It is given that primary semi-axes are a_1, a_2, a_3.

$\therefore \qquad a^2 - \lambda_1 = a_1^2, \qquad\qquad a^2 - \lambda_2 = a_2^2, \qquad\qquad a^2 - \lambda_3 = a_3^2$

$\Rightarrow \qquad \lambda_1 = a^2 - a_1^2, \qquad\qquad \lambda_2 = a^2 - a_2^2, \qquad\qquad \lambda_3 = a^2 - a_3^2$

Putting these values of $\lambda_1, \lambda_2, \lambda_3$, the results follow.

Note. The parameters $\lambda_1, \lambda_2, \lambda_3$ are called the *elliptic co-ordinates* of P with reference to the conicoid $x^2/a^2 + y^2/b^2 + z^2/c^2 = 1$.

4. *Prove that the locus of umbilics of a system of confocal ellipsoids is the focal hyperbola.*

(*Gorakhpur, 2000*)

Sol. Equation of the confocal ellipsoid is

$$x^2/(a^2 - \lambda) + y^2/(b^2 - \lambda) + z^2/(c^2 - \lambda) = 1 \qquad\qquad ...(i)$$

The umbilics of (*i*) are (α, β, γ), then

$$\alpha = \pm \dfrac{\sqrt{a^2 - \lambda}\ \sqrt{a^2 - b^2}}{\sqrt{a^2 - c^2}}, \quad \beta = 0, \quad \gamma = \pm \dfrac{\sqrt{c^2 - \lambda}\ \sqrt{b^2 - c^2}}{\sqrt{a^2 - c^2}}$$

$\therefore \qquad a^2 - \lambda = \dfrac{\alpha^2(a^2 - c^2)}{(a^2 - b^2)}, \quad c^2 - \lambda = \dfrac{\gamma^2(a^2 - c^2)}{(b^2 - c^2)}, \quad \beta = 0$

$\Rightarrow \qquad \dfrac{\alpha^2}{(a^2 - b^2)} - \dfrac{\gamma^2}{(b^2 - c^2)} = 1, \quad \beta = 0$

Hence, the locus of umbilics (α, β, γ) is

$$x^2/(a^2 - b^2) - z^2/(b^2 - c^2) = 1, \quad y = 0$$

which represents a focal hyperbola.

5. *What loci are represented by the equations in elliptic co-ordinates :*

(*i*) $\lambda_1 + \lambda_2 + \lambda_3 = constant,$ (*ii*) $\lambda_2\lambda_3 + \lambda_3\lambda_1 + \lambda_1\lambda_2 = constant,$ *and* (*iii*) $\lambda_1\lambda_2\lambda_3 = constant$?

Sol. Elliptic co-ordinates $\lambda_1, \lambda_2, \lambda_3$ are the roots of the equation

$$f(\lambda) \equiv (a^2 - \lambda)(b^2 - \lambda)(c^2 - \lambda) - \alpha^2(b^2 - \lambda)(c^2 - \lambda) - \beta^2(c^2 - \lambda)(a^2 - \lambda)$$
$$- \gamma^2(a^2 - \lambda)(b^2 - \lambda) = 0$$

$\Rightarrow \qquad \lambda^3 - \lambda^2(a^2 + b^2 + c^2 - \alpha^2 - \beta^2 - \gamma^2)$
$$+ \lambda(a^2b^2 + b^2c^2 + c^2a^2 - \alpha^2b^2 - \alpha^2c^2 - \beta^2c^2 - \beta^2a^2 - \gamma^2a^2 - \gamma^2b^2)$$
$$- (a^2b^2c^2 - \alpha^2b^2c^2 - \beta^2c^2a^2 - \gamma^2a^2b^2) = 0$$

$$\Rightarrow \qquad \lambda_1 + \lambda_2 + \lambda_3 = a^2 + b^2 + c^2 - \alpha^2 - \beta^2 - \gamma^2$$

$$\lambda_1\lambda_2 + \lambda_2\lambda_3 + \lambda_3\lambda_1 = a^2b^2 + b^2c^2 + c^2a^2 - (b^2 + c^2)\,\alpha^2 - (c^2 + a^2)\,\beta^2 - (a^2 + b^2)\,\gamma^2$$

and

$$\lambda_1\lambda_2\lambda_3 = a^2b^2c^2 - \alpha^2b^2c^2 - \beta^2c^2a^2 - \gamma^2a^2b^2$$

(i) $\lambda_1 + \lambda_2 + \lambda_3 = $ Constant

$$\Rightarrow \qquad a^2 + b^2 + c^2 - \alpha^2 - \beta^2 - \gamma^2 = \text{Constant} = k^2 \text{ (say)}$$

$\therefore$ Locus of (α, β, γ) is

$$x^2 + y^2 + z^2 = a^2 + b^2 + c^2 - k^2$$

which is a sphere.

(ii) $\lambda_1\lambda_2 + \lambda_2\lambda_3 + \lambda_3\lambda_1 = $ Constant

$$\Rightarrow \qquad a^2b^2 + b^2c^2 + c^2a^2 - (b^2 + c^2)\,\alpha^2 - (c^2 + a^2)\,\beta^2 - (a^2 + b^2)\,\gamma^2 = \text{Constant} = k^4 \text{ (say)}$$

$\therefore$ The locus of (α, β, γ) is

$$(b^2 + c^2)\,x^2 - (c^2 + a^2)\,y^2 - (a^2 + b^2)\,z^2 = a^2b^2 + b^2c^2 + c^2a^2 - k^4.$$

This represents an ellipsoid.

(iii) $\lambda_1\lambda_2\lambda_3 = $ Constant

$$\Rightarrow \qquad a^2b^2c^2 - \alpha^2b^2c^2 - \beta^2c^2a^2 - \gamma^2a^2b^2 = \text{Constant}$$

$$\Rightarrow \qquad \alpha^2/a^2 + \beta^2/b^2 + \gamma^2/c^2 = 1 + \text{Constant} = \text{Constant}$$

$\therefore$ Locus of (α, β, γ) is

$$x^2/a^2 + y^2/b^2 + z^2/c^2 = \text{Constant}.$$

This is an ellipsoid.

EXERCISES

1. Prove that the equation to the confocal through the point of the focal ellipse whose eccentric angle is α is

$$\frac{x^2}{(a^2 - b^2)\cos^2 \alpha} - \frac{y^2}{(a^2 - b^2)\sin^2 \alpha} + \frac{z^2}{(c^2 - a^2 \sin^2 \alpha - b^2 \cos^2 \alpha)} = 1.$$

(Avadh, 1997; Gorakhpur, 1995, 2000)

2. A given plane and parallel tangent plane to a conicoid are at a distance p and p_0 from the centre. Prove that the parameter of the confocal conicoid which touches the plane is $(p_0^2 - p^2)$. *(Gorakhpur, 1999, 2003)*

3. Show that the locus of the point of intersection of three planes mutually at right angles, each of which touches one of three given confocals, is a sphere. *(Gorakhpur, 1997)*

4. Show that the two confocal paraboloids cut everywhere at right angles.

5. Prove that the perpendiculars from the origin to the tangent planes to the ellipsoid which touch it along its curve of intersection with the confocal whose parameter is λ, lie on the cone

$$\frac{a^2x^2}{(a^2 - \lambda)} + \frac{b^2y^2}{(b^2 - \lambda)} + \frac{c^2z^2}{(c^2 - \lambda)} = 0.$$

6. If a straight line touches two conicoids confocal with a given conicoid then show that the tangent planes at the points of contact will be at right angles

12.4. CONFOCALS THROUGH A POINT ON A CONICOID

To prove that the parameters of the two confocals through any point P of a conicoid are equal to the square of the axes of the central section of the conicoid which is parallel to the tangent plane at P, and the normals at P to the confocals are parallel to the axes of that section.

Let $P(x_1, y_1, z_1)$ be any point on the conicoid

$$x^2/a^2 + y^2/b^2 + z^2/c^2 = 1 \qquad \qquad ...(i)$$

Let a confocal conicoid be

$$x^2/(a^2 - \lambda) + y^2/(b^2 - \lambda) + z^2/(c^2 - \lambda) = 1 \qquad \qquad ...(ii)$$

If P lies on (ii), then

$$x_1^2/(a^2 - \lambda) + y_1^2/(b^2 - \lambda) + z_1^2/(c^2 - \lambda) = 1 \qquad \qquad ...(iii)$$

Also,
$$x_1^2/a^2 + y_1^2/b^2 + z_1^2/c^2 = 1 \qquad \qquad ...(iv)$$

From (iii) and (iv), we get

$$x_1^2/(a^2 - \lambda) + y_1^2/(b^2 - \lambda) + z_1^2/(c^2 - \lambda) = x_1^2/a^2 + y_1^2/b^2 + z_1^2/c^2$$

$$\Rightarrow \qquad \frac{x_1^2}{a^2(a^2 - \lambda)} + \frac{y_1^2}{b^2(b^2 - \lambda)} + \frac{z_1^2}{c^2(c^2 - \lambda)} = 0 \qquad \qquad ...(v)$$

Equation of the central section of the given conicoid parallel to the tangent plane at P is

$$xx_1/a^2 + yy_1/b^2 + zz_1/c^2 = 0 \qquad \qquad ...(vi)$$

and the squares of the semi-axes of this section are given by

$$\frac{x_1^2}{a^2(a^2 - r^2)} + \frac{y_1^2}{b^2(b^2 - r^2)} + \frac{z_1^2}{c^2(c^2 - r^2)} = 0 \qquad \qquad ...(vii)$$

Hence, the values of λ are the squares of the semi-axes of this section.

Again the direction cosines (l, m, n) of the semi-axis of length r are given by

$$\frac{l}{x_1/(a^2 - r^2)} = \frac{m}{y_1/(b^2 - r^2)} = \frac{n}{z_1/(c^2 - r^2)}$$

so that the axis is parallel to the normal at (x_1, y_1, z_1) to the confocal conicoids. Hence, the theorem.

12.4.1. Locus of Poles of a Plane With Respect to Confocals

To prove that the locus of the poles of a given plane with respect to a system of confocal conicoids is the normal to the plane at the point of contact with the confocal.

(*Gorakhpur, 1999, 2002*)

Let given plane be $\qquad \qquad lx + my + nz = 1 \qquad \qquad ...(i)$

and the equation of confocal be

$$x^2/(a^2 - \lambda) + y^2/(b^2 - \lambda) + z^2/(c^2 - \lambda) = 1 \qquad \qquad ...(ii)$$

The polar plane of the point (x', y', z') is

$$xx'/(a^2 - \lambda) + yy'/(b^2 - \lambda) + zz'/(c^2 - \lambda) = 1 \qquad \qquad ...(iii)$$

On comparing it with (i), we have

$$x'/(a^2 - \lambda) = l, \ y'/(b^2 - \lambda) = m, \ z'/(c^2 - \lambda) = n$$

$$\Rightarrow \qquad x'/l - a^2 = y'/m - b^2 = z'/n - c^2 = -\lambda$$

and the locus of the pole is the straight line whose equations are

$$\frac{x - a^2 l}{l} = \frac{y - b^2 m}{m} = \frac{z - c^2 n}{n}$$

These lines are at right angles to the given plane. Further, the pole with respect to that confocal which touches the plane also lies on this line. But this pole is the point of contact of the plane and the conicoid. Hence, the proposition.

12.4.2. Normals to the Confocals Through a Point

Let the confocals of the conicoid

$$x^2/a^2 + y^2/b^2 + z^2/c^2 = 1 \qquad \ldots(i)$$

which pass through $P(\alpha, \beta, \gamma)$ have parameters $\lambda_1, \lambda_2, \lambda_3$ and let p_1, p_2, p_3 be the perpendiculars from $(0, 0, 0)$, the centre of conicoid to the tangent planes at P to the confocals.

The equations of normal at $P(\alpha, \beta, \gamma)$ to the confocal of parameter λ_1 are

$$\frac{x - \alpha}{p_1 \alpha / (a^2 - \lambda_1)} = \frac{y - \beta}{p_1 \beta / (b^2 - \lambda_1)} = \frac{z - \gamma}{p_1 \gamma (c^2 - \lambda_1)} \qquad \ldots(ii)$$

The co-ordinates of any point Q on it $(PQ = r)$ are

$$\left[\alpha \left(1 + \frac{p_1 r}{a^2 - \lambda_1} \right), \ \beta \left(1 + \frac{p_1 r}{b^2 - \lambda_1} \right), \ \gamma \left(1 + \frac{p_1 r}{c^2 - \lambda_1} \right) \right].$$

The polar plane of P, w.r.t. the given conicoid is

$$\frac{\alpha x}{a^2} + \frac{\beta y}{b^2} + \frac{\gamma z}{c^2} = 1 \qquad \ldots(iii)$$

If Q lies in (iii), then

$$\frac{\alpha^2}{a^2} \left(1 + \frac{p_1 r}{a^2 - \lambda_1} \right) + \frac{\beta^2}{b^2} \left(1 + \frac{p_1 r}{b^2 - \lambda_1} \right) + \frac{\gamma^2}{c^2} \left(1 + \frac{p_1 r}{c^2 - \lambda_1} \right) = 1 \qquad \ldots(iv)$$

Also

$$\frac{\alpha^2}{a^2 - \lambda_1} + \frac{\beta^2}{b^2 - \lambda_1} + \frac{\gamma^2}{c^2 - \lambda_1} = 1 \qquad \ldots(v)$$

Subtracting (iv) from (iii), we get

$$\left[\frac{\alpha^2}{a^2 (a^2 - \lambda_1)} + \frac{\beta^2}{b^2 (b^2 - \lambda_1)} + \frac{\gamma^2}{c^2 (c^2 - \lambda_1)} \right] (p_1 r - \lambda_1) = 0.$$

Hence, $\qquad\qquad p_1 r - \lambda_1 = 0 \Rightarrow r = PQ = \lambda_1 / p_1.$

Similarly, we can show that if the normals at P to the other two confocals (parameters λ_2, λ_3) meet the polar plane of P in R and S, then

$$PR = \lambda_1 / p_2 \text{ and } PS = \lambda_3 / p_3.$$

Corollary. Putting $p_1 r = \lambda_1$, the co-ordinates of Q become :

$$\alpha \left(1 + \frac{\lambda_1}{a^2 - \lambda_1} \right), \ \beta \left(1 + \frac{\lambda_1}{b^2 - \lambda_1} \right), \ \gamma \left(1 + \frac{\lambda_1}{c^2 - \lambda_1} \right)$$

$$\Rightarrow \qquad \left(\frac{a^2 \alpha}{a^2 - \lambda_1}, \ \frac{b^2 \beta}{b^2 - \lambda_1}, \ \frac{c^2 \gamma}{c^2 - \lambda_1} \right)$$

Hence the equation of the polar plane of Q with regard to the conicoid is

$$\frac{\alpha x}{a^2 - \lambda_1} + \frac{\beta y}{b^2 - \lambda_1} + \frac{\gamma z}{c^2 - \lambda_1} = 1$$

which is the same as the tangent plane to the confocal at the point $P(\alpha, \beta, \gamma)$. This tangent plane contains the normals PR and PS. Hence, the polar plane of Q is the plane PRS. In a similar manner, it can be proved that the polar plane of R in the plane PQS, the polar plane of S in the plane PQR and the polar plane of P is the plane QRS.

Hence, *tetrahedron PQRS is self-polar with respect to the given conicoid.*

Remark : We have seen that the tetrahedron $PQRS$ is self-polar with respect to the conicoid. It follows from it that the triangle QRS is self-polar with regard to the common section of the conicoid (i) and the enveloping cone by the plane QRS. Hence, the normals PQ, PR and PS are the conjugate diameters of the enveloping cone with the vertex at P. Since PQ, PR and PS are mutually orthogonal, they are the principal axes of the enveloping cone with the vertex at the point P.

12.4.3. Enveloping Cone

Let us take P as origin, the tangent plane at P to the three confocals as the co-ordinate planes, and the normals PQ, PR and PS as the co-ordinate axes. Then the equation to the enveloping cone is of the form

$$Ax^2 + By^2 + Cz^2 = 0 \qquad \qquad ...(i)$$

The centre C of the conicoid is $(-p_1, -p_2, -p_3)$ and therefore, the equations to the line PC are

$$x/p_1 = y/p_2 = z/p_3 \qquad \qquad ...(ii)$$

As the centre of the section of the cone or the conicoid by the plane QRS lies on PC, its co-ordinates must be (kp_1, kp_2, kp_3).

Then the equation of QRS will be

$$Ap_1(x - kp_1) + Bp_2(y - kp_2) + Cp_3(z - kp_3) = 0 \qquad \qquad ...(iii)$$

Again the normals being the axes of reference, the plane QRS makes intercepts λ_1/p_2, λ_2/p_2, λ_3/p_3 on them (§ 12.3.2). Hence, the equation is also given by

$$\frac{x}{\lambda_1/p_1} + \frac{y}{\lambda_2/p_2} + \frac{z}{\lambda_3/p_3} = 1$$

$$\Rightarrow \qquad \frac{p_1 x}{\lambda_1} + \frac{p_2 y}{\lambda_2} + \frac{p_3 z}{\lambda_3} = 1 \qquad \qquad ...(iv)$$

Hence, $$\frac{A}{1/\lambda_1} = \frac{B}{1/\lambda_2} = \frac{C}{1/\lambda_3}$$

Therefore, the equation of enveloping cone becomes

$$x^2/\lambda_1 + y^2/\lambda_2 + z^2/\lambda_3 = 0 \qquad \qquad ...(v)$$

$$(Gorakhpur, 1996)$$

12.4.4. Corresponding Point

Def. Two points (x_1, y_1, z_1) and (ξ_1, η_1, ζ_1) one on each of the coaxial conicoids whose equation are

$$x^2/a^2 + y^2/b^2 + z^2/c^2 = 1 \qquad \qquad ...(i)$$

and $$x^2/\alpha^2 + y^2/\beta^2 + z^2/\gamma^2 = 1 \qquad \qquad ...(ii)$$

are said to correspond when

$$\frac{x_1}{a} = \frac{\xi_1}{\alpha}, \frac{y_1}{b} = \frac{\eta_1}{\beta}, \frac{z_1}{c} = \frac{\zeta_1}{\gamma} \qquad \qquad ...(iii)$$

In order that real points on one conicoid may correspond to real points on the other, the two surfaces must be of the same nature and must be similarly placed.

Let $P(x_1, y_1, z_1)$ and $Q(x_2, y_2, z_2)$ be the two points on the first conicoid and $P'(\xi_1, \eta_1, \zeta_1)$ and $Q'(\xi_2, \eta_2, \zeta_2)$ be the corresponding points on the other conicoid which is confocal to the first, we have

$$\frac{x_1}{a} = \frac{\xi_1}{\alpha}, \frac{y_1}{b} = \frac{\eta_1}{\beta}, \frac{z_1}{c} = \frac{\zeta_1}{\gamma}$$

$$\frac{x_2}{a} = \frac{\xi_2}{\alpha}, \frac{y_2}{b} = \frac{\eta_2}{\beta}, \frac{z_2}{c} = \frac{\zeta_2}{\gamma}$$

and

$$a^2 - \alpha^2 = b^2 - \beta^2 = c^2 - \gamma^2 = \lambda$$

Now, $PQ'^2 = (x_1 - \xi_2)^2 + (y_1 - \eta_2)^2 + (z_1 - \zeta_2)^2$

$$= \left(\frac{a}{\alpha}\xi_1 - \frac{\alpha}{a}x_2\right)^2 + \left(\frac{b}{\beta}\eta_1 - \frac{\beta}{b}y_2\right)^2 + \left(\frac{c}{\gamma}\zeta_1 - \frac{\gamma}{c}z_2\right)^2$$

and

$$P'Q^2 = (x_2 - \xi_1)^2 + (y_2 - \eta_1)^2 + (z_2 - \zeta_1)^2$$

$$\Rightarrow \quad PQ'^2 - P'Q^2 = \sum\left[\left(\frac{a}{\alpha}\xi_1 - \frac{\alpha}{a}x\right)^2 - (x_2 - \zeta_1)^2\right]$$

$$= (a^2 - \alpha^2)\left(\frac{\xi_1^2}{\alpha^2} - \frac{x_2^2}{a^2}\right) + (b^2 - \beta^2)\left(\frac{\eta_1^2}{\beta^2} - \frac{y_2^2}{b^2}\right)$$

$$+ (c^2 - \gamma^2)\left(\frac{\zeta_1^2}{\gamma^2} - \frac{z_2^2}{c^2}\right)$$

$$= \lambda\left[\left(\frac{\xi_1^2}{\alpha^2} + \frac{\eta_1^2}{\beta^2} + \frac{\zeta_1^2}{\gamma^2}\right) - \left(\frac{x_2^2}{a^2} + \frac{y_2^2}{b^2} + \frac{z_2^2}{c^2}\right)\right] = \lambda(1 - 1) = 0$$

$$\therefore \qquad PQ' = P'Q.$$

Hence, the distance between two points one on each of the two confocal ellipsoids is equal to the distance between the two corresponding points.

12.5. EQUATION TO CONICOID REFERRED TO THE NORMALS AS AXES

(Gorakhpur, 1995, 99)

Let three conicoids confocal with a given conicoid $x^2/a^2 + y^2/b^2 + z^2/c^2 = 1$ pass through a given point P and PQ, PR, PS the normals at P to the confocals, meet the polar plane of P with respect to the given conicoid in Q, R, S. Now we are to find the equation of the conicoid with reference to the normals PQ, PR and PS as co-ordinate axes.

The conicoid will be having contact with the cone along the section of the cone and the plane QRS and hence the equation of the conicoid will be of the form

$$\left(\frac{x^2}{\lambda_1} + \frac{y^2}{\lambda_2} + \frac{z^2}{\lambda_3}\right) = k\left(\frac{p_1 x}{\lambda_1} + \frac{p_2 y}{\lambda_2} + \frac{p_3 z}{\lambda_3} - 1\right)^2 \qquad \ldots(i)$$

The centre $O(-p_1, -p_2, -p_3)$ of the conicoid bisects all chords passing through it. The equations of the chord parallel to x-axis, i.e., PQ, are given by

$$\frac{x + p_1}{1} = \frac{y + p_2}{0} = \frac{z + p_3}{0} = r \text{ (say)} \qquad \ldots(i)$$

Let the chord (*ii*) meets the conicoid (*i*) in the point $(r - p_1, - p_2, - p_3)$. Then

$$\frac{(r - p_1)^2}{\lambda_1} + \frac{p_2{}^2}{\lambda_2} + \frac{p_3{}^2}{\lambda_3} = k\left[\frac{p_1(r - p_1)}{\lambda_1} - \frac{p_2{}^2}{\lambda_2} - \frac{p_3{}^2}{\lambda_3} - 1\right]^2 \qquad ...(iii)$$

The equation (*iii*) being a quadratic in r shows that the chord (*ii*) meets the conicoid (*i*) in two points. Since the centre is the middle point of the chord, the two values of r should be equal in magnitude but opposite in signs. Hence if r_1 and r_2 be the roots of (*iii*), then $r_1 + r_2 = 0$.

$\Rightarrow$ coeff. of $r = 0$

$$\Rightarrow \qquad \frac{2p_1}{\lambda_1} + \frac{2kp_1}{\lambda_1}\left(\frac{p_1{}^2}{\lambda_1} + \frac{p_2{}^2}{\lambda_2} + \frac{p_3{}^2}{\lambda_3} + 1\right) = 0$$

$$\Rightarrow \qquad \frac{1}{k} = \frac{p_1{}^2}{\lambda_1} + \frac{p_2{}^2}{\lambda_2} + \frac{p_3{}^2}{\lambda_3} + 1$$

Putting the value of k in (*i*), the equation of the conicoid is

$$\left(\frac{x^2}{\lambda_1} + \frac{y^2}{\lambda_2} + \frac{z^2}{\lambda_3}\right)\left(\frac{p_1{}^2}{\lambda_1} + \frac{p_2{}^2}{\lambda_2} + \frac{p_3{}^2}{\lambda_3} + 1\right) = \left(\frac{p_1 x}{\lambda_1} + \frac{p_2 y}{\lambda_2} + \frac{p_3 z}{\lambda_3} - 1\right)^2.$$

EXAMPLES

1. *Three conicoids confocal with a given conicoid $x^2/a^2 + y^2/b^2 + z^2/c^2 = 1$ pass through a given point P and PQ, PR, PS the normals at P to the confocals, meet the polar plane of P with respect to the given conicoid in Q, R, S. Prove that the tetrahedron PQRS is self-polar with respect to the given conicoid.*

Sol. The co-ordinates of the point Q (§ 12.3.2) are

$$\left[\alpha\left(1 + \frac{p_1 r}{a^2 - \lambda_1}\right), \beta\left(1 + \frac{p_1 r}{b^2 - \lambda_1}\right), \gamma\left(1 + \frac{p_1 r}{c^2 - \lambda_1}\right)\right]$$

where $p_1 r = \lambda_1$. Hence, the co-ordinates reduce to

$$\left(\frac{a^2\alpha}{a^2 - \lambda_1}, \frac{b^2\beta}{b^2 - \lambda_1}, \frac{c^2\gamma}{c^2 - \lambda_1}\right).$$

Polar plane of Q with respect to the given conicoid is

$$\frac{\alpha x}{a^2 - \lambda_1} + \frac{\beta y}{b^2 - \lambda_1} + \frac{\gamma z}{c^2 - \lambda_1} = 1$$

which is also the tangent plane at P to the confocal whose parameter is λ_1, *i.e.*, the plane perpendicular to PQ.

But the normals to the three confocals through P, *viz*., PQ, PR, PS are mutually perpendicular. Therefore, the tangent plane at P to the first confocal is the plane PRS.

It follows that the polar plane of Q is PRS, and similarly, the polar planes of R and S are PSQ and PRQ, while the polar plane of P is QRS. Hence, the tetrahedron $PQRS$ is self-polar with respect to the conicoid.

2. *Prove that the difference of the squares of the perpendiculars from the centre on any two parallel tangent planes to two given confocal conicoids is constant.*

Sol. Let the two confocal conicoids of

$$\frac{x^2}{a^2} + \frac{y^2}{b^2} + \frac{z^2}{c^2} = 1$$

be

$$\frac{x^2}{a^2 - \lambda_1} + \frac{y^2}{b^2 - \lambda_2} + \frac{z^2}{c^2 - \lambda_1} = 1 \qquad \ldots(i)$$

and

$$\frac{x^2}{a^2 - \lambda_2} + \frac{y^2}{b^2 - \lambda_2} + \frac{z^2}{c^2 - \lambda_2} = 1 \qquad \ldots(ii)$$

where λ_1 and λ_2 are constants.

Now, if p_1 and p_2 be lengths of perpendiculars from the centre on the two parallel planes

$$lx + my + nz = p_1 \qquad \ldots(iii)$$
and
$$lx + my + nz = p_2 \qquad \ldots(iv)$$

where (l, m, n) are direction cosines of the normals to these planes.

$\therefore$ If (iii) is a tangent plane of (i), we have

$$l^2 (a^2 - \lambda_1) + m^2 (b^2 - \lambda_1) + n^2 (c^2 - \lambda_1) = p_1^2$$

Similarly, $l^2 (a^2 - \lambda_2) + m^2 (b^2 - \lambda_2) + n^2 (c^2 - \lambda_2) = p_2^2.$

On subtraction, we have

$$(p_2^2 - p_1^2) = l^2 (\lambda_2 - \lambda_1) + m^2 (\lambda_2 - \lambda_1) + n^2 (\lambda_2 - \lambda_1)$$
$$= (l^2 + m^2 + n^2) (\lambda_2 - \lambda_1) = \lambda_2 - \lambda_1 = \text{Constant.}$$

3. *OP, OQ, OR are conjugate diameters of an ellipsoid and P', Q', R' are the points of a concentric sphere corresponding to P, Q, R. Prove that OP', OQ', OR' are mutually perpendicular.*

Sol. Let the co-ordinates of P, Q and R be (x_r, y_r, z_r), $r = 1, 2, 3$. Now if OP, OQ and OR are conjugate diameters of the ellipsoid

$$\frac{x^2}{a^2} + \frac{y^2}{b^2} + \frac{z^2}{c^2} = 1 \qquad \ldots(i)$$

then we must have

$$\frac{x_1^2}{a^2} + \frac{y_1^2}{b^2} + \frac{z_1^2}{a^2} = 1, \qquad \frac{x_2^2}{a^2} + \frac{y_2^2}{b^2} + \frac{z_2^2}{c^2} = 1,$$

$$\frac{x_3^2}{a^2} + \frac{y_3^2}{b^2} + \frac{z_3^2}{c^2} = 1, \qquad \frac{x_1 x_2}{a^2} + \frac{y_1 y_2}{b^2} + \frac{z_1 z_2}{c^2} = 0,$$

$$\frac{x_2 x_3}{a^2} + \frac{y_2 y_3}{b^2} + \frac{z_2 z_3}{c^2} = 0, \qquad \frac{x_3 x_1}{a^2} + \frac{y_3 y_1}{b^2} + \frac{z_3 z_1}{c^2} = 0 \qquad \ldots(ii)$$

Now, any sphere concentric with ellipsoid is

$$x^2 + y^2 + z^2 = r^2 \qquad \ldots(iii)$$

Let $P'(\xi_1, \eta_1, \zeta_1)$, $Q'(\xi_2, \eta_2, \zeta_2)$ and $R'(\xi_3, \eta_3, \zeta_3)$ be the points of the sphere (iii) corresponding to the points P, Q and R respectively. Then we must have

$$\frac{x_1}{a} = \frac{\xi_1}{r}, \frac{y_1}{b} = \frac{\eta_1}{r}, \frac{z_1}{c} = \frac{\zeta_1}{r} \text{ etc.}$$

Now, direction ratios of OP', OQ' and OR' are

$$\xi_1, \eta_1, \zeta_1; \xi_2, \eta_2, \zeta_2 \text{ and } \xi_3, \eta_3, \zeta_3$$

respectively.

Now,
$$\xi_1\xi_2 + \eta_1\eta_2 + \zeta_1\zeta_2 = \frac{rx_1}{a}\cdot\frac{rx_2}{a} + \frac{ry_1}{b}\cdot\frac{ry_2}{b} + \frac{rz_1}{c}\cdot\frac{rz_2}{c}$$

$$= r^2\left(\frac{x_1x_2}{a^2} + \frac{y_1y_2}{b^2} + \frac{z_1z_2}{c^2}\right) = 0.$$

$\Rightarrow$ OP' is perpendicular to OQ'.

Similarly we can prove that OP' is perpendicular to OR' and OQ' is perpendicular to OR'.

Hence OP', OQ' and OR' are mutually perpendicular.

4. *P and Q are any points on a generator of a hyperboloid and P' and Q' are the corresponding points on a second hyperboloid. Prove that P' and Q' lie on a generator of the latter.*

Sol. Let P and Q be the points (x_1, y_1, z_1) and (x_2, y_2, z_2) on the hyperboloid

$$x^2/a^2 + y^2/b^2 + z^2/c^2 = 1 \qquad \text{...(i)}$$

Let P' and Q' be the points (ξ_1, η_1, ζ_1) and (ξ_2, η_2, ζ_2) on the hyperboloid

$$x^2/\alpha^2 + y^2/\beta^2 + z^2/\gamma^2 = 1 \qquad \text{...(ii)}$$

Let P' and Q' be the corresponding points of P and Q, hence

$$\frac{x_1}{a} = \frac{\xi_1}{\alpha}, \quad \frac{y_1}{b} = \frac{\eta_1}{\beta}, \quad \frac{z_1}{c} = \frac{\zeta_1}{\gamma}$$

and
$$\frac{x_2}{a} = \frac{\xi_2}{a}, \quad \frac{y_2}{b} = \frac{\eta_2}{\beta}, \quad \frac{z_2}{c} = \frac{\zeta_2}{\gamma} \qquad \text{...(iii)}$$

Since P and Q lie on a generator of the first hyperboloid, hence each lies on the tangent plane at the other, the condition for which is

$$\frac{x_1x_2}{a^2} + \frac{y_1y_2}{b^2} - \frac{z_1z_2}{c^2} = 1$$

by (iii)

$$\frac{\xi_1\xi_2}{\alpha^2} + \frac{\eta_1\eta_2}{\beta^2} - \frac{\zeta_1\zeta_2}{\gamma^2} = 1$$

which shows that the point P' (or Q') lies on tangent plane to the second hyperboloid at Q' (or P').

Hence, P' and Q' lie on a generator of the second hyperboloid.

EXERCISES

1. If λ and μ are the parameters of the confocal hyperboloids through a point P on the ellipsoid $x^2/a^2 + y^2/b^2 + z^2/c^2 = 1$, then prove that the perpendicular from the centre to the tangent plane at P to the ellipsoid is $abc/\sqrt{\lambda\mu}$. Prove that the perpendiculars to the tangent planes to the hyperboloids are

$$\left[\frac{(a^2 - \lambda)(b^2 - \lambda)(c^2 - \lambda)}{\lambda(\lambda - \mu)}\right]^{1/2} \quad \text{and} \quad \left[\frac{(a^2 - \mu)(b^2 - \mu)(c^2 - \mu)}{\mu(\mu - \lambda)}\right]^{1/2}$$

(Gorakhpur, 1997; Avadh, 1996)

2. If $\lambda_1, \lambda_2, \lambda_3$ are the parameters of three confocals to $x^2/a^2 + y^2/b^2 + z^2/c^2 = 1$ that pass through P, prove that the perpendiculars from the centre of the tangent plane at P are

$$\left[\frac{(a^2 - \lambda_1)(b^2 - \lambda_1)(c^2 - \lambda_1)}{(\lambda_2 - \lambda_1)(\lambda_3 - \lambda_1)}\right]^{1/2} \quad \text{etc.}$$

3. Show that two confocal paraboloids cut everywhere at right angles.

4. If P is a point on an ellipsoid and P' is the corresponding point on a confocal whose parameter is λ, then prove that $OP^2 - OP'^2 = \lambda$, where O is the centre.

5. Find the equation to the conicoid $x^2/a^2 + y^2/b^2 + z^2/c^2 = 1$ referred to the normals to its confocals through any point P as co-ordinates axes.

$$\left[\textbf{Ans.} \ \left(\frac{x^2}{\lambda_1} + \frac{y^2}{\lambda_2} + \frac{z^2}{\lambda_3}\right)\left(\frac{p_1^{\,2}}{\lambda_1} + \frac{p_2^{\,2}}{\lambda_2} + \frac{p_3^{\,2}}{\lambda_3} + 1\right) = \left(\frac{p_1 x}{\lambda_1} + \frac{p_2 y}{\lambda_2} + \frac{p_3 z}{\lambda_3} - 1\right)^2\right]$$

6. If $a_1, b_1, c_1; a_2, b_2, c_2; a_3, b_3, c_3$ are the axes of the confocals to $x^2/\alpha^2 + y^2/\beta^2 + z^2/\gamma^2 = 1$ which pass through a point (ξ, η, ζ) and p_1, p_2, p_3 are the perpendiculars from the centre to the tangent planes to the confocals at the point, prove that

    (i) $\xi^2 + \eta^2 + \zeta^2 = a_1^{\,2} + b_2^{\,2} + c_3^{\,2}$ *(Gorakhpur, 1998)*

    (ii) $p_1^{\,2}/a_1^{\,2} + p_2^{\,2}/a_2^{\,2} + p_3^{\,2}/a_3^{\,2} = 1$

    (iii) $\dfrac{p_1^{\,2}}{a_1^{\,2} - \alpha^2} + \dfrac{p_2^{\,2}}{a_2^{\,2} - \alpha^2} + \dfrac{p_3^{\,2}}{a_3^{\,2} - \alpha^2} - 1 = \dfrac{\alpha^2 \beta^2 \gamma^2}{(a_1^{\,2} - \alpha^2)(a_2^{\,2} - \alpha^2)(a_3^{\,2} - \alpha^2)}.$

12.6. FOCUS AND DIRECTRIX

There are two definitions of a conicoid which correspond to the focus and directrix definition of a conic.

I. The definition according to *Maccullagh* is as follows :

The conicoid is the locus of a point which moves so that its distance from a fixed point is in a constant ratio to its distance from a given straight line measured parallel to a given plane.

The fixed point is called the *focus* and the given line the *directrix*.

Let the given plane be $z = 0$ and the point of intersection of the given line and given plane be the origin. Choosing rectangular axes, let the fixed point be (α, β, γ) and the given line be

$$x/l = y/m = z/n \qquad\qquad \text{...(i)}$$

Let (ξ, η, ζ) be any point on the locus. Then the plane through it parallel to $z = 0$ will meet the given line in the point $(l\zeta/n, m\zeta/n, \zeta)$.

The distance of (ξ, η, ζ) from the line measured parallel to the given plane is, therefore,

$$\sqrt{\{(\xi - l\zeta/n)^2 + (\eta - m\zeta/n)\}^2}$$

Hence, according to the definition, the locus will be

$$(x - \alpha)^2 + (y - \beta)^2 + (z - \gamma)^2 = k^2 \{(x - lz/n)^2 + (y - mz/n)^2\} \qquad \text{...(ii)}$$

This is the equation of conicoid.

This conicoid is of the form

$$\lambda\varphi - (u^2 + v^2) = 0 \qquad\qquad \text{...(iii)}$$

where $\varphi = (x - \alpha)^2 + (y - \beta)^2 + (z - \gamma)^2$ and $u = 0$, $v = 0$ represent planes.

II. The other definition is due to *Salmon* and is as follows :

The conicoid is the locus of a point the square of whose distance from a fixed point varies as the product of its distances from two given planes.

The fixed point is called the *focus* and the line of intersection of the two given planes the *directrix*.

Clearly, the equation of the locus is of the form

$$(x - \alpha)^2 + (y - \beta)^2 + (z - \gamma)^2 = k^2 (lx + my + nz + p)(l'x + m'y + n'z + p')$$

which is the equation of the conicoid.

This is of the form $\lambda\varphi - uv = 0$, where φ, u, v have the same meaning as before.

Now in either case if $S = 0$ represents the locus of the point, then

$$S - \lambda\varphi = 0$$

represents a pair of planes, which are imaginary in Case I and real in Case II. But their line of intersection, viz., $u = 0 = v$ is real in both cases.

Thus, we have the following rule for finding the focus and directrix of a conicoid :

If $S = 0$ is the equation to a conicoid and λ, α, β, γ are constants such that the equations $S - \lambda\varphi = 0$ represents two planes (real or imaginary), then (α, β, γ) is a focus and the line of intersection of the two planes is the corresponding directrix.

12.6.1. Foci of $ax^2 + by^2 + cz^2 = 1$

From § 12.4, if (α, β, γ) is the focus, then

$$ax^2 + by^2 + cz^2 - 1 - \lambda\left[(x - \alpha)^2 + (y - \beta)^2 + (z - \gamma)^2\right] \qquad \text{...}(i)$$

must be the product of two linear factors.

Hence, λ must be equal to a, or b, or c.

(*i*) When $\lambda = a$, (*i*) becomes

$$(b - a) y^2 + (c - a) z^2 + 2a\alpha x + 2a\beta y + 2a\gamma z - a (\alpha^2 + \beta^2 + \gamma^2) - 1$$

$$\Rightarrow \quad (b - a)\left(y + \frac{a\beta}{b - a}\right)^2 + (c - a)\left(z + \frac{a\gamma}{c - a}\right)^2 - \frac{ab\beta^2}{b - \alpha} - \frac{ac\gamma^2}{c - a} - 1 + 2a\alpha x - a\alpha^2.$$

In order that this may be resolved into two linear factors, we must have $a = 0$, and

$$\frac{ab\beta^2}{b - a} + \frac{ac\gamma^2}{c - a} + 1 = 0 \quad \Rightarrow \quad \frac{\beta^2}{(1/b - 1/a)} + \frac{\gamma^2}{(1/c - 1/a)} = 1$$

(*ii*) Similarly, when $\lambda = b$, we have

$$\beta = 0 \text{ and } \frac{\alpha^2}{(1/a - 1/c)} + \frac{\beta^2}{(1/b - 1/c)} = 1$$

and

(*iii*) When $\lambda = c$, we have

$$\gamma = 0 \text{ and } \frac{\alpha^2}{(1/a - 1/c)} + \frac{\beta^2}{(1/b - 1/c)} = 1$$

There are, therefore, three conics, one in each principal plane on which the principal foci lie.

If the surface is the ellipsoid

$$x^2/a^2 + y^2/b^2 + z^2/c^2 = 1 \ (a > b > c)$$

the conics on which the foci lie are

$$x = 0, \ y^2/(b^2 - a^2) + z^2/(c^2 - a^2) = 1$$
$$y = 0, \ z^2/(c^2 - b^2) + x^2/(a^2 - b^2) = 1$$
$$z = 0, \ x^2/(a^2 - c^2) + y^2/(b^2 - c^2) = 1$$

and

Of these, the first is imaginary, while the other two are real.

These are known as *focal conics*, the one being an ellipse and the other a hyperbola. They are also the boundaries of limiting case of confocal conicoids as shown in § 12.1.

It is obvious that confocal conicoids have the same focal conics.

EXAMPLES

1. *Show that the focal conics of a paraboloid are two parabolas.*

Sol. Let the equation of the paraboloid be

$$ax^2 + by^2 = 2z \qquad \ldots(i)$$

Let (α, β, γ) be a focus. Then

$$ax^2 - by^2 - 2z - \lambda\{(x-\alpha)^2 + (y-\beta)^2 + (z-\gamma)^2\} = 0 \qquad \ldots(ii)$$

represents a pair of planes.

(i) When $\lambda = a$, then from (ii)

$$2a\alpha x - a\alpha^2 + (b-a)y^2 + 2a\beta y - a\beta^2 - az^2 + 2(a\gamma - 1)z - a\gamma^2 = 0$$

$$\Rightarrow \quad 2a\alpha x - a\alpha^2 + (b-a)\left(y + \frac{a\beta}{b-a}\right)^2 - a\left(z - \frac{a\gamma - 1}{a}\right)^2 - \frac{ab\beta^2}{b-a} - \frac{2a\gamma - 1}{a} = 0$$

This will represent two planes, if

$$\alpha = 0 \text{ and } \frac{ab\beta^2}{b-a} + \frac{2a\gamma - 1}{a} = 0 \qquad \ldots(iii)$$

(ii) When $\lambda = b$, then

$$(a-b)x^2 + 2b\alpha x - b\alpha^2 - 2b\beta y - b\beta^2 - bz^2 - 2(b\gamma - 1)z - b\gamma^2 = 0$$

$$\Rightarrow \quad (a-b)\left(x + \frac{b\alpha}{a-b}\right)^2 + 2b\beta y - b\beta^2 - b\left(z - \frac{b\gamma - 1}{b}\right)^2 - \frac{abz^2}{a-b} - \frac{2b\gamma - 1}{b} = 0$$

and in order that this may represent two planes we must have

$$\beta = 0 \text{ and } \frac{ab\alpha^2}{a-b} + \frac{2b\gamma - 1}{b} = 0 \qquad \ldots(iv)$$

From eqns. (iii) and (iv), we have that the foci of the paraboloid lie on the conics

$$x = 0, \quad \frac{y^2}{1/a - 1/b} + 2z - \frac{1}{a} = 0$$

and

$$y = 0, \quad \frac{x^2}{1/b - 1/a} + 2z - \frac{1}{b} = 0$$

These are two parabolas and are known as the *focal parabolas* of the paraboloid.

2. *Through a straight line in one of the principal planes, tangent planes are drawn to a system of confocals. Prove that the points of contact lie on a plane and that the normals at these points pass through a fixed point in the principal plane.*

Sol. The tangent plane to a confocal

$$x^2/(a^2 - \lambda) + y^2/(b^2 - \lambda) + z^2/(c^2 - \lambda) = 1 \qquad \ldots(i)$$

and the point (x', y', z') is

$$xx'/(a^2 - \lambda) + yy'/(b^2 - \lambda) + zz'/(c^2 - \lambda) = 1 \qquad \ldots(ii)$$

This passes through the given line

$$\left. \begin{array}{r} lx + my = 1 \\ z = 0 \end{array} \right\} \qquad \ldots(iii)$$

in the xy-plane if $\qquad x'/(a^2 - \lambda) = l$ and $y'/(b^2 - \lambda) = m$

Eliminating λ, we have $\qquad x'/l - y'/m = a^2 - b^2$

Therefore, the points of contact of tangent planes through the given line in the xy-plane, lie on the plane

$$x/l - y/m = a^2 - b^2 \qquad\qquad ...(iv)$$

The normal at (x', y', z') is

$$\frac{x - x'}{x'/(a^2 - \lambda)} = \frac{y - y'}{y'/(b^2 - \lambda)} = \frac{z - z'}{z'/(c^2 - \lambda)} \qquad\qquad ...(v)$$

This meets the plane $z = 0$, where

$$\frac{x - x'}{l} = \frac{y - y'}{m} = -(c^2 - \lambda)$$

$$\Rightarrow \qquad \frac{x}{l} = \frac{x'}{l} - c^2 + a^2 - (a^2 - \lambda) = a^2 - c^2$$

Similarly,

$$y/m = b^2 - c^2$$

Hence, the normal at the point of contact passes through a fixed point in the xy-plane.

EXERCISES

1. Find the equations to the focal conics of the hyperboloid $x^2 + yz - 2 = 0$.

> [**Ans.** $x = 0$, $y^2 + z^2 + 4yz = 0$ and $y = z$, $2x^2 + 3y^2 = 12$]

2. Find the focal conics of the cone

$$ax^2 + by^2 + cz^2 = 0.$$

$$\left[\textbf{Ans.}\ y = 0,\ \frac{z^2}{1/c - 1/b} + \frac{x^2}{1/a - 1/b} = 0 \text{ and } z = 0,\ \frac{x^2}{1/a - 1/c} + \frac{y^2}{1/b - 1/c} = 0 \right]$$

OBJECTIVE QUESTIONS

I. Multiple Choice Questions

Note : *For each of the following questions, four alternatives are given for the answer. Only one of them is correct. Choose the correct alternative.*

1. Three conicoids confocal with a given central conicoid will pass through a :

(*a*) given line   (*b*) given conic   (*c*) given point   (*d*) None of these.

2. Conicoids confocal with a given conicoid touch a given :

(*a*) plane   (*b*) line   (*c*) conic   (*d*) conicoid itself.

3. Tangent planes at a point to the three confocals which pass through it :

(*a*) meet in a line   (*b*) intersect at a point

(*c*) are mutually perpendicular   (*d*) None of these.

4. Locus of umbilics of a system of confocal ellipsoids is :

(*a*) focal ellipse   (*b*) focal hyperbola   (*c*) focal parabola   (*d*) None of these.

5. Locus of a point the square of whose distance from a fixed point varies as the product of its distances from two given planes is :

(*a*) sphere   (*b*) conicoid   (*c*) plane   (*d*) cone.

6. Focal conics of a paraboloid are :

(*a*) one parabola one ellipse   (*b*) one ellipse one hyperbola

(*c*) one parabola one hyperbola   (*d*) two parabolas.

7. How many conicoids confocal with a given ellipsoid pass through any point ?

(*a*) One   (*b*) Two   (*c*) Three   (*d*) Four.

8. What locus is represented by the equation $\lambda_1 + \lambda_2 + \lambda_3 = $ constant, where λ's are elliptic co-ordinates ?

   (*a*) Sphere   (*b*) Paraboloid   (*c*) Ellipsoid   (*d*) None of these.

9. Tangent planes to two confocals at any common point are :

   (*a*) parallel   (*b*) coincident   (*c*) perpendicular   (*d*) None of these

10. The two confocal paraboloids cut everywhere at an angle :

   (*a*) $\pi/4$ (*b*) $\pi/3$ (*c*) $\pi/2$ (*d*) None of these.

ANSWERS

1. (*c*)	**2.** (*a*)	**3.** (*c*)	**4.** (*b*)	**5.** (*b*)
6. (*d*)	**7.** (*c*)	**8.** (*a*)	**9.** (*c*)	**10.** (*c*)

II. Fill in the Blanks

Note : *Fill in the blanks "......." so that the following statements are complete and correct.*

1. The conicoids whose principal sections have the ..... are known as confocal conicoids.
2. ..... paraboloids confocal with a given paraboloid pass through a given point.
3. The product of eccentricities of the ..... of an ellipsoid is unity.
4. Three conicoids confocal with a given ellipsoid pass through any point are ....., one a hyperboloid of one sheet and other a hyperboloid of two sheets.
5. The locus represented by $\lambda_2\lambda_2 + \lambda_3\lambda_1 + \lambda_1\lambda_2 = $ constant, where λ's are elliptic co-ordinates is an ..... .
6. The tangent planes to two confocals at any common point are ..... .
7. Focal conics of a paraboloid are two ..... .
8. Distance between two points one on each of the two confocal conicoids is equal to the distance between the two ..... points.

ANSWERS

1. same foci;	**2.** three;	**3.** focal conics;	**4.** ellipsoid;
5. ellipsoid;	**6.** perpendicular;	**7.** parabolas;	**8.** corresponding.

III. True/False Statements

Note : *Write 'T' for true and 'F' for false statements.*

1. Through any point there pass three conicoids confocal with a given ellipsoid, *viz.*, one ellipsoid and two hyperboloids of one sheet.
2. The locus represented by $\lambda_1 + \lambda_2 + \lambda_3 = $ constant, where λ's are elliptic co-ordinates is a hyperboloid of one sheet.
3. The conicoids whose principal sections have the same foci are called confocal conicoids.
4. Three paraboloids confocal with a given paraboloid pass through given point — two elliptic and one hyperbolic.
5. The product of eccentricities of the focal conics of an ellipsoid is unity.
6. The tangent plane to two confocals at any common point are always parallel.
7. Normals to the three confocals through the point P are the axes of the enveloping cone whose vertex is P.
8. Locus of the umbilics of a system of confocal ellipsoids is the focal parabola.

ANSWERS

1. F	**2.** F	**3.** T	**4.** T	**5.** T	**6.** F	**7.** T	**8.** F

APPENDIX II

Spherical Polar and Cylindrical Co-ordinates

Various systems of co-ordinates have been devised to meet different types of problems which arise in Geometry and in various applications of the same. Cartesian system which is one of these has already been introduced and this is the one system with which we have been concerned all along. It is now proposed to introduce two more systems, *viz.*, :

1. *Cylindrical Polar*,   2. *Spherical Polar*,

which are often found useful in various applications.

1. Cylindrical Polar Co-ordinates

Let P be a given point.

Draw PN perpendicular to the XY-plane, N being the foot of the perpendicular.
We write

$$ON = r, \angle XON = \theta, NP = z.$$

Then r, θ, z are called the *cylindrical polar co-ordinates* of the point P.

It will be seen that r, θ are the usual polar co-ordinates of the projection N in the XY-plane of the point P referred to O as the pole and OX as the initial line.

If x, y, z be the cartesian co-ordinates of P referred to OX, OY, OZ as the three axes, we may easily obtain the following formulae giving relations between x, y, z and r, θ, z :

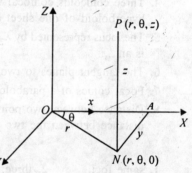

Fig. 51

$$x = r \cos \theta, \ y = r \sin \theta, \ z = z.$$

Ex. What are the surfaces represented by :

(*i*) r = constant; (*ii*) θ = constant; (*iii*) z = constant ?

2. Spherical Polar Co-ordinates

Let N be the foot of the perpendicular from P on the XY-plane.
We write

$$OP = r, \angle POZ = \theta, \angle XON = \phi.$$

It may be easily seen that ϕ can also be described as the angle between the planes POZ and XOZ.

Then r, θ, ϕ are known as the *spherical polar co-ordinates* of P.

We now obtain the formulae of transformation between x, y, z and r, θ, ϕ.

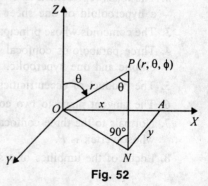

Fig. 52

Draw $NA \perp OX$. We have $\angle OPN = \theta$.

From the right-angled triangle OPN, we have

$$Z - NP = OP \cos \theta = r \cos \theta,$$
$$ON = OP \sin \angle OPN = r \sin \theta.$$

Again, from the right-angled triangle OAN, we have

$$x = OA - ON \cos \phi - r \sin \theta \cos \phi,$$
$$y = NA - ON \sin \phi - r \sin \theta \cos \phi.$$

Thus, we have the following formulae of transformation :

$$x = r \sin \theta \cos \phi, \; y = r \sin \theta \cos \phi, \; z = r \cos \theta.$$

Surfaces represented by :

(i) r = constant; (ii) θ = constant; (iii) ϕ = constant.

The reader may easily verify that

(i) r = constant represents a sphere with its centre at the origin.

(ii) θ = constant represents a right circular cone with its vertex at the origin and OZ as its axis.

(iii) ϕ = constant represents a semi-plane through OZ.

It may be easily verified that if a point, r, θ, ϕ varies in the interior of a sphere whose centre is at the origin and the radius is a; then r varies from 0 to a; ϕ varies from 0 to 2π; θ varies from 0 to π.

Attention: Students

We request you, for your frank assessment, regarding some of the aspects of the book, given as under:

14516   **ANALYTICAL SOLID GEOMETRY**
Shanti Narayan & P.K. Mittal   *Reprint 2019*

Please fill up the given spaces in neat capital letters. Add additional sheet(s) if the space provided is not sufficient, and if so required.

(i)   What topic(s) of your syllabus that are important from your examination point of view are not covered in the book ?

....
....
....
....

(ii)   What are the chapters and/or topics, wherein the treatment of the subject-matter is not systematic or organised or updated?

....
....
....
....

(iii)   Have you come across misprints/mistakes/factual inaccuracies in the book? Please specify the chapters, topics and the page numbers.

....
....
....
....
....

(iv)   Name top three books on the same subject (in order of your preference - 1, 2, 3) that you have found/heard better than the present book? Please specify in terms of quality (in all aspects).

1 ....
....
2 ....
....
3 ....
....

(v) Further suggestions and comments for the improvement of the book:

....

....

....

....

....

Other Details:

(i) Who recommended you the book? (Please tick in the box near the option relevant to you.)

☐ Teacher   ☐ Friends   ☐ Bookseller

(ii) Name of the recommending teacher, his designation and address:

....

....

....

(iii) Name and address of the bookseller you purchased the book from:

....

....

....

(iv) Name and address of your institution (Please mention the University or Board, as the case may be)

....

....

....

(v) Your name and complete postal address:

....

....

....

(vi) Write your preferences of our publications (1, 2, 3) you would like to have

....

....

The best assessment will be awarded half-yearly. The award will be in the form of our publications, as decided by the Editorial Board, amounting to Rs. 300 (total).

Please mail the filled up coupon at your earliest to:
Editorial Department
S. CHAND & COMPANY LTD.
Post Box No. 5733, Ram Nagar,
New Delhi 110 055